C0-BFC-117

JEFFERSON COLLEGE
3 6021 00026 2752

The Discovery of Fiction

Thomas E. Sanders
Miami-Dade Junior College

Scott, Foresman and Company

Library of Congress Catalog Card #67-16957

Printed in the United States of America.
Regional offices of Scott, Foresman and Company are located in Atlanta, Dallas, Glenview, Palo Alto, and Oakland, N.J.

Acknowledgements

"**A Mother's Tale.**" "A Mother's Tale" by James Agee. Copyright © 1952 by The James Agee Trust. Reprinted by permission. Originally appeared in *Harper's Bazaar.* "**Rashōmon.**" From *Rashōmon & Other Stories* by Ryūnosuke Akutagawa. By permission of Liveright, Publishers, N.Y. Copyright © 1952 by Liveright, Publishers. "**Hands.**" From *Winesburg, Ohio* by Sherwood Anderson. Copyright 1919 by B. W. Huebsch, Inc., 1947 by Eleanor Copenhaver Anderson. Reprinted by permission of The Viking Press, Inc. Excerpt from ***A Story Teller's Story.*** From *A Story Teller's Story* by Sherwood Anderson. Reprinted by permission of Harold Ober Associates Inc. Copyright © 1924 by B. W. Huebsch, Inc., renewed 1951 by Eleanor Copenhaver Anderson. "**The Squatter.**" From Djuna Barnes, *Nightwood.* Copyright © 1937 by Djuna Barnes. Reprinted by permission of the author and New Directions Publishing Corporation. "**By the Waters of Babylon.**" From *Selected Works of Stephen Vincent Benét.* Holt, Rinehart and Winston, Inc. Copyright, 1937, by Stephen Vincent Benét. Reprinted by permission of Brandt & Brandt. "**The Scythe.**" Copyright 1943 by Ray Bradbury. Reprinted by permission of the Harold Matson Company, Inc. "**The Turtle.**" Reprinted by permission of Harold Ober Associates Inc. Copyright © 1965 by Paul Brodeur. First published in *The Saturday Evening Post.* "**Incident on the Tenth Floor.**" "Incident on the Tenth Floor" by Jeff Brown. Reprinted by permission of Harold Ober Associates Inc. Copyright © 1966 by The Curtis Publishing Company. "**Adolph Hitler, Judy Mauritz, and the Clear Blue Sky of Japan.**" From *december* Magazine, Volume VIII, No. 1. Copyright 1966 by C. L. Johnson, Publisher. Reprinted by permission. "**Torch Song.**" Reprinted from John Cheever's *The Enormous Radio and Other Stories,* by permission of the publishers, Funk & Wagnalls, N.Y. Excerpt from "**On Writing and Bad Writing.**" From "On Writing and Bad Writing" by John Ciardi. Copyright 1962 by Saturday Review Associates, Inc. Reprinted by permission. "**Little Memento.**" From *Fancies and Goodnights* by John Collier, copyright © 1931, 1937, 1938, 1939, 1940, 1941, 1942, 1943, 1944, 1951 by John Collier. Reprinted by permission of the Harold Matson Company, Inc. "**The Unwanted.**" "The Unwanted" by Mary Elizabeth Counselman. Copyright 1950 by *Weird Tales.* Reprinted by permission of Renown Publications, Inc. "**The Upturned Face.**" Reprinted from *Stephen Crane: An Omnibus.* Published 1930, 1952 by Alfred A. Knopf, Inc. "**Pig.**" © Copyright 1959 by Roald Dahl. Reprinted from *Kiss Kiss,* by Roald Dahl, by permission of Alfred A. Knopf, Inc. Excerpt from the translator's note to ***The Story of O.*** From the translator's note to *The Story of O* by Pauline Réage, Translated from the French by Sabine d'Estrée, Copyright © 1965 by Grove Press, Inc. "**Some of the Time, All of the Time.**" "Some of the Time, All of the Time" by Sonya Dorman. Reprinted by permission of John Schaffner, Literary Agent. Copyright © 1965 by The Curtis Publishing Company. "**The Question My Son Asked.**" "The Question My Son Asked" by Stanley Ellin. Reprinted by permission of Curtis Brown, Ltd. Copyright © 1963 by Davis Publications, Inc. "**Our Lady's Juggler.**" Reprinted by permission of Dodd, Mead & Company, Inc. from *Mother of Pearl* by Anatole France. "**The Punch.**" Reprinted by permission of Russell & Volkening, Inc. agents for the author. Copyright © 1965 by Bruce Jay Friedman. "**The Death of the Hired Man.**" From *Complete Poems of Robert Frost.* Copyright 1930, 1939 by Holt, Rinehart and Winston, Inc. Copyright © 1958 by Robert Frost. Copyright © 1967 by Lesley Frost Ballantine. Reprinted by permission of Holt, Rinehart and Winston, Inc. "**The Dinner Party.**" "The Dinner Party" by Mona Gardner. Copyright 1942 by Saturday Review Associates, Inc. Reprinted by permission of the copyright holder and *The Reader's Digest.* A condensation of "The Dinner Party" appeared in the March 1942 *The Reader's Digest.* "**A Jury of Her Peers.**" Copyright 1946 by Susan Glaspell. Reprinted by permission of the Estate of Susan Glaspell. "**A Discovery in the Woods.**" From *A Sense of Reality* by Graham Greene. Copyright © by Graham Greene. Reprinted by permission of The Viking Press, Inc. "**A Question of Blood.**" Copyright 1937 by Ernest Haycox. Copyright renewed 1965 by Jill Marie Haycox. Used by permission of Jill Marie Haycox, Executrix of the Estate of Ernest Haycox, and the Scott Meredith Literary Agency, Inc. "**The Slaughter-House.**" "The Slaughter-House" by Alfred Hayes. Reprinted by permission of the author. "**A Clean, Well-Lighted Place.**" "A Clean, Well-Lighted Place" (Copyright 1933 Charles Scribner's Sons; renewal copyright © 1961 by Ernest Hemingway) is reprinted with the permission of Charles Scribner's Sons from *Winner Take Nothing* by Ernest Hemingway. Excerpt from ***Death in the Afternoon.*** Reprinted with the permission of Charles Scribner's Sons from *Death in the Afternoon,* pages 191–192, by Ernest Hemingway. Copyright 1932 Charles Scribner's Sons; renewal copyright © 1960 Ernest Hemingway. "**An Invitation to Etsujim.**" From *An Introduction to Haiku* by Harold G. Henderson. Copyright © 1958 by Harold G. Henderson. Reprinted by permission of Doubleday & Company, Inc. "**The Terrapin.**" "The Terrapin" by Patricia Highsmith. Copyright © 1962 by Davis Publications, Inc. Appeared originally in *Ellery Queen's Mystery Magazine.* Reprinted by permission of McIntosh and Otis, Inc. "**The World Outside.**" "The World Outside" by Barbara Holland. From the March 1965 issue of *Redbook* Magazine. Copyright © 1965 by the McCall Corporation. Reprinted by permission of McIntosh and Otis, Inc. "**On the Genesis of The Real Thing.**" From *The Notebooks of Henry James,* edited by F. O. Matthiessen and Kenneth Murdock. Copyright 1947 by Oxford University Press, Inc. Reprinted by permission. **"The Real Thing."** "The Real Thing" is reprinted with the permission of Charles Scribner's Sons from Volume XVIII, *The Novels and Tales of Henry James.* Copyright 1909 Charles Scribner's Sons; renewal copyright 1937 Henry James. **"The Run on the Cherokee Strip."** From *The Cherokee Strip* by Marquis James. Copyright 1945 by Marquis James. Reprinted by permission of The Viking Press, Inc. **"Miss Tempy's Watchers."** From *The Country of the Pointed Firs* by Sarah Orne Jewett. Originally published by Houghton Mifflin Company. **"Fulvous Yellow."** "Fulvous Yellow" by Stanley Kauffmann. Copyright, 1948, by *Story* Magazine, Inc. Reprinted by permission of Brandt & Brandt. **"Shuffle, Deal."** From *The Miami News,* Sept. 19, 1966, by John Keasler, *Miami News* Columnist. Reprinted by permission of the author. Excerpt from ***Babbitt.*** From *Babbitt* by Sinclair Lewis. Copyright 1922 Harcourt, Brace & Company, Inc.; Copyright 1950 Sinclair Lewis. Reprinted by permission of Ernst, Cane, Berner & Gitlin for the Estate of Sinclair Lewis. **"All Gold Cañon."** "All Gold Cañon" by Jack London. Reprinted by permission of Irving Shepard, Copyright Owner. Excerpt from ***Vestal Fire.*** From *Vestal Fire* by Sir Compton Mackenzie. Copyright Chatto & Windus 1927, New Phoenix Library, 1957. Reprinted by permission of Joyce Weiner Associates, London. **"Miss Brill."** Copyright 1922 by Alfred A. Knopf, Inc. and renewed 1950 by John Middleton Murry. Reprinted from *The Short Stories of Katherine Mansfield* by permission of the publisher. **"The Three Fat Women of Antibes."** Copyright 1933 by W. Somerset Maugham from the book *The Mixture as Before* by W. Somerset Maugham. Reprinted by permission of Doubleday & Company, Inc. Excerpt from the Foreword to ***The Square Root of Wonderful.*** From the Foreword to *The Square Root of Wonderful* by Carson McCullers. Copyright © 1958 by Houghton Mifflin Company. Reprinted by permission of the publisher. **"A Tree. A Rock. A Cloud."** From *The Ballad of the Sad Cafe* by Carson McCullers. Reprinted by permission of Houghton Mifflin Company. Copyright 1942 by Carson McCullers. Excerpt from ***Peyton Place.*** From *Peyton Place* by Grace Metalious. Copyright 1956 by Grace Metalious. Reprinted by permission of Simon and Schuster, Inc., publishers. **"A Good Man Is Hard to Find."** Copyright, 1953, by Flannery O'Connor. Reprinted from her volume *A Good Man Is Hard to Find and Other Stories* by permission of Harcourt, Brace & World, Inc. **"The Terrible Miss Dove."** Reprinted by permission of Dodd, Mead & Company, Inc. from *The Finer Things of Life* by Frances Gray Patton. Copyright 1946, 1947, 1948, 1949, 1950, 1951 by Frances Gray Patton. Copyright 1946 by The Curtis Publishing Company. **"The Mugging."** "The Mugging" by Edward L. Perry, originally titled "A Mugging at Midnight," is reprinted by permission of the author. Excerpt from **"*Noon Wine:* The Sources."** From "*Noon Wine:* The Sources" by Katherine Anne Porter. © Copyright 1956 by Katherine Anne Porter. Reprinted by permission of the author. **"A Secret for Two."** "A Secret for Two" by Quentin Reynolds. Copyright © 1936 Crowell-Collier Publishing Co. Reprinted by permission of The Estate of Quentin Reynolds. **"My Papa's Waltz."** Copyright 1942 by Hearst Magazines, Inc. from the book *The Collected Poems of Theodore Roethke.* Reprinted by permission of Doubleday & Company, Inc. Originally appeared in *Harper's Bazaar.* **"The Open Window."** From *The Complete Short Stories of Saki* (H. H. Munro). All rights reserved. Reprinted by permission of The Viking Press, Inc. **"Love for a Hand."** Copyright 1952 by Karl Shapiro. Reprinted from *Poems 1940–1953,* by Karl Shapiro, by permission of Random House, Inc. Originally appeared in *The New Yorker.* Excerpt from ***A Prosody Handbook.*** (VII) "Aesthetic Distance" (pp. 104–105) in *A Prosody Handbook* by Karl Shapiro and Robert Beum. Copyright © 1965 by Karl Shapiro and Robert Beum. Reprinted by permission of Harper & Row, Publishers. **"The People Next Door."** "The People Next Door" by Pauline Smith. Copyright 1952 by Grace Publishing Company, Inc. Reprinted by permission of the copyright owner. **"The Echo and the Nemesis."** Reprinted from *Children Are Bored on Sunday* by Jean Stafford, by permission of Farrar, Straus & Giroux, Inc. Copyright 1950 by Jean Stafford. First appeared in *The New Yorker* as "The Nemesis." Excerpt from ***An Introduction to Fiction.*** From *An Introduction to Fiction,* by Robert Stanton, copyright © 1965 by Holt, Rinehart and Winston, Inc. Excerpt from ***The Grapes of Wrath.*** From *The Grapes of Wrath* by John Steinbeck. Copyright 1939, 1967 by John Steinbeck. Reprinted by permission of The Viking Press, Inc. **"Bianca's Hands."** Reprinted from *E Pluribus Unicorn* by Theodore Sturgeon. By permission of Abelard-Schuman, Ltd. All rights reserved. Copyright 1953 by Theodore Sturgeon. **"A Glass of Blessings."** "A Glass of Blessings" by Glendon Swarthout. From *Esquire.* Copyright © 1958, Glendon Swarthout. Reprinted by permission of A. Watkins, Inc. **"Joy Cometh in the Morning."** "Joy Cometh in the Morning" by Dorothy Thomas, from the December 1966 issue of *Redbook* Magazine, Copyright © by McCall Corporation 1966. Reprinted by permission of the author. Excerpt from the **"Maugham Obituary."** Reprinted by permission from *TIME The Weekly Newsmagazine;* © Time Inc. 1965. **"Scouse Bible."** Reprinted courtesy of UPI. **"All Our Yesterdays."** "All Our Yesterdays" by Beb Vuyk. From the Winter 1961–1962 Number of *The Literary Review,* published by Fairleigh Dickinson University, Teaneck, New Jersey. **"Death of a Travelling Salesman."** From *A Curtain of Green and Other Stories,* copyright, 1941, by Eudora Welty. Reprinted by permission of Harcourt, Brace & World, Inc. Excerpt from **"The Reading and Writing of Short Stories."** From "The Reading and Writing of Short Stories" by Eudora Welty from *The Atlantic Monthly,* March, 1949. Copyright © 1949 by Eudora Welty. Reprinted by permission of Russell & Volkening, Inc. **"The Use of Force."** From William Carlos Williams, *The Farmers' Daughters.* Copyright 1938 by William Carlos Williams. Reprinted by permission of New Directions Publishing Corporation.

Table of Contents

Foreword

I never knew Alan Swallow, and there was nothing personal in the correspondence we engaged in many years ago. We were just two young teachers trying to help students discover the American West. Over the years, as Alan moved ahead in his publishing operation, where he was "editor, printer, first reader, and final word," I reviewed his books and once wrote a full column about him. More recently, he came to represent to me the individual voice in American publishing.

Now I stand for a moment in his place. At the time of Alan's death on November 27, 1966, he was beginning to gather notes for a foreword to this book. All over America friends and former students mourned his passing. One of his ex-students, Mark Harris of San Francisco State College, wrote in the New York *Times:* "His books and his students . . . have worked their effect not only upon American literature but upon our general thought: minds well-trained in literature begin to understand the world as well. Himself poet, he was the unacknowledged legislator."

Another former student, Tom Sanders, would look up from his manuscript and think of his old teacher. Tom thought he knew his way around in the world of modern literature when in 1949 he entered graduate school at Denver University. But his horizons widened when he fell under the spell of young Professor Swallow, a short, stocky strawberry blond with a magnificent temper and a way of getting through to students. Alan was dividing his time between teaching and publishing. He was head of the university press, and he was already laying the foundation for his private publishing, turning out modest chapbooks with hand-set type on a second-hand press.

Alan's old students begin to sound a little vague and mystical when they talk about his teaching. Tom Sanders says, "He was the most incredible teacher I've ever known. Though he never taught a thing, what we needed to know we learned." The old crowd speaks of his feeling for words and for the literature of America. In the classroom and out, his business was exploring man's dignity and man's hope. Mark Harris comments on things the young teacher never taught, but waited patiently for the students to learn. "His method," Harris says, "must have been the method of liberated readers in all ages. The separation of mind from prejudice is the root of justice."

For most boys who dream of becoming writers and critics, there are moments of doubt when they suspect that the bright world they aspire to is more myth than fact. Alan Swallow couldn't take his students out into the world, but he brought the world into his home—a lesson in magic for the boys from the hillside farms, the small towns, and the high mountain valleys. In his living room they listened to the talk of visitors like James T. Farrell, Archibald MacLeish, Yvor Winters, Allen Tate, Janet Lewis, and J. V. Cunningham. The big world opened, and students walked in.

One of them, the man who made this book, hopes *The Discovery of Fiction* keeps the faith with his old teacher. I'm sure it does. The book exhibits a sophisticated knowledge of literature. The author's style is interesting and lively. And finally, as it was in the classroom long ago, the emphasis is always on the text. Does Tom hear Alan's voice: "Beware of paraphrase. Why do you like it? Go back to the story or poem. Subjectivity is out."

The mark of the teacher is on the student. Alan Swallow distilled his philosophy of education and publishing in a poem, "For My Students." These two stanzas suggest why his students find it hard to forget him:

What is unnamed, we heal,
What is unopened, tear and close.
What is unclean
We suffer, and experiment with hope.

What is within, discover;
What is without, bring warm to home.
Whatever seems in wonder,
We hold, and give it shape of hope.

Fred Shaw
Dean of Academic Affairs
Miami-Dade Junior College South

Preface

When the writing skills of children develop naturally, poetry precedes prose, giving way to longer forms as the child's memory develops and he learns to include information several paragraphs before its actual need arises. The development of a child's reading skills follows the same basic pattern; yet, by the time he reaches high school, a curious thing often happens. He loses the ability to read short poems with comprehension and he tends to read longer prose forms for little more than plot. With the loss of his primitive poetic responses, in other words, he also loses the ability to recognize and retain innuendo in dialog, analogy in description, and subtlety in character response—all of which create a reader's understanding of character. Reading merely for plot, the student finds no personal meaning in a story, recognizes no analogous applications. He reads to be amused, and, deprived of subtlety, important fiction is not amusing. The student becomes, consequently, either a nonreader or a poor reader.

The Discovery of Fiction begins with a refresher chapter devoted to poetic principles, the remainder of the book developing reading skills as they grow from those beginnings. Because prose forms create problems for both students and teachers in the simple logistics of page numbers, a new approach is adopted in this book. Certain stories appear in one type face, textual matter in another. An uninterrupted reading of these stories requires only that the reader follow the numbered paragraphs of the story, skipping over the textual material. Then, on rereading the story, he can pause at the end of a half-scene or scene and examine the components of the narrative, understanding the structure as it has been built by the author. The final analysis and personal application of the story, of course, remain the province of the teacher and the student.

In the main, I have preferred the unfamiliar rather than the widely-anthologized story. (Teachers deserve fresh material too!) Differentiating among pulp, slick, and quality stories rests, of course, on literary discrimination, and that topic is carefully considered throughout the book. Style has always presented the greatest problems in the classroom and, for that reason, the most analytical chapter—and one of the longest—is devoted to that area. With over sixty selections, the book in effect contains its own anthology and can be supplemented by any of the excellent collections of traditional stories available at minimal cost on newsracks.

Many people have made this book possible. Without them, it would not exist. Grace J. McAlister, Louise Forshaw, and Walter W. Peek have supplied impetus when I had none. William J. Heim, Jr., Mary Mereness, Josephine Curto, Bettye Lou and Manny Nicolaides, Naomi Pratt, Phyllis Eisman, and Frank Hester have been friends through it all. (And who would dare disappoint friends?) My teachers deserve more credit than I can give. Nelle Bagain (grade 2), Willow McLain (grade 5), Billie Marie Douthatt (grade 8), Velma Adams (grade 10), and Etta Bruton (freshman, college) taught me to read—at, I am sure, no small expense to their dedication and patience. Solomon Lichter gave me license to teach others to read as few educators dare today. Ambrose Garner protected my academic freedom to teach—obtrusively and firmly. Marie Joffre acted as unofficial librarian. Helen Isaacson and Barbara Stewart of Scott, Foresman and Company have worked on my books with an enthusiasm and dedication far exceeding the call of duty. Bobbie Ossip, Stan Miron, Ron DeMaris, June Seligman, and Bernice Miller gave invaluable help in suggesting approaches. And thousands of students, thousands of writers supplied reasons for the book. I hope it serves all of them as well as they deserve.

Thomas E. Sanders
Miami, Florida
1967

For the living and the dead
Verne Reaves
and
Alan Swallow
with the wish they could
have known each
other

CHAPTER I

And Every Man a Poet

Every man is a teller of tales. Some are more accomplished than others, but none escapes the impulse—even the necessity—of narration. In the course of an ordinary day, for example, you may be called upon to construct a bit of biography when asked why you do not have an assignment. You begin: "I had just sat down to study last night when. . . ." Or, conversationally, you may recount some anecdote: "That reminds me of the mortuary science student in a family living class who. . . ." Or you may narrate a fantasy: "I had the wildest dream last night. I was at a formal dance and everyone else. . . ."

You employ such narratives for a variety of reasons, all beginning in the necessity to communicate an idea that, simply stated, would lack impact. With the materials of the storyteller's art, you embellish facts to add interest, distort or minimize truth with overstatement or understatement, and create fiction to vitalize dull reality. Your approach to the narrative will be unique, for you incorporate the totality of your own personality in the recounting, but you will follow a multiplicity of rules and precedents established by centuries of inventive people. The more widely read you are, the more imitative, the more imaginative, the more interesting and successful you will be in reaching your audience. And there again you share the storyteller's art: without an audience, there is no reason for you to be inventive.

Knowing this basic truth, you consciously strive to spin a more elaborate fiction, to make it more interesting, to capture your listener. And you envy the friend who "can really tell a joke" or who is successful in amorous conquests because he "has a line you could hang laundry on." If you hear an amusing joke, read an interesting fact, or encounter a colorful phrase, you may consciously attempt to file it in your memory so it will be available when you need an arresting item to embellish your conversation.

Unconsciously, you are engaging in the storyteller's craft by practicing *observation* (examining experience so you can remember salient features by mentally filing the material where you can find it later). At some future time, the need will arise, and you will practice the second step, that of *selection* (choosing from stored experience that material which will most immediately and best fit the circumstances and contribute to the total impression you desire). Writers, realizing their memories are limited and imperfect, usually keep physical files or journals wherein they preserve such materials, and these journals become invaluable to the serious reader when he attempts a critical paper on an author's work.

When the time comes and you need a clever joke, an interesting anecdote, or a novel phrase, you will select the material and present it in the fewest, best, most colorful words you can command. This is the practice of *economy* (paring language of excess words, allowing similes and metaphors to create brief analogies that would be boring in lengthy explanation). At this point, you are a prose writer without a pencil. But you are also, simultaneously, a poet. For no writer of prose fiction exists who, at one and the same time, is not something of a poet. He may not consider himself one, but his work will contain a variety of poetic techniques, consciously and unconsciously employed to achieve *compression* (the reduction of all elements—words, characters, and incidents—to the minimum number necessary to gain the maximum effect).

This connection between the art of the storyteller and the art of the poet points up the aesthetic and historical interrelationship of the two forms. Both the poet and the storyteller deal with intense emotions, depths of insight, character revelations, and evaluations of incident, and the prose fiction writer will be successful in communicating with you, the reader, in direct relation to his ability to incorporate and use the poetic techniques developed by centuries of poets who preceded him. You, on the other hand, must also understand something of those techniques if you are to respond with your intellect as well as with your emotions.

The fact is that, except for King Alfred's *Handbook* (A.D. 887) and the King James Bible (A.D. 1611), there was little distinguished prose in English until the middle of the seventeenth century. And even the prose of the Bible (the *Handbook* is not extant) is not sharply different from poetry. Generally speaking, the scannable line separates them, for prose may not be *scanned* (the process of marking the regularly repeated accents—the *rhythm*—of poetry). However, much of the Bible scans easily while some modern, cadenced poetry will not seem to scan at all. Extreme compressions, a yoking of seemingly disparate ideas into metaphors and similes, abstract symbols—all are more apparent in poetry, but they also exist in prose. Nor is length the determining difference, since brevity is observable in both forms, and some epic poems are as long as novels. Prose allows greater flexibility in the writing than does poetry, however, for the author is not confined to rhythm. He may disregard it utterly if the words needed to express an idea lack harmony of sound. He may employ it, however, when and if it adds dimension to his work. And some of the best prose writers are masterful at weaving rhythm in and out of their work so skillfully that the unobservant reader scarcely notices a change in tempo.

The early poets, quite conscious of their audiences, soon recognized the need to make every word work at both its *denotative* (the literal, dictionary definition) and its *connotative* (the associative, picture-producing creator of attitudes) level. They learned to create *images* (pictures visualized on the screen of the mind) with one word (such as *snake*), with combined sounds (*still, stealthy snake, snarled and coiled*), and with a yoking of seemingly unrelated ideas (*He stood, like a stealthy snake, and waited*). Then they added rhythm (a regularly recurring beat) to intensify response (*So still he stood, a stealthy snake, his spirit snarled and coiled*), for they discovered any ancient theme poetically stated creates an identification reaction in an audience.

As those discoveries grew in time, they became the poet's rules and laws. *Snake* denotes one of nature's reptiles; but it also connotes an ancient *symbol* (that which represents a thing which cannot, itself, be expressed). So *snake* became incarnate sin, sly wisdom, enemy of man, dark knowledge so desirable, so stumbled on but seldom found when sought with conscious knowledge.* Then, used as central element, it became an *allegory* (a narrative in which abstractions become concrete so the reader can understand them) in "Genesis," where Satan is the snake in Eden's innocence.

The early audiences had no books; their memories had to serve as the page where, heard but once, the words were penned—if they were to be remembered. Since the *metaphor* (a comparison stating one thing *is* another: *Bill and Mary would be happy but John is the snake in their garden*) and the *simile* (a comparison employing the words *like, as,* or

*Thomas Carlyle says (in *Sartor Resartus*) that in a symbol "the Infinite is made to blend itself with the Finite, to stand visible, and as it were, attainable there."

than: John is like a snake in Bill and Mary's Eden) create memorable pictures, the poet used them when he could. He combined them with easily remembered *rhyme* (a correspondence of sound) in the free-ranging forms of *assonance* (repeated vowel sounds: *caught, straight and pale, the snake, dead stick*), *consonance* (repeated internal consonant sounds: *clipped sharply and impaled upon*), and *alliteration* (repeated initial sounds: *God's wrath,* th*at* th*orn,* th*in, tipped with starkness*), and the limited forms such as *masculine rhyme* (a correspondence of vowels in accented syllables: *stick-thick*), *feminine rhyme* (corresponding vowels in two consecutive syllables, the second of which is unaccented: *starkness-darkness*), and *slant rhyme* (a near but inexact correspondence of vowels: *upon-strong*). Because rhyme creates an echo in the mind, it forces memory to work. *Imagery* (the metaphors and similes) is sharper than mere denotative words, and rhythm enforces further memory.

Read these six lines, then, and notice how poetic usage makes them vivid:

Caught straight and pale, the snake, dead stick,
Clipped sharply and impaled upon
God's wrath (that thorn, thin, tipped with starkness
Of wit) breathed panic dark and thick
As his oppressive length, once strong,
Dropped, a broken lance, into darkness.

Another poetic device startles the reader in line 4. Called *saṁvegha,* it is "poetic shock" induced by the writer's leading you to expect one idea but developing another, both of which join in your mind. The word *starkness* at the end of line 3 seems to complete the thought. However, the line runs over into the next one before it is completed—and then in an unanticipated word.

Now observe how all these poetic devices work in a complete poem first published in an American magazine of large circulation:

My Papa's Waltz

The whiskey on your breath
Could make a small boy dizzy;
But I hung on like death:
Such waltzing was not easy.

We romped until the pans
Slid from the kitchen shelf;
My mother's countenance
Could not unfrown itself.

The hand that held my wrist
Was battered on one knuckle;
At every step you missed
My right ear scraped a buckle.

You beat time on my head
With a palm caked hard by dirt,
Then waltzed me off to bed
Still clinging to your shirt.

Theodore Roethke

In four *quatrains* (four-line stanzas wherein at least two lines rhyme), a literal picture is painted, animated startlingly, and lifted into symbolism. Three *iambs* (an unaccented syllable followed by an accented one) to the line create the 3/4 time rhythm of the waltz, but the tempo is violated drunkenly by feminine rhyme which adds an additional unaccented syllable to lines 2, 4, 10, and 12. The awkward inebriation is further revealed in the initial foot, a *trochee* (an accented syllable followed by an unaccented one), of line 6 and the *anapest* (two unaccented syllables followed by an accented one) which opens line 14. With subtle violations of the rhythm, each stanza reveals the staggering agony of the dance.

Denotatively, the words describe a small boy's memory of an evening when his father, not quite sober, danced him about the kitchen and waltzed him off to bed as his mother frowned at the performance. Connotatively, much greater depths are revealed. The father's breath "could" make a small boy dizzy, implying it did not, a poetic *understatement* (a statement that suggests much more than it reveals directly). A completely terrified child would succumb to smell *plus* terror; this child did not. With determination, he "hung on like death," a simile which reveals that this was not a physical act (as it definitely is in the last line of the poem) but one of desire to participate, one of clinging to the experience. That the "waltzing was not easy" reveals through *litotes* (understatement in negative form meaning the exact opposite of the statement) that the dance was difficult for the child to execute, though he was determined to participate. Nor was it unpleasant. "We romped" indicates the pleasure of the experience for the child, even though the mother disapproved. As a person, she scarcely exists in the child's memory, however. Her face represents the whole woman; she was a surface, merely a visual experience. *Synecdoche* (the use of the most important or distinctive part as representative of the whole) reduces her to a disapproving countenance which she, as a total person, is too weak to control. It acts independently of her will. Poetically she is characterized as exceedingly weak—in her son's eyes.

Subtle observation reveals a great deal about the father. "The hand that held my wrist/Was battered on one knuckle" suggests the father had been involved in a fight and landed at least one good punch. The child notices and comments on this minor feature, indicating concern and love for the father. A terrified child would not see such a small detail. Physical size of the child is established in the buckle-ear relationship, and, lest pity or emotional response lead you to read this as a cruel line, remember the easy way children accommodate pain, often associating it with pleasure. Notice also the "ear scraped a buckle;" it was not scraped *by* the buckle. Careful reading of the line reveals no pain. The fourth stanza reveals the father's other hand. It beats "time" (notice again: this is not a pain-filled line) and is "caked hard by dirt." In that fight, the father had been felled by at least one blow, his palm being dirtied as he fell on it. That only *one* palm is so soiled indicates he had not been completely flattened, knowledge impressive enough for the child to note. Only now does the symbolism of the final line emerge. As they danced, the child's ear scraped a buckle; therefore, his hands were clutched around the father's legs. Now the child has been lifted, held tight in an embrace he returned: "clinging to your shirt." Physical the shirt may be, but it is also *metonymy* (the name of one thing used for another which it represents). Covering the chest and the heart, that shirt symbolizes the love the boy clings to so desperately.

A less careful, more emotional reading might have convinced you the child was terrified by the father, that the mother was a "good" but defeated woman afraid to interfere. However, the *motion* of the poem (the movement in time used to establish or develop an idea) is an arrested moment from line 1 through line 14. The word *then* serves as *transition* (a word, phrase, repetition, or suggested association that marks the passing from one idea to another) and *pivot* (the point at which motion stops) in order that *countermotion* (a change of mood or tone within the work to intensify, clarify, or reveal the main idea) may be revealed. The *tone* (dominant quality of sound that establishes the reader's attitude) is one of bewilderment and ambivalence, but the *mood* (the feeling that emerges as emotional atmosphere in which the reader exists as he reads) is one of childlike simplicity and clarity, and the reader recalls those moments in his own youth when the big, male father seemed so wonderfully overwhelming as he expressed love in the only way he could—roughly. That those moments are rare makes them doubly memorable even if they are the result of inhibitions released only under the urgings of alcohol.

As a reader, you can become intensely involved in such a poem, not because it makes a statement, but because it opens memory for you and allows you to assess your own experiences and attitudes in relation to that which, theoretically, does not actually apply to you. Two readers, reading emotionally and without careful attention, may well find this poem to mean two entirely different things. If memories of the father are unpleasant, it will be a savage experience. If memories are pleasant, it will be an exhilarating one. The careful reader will find it rewarding as he compares the vicarious experience to his actual stored memories—whether they be pleasant or unpleasant.

Now, with this understanding (or refresher) of poetic techniques, we can return to our discussion of fiction. While its realm is large, embracing many forms, our concern here will be primarily with the short story. As short stories are, broadly speaking, composed of four distinct prose forms working together, we will study them in the following order: simple narrative, description, character, and dialog. Then we will see how they are combined with other elements to create stories that amuse, instruct, and reveal—in short, stories that are worth reading.

Basic to all prose and poetry is an element called *scene.* Since every reportable incident has its origin in an observed phenomenon, a happening, or a series of related happenings, the creative process of writing must spring from a scene of some sort. "Scene," in this sense, is the physical and emotional place where the observation or happening occurs. Sensory perceptions are necessarily involved in geographical scene because, within a geographic framework, that which triggers the author's creative awareness becomes obvious only through his five senses.

Standing at a given geographic location, the author sees the scene from a *vantage point* (literally, from above or below, from north or south, from inside or outside) which is limited by geography and such considerations as the size of the viewer. In "My Papa's Waltz," for instance, the pans on the kitchen shelf, the mother's countenance, the bulk of the father's body are all above the poet. He becomes even smaller than the second line indicates. And the figures assume large proportion above him—proportion that is emotional as well as physical—because his vantage point forces him to look up until the last two lines when he is raised into the upper reaches of the scene. And at that point, the shift in scene contributes to the countermotion of the poem. An integral part of scene, in this sense, is *setting* (locale in time—as a church in Rome during World War II) which, in this poem, is the kitchen one night. As reaction to that setting is changed by events that have happened outside it in earlier time, a second element of the scene emerges: *point of view*—an attitude brought to bear on the scene by the author. If he dislikes what he sees, his point of view will be disapproving; if he enjoys it, his point of view will be approving. That point of view creates the *tone* of the story, the overall impression that comes through to the reader—humor, pathos, irony, sincerity, and so on. (See pp. 20–21 and 199–232 for a fuller discussion of point of view.)

A second aspect of the word *scene* suggests the divisions of a written work. A scene, in this sense, is a continuous section of action within one setting. Poems and short stories may be constructed of only one scene (as is "My Papa's Waltz") or of several scenes connected by various methods. Chief among them are the following: (1) transitional words and phrases such as *then* or *the next morning;* (2) *exposition* (a presentation of essential information in capsule form, an explanation free of description); and (3) *panorama* (basic exposition to which has been added some of the descriptive matter of scene but not enough to create more than a blurred impression of several scenes passing by in rapid motion).

If an author observes sensitively and reports freshly without violating his point of view, the reader will be aware of a third aspect of scene: a feeling that what he is reading is happening *as he reads,* a sense of "now-ness." However, if the author violates geographical or chronological point of view, confusion will cloud his work. If he is unclear in his attitudinal point of view (tone), or if he changes it without effective transition, confusion will pervade the work. We speak of a "sense of scene" if we are unaware the work we are reading is not actually happening. If we are so involved in the work that it seems more real than the actual moment in which we are reading it, it has a sense of scene.

Vardis Fisher, author of the "Testament of Man" series of novels, says a sense of scene depends on the author's sense of reality. Advising beginning writers, he notes:

> The reader should never sense your presence in the scene or anywhere around it: the more you impose on your people your values, judgments and views the less convincing they are likely to be. That scene is best, other things being equal, about which we cannot say whether it was written by a man or a woman, about which we cannot know what the author thinks of his characters. The reader has a strong sense of the author's presence when he manipulates instead of letting the scene develop in accordance with the reality of the characters in it.*

* *God or Caesar: The Writing of Fiction for Beginners* (Caldwell, Idaho, 1953), p. 111.

Originality results, usually, not from the new (for there is probably no such thing) but from a faithful reporting of sensory reaction as the writer perceives it. But since no one has ever "known" anything exactly as the author does, the reader's *reaction* will be new. Faithful reporting is an honest, clear, vivid sharing. The reader reads for that sharing, and he is delighted when it occurs. The faithful reporter will include the immediately obvious as well as that which the reader might miss from personal observation. To "see" anything, the writer must perceive it with all five senses—not with the eye alone. Smoke, for instance, can be seen, touched, tasted, smelled, and heard. But perceptive people will not see cigarette smoke and smoke from steaks being charcoal-broiled as the same kind of smoke. They aren't. One is dry, nonfat; the other is not. One is pearly; the other is mottled. One is clinging; the other is not. If you broaden your perception of smoke to include fog, you will assuredly see differences. When you become very perceptive, you will see subtle similarities also. The reporting of subtle similarities creates good prose, and the reader can learn to be more perceptive than he is by studying the author's word choices.

Once a writer translates those differences and similarities into words which will create a memory of smoke or fog you have seen but forgotten, his prose becomes effective. It creates that memory because he reports the details you once saw without the careful focus he now supplies. His reporting will open your perception, and you will share his experience because it combines with yours. Poets use forms such as the seventeen-syllable *haiku* (a Japanese form designed to start a chain of memory in the reader's mind) to attempt merely to make you remember what you have once seen or experienced, leaving the interpretation of the sight or experience up to you:

An Invitation to Etsujim

Snow that we two
looked at together—this year
has it fallen anew?

Matsuo Basho
(tr. Harold G. Henderson)

But once the prose writer has re-created an experience, he is ready (obliged) to interpret its meaning for you. That successful interpretation *is* the short story. Within the framework of that interpretation, change usually occurs in a central character, and that too characterizes the short story.

The change itself may be very subtle; certainly it will be gradual. In life, people are not apt to change their attitudes quickly, and the short story is an interpretative re-creation of life. If, in a short story, a character, as a result of an experience, suddenly "comes to realize" something and is, thereby, changed for the better, you probably are reading a very poor short story. If, on the other hand, he modifies a view as a result of one incident, modifies it further as a result of a second or complicating incident, and realizes a reversal of attitude as a result of a crisis or climax arising out of the web of interwoven incidents, you probably are reading a pretty good short story. The story so constructed will probably communicate itself to you—if the author's point of view is logical and unviolated. Finally, if he has focused on the meaningful part of experience and interpreted it intelligently in scenes growing out of one another in an ordered fashion that you can understand and follow, involving you so you identify with the characters, you definitely are reading a good short story.

The "shared experience"—which comes from an author's faithful reporting of a meaningful part of experience—is a two-way street: it proves gratifying to both the reader and the writer. As a young author recently wrote:

> . . . A good writer always keeps in mind that he has to communicate with his reader, and he knows the rules of the game by memory. But really his goal is to reveal himself. He may not, like Shakespeare, even mention himself, but he is probing what is there inside himself. If he does that well, he ends up not with merely a catharsis or a detailed contemplation of his own navel, but with something universal and applicable to a great many more people than just himself. We are terribly limited creatures; and yet we are virtually all things that exist. The trick is to get at and describe what we are and put it into the possession of others. That motive seems to me both selfish and wonderfully humble.°

And that is as good a description of the purpose of fiction as any I know.

Before you examine the components of prose in isolation, it will be helpful to examine two short stories that quite obviously utilize poetic principles. The first was written several thousand years ago. (Contrary to popular belief, the short story is not of recent invention.) As you read it, notice the *story line* (the progression of scenes growing out of each other to reach a logical, interesting conclusion). As each scene change occurs, number it. Notice how each leads into the next, how each is dependent on the one before it. Notice also the skillful inter-

° Verne Reaves, letter to the author, August 29, 1966.

weaving of description, character studies, and dialog. All combine to create a single, unified experience which is interpreted in a logical, clear way to satisfy you as a reader.

The *allusions* (references to an historical person or event, a place connotatively rich in association, and so on) to contemporary customs in the story were, obviously, clear to the audience for which the story was written. A careful reading today reveals enough of the custom—even after many years—to make the story meaningful. Should the custom elude you, however, it was as follows: If an adult male died without a male heir, a kinsman of the man could sire a child with the widow. In fact, it was his duty as a kinsman to do so. The child bore the dead man's name and was considered his natural son. However, as the son of the biological father, he might claim inheritance through two men. As a result, the nameless kinsman was anxious to claim the land of Elimelech, but he was unwilling to jeopardize the inheritance of the children who bore his name. Boaz reveals his astuteness as he outlines the conditions under which the desirable land may be claimed.

Paragraphs are numbered for reference. Read the story first in its entirety by reading *only* the numbered paragraphs; then come back and read the story again *with* the discussions.

The Book of Ruth

1 Now it came to pass in the days when the judges ruled, that there was a famine in the land. And a certain man of Beth-lehem-judah went to sojourn in the country of Moab, he, and his wife, and his two sons. And the name of the man was Elimelech, and the name of his wife Naomi, and the name of his two sons Mahlon and Chilion, Ephrathites of Beth-lehem-judah. And they came into the country of Moab, and continued there.

2 And Elimelech Naomi's husband died; and she was left, and her two sons. And they took them wives of the women of Moab; the name of the one was Orpah, and the name of the other Ruth: and they dwelled there about ten years. And Mahlon and Chilion died also both of them; and the woman was left of her two sons and her husband.

The first two paragraphs are *straight narrative* (factual recitation of material, unembellished by non-essential matter) of *enveloping action.* Sometimes called *exposition,* enveloping action is designed to introduce the characters and give meaning to the scenes that follow. Out of enveloping action grow the *generating circumstances,* which introduce the chief characters' dilemmas or elements of *conflict.* Conflict is, basically, the struggle man undergoes as he lives his life. It may be physical, as when a man fights an animal, another man, a storm, or anything that may defeat or kill him. Or conflict may be mental, as when a man engages in the exchanges of business or interpersonal family relationships. Or it may be spiritual, as when a man struggles with his moral, religious, or social beliefs.

The prose of this passage and of the rest of the work should be carefully considered if you are to enjoy and understand it completely. Originally written in Hebrew, "The Book of Ruth" followed the Oriental tradition of *cadencial verse*—verse that does not divide into lines of regularly recurring rhythm patterns as does English poetry. Instead, it utilizes the entire *stanza* (the poetic division comparable to a paragraph in prose) to create a rhythm pattern resting on emphasis supplied by the natural modulations of the voice. These natural modulations result in an irregular spacing of accents to create cadences of sound that are pleasing to the ear in the same way speech is when vocabulary, syntax, and rhythm are highly organized. Such cadences are musical in their phrasal groupings—not musical in the sense of being timed with a metronome, but musical as the lyrics of songs are when a good singer rearranges word stress and tempo to create his own unique style. Attempting to retain the *flavor* (the characteristic quality, the distinctive nature of sound in the original) of the Hebraic verse, the King James translators emphasized the cadences of English—sometimes to the detriment of accuracy. Notice how the cadences form naturally as you read

Now it came to pass/ in the days/ when the judges ruled,/ that there was a famine/ in the land./ And a certain man/ of Beth-lehem-judah/ went to sojourn/ in the country of Moab,/ he,/ and his wife,/ and his two sons.

Compare those cadences with the lack of rhythm in the Theophile J. Meek translation in the *Goodspeed Bible,* a closer approximation of the prose you are accustomed to reading in newspapers and magazines:

In the time when the judges were in power a famine occurred in the land; so a certain man from Bethlehem in Judah emigrated to the country of Moab, along with his wife and two sons.°

As Alexander Pope once noted:

° *The Complete Bible, An American Translation* (Chicago, 1960).

> 'Tis not enough no harshness gives offense;
> The sound must seem an echo to the sense.
> *An Essay on Criticism* (*ll.* 364–365)

An extra dimension is added to the King James version as rhythm makes its unique contribution.

3 Then she arose with her daughters-in-law, that she might return from the country of Moab; for she had heard in the country of Moab how that the Lord had visited His people in giving them bread. Wherefore she went forth out of the place where she was, and her two daughters-in-law with her; and they went on the way to return unto the land of Judah. And Naomi said unto her two daughters-in-law, "Go, return each to her mother's house: the Lord deal kindly with you, as ye have dealt with the dead, and with me. The Lord grant you that ye may find rest, each of you in the house of her husband." Then she kissed them; and they lifted up their voice, and wept. And they said unto her, "Surely we will return with thee unto thy people."

4 And Naomi said, "Turn again, my daughters: why will ye go with me? are there yet any more sons in my womb, that they may be your husbands? Turn again, my daughters, go your way; for I am too old to have an husband. If I should say, I have hope, if I should have an husband also to-night, and should also bear sons; would ye tarry for them till they were grown? would ye stay for them from having husbands? nay, my daughters, for it grieveth me much for your sakes that the hand of the Lord is gone out against me."

5 And they lifted up their voice, and wept again: and Orpah kissed her mother-in-law; but Ruth clave unto her. And she said, "Behold, thy sister-in-law is gone back unto her people, and unto her gods: return thou after thy sister-in-law." And Ruth said, "Intreat me not to leave thee, or to return from following after thee: for whither thou goest, I will go; and where thou lodgest, I will lodge: thy people shall be my people, and thy God my God: where thou diest, will I die, and there will I be buried: the Lord do so to me, and more also, if ought but death part thee and me."

Paragraphs 3, 4, and 5 constitute the first scene, the exchange between Naomi and her daughters-in-law. Ruth and Orpah are compared in their loyalty to Naomi and contrasted in their decisiveness. Ruth emerges as a much clearer character through the focusing action. *Focus* is emphasis achieved by centering the reader's attention on a character, object, or attitude. Had Orpah not been introduced into the story for this comparative focusing action, Ruth's determination would be much less interesting.

Few passages are more often quoted than Ruth's speech from the King James translation. It has appealed to lovers and lovers of language from the time of its first appearance. Removed from context, it frequently adds its own note of fidelity and permanence to marriage ceremonies. That it is a remarkable blending of sound and sense designed to intensify emotion cannot be denied. Compare it with the Meek translation of the passage:

"Do not press me to leave you, to turn back from following you; for wherever you go, I will go; and wherever you lodge, I will lodge; your people shall be my people, and your god my god; wherever you die, I will die, and there will I be buried. May the LORD requite me and worse, if even death separates me from you."

The comparison should leave no doubt of the efficacy of the poetic treatment.

6 When she saw that she was steadfastly minded to go with her, then she left speaking unto her. So they two went until they came to Beth-lehem. And it came to pass, when they were come to Beth-lehem, that all the city was moved about them, and they said, "Is this Naomi?" And she said unto them, "Call me not Naomi, call me Mara: for the Almighty hath dealt very bitterly with me. I went out full, and the Lord hath brought me home again empty: why then call ye me Naomi, seeing the Lord hath testified against me, and the Almighty hath afflicted me?"

Paragraph 6 is a transition, serving to move the reader from one point in geographical time to another. Symbolism is, unfortunately, lost in the English translation, for *Naomi* meant "pleasant" in Hebrew; *Mara* meant "bitter."

7 So Naomi returned, and Ruth the Moabitess, her daughter-in-law, with her, which returned out of the country of Moab: and they came to Beth-lehem in the beginning of barley harvest. And Naomi had a kinsman of her husband's, a mighty man of wealth, of the family of Elimelech; and his name was Boaz. And Ruth the Moabitess said unto Naomi, "Let me now go to the field, and glean ears of corn after him in whose sight I shall find grace." And she said unto her, "Go, my daughter." And she went, and came, and gleaned in the field after the reapers: and her hap was to light on a part of the field belonging unto Boaz, who was of the kindred of Elimelech.

8 And, behold, Boaz came from Beth-lehem, and said unto the reapers, "The Lord be with you." And they answered him, "The Lord bless thee." Then said Boaz unto his servant that was set over the reapers, "Whose damsel is this?" And the

servant that was set over the reapers answered and said, "It is the Moabitish
damsel that came back with Naomi out of the country of Moab: and she said, I
pray you, let me glean and gather after the reapers among the sheaves: so she
came, and hath continued even from the morning until now, that she tarried a
little in the house."

9 Then said Boaz unto Ruth, "Hearest thou not, my daughter? Go not to glean in
another field, neither go from hence, but abide here fast by my maidens: let thine
eyes be on the field that they do reap, and go thou after them: have I not charged
the young men that they shall not touch thee? and when thou art athirst, go unto
the vessels, and drink of that which the young men have drawn."

10 Then she fell on her face, and bowed herself to the ground, and said unto
him, "Why have I found grace in thine eyes, that thou shouldest take knowledge of
me, seeing I am a stranger?"

11 And Boaz answered and said unto her, "It hath fully been shewed me, all that
thou hast done unto thy mother-in-law since the death of thine husband: and how
thou hast left thy father and thy mother, and the land of thy nativity, and art
come unto a people which thou knewest not heretofore. The Lord recompense thy
work, and a full reward be given thee of the Lord God of Israel, under whose wings
thou art come to trust."

12 Then she said, "Let me find favor in thy sight, my lord; for that thou hast
comforted me, and for that thou hast spoken friendly unto thine handmaid, though
I be not like unto one of thine handmaidens."

13 And Boaz said unto her, "At mealtime come thou hither, and eat of the bread,
and dip thy morsel in the vinegar." And she sat beside the reapers: and he reached
her parched corn, and she did eat, and was sufficed, and left. And when she was
risen up to glean, Boaz commanded his young men, saying, "Let her glean even
among the sheaves, and reproach her not: and let fall also some of the handfuls
of purpose for her, and leave them, that she may glean them, and rebuke her not."

Paragraphs 7–13 constitute a scene of *rising action*—that is, action growing out of the generating circumstances when complications occur. *Complications* result when a person or situation forces a character to react in some way. Boaz is introduced and his concern with honor is *foreshadowed* (hinted at or suggested in advance).

14 So she gleaned in the field until even, and beat out that she had gleaned: and
it was about an ephah of barley. And she took it up, and went into the city: and
her mother-in-law saw what she had gleaned: and she brought forth, and gave to her
that she had reserved after she was sufficed. And her mother-in-law said unto her,
"Where hast thou gleaned to-day? and where wroughtest thou? blessed be he that
did take knowledge of thee."

15 And she shewed her mother-in-law with whom she had wrought, and said, "The man's name with whom I wrought to-day is Boaz." And Naomi said unto her daughter-in-law, "Blessed be he of the Lord, who hath not left off His kindness to the living and to the dead." And Naomi said unto her, "The man is near of kin unto us, one of our next kinsmen."

16 And Ruth the Moabitess said, "He said unto me also, Thou shalt keep fast by my young men, until they have ended all my harvest."

17 And Naomi said unto Ruth her daughter-in-law, "It is good, my daughter, that thou go out with his maidens, that they meet thee not in any other field." So she kept fast by the maidens of Boaz to glean unto the end of barley harvest and of wheat harvest; and dwelt with her mother-in-law.

18 Then Naomi her mother-in-law said unto her, "My daughter, shall I not seek rest for thee, that it may be well with thee? And now is not Boaz of our kindred, with whose maidens thou wast? Behold, he winnoweth barley to-night in the threshing-floor. Wash thyself therefore, and anoint thee, and put thy raiment upon thee, and get thee down to the floor: but make not thyself known unto the man, until he shall have done eating and drinking. And it shall be, when he lieth down, that thou shalt mark the place where he shall lie, and thou shalt go in, and uncover his feet, and lay thee down; and he will tell thee what thou shalt do."

19 And she said unto her, "All that thou sayest unto me I will do."

Paragraphs 14–17 reveal the complicating element of Naomi's awareness and cleverness. They also serve as narrative transition. Paragraphs 18–19 add the complicating element of intrigue in further rising action, intrigue delightfully fostered by the translators. Notice the power of Naomi's instructions as cadences flow with rising intensity to that point where Boaz shall retire. Then, recognizing the emotional identification with the poetically stated ancient theme, the translators employed the iambs and anapests so familiar to their Shakespearean audiences. Those *feet* (groups of syllables working together as rhythm units) are *rising meter* (in measured bursts, they rise to meet the accented syllable and give it power) and they create the sounds of joy. And, if an iamb rises to joy, the anapest is even more joyous because it rises farther.

Now read the lines in their English measure. A rocker indicates an unaccented syllable; a dash marks the accented one. The feet are separated by *virgules* (straight lines separating poetic feet) to reveal four feet to each line except the second, third, and fifth. The *tetrameter* line (one containing four feet) is a useful one for subtle persuasion, for its lilting delicacy belies the seriousness of its sense. Line 2 shortens to *trimeter* (three feet) to emphasize the command; line 3 reduces farther still to *dimeter* (two feet) to reinforce the order; line 5 repeats the technique:

⏑ — ⏑ — ⏑ ⏑ — ⏑ —
And it|shall be,|when he li|eth down,

⏑ — ⏑ — ⏑ —
that thou|shalt mark|the place

⏑ — ⏑ —
where he|shall lie,

⏑ — ⏑ — ⏑ ⏑ ⏑ — ⏑ ⏑ —
and thou|shalt go in,|and uncov|er his feet,

⏑ — ⏑ —
and lay|thee down;

⏑ — ⏑ — ⏑ ⏑ — — —
and he|will tell thee|what thou|shalt do.

Naomi reveals her cleverness in the speech, and she is clever enough to temper it with subtle, promised delights. The second feet of lines 4 and 6 are *amphibrachs* (three-syllable feet accented in the middle to create a rhythm that Samuel Taylor Coleridge says "hastes with a stately stride"). Naomi suggests Ruth "shalt go in" with proud haste and Boaz will respond in kind and "will tell thee" the next instruction. And Ruth is commanded to follow his order. Naomi does not belabor the point; she merely employs the *spondee* (two equally accented syllables), a poetic foot of great power. Ruth has little choice but to obey—even if she were so inclined.

20 And she went down unto the floor, and did according to all that her mother-
in-law bade her. And when Boaz had eaten and drunk, and his heart was merry, he
went to lie down at the end of the heap of corn: and she came softly, and uncov-
ered his feet, and laid her down. And it came to pass at midnight, that the man
was afraid, and turned himself: and, behold, a woman lay at his feet. And he said,
"Who art thou?" And she answered, "I am Ruth thine handmaid: spread therefore
thy skirt over thine handmaid; for thou art a near kinsman."
21 And he said, "Blessed be thou of the Lord, my daughter: for thou hast shewed
more kindness in the latter end than at the beginning, inasmuch as thou followedst
not young men, whether poor or rich. And now, my daughter, fear not; I will do to
thee all that thou requirest: for all the city of my people doth know that thou are a
virtuous woman. And now it is true that I am thy near kinsman: howbeit there is a
kinsman nearer than I. Tarry this night, and it shall be in the morning, that if he
will perform unto thee the part of a kinsman, well; let him do the kinsman part:
but if he will not do the part of a kinsman to thee, then will I do the part of a kins-
man to thee, as the Lord liveth: lie down until the morning."

Paragraphs 20–21 reveal conflict within Boaz, the resolution of which was foreshadowed in paragraphs 7–13.

22 And she lay at his feet until the morning: and she rose up before one could know another. And he said, "Let it not be known that a woman came into the floor." Also he said, "Bring the vail that thou hast upon thee, and hold it." And when she held it, he measured six measures of barley, and laid it on her: and she went into the city.

23 And when she came to her mother-in-law, she said, "Who art thou, my daughter?" And she told her all that the man had done to her. And she said, "These six measures of barley gave he me; for he said to me, Go not empty unto thy mother-in-law." Then said she, "Sit still, my daughter, until thou know how the matter will fall: for the man will not be in rest, until he have finished the thing this day."

Paragraphs 22–23 intensify and heighten the *suspense* (excitement generated to make the reader want to know "What will happen next?"). The suspense device here is time. Detective stories utilize this suspense device regularly, as do sports stories. Naomi's wisdom is further revealed.

24 Then went Boaz up to the gate, and sat him down there: and, behold, the kinsman of whom Boaz spake came by; unto whom he said, "Ho, such a one! turn aside, sit down here." And he turned aside, and sat down. And he took ten men of the elders of the city, and said, "Sit ye down here." And they sat down. And he said unto the kinsman, "Naomi, that is come again out of the country of Moab, selleth a parcel of land, which was our brother Elimelech's: and I thought to advertise thee, saying, Buy it before the inhabitants, and before the elders of my people. If thou wilt redeem it, redeem it: but if thou wilt not redeem it, then tell me, that I may know: for there is none to redeem it beside thee; and I am after thee."

25 And he said, "I will redeem it."

26 Then said Boaz, "What day thou buyest the field of the hand of Naomi, thou must buy it also of Ruth the Moabitess, the wife of the dead, to raise up the name of the dead upon his inheritance."

27 And the kinsman said, "I cannot redeem it for myself, lest I mar mine own inheritance: redeem thou my right to thyself; for I cannot redeem it." Now this was the manner in former time in Israel concerning redeeming and concerning changing, for to confirm all things; a man plucked off his shoe, and gave it to his neighbor: and this was a testimony in Israel. Therefore the kinsman said unto Boaz, "Buy it for thee." So he drew off his shoe.

28 And Boaz said unto the elders, and unto all the people, "Ye are witnesses this day, that I have bought all that was Elimelech's, and all that was Chilion's and Mahlon's, of the hand of Naomi. Moreover, Ruth the Moabitess, the wife of Mahlon, have I purchased to be my wife, to raise up the name of the dead upon his inheritance, that the name of the dead be not cut off from among his brethren, and from the gate of his place: ye are witnesses this day."

[29]And all the people that were in the gate, and the elders, said, "We are witnesses. The Lord make the woman that is come into thine house like Rachel and like Leah, which two did build the house of Israel: and do thou worthily in Ephratah, and be famous in Beth-lehem: and let thy house be like the house of Pharez, whom Tamar bore unto Judah, of the seed which the Lord shall give thee of this young woman."

Paragraphs 24–29 lead to the *climax* (the point of highest interest in the story) as Boaz skillfully bargains and wins the right of redemption.

[30]So Boaz took Ruth, and she was his wife: and when he went in unto her, the Lord gave her conception, and she bare a son. And the women said unto Naomi, "Blessed be the Lord, which hath not left thee this day without a kinsman, that his name may be famous in Israel. And he shall be unto thee a restorer of thy life, and a nourisher of thine old age: for thy daughter-in-law, which loveth thee, which is better to thee than seven sons, hath born him." And Naomi took the child, and laid it in her bosom, and became nurse unto it. And the women her neighbors gave it a name, saying, "There is a son born to Naomi"; and they called his name Obed: he is the father of Jesse, the father of David. □

Paragraph 30 constitutes a *denouement* or solution, the careful tying up of all loose ends so that the reader is left with no unanswered questions. Detective stories employ this device today while most other kinds of stories end at the climax or immediately afterward.

In ten scenes, the author introduces three main characters (Naomi, Ruth, Boaz) and two foil characters (Orpah and the unnamed kinsman). *Foil characters* are those introduced to illuminate the qualities of a main character through comparison or contrast. They may also be needed to further the action of the story by their presence or behavior.

A theme emerges as we see Ruth's devotion triumph and Naomi's acceptance and cleverness sustain her. While this story suffers because of our religious involvement with it, an objective reading reveals Ruth to be a *stock character* (one who reacts completely predictably) in the manipulative exchange between Boaz and Naomi. Boaz, of course, never realizes he has been outmaneuvered by two women. Naomi becomes an interesting character as a result of her selfish motives, but she remains noble because of her desire to see Ruth safely married and the mother of a child bearing Mahlon's name, thus securing the line. Through helping Ruth achieve her destiny, Naomi also achieves her own.

The translators of the King James Bible were poets first, prose writers second. Thus, this early short story is written in straight narrative *poetic prose* (a blending of the best of poetic devices and prose elements). It utilizes the most common of all plots: boy wants girl, boy might not get girl, boy is self-sufficient, so boy gets girl. If you can divorce the story from its religious context, you can see how simple and interesting it is from a literary standpoint. While little description is employed and attention to character development is weak, the dialog and implicit material couple with the narrative flow to create a well-rounded story.

Now, reread the story, observing the *narrative flow* (the speed of the story line as it slows to focus on a scene or speeds along on panorama and exposition), dialog, and scene structure.

Since narrative techniques vary, another writer telling the same story might choose to begin the action nearer the climax and utilize flashbacks. A *flashback* is a scene that occurred chronologically before the story begins but which must be brought in to give meaning to incidents within the story. A variety of points of view might also be used. The story is now told from an *objective* (sometimes called *dramatic*) point of view. The objective point of view allows the writer to report everything he cares to, regardless of geography and time. However, as it is objective, he reports only externals in dialog and action, examining thoughts of none of the characters and making no speculations or assessments. But another writer might decide to use a *limited omniscient* point of view. He could then examine the thoughts of *one* character and any actions that character observes or takes part in. For example, Boaz could be interestingly handled with limited omnisciency; however, the author would lose the scenes between Ruth and Naomi. Using the *omniscient* point of view, though, the author could free himself from *any* limitations, entering *any* character's thoughts at will, roaming freely in space and time, being as subjective as he wished. And still another possibility would be a *first person* point of view. In such a case, the story would focus on Naomi—using the personal pronoun *I,* she could recount the incidents from her vantage point as she observed or heard reports of incidents. The first person point of view would involve more scenes, however, as the kinsman would have to report to Naomi his exchange with Boaz. Or the author might write her account as she tells it many years later, which would allow the possibility of dramatic irony, since the reader could be made aware of things from her narrative that she, as a character, could not assess because of her personal involvement.

From examining the point of view possibilities, you can see how that choice broadens or confines the story possibilities. Each point of view possibility changes the story, enriching or limiting its scope, and, as you become increasingly aware of it, you will appreciate its contribution to the short story. One reason there is no simple definition of the short story has to do with point of view: the short story is a highly flexible form, allowing extensive experimentation and combinations of possibilities. In Chapter V, we will have more to say about point of view.

Since the "Book of Ruth" is structured on straight narrative and dialog, "The Scythe" by Ray Bradbury should offer an interesting contrast. It is structured on description, dialog, and character analysis. Notice that the scenes are numbered for you with roman numerals. As you read, you should label the paragraphs of enveloping action, underline descriptive passages, place parentheses around phrases which reveal character, label rising action paragraphs, and indicate each complication as it is introduced into the story. You will recognize the poetic prose of this story because it refuses to be ignored. Examine the logic of poetic devices as they are employed. You should also notice that all the elements combine to create *verisimilitude* (believability—a vital ingredient of any writing) at the *moment of illumination* (that point at which a character understands something about life, or at which the reader understands the reason the author wanted to tell the story—this point is called the *pivot* in poetry). Is the moment of illumination also the climax? It may or may not be in a given story.

Symbolism is employed throughout the narrative in "The Scythe," and you should begin now to isolate symbolic matter in your reading. All literature that has endured is, in some way, symbolic. If it means something beyond the moment's amusement, literature must be applicable to any period, not only to the time in which it is written. Symbols, as we have said, are the signs which characterize larger ideas: flags are symbols of countries; Hermes (Mercury) is the symbol of rapid communication; the cross is a symbol of death and resurrection. Symbolism is the art of using symbols to suggest subtle, intangible truths of an elaborate nature. As ideas and attitudes cluster around a symbol, the elaboration on and interweaving of the symbol create a growing awareness in the reader of a truth that could not otherwise be expressed. You can easily identify the scythe as a symbol of harvesting that which is ripe, whether it be grain or human life. As you read "The Scythe," notice the growth of the symbol as it becomes the instrument of the "grim reaper," and then how the "grim" element becomes ironically paramount.

In seventeen scenes, Bradbury tells an engrossing tale, chronologically constructed without flashback. Necessary background material is supplied in dialog and *interior monolog* (a character's revealed thoughts as he seems to speak to himself). A timeless agrarian atmosphere grows out of the geographical setting. A desperate inevitability sets the mood from the beginning. The tone of the story is apocalyptic as a result of the pastoral setting, the religious references, and the implicit allusion to the "grim reaper."

Read the story first by skipping the discussions between the scenes. Then go back and reread it with the discussions.

The Scythe

by Ray Bradbury

I 1 Quite suddenly there was no more road. It ran down the valley like any other road, between slopes of barren, stony ground and live oak trees, and then past a broad field of wheat standing alone in the wilderness. It came up beside the small white house that belonged to the wheat field and then just faded out, as though there was no more use for it.

2 It didn't matter much, because just there the last of the gas was gone. Drew Erickson braked the ancient car to a stop and sat there, not speaking, staring at his big, rough farmer's hands.

3 Molly spoke, without moving where she lay in the corner beside him. "We must of took the wrong fork back yonder."

4 Drew nodded.

5 Molly's lips were almost as white as her face. Only they were dry, where her skin was damp with sweat. Her voice was flat, with no expression in it.

6 "Drew," she said. "Drew, what are we a-goin' to do now?"

7 Drew stared at his hands. A farmer's hands, with the farm blown out from under them by the dry, hungry wind that never got enough good loam to eat.

8 The kids in the back seat woke up and pried themselves out of the dusty litter of bundles and bedding. They poked their heads over the back of the seat and said:

9 "What are we stoppin' for, Pa? Are we gonna eat now, Pa? Pa, we're awful hungry. Can we eat now, Pa?"

10 Drew closed his eyes. He hated the sight of his hands.

11 Molly's fingers touched his wrist. Very light, very soft. "Drew, maybe in the house there they'd spare us somethin' to eat?"

12 A white line showed around his mouth. "Beggin'," he said harshly. "Ain't none of us ever begged before. Ain't none of us ever goin' to."

13 Molly's hand tightened on his wrist. He turned and saw her eyes. He saw the eyes of Susie and little Drew, looking at him. Slowly all the stiffness went out of his neck and his back. His face got loose and blank, shapeless like a thing that has

been beaten too hard and too long. He got out of the car and went up the path to the house. He walked uncertainly, like a man who is sick, or nearly blind.

Scenes I–IV establish the situation and generating circumstances of the plot. They are, therefore, enveloping action. In scene I, description involves the reader as action verbs and poetic rhythms create the scene. Irony suggests that the road ends and the gas runs out simultaneously in accordance with fate. All characters are introduced in this scene, but the focus is on Drew. This is his story, told from his point of view—he is the focus of limited omnisciency. The reader never observes anything except as Drew observes it. Notice how an understanding of Molly results from Drew's focusing his point of view on her. His conflict is established early: he is in conflict with himself, though that conflict will take many forms in the story. His hands, which are to be so important, serve as a focal point in characterization from the very beginning, and they remain dominant throughout the story. Molly's desperation and determination are suggested also. Did you notice poetic devices such as the personification of the wind? (*Personification* is the attribution of human qualities to inanimate objects or abstractions.) Point out other devices, for instance, the farm blown out from under Drew's hands.

II 14 The door of the house was open. Drew knocked three times. There was nothing inside but silence, and a white window curtain moving in the slow, hot air.

15 He knew it before he went in. He knew there was death in the house. It was that kind of silence.

16 He went through a small, clean living room and down a little hall. He wasn't thinking anything. He was past thinking. He was going toward the kitchen, unquestioning, like an animal.

17 Then he looked through an open door and saw the dead man.

18 He was an old man, lying out on a clean white bed. He hadn't been dead long; not long enough to lose the last quiet look of peace. He must have known he was going to die, because he wore his grave clothes—an old black suit, brushed and neat, and a clean white shirt and a black tie.

19 A scythe leaned against the wall beside the bed. Between the old man's hands there was a blade of wheat, still fresh. A ripe blade, golden and heavy in the tassel.

20 Drew went into the bedroom, walking soft. There was a coldness on him. He took off his broken, dusty hat and stood by the bed, looking down.

21 The paper lay open on the pillow beside the old man's head. It was meant to be read. Maybe a request for burial, or to call a relative. Drew scowled over the words, moving his pale, dry lips.

22 *To him who stands beside me at my death bed:* Being of sound mind, and alone in the world as it has been decreed, I, John Buhr, do give and bequeath this farm, with all pertaining to it, to the man who is to come. Whatever his name or origin shall be, it will not matter. The farm is his, and the wheat; the scythe, and the task ordained thereto. Let him take them freely, and without question—and remember that I, John Buhr, am only the giver, not the ordainer. To which I set my hand and seal this third day of April, 1938. (Signed) John Buhr. *Kyrie eléison!*

The second scene introduces the three foreshadowing elements: silence, the scythe, and the wheat. The living and the dead are sharply contrasted in appearance, further detailing Drew's character. His hat is "broken and dusty." Is this synecdoche? Examine the tone of the old man's note. It is as cadenced as anything in "The Book of Ruth," and the language has the flavor of the King James Bible. The final words of the note are a prayer meaning "The Lord have mercy upon us," an *ambiguity* (the expression of ideas in language designed to convey more than one idea) that is also *poetic irony* (a condition which is the tragic reverse of what the character thinks). Drew may assume the ritualized words are merely the equivalent of *amen,* but he will learn the old man is literally asking mercy for himself and Drew.

III 23 Drew walked back through the house and opened the screen door. He said, "Molly, you come in. Kids, you stay in the car."

24 Molly came inside. He took her to the bedroom. She looked at the will, the scythe, the wheat field moving in a hot wind outside the window. Her white face tightened up and she bit her lips and held onto him. "It's too good to be true. There must be some trick to it."

25 Drew said, "Our luck's changin', that's all. We'll have work to do, stuff to eat, somethin' over our heads to keep rain off." He touched the scythe. It gleamed like a half-moon. Words were scratched on its blade: WHO WIELDS ME—WIELDS THE WORLD! It didn't mean much to him, right at that moment.

26 "Drew," Molly asked, staring at the old man's clasped hands, "why—why's he holdin' that wheat-stalk so hard in his fingers?"

27 Just then the heavy silence was broken by the sound of the kids scrambling up the front porch. Molly gasped.

IV 28 They lived in the house. They buried the old man on a hill and said some words over him, and came back down and swept the house and unloaded the car and had something to eat, because there was food, lots of it, in the kitchen; and they did nothing for three days but fix the house and look at the land and lie in the good beds, and then look at one another in surprise that all this was happening this way, and their stomachs were full and there was even a cigar for him to smoke in the evenings.

29There was a small barn behind the house and in the barn a bull and three cows; and there was a well-house, a spring-house, under some big trees that kept it cool. And inside the well-house were big sides of beef and bacon and pork and mutton, enough to feed a family five times their size for a year, two years, maybe three. There was a churn and a box of cheese there, and big metal cans for the milk.

The third scene reveals Molly's character as she accepts serendipitous good luck—a dramatically ironic moment. That irony is intensified in foreshadowing (her fear of trickery), a foreshadowing strengthened in its effect when she is startled by life sounds (the children) shattering the silence of death in the house. Explain the woeful alliteration of the scythe's inscription. Why might the line following the inscription be called "masterful understatement?"

The fourth scene is transitional narrative covering three days. It prepares the reader for the rising action which is to come. Verbs-of-being are skillfully employed in paragraph 2 of this scene. The essentials *exist* in this house. The religious tone is also fully realized in this three-day transition as the reader associates the seventy-two hours with Christ's death and resurrection. Simple exposition is avoided in this scene, and panorama allows the three days to sweep by on a series of small pictures skillfully sketched to suggest a large canvas the reader must examine hurriedly in passing.

V 30On the fourth morning Drew Erickson lay in bed looking at the scythe, and he knew it was time for him to work because there was ripe grain in the long field; he had seen it with his eyes, and he did not want to get soft. Three days sitting were enough for any man. He roused himself in the first fresh smell of dawn and took the scythe and held it before him as he walked out into the field. He held it up in his hands and swung it down.

31It was a big field of grain. Too big for one man to tend, and yet one man had tended it.

32At the end of the first day of work, he walked in with the scythe riding his shoulder quietly, and there was a look on his face of a puzzled man. It was a wheat field the like of which he had never seen. It ripened only in separate clusters, each set off from the others. Wheat shouldn't do that. He didn't tell Molly. Nor did he tell her the other things about the field. About how, for instance, the wheat rotted within a few hours after he cut it down. Wheat shouldn't do that, either. He was not greatly worried. After all, there was food at hand.

Scenes V–XV are devoted to rising action. Suspense is built, step by logical step, while unity is achieved through unbroken chronology. Complications are introduced coherently, each one a little more intense than the last.

The fifth scene pinpoints Drew's silent conflict with nature. The wheat grows strangely, irregularly, "unnaturally." Notice how silence is woven into the scene. And notice how personification begins to enlarge the scythe symbol.

VI [33]The next morning the wheat he had left rotting, cut down, had taken hold and come up again in little green sprouts, with tiny roots, all born again.

[34]Drew Erickson rubbed his chin, wondered what and why and how it acted that way, and what good it would be to him—he couldn't sell it. A couple of times during the day he walked far up in the hills to where the old man's grave was, just to be sure the old man was there, maybe with some notion he might get an idea there about the field. He looked down and saw how much land he owned. The wheat stretched three miles in one direction toward the mountains, and was about two acres wide, patches of it in seedlings, patches of it golden, patches of it green, patches of it fresh cut by his hand. But the old man said nothing concerning this; there were a lot of stones and dirt in his face now. The grave was in the sun and the wind and silence. So Drew Erickson walked back down to use the scythe, curious, enjoying it because it seemed important. He didn't know just why, but it was. Very, very important.

[35]He couldn't just let the wheat stand. There were always new patches of it ripened, and in his figuring out loud to no one in particular he said, "If I cut the wheat for the next ten years, just as it ripens up, I don't think I'll pass the same spot twice. Such a damn big field." He shook his head. "That wheat ripens just so. Never too much of it so I can't cut all the ripe stuff each day. That leaves nothin' but green grain. And the next mornin', sure enough, another patch of ripe stuff. . . ."

Drew's conflict becomes more obvious in the sixth scene when he is forced into conflict with himself as well as with nature. Another element of conflict becomes obvious (fate? God?) when Drew is impelled to cut the wheat. Explain the effect of rhythm in "The grave was in the sun and the wind and silence." How do sound and sense combine to suggest something that is unstated?

VII [36]It was damned foolish to cut the grain when it rotted as quick as it fell. At the end of the week he decided to let it go a few days.

[37]He lay in bed late, just listening to the silence in the house that wasn't anything like death silence, but a silence of things living well and happily.

38 He got up, dressed, and ate his breakfast slowly. He wasn't going to work. He went out to milk the cows, stood on the porch smoking a cigarette, walked about the backyard a little and then came back in and asked Molly what he had gone out to do.

39 "Milk the cows," she said.

40 "Oh, yes," he said, and went out again. He found the cows waiting and full, and milked them and put the milk cans in the spring-house, but thought of other things. The wheat. The scythe.

41 All through the morning he sat on the back porch rolling cigarettes. He made a toy boat for little Drew and one for Susie, and then he churned some of the milk into butter and drew off the buttermilk, but the sun was in his head, aching. It burned there. He wasn't hungry for lunch. He kept looking at the wheat and the wind bending and tipping and ruffling it. His arms flexed, his fingers, resting on his knee as he sat again on the porch, made a kind of grip in the empty air, itching. The pads of his palms itched and burned. He stood up and wiped his hands on his pants and sat down and tried to roll another cigarette and got mad at the mixings and threw it all away with a muttering. He had a feeling as if a third arm had been cut off of him, or he had lost something of himself. It had to do with his hands and his arms.

42 He heard the wind whisper in the field.

43 By one o'clock he was going in and out of the house, getting underfoot, thinking about digging an irrigation ditch, but all the time really thinking about the wheat and how ripe and beautiful it was, aching to be cut.

44 "Damn it to hell!"

45 He strode into the bedroom, took the scythe down off its wall-pegs. He stood holding it. He felt cool. His hands stopped itching. His head didn't ache. The third arm was returned to him. He was intact again.

46 It was instinct. Illogical as lightning striking and not hurting. Each day the grain must be cut. It had to be cut. Why? Well, it just did, that was all. He laughed at the scythe in his big hands. Then, whistling, he took it out to the ripe and waiting field and did the work. He thought himself a little mad. Hell, it was an ordinary-enough wheat field, really, wasn't it? Almost.

The seventh scene sharpens Drew's conflict. Examine the different "silences" in the house to see if you can detect how they are created by poetically constructed sound patterns utilizing the letters *s* and *l*. Personification and rhythm combine to create the sense of "but the sun was in his head, aching. It burned there." Eleven words create a vivid picture in poetry that you probably could not duplicate in a hundred words of prose. If you disagree, attempt such duplication as a writing exercise. Explain "He wasn't hungry for lunch," noticing the effect of cadence combined with ambiguity.

Personification has now endowed the scythe with imperativeness. Symbolically, it has become a part of Drew. And *h, r, d, w,* and *n* combine in alliteration and consonance with *i* and *e* assonance to create *onomatopoeia* (a sound pattern that creates the sound literally—as *bang* or "He heard the wind whisper in the field") as personified nature of the field summons him. His "Damn it to hell!" may seem little more than an exclamation of disgust, but ambiguity and irony pervade the words. As the symbol claims Drew completely, he is again complete. And the act of completion is "illogical as lightning striking"—a comparison bright with assonance and alliteration, but shocking in saṁvegha as it fails to shock: "and not hurting." *Hell* in the last sentence is poetically ironic again as it is definitely removed from a religious context and used as simple interjection. That it can be so casually employed is the epitome of irony, and Drew's interior monolog reveals his near-awareness of that irony.

VIII [47]The days loped away like gentle horses.

[48]Drew Erickson began to understand his work as a sort of dry ache and hunger and need. Things built in his head.

[49]One noon, Susie and little Drew giggled and played with the scythe while their father lunched in the kitchen. He heard them. He came out and took it away from them. He didn't yell at them. He just looked very concerned and locked the scythe up after that, when it wasn't being used.

[50]He never missed a day, scything.

[51]Up. Down. Up, down, and across. Back and up and down and across. Cutting. Up. Down.

[52]Up.

[53]Think about the old man and the wheat in his hands when he died.

[54]Down.

[55]Think about this dead land, with wheat living on it.

[56]Up.

[57]Think about the crazy patterns of ripe and green wheat, the way it grows!

[58]Down.

[59]Think about . . .

[60]The wheat whirled in a full yellow tide at his ankles. The sky blackened. Drew Erickson dropped the scythe and bent over to hold his stomach, his eyes running blindly. The world reeled.

[61]"I've killed somebody!" he gasped, choking, holding to his chest, falling to his knees beside the blade. "I've killed a lot—"

[62]The sky revolved like a blue merry-go-round at the county fair in Kansas. But no music. Only a ringing in his ears.

The eighth scene is pivotal. The opening sentence is a beautiful transition, poetically rich and revelatory of Drew's agrarian thought processes. Personification and simile create vivid imagery as repeated *l* sounds lilt through the loping rhythm of the line and close it, like a day, on a gentle, unaccented syllable. In the act of scything, *free verse* (verse freed from the traditional rules of regular rhythm and rhyme, but still restrained by such impositions as repetition and parallel grammatical structure) creates a vivid picture of action interwoven with interior monolog until the moment of illumination occurs for Drew. The reader has suspected this truth, but *his* moment of illumination is yet to come. Then, completing the poetic tapestry, the final paragraph refers obliquely to the opening one. Gentle horses lope around the platform of that agrarian county fair merry-go-round which is as blue as the days of sentence 1.

IX [63]Molly was sitting at the blue kitchen table peeling potatoes when he blundered into the kitchen, dragging the scythe behind him.

[64]"Molly!"

[65]She swam around in the wet of his eyes.

[66]She sat there, her hands fallen open, waiting for him to finally get it out.

[67]"Get the things packed," he said, looking at the floor.

[68]"Why?"

[69]"We're leaving," he said, dully.

[70]"We're leaving?" she said.

[71]"That old man. You know what he did here? It's the wheat, Molly, and this scythe. Every time you use the scythe on the wheat a thousand people die. You cut across them and—"

[72]Molly got up and put the knife down and the potatoes to one side and said, understandingly, "We traveled a lot and haven't eaten good until the last month here, and you been workin' every day and you're tired—"

[73]"I hear voices, sad voices, out there. In the wheat," he said. "Tellin' me to stop. Tellin' me not to kill them!"

[74]"Drew!"

[75]He didn't hear her. "The field grows crooked, wild, like a crazy thing. I didn't tell you. But it's wrong."

[76]She stared at him. His eyes were blue glass, nothing else.

[77]"You think I'm crazy," he said, "but wait 'til I tell you. Oh, God, Molly, help me; I just killed my mother!"

[78]"Stop it!" she said firmly.

[79]"I cut down one stalk of wheat and I killed her. I felt her dyin', that's how I found out just now—"

[80]"Drew!" Her voice was like a crack across the face, angry and afraid now. "Shut up!"

[81]He mumbled. "Oh—Molly—"

[82]The scythe dropped from his hands, clamored on the floor. She picked it up with a snap of anger and set it in one corner. "Ten years I been with you," she said. "Sometimes we had nothin' but dust and prayers in our mouths. Now, all this good luck sudden, and you can't bear up under it!"

[83]She brought the Bible from the living room.

[84]She rustled its pages over. They sounded like the wheat rustling in a small, slow wind. "You sit down and listen," she said.

[85]A sound came in from the sunshine. The kids, laughing in the shade of the large live oak beside the house.

[86]She read from the Bible, looking up now and again to see what was happening to Drew's face.

Repeated color (*blue kitchen table*) creates a gentle transition into the ninth scene which is focused, through Drew's point of view, on Molly. Her strength and his fear create a new conflict in him, a conflict now including Molly, fate or God, and nature. Poetry elevates the language to onomatopoeia as the reader hears the wheat field struggling tensely against the Bible in Drew's mind. Ironically, he does not understand that the tension is in himself. "She rustled its pages over. They sounded like the wheat rustling in a small, slow wind. 'You sit down and listen,' she said."

X [87]She read from the Bible each day after that. The following Wednesday, a week later, when Drew walked down to the distant town to see if there was any General Delivery mail, there was a letter.

[88]He came home looking two hundred years old.

[89]He held the letter out to Molly and told her what it said in a cold, uneven voice.

[90]"Mother passed away—one o'clock Tuesday afternoon—her heart—"

[91]All that Drew Erickson had to say was, "Get the kids in the car, load it up with food. We're goin' on to California."

[92]"Drew—" said his wife, holding the letter.

[93]"You know yourself," he said, "this is poor grain land. Yet look how ripe it grows. I ain't told you all the things. It ripens in patches, a little each day. It ain't right. And when I cut it, it rots! And next mornin' it comes up without any help, growin' again! Last Tuesday, a week ago, when I cut the grain it was like rippin' my own flesh. I heard somebody scream. It sounded just like—And now, today, this letter."

94 She said, "We're stayin' here."

95 "Molly."

96 "We're stayin' here, where we're sure of eatin' and sleepin' and livin' decent and livin' long. I'm not starvin' my children down again, ever!"

97 The sky was blue through the windows. The sun slanted in, touching half of Molly's calm face, shining one eye bright blue. Four or five water drops hung and fell from the kitchen faucet slowly, shining, before Drew sighed. The sigh was husky and resigned and tired. He nodded, looking away. "All right," he said. "We'll stay."

98 He picked up the scythe weakly. The words on the metal leaped up with a sharp glitter.

99 WHO WIELDS ME—WIELDS THE WORLD!

100 "We'll stay. . . ."

The tenth scene intensifies the conflict—Drew is defeated by the combination of conflicting elements. The colors green, blue, and yellow have been used repeatedly in the story thus far. They represent, of course, earth, air, and fire (both sun and ripening wheat); and, as it drips from the faucet, water completes this allusion to the four elements of life. For Drew, it has become a very long life. *Hyperbole* (gross exaggeration used to achieve emphasis in effect) makes him look "two hundred years old." And all eternity seems to reside in the woeful *w*'s of the close of the scene from the words "We'll stay" in paragraph 97 to the words "We'll stay" in paragraph 100.

XI 101 Next morning he walked to the old man's grave. There was a single fresh sprout of wheat growing in the center of it. The same sprout, reborn, that the old man had held in his hands weeks before.

102 He talked to the old man, getting no answers.

103 "You worked the field all your life because you *had* to, and one day you came across your own life growin' there. You knew it was yours. You cut it. And you went home, put on your grave clothes, and your heart gave out and you died. That's how it was, wasn't it? And you passed the land on to me, and when I die, I'm supposed to hand it over to someone else."

104 Drew's voice had awe in it. "How long a time has this been goin' on? With nobody knowin' about this field and its use except the man with the scythe . . . ?"

105 Quite suddenly he felt very old. The valley seemed ancient, mummified, secretive, dried and bent and powerful. When the Indians danced on the prairie it had been here, this field. The same sky, the same wind, the same wheat. And, before the Indians? Some Cro-Magnon, gnarled and shag-haired, wielding a crude wooden scythe, perhaps, prowling down through the living wheat. . . .

106 Drew returned to work. Up, down. Up, down. Obsessed with the idea of being

the wielder of *the* scythe. He, himself! It burst upon him in a mad, wild surge of strength and horror.

107 Up! WHO WIELDS ME! Down! WIELDS THE WORLD!

108 He had to accept the job with some sort of philosophy. It was simply his way of getting food and housing for his family. They deserved eating and living decent, he thought, after all these years.

109 Up and down. Each grain a life he neatly cut into two pieces. If he planned it carefully—he looked at the wheat—why, he and Molly and the kids could live forever!

110 Once he found the place where the grain grew that was Molly and Susie and little Drew he would never cut it.

111 And then, like a signal, it came, quietly.

112 Right there, before him.

113 Another sweep of the scythe and he'd cut them away.

114 Molly, Drew, Susie. It was certain. Trembling, he knelt and looked at the few grains of wheat. They glowed at his touch.

115 He groaned with relief. What if he had cut them down, never guessing? He blew out his breath and got up and took the scythe and stood back away from the wheat and stood for a long while looking down.

116 Molly thought it awfully strange when he came home early and kissed her on the cheek, for no reason at all.

XII 117 At dinner, Molly said, "You quit early today? Does—does the wheat still spoil when it falls?"

118 He nodded and took more meat.

119 She said, "You ought to write to the Agriculture people and have them come look at it."

120 "No," he said.

121 "I was just suggestin'," she said.

122 His eyes dilated. "I got to stay here all my life. Can't nobody else mess with that wheat; they wouldn't know where to cut and not to cut. They might cut the wrong parts."

123 "What wrong parts?"

124 "Nothin'," he said, chewing slowly. "Nothin' at all."

125 He slapped his fork down, hard. "Who knows *what* they might want to do! Those government men! They might even—might even want to plow the whole field under!"

126 Molly nodded. "That's just what it needs," she said. "And start all over again, with new seed."

127 He didn't finish eating. "I'm not writin' any gover'ment, and I'm not handin' this field over to no stranger to cut, and that's that!" he said, and the screen door banged behind him.

XIII [128]He detoured around that place where the lives of his children and his wife grew up in the sun, and used his scythe on the far end of the field where he knew he would make no mistakes.

[129]But he no longer liked the work. At the end of an hour he knew he had brought death to three of his old, loved friends in Missouri. He read their names in the cut grain and couldn't go on.

[130]He locked the scythe in the cellar and put the key away. He was done with the reaping, done for good and all.

In the eleventh scene, free verse again dominates a portion of the narrative. Prose lacks the power to evoke the sense of time past, time present, and time to come as it is created in paragraphs 105 through 107. Symbol becomes allegory as Drew equates himself with the long train of reapers in "except the man with the scythe." Repetition in "The same sky, the same wind, the same wheat" beats in the reader's temples with the insistence of racing blood. And the scythe becomes *the* scythe.

Survival of the family is added as a conflicting element which leads into the twelfth scene, creating verisimilitude in Drew's decision (even determination) to stay. Logically, scene thirteen presents his determination to stop *all* death. Irony rests heavily in the final line: Is his decision for "good" because it is for "all"?

XIV [131]He smoked his pipe in the evening, on the front porch, and told the kids stories to hear them laugh. But they didn't laugh much. They seemed withdrawn, tired and funny, like they weren't his children any more.

[132]Molly complained of a headache, dragged around the house a little, went to bed early and fell into a deep sleep. That was funny, too. Molly always stayed up late and was full of vinegar.

[133]The wheat field rippled with moonlight on it, making it into a sea.

[134]It wanted cutting. Certain parts needed cutting *now.* Drew Erickson sat, swallowing quietly, trying not to look at it.

[135]What'd happen to the world if he never went in the field again? What'd happen to people ripe for death, who waited the coming of the scythe?

[136]He'd wait and see.

[137]Molly was breathing softly when he blew out the oil lamp and got to bed. He couldn't sleep. He heard the wind in the wheat, felt the hunger to do the work in his arms and fingers.

[138]In the middle of the night he found himself walking in the field, the scythe in his hands. Walking like a crazy man, walking and afraid, half-awake. He didn't remember unlocking the cellar door, getting the scythe, but here he was in the moonlight, walking in the grain.

[139]Among these grains there were many who were old, weary, wanting so very much to sleep. The long, quiet, moonless sleep.

[140]The scythe held him, grew into his palms, forced him to walk.

[141]Somehow, struggling, he got free of it. He threw it down, ran off into the wheat, where he stopped and went down on his knees.

[142]"I don't want to kill anymore," he said. "If I work with the scythe I'll have to kill Molly and the kids. Don't ask me to do that!"

[143]The stars only sat in the sky, shining.

The fourteenth scene foreshadows the death-in-life of Drew's family as his inner conflict grows. He recognizes self-interest, duty, and responsibility, but love and fear are greater than these. Richly evocative, the final line of the scene defies analysis. In structure, it is *pure poetry* (poetry designed to create response through sound and personal response of the reader). It doesn't *mean* anything except what the reader wishes it to mean. Nor is his response logical. Springing from his inner self, that response is usually so unique and intense he cannot explain it. Nor should he try. Because the line is pure poetry, its meaning is as vast as the sky it includes.

XV [144]Behind him, he heard a dull, thumping sound.

[145]Something shot up over the hill into the sky. It was like a living thing, with arms of red color, licking at the stars. Sparks fell into his face. The thick, hot odor of fire came with it.

[146]The house!

[147]Crying out, he got sluggishly, hopelessly, to his feet, looking at the big fire.

[148]The little white house with the live oaks was roaring up in one savage bloom of fire. Heat rolled over the hill and he swam in it and went down in it, stumbling, drowning over his head.

[149]By the time he got down the hill there was not a shingle, bolt or threshold of it that wasn't alive with flame. It made blistering, crackling, fumbling noises.

[150]No one screamed inside. No one ran around or shouted.

[151]He yelled in the yard. "Molly! Susie! Drew!"

[152]He got no answer. He ran close in until his eyebrows withered and his skin crawled hot like paper burning, crisping, curling up in tight little curls.

[153]"Molly! Susie!"

[154]The fire settled contentedly down to feed. Drew ran around the house a dozen times, all alone, trying to find a way in. Then he sat where the fire roasted his body and waited until all the walls had sunken down with fluttering crashes, until the last ceilings bent, blanketing the floors with molten plaster and scorched lathing. Until the flames died and smoke coughed up, and the new day came slowly; and there was nothing but embering ashes and an acid smoldering.

155 Disregarding the heat fanning from the leveled frames, Drew walked into the ruin. It was still too dark to see much. Red light glowed on his sweating throat. He stood like a stranger in a new and different land. Here—the kitchen. Charred tables, chairs, the iron stove, the cupboards. Here—the hall. Here the parlor and then over here was the bedroom where—

156 Where Molly was still alive.

157 She slept among fallen timbers and angry-colored pieces of wire spring and metal.

158 She slept as if nothing had happened. Her small white hands lay at her sides, flaked with sparks. Her calm face slept with a flaming lath across one cheek.

159 Drew stopped and didn't believe it. In the ruin of her smoking bedroom she lay on a glittering bed of sparks, her skin intact, and her breast rising, falling, taking air.

160 "Molly!"

161 Alive and sleeping after the fire, after the walls had roared down, after ceilings had collapsed upon her and flame had lived all about her.

162 His shoes smoked as he pushed through piles of fuming litter. It could have seared his feet off at the ankles, he wouldn't have known.

163 "Molly . . ."

164 He bent over her. She didn't move or hear him, and she didn't speak. She wasn't dead. She wasn't alive. She just lay there with the fire surrounding her and not touching her, not harming her in any way. Her cotton nightgown was streaked with ashes, but not burnt. Her brown hair was pillowed on a tumble of red-hot coals.

165 He touched her cheek, and it was cold, cold in the middle of hell. Tiny breaths trembled her half-smiling lips.

166 The children were there, too. Behind a veil of smoke he made out two smaller figures huddled in the ashes sleeping.

167 He carried all three of them out to the edge of the wheat field.

168 "Molly. Molly, wake up! Kids! Kids, wake up!"

169 They breathed and didn't move and went on sleeping.

170 "Kids, wake up! Your mother is—"

171 Dead? No, not dead. But—

172 He shook the kids as if they were to blame. They paid no attention; they were busy with their dreams. He put them back down and stood over them, his face cut with lines.

173 He knew why they'd slept through the fire and continued to sleep now. He knew why Molly just lay there, never wanting to laugh again.

174 The power of the wheat and the scythe.

175 Their lives, supposed to end yesterday, May 30th, 1938, had been prolonged simply because he refused to cut the grain. They should have died in the fire. That's the way it was meant to *be*. But since he had not used the scythe, nothing could

hurt them. A house had flamed and fallen and still they lived, caught halfway, not dead, not alive. Simply—waiting. And all over the world thousands more just like them, victims of accidents, fires, disease, suicide, waited, slept just like Molly and her children slept. Not able to die, not able to live. All because a man was afraid of harvesting the ripe grain. All because one man thought he could stop working with a scythe and never work with that scythe again.

176 He looked down upon the children. The job had to be done every day and every day with never a stopping but going on, with never a pause, but always the harvesting, forever and forever and forever.

Scene XV creates a poetically dynamic fire. Personified in the simile "like a living thing," it has red arms, and it licks at the stars the reader has so recently been lost among. Heat sears him in the process. That fire blooms, roars, and fumbles through the house before it finally settles "contentedly down to feed." Finally it dies in "embering ashes and an acid smoldering"—imagery that lies hot on the skin and stings the nose with odors burned out of sound.

Isolation stretches around Drew as he stands "like a stranger in a new and different land" before "the bedroom where—," where saṁvegha supplies the vivid poetic shock of "Where Molly was still alive." Again "hell" intrudes itself, ambiguously again. She lies "in the middle of hell"—a hell of heat, a hell of disaster, and a hell of his own making, for it is an inconceivable geographical spot transplanted to a rational earth. And now the living death forced on his family brings awareness of what love and responsibility demand. And the demand is eternal.

XVI 177 All right, he thought. All right. I'll use the scythe.

178 He didn't say good-by to his family. He turned with a slow-feeding anger and found the scythe and walked rapidly, then he began to trot, then he ran with long jolting strides into the field, raving, feeling the hunger in his arms, as the wheat whipped and flailed his legs. He pounded through it, shouting. He stopped.

179 "Molly!" he cried, and raised the blade and swung it down.

180 "Susie!" he cried. "Drew!" And swung the blade down again.

181 Somebody screamed. He didn't turn to look at the fire-ruined house.

182 And then, sobbing wildly, he rose above the grain again and again and hewed to left and right and to left and to right and to left and to right. Over and over and over! Slicing out huge scars in green wheat and ripe wheat, with no selection and no care, cursing, over and over, swearing, laughing, the blade swinging up in the sun and falling in the sun with a singing whistle! Down!

183 Bombs shattered London, Moscow, Tokyo.

184 The blade swung insanely.

185 And the kilns of Belsen and Buchenwald took fire.

186 The blade sang, crimson wet.

187 And mushrooms vomited out blind suns at White Sands, Hiroshima, Bikini, and up, through, and in continental Siberian skies.

188 The grain wept in a green rain, falling.

189 Korea, Indo-China, Egypt, India trembled; Asia stirred, Africa woke in the night. . . .

190 And the blade went on rising, crashing, severing, with the fury and the rage of a man who has lost and lost so much that he no longer cares what he does to the world.

XVII 191 Just a few short miles off the main highway, down a rough dirt road that leads to nowhere, just a few short miles from a highway jammed with traffic bound for California.

192 Once in a while during the long years a jalopy gets off the main highway, pulls up steaming in front of the charred ruin of a little white house at the end of the dirt road, to ask instructions from the farmer they see just beyond, the one who works insanely, wildly, without ever stopping, night and day, in the endless fields of wheat.

193 But they get no help and no answer. The farmer in the field is too busy, even after all these years; too busy slashing and chopping the green wheat instead of the ripe.

194 And Drew Erickson moves on with his scythe, with the light of blind suns and a look of white fire in his never-sleeping eyes, on and on and on. . . . □

Scene XVI presents the climax of the story. Drew kills his family; then, maddened, he reaps blindly, not discriminating between green and ripe patches. The moment of illumination now occurs for the reader as he suddenly sees a "reason" for "reasonless" war in the violence of verse freed to create violence.

Scene XVII is denouement, bringing the story full circle. A subtle social comment seems to rest in the prolonging of useless life as the young die in war.

"The Scythe" is both fantasy and allegory, but it is believable because it is logically developed, interestingly told, and subtle in enlisting the reader's sympathy through poetic devices—particularly allusion. The reader can accept the basic premise of the story because he is already familiar with certain elements of the plot.

While these two short stories have little in common except agrarian setting, both exhibit carefully planned, effective narrative structure. In both, the author isolated the meaning he wished to reveal to his reader. Then, choosing a series of scenes that would convey that message or theme, he built on the foundation of them. Scene flows into scene, the narrative flow slowing or speeding along at the author's command in each story until a logical, acceptable conclusion results. The reader is satisfied.

Suggested Activity. Choose a story you know and like. Examine it, marking the scenes. Label them as enveloping action, generating circumstances, rising action, climax, and denouement (but remember, not all stories *have* a denouement). Isolate poetic devices. Discover the uses of description in the story. How is straight narrative used? How do the character sketch and description work together? What are the transitional devices? Is there a pivotal scene containing the moment of illumination? What is the theme? It will supply a very abbreviated *précis* (a shortcut or a brief; abstracted thought, reduced to the pithiest essence possible) of the story.

Suggested Assignments. 1. Read "The Upturned Face," which follows. Write a three-paragraph analysis of the structure of the story. Be sure to indicate the enveloping action, generating circumstances, rising action, climax, and denouement (if there is one).

2. In three paragraphs, discuss the element of conflict in this story. Do not oversimplify in haste.

3. Discuss the realism of the dialog. What makes it seem true to life or unreal, whichever you feel the case to be?

The Upturned Face

by Stephen Crane

1 "What will we do now?" said the adjutant, troubled and excited.

2 "Bury him," said Timothy Lean.

3 The two officers looked down close to their toes where lay the body of their comrade. The face was chalk-blue; gleaming eyes stared at the sky. Over the two upright figures was a windy sound of bullets, and on the top of the hill Lean's prostrate company of Spitzbergen infantry was firing measured volleys.

4 "Don't you think it would be better—" began the adjutant. "We might leave him until tomorrow."

5 "No," said Lean. "I can't hold that post an hour longer. I've got to fall back, and we've got to bury old Bill."

6 "Of course," said the adjutant, at once. "Your men got entrenching tools?"

7 Lean shouted back to his little line, and two men came slowly, one with a pick, one with a shovel. They started in the direction of the Rostina sharpshooters. Bullets cracked near their ears. "Dig here," said Lean gruffly. The men, thus caused to lower their glances to the turf, became hurried and frightened, merely because they could not look to see whence the bullets came. The dull beat of the pick striking the earth sounded amid the swift snap of close bullets. Presently the other private began to shovel.

8 "I suppose," said the adjutant, slowly, "we'd better search his clothes for—things."

9 Lean nodded. Together in curious abstraction they looked at the body. Then Lean stirred his shoulders suddenly, arousing himself.

10 "Yes," he said, "we'd better see what he's got." He dropped to his knees, and his hands approached the body of the dead officer. But his hands wavered over the buttons of the tunic. The first button was brick-red with drying blood, and he did not seem to dare touch it.

11 "Go on," said the adjutant, hoarsely.

12 Lean stretched his wooden hand, and his fingers fumbled the blood-stained buttons. At last he rose with ghastly face. He had gathered a watch, a whistle, a pipe, a tobacco pouch, a handkerchief, a little case of cards and papers. He looked at the adjutant. There was a silence. The adjutant was feeling that he had been a coward to make Lean do all the grisly business.

13 "Well," said Lean, "that's all, I think. You have his sword and revolver?"

14 "Yes," said the adjutant, his face working, and then he burst out in a sudden strange fury at the two privates. "Why don't you hurry up with that grave? What are you doing, anyhow? Hurry, do you hear? I never saw such stupid—"

15 Even as he cried out in his passion the two men were laboring for their lives. Ever overhead the bullets were spitting.

16 The grave was finished. It was not a masterpiece—a poor little shallow thing. Lean and the adjutant again looked at each other in a curious silent communication.

17 Suddenly the adjutant croaked out a weird laugh. It was a terrible laugh, which had its origin in that part of the mind which is first moved by the singing of the nerves. "Well," he said humorously to Lean, "I suppose we had best tumble him in."

18 "Yes," said Lean. The two privates stood waiting, bent over their implements. "I suppose," said Lean, "it would be better if we laid him in ourselves."

19 "Yes," said the adjutant. Then, apparently remembering that he

had made Lean search the body, he stooped with great fortitude and took hold of the dead officer's clothing. Lean joined him. Both were particular that their fingers should not feel the corpse. They tugged away; the corpse lifted, heaved, toppled, flopped into the grave, and the two officers, straightening, looked again at each other—they were always looking at each other. They sighed with relief.

20 The adjutant said, "I suppose we should—we should say something. Do you know the service, Tim?"

21 "They don't read the service until the grave is filled in," said Lean, pressing his lips to an academic expression.

22 "Don't they?" said the adjutant, shocked that he had made the mistake. "Oh, well," he cried, suddenly, "let us—let us say something—while he can hear us."

23 "All right," said Lean. "Do you know the service?"

24 "I can't remember a line of it," said the adjutant.

25 Lean was extremely dubious. "I can repeat two lines, but—"

26 "Well, do it," said the adjutant. "Go as far as you can. That's better than nothing. And the beasts have got our range exactly."

27 Lean looked at his two men. "Attention!" he barked. The privates came to attention with a click, looking much aggrieved. The adjutant lowered his helmet to his knee. Lean, bareheaded, stood over the grave. The Rostina sharpshooters fired briskly.

28 "O Father, our friend has sunk in the deep waters of death, but his spirit has leaped toward Thee as the bubble arises from the lips of the drowning. Perceive, we beseech, O Father, the little flying bubble, and—"

29 Lean, although husky and ashamed, had suffered no hesitation up to this point, but he stopped with a hopeless feeling and looked at the corpse.

30 The adjutant moved uneasily. "And from Thy superb heights—" he began, and then he too came to an end.

31 "And from Thy superb heights," said Lean.

32 The adjutant suddenly remembered a phrase in the back part of the Spitzbergen burial service, and he exploited it with the triumphant manner of a man who has recalled everything, and can go on.

33 "O God, have mercy—"

34 "O God, have mercy—" said Lean.

35 "Mercy," repeated the adjutant, in quick failure.

36 "Mercy," said Lean. And then he was moved by some violence of feeling, for he turned suddenly upon his two men and tigerishly said, "Throw the dirt in."

37 The fire of the Rostina sharpshooters was accurate and continuous.

38 One of the aggrieved privates came forward with his shovel. He lifted his first shovel load of earth, and for a moment of inexplicable hesitation it was held poised above this corpse, which from its chalk-blue face looked keenly out from the grave. Then the soldier emptied his shovel on—on the feet.

39 Timothy Lean felt as if tons had been swiftly lifted from off his forehead. He had felt that perhaps the private might empty the shovel on—on the face. It had been emptied on the feet. There was a great point gained there—ha, ha!—the first shovelful had been emptied on the feet. How satisfactory!

40 The adjutant began to babble. "Well, of course—a man we've messed with all these years—impossible—you can't, you know, leave your intimate friends rotting on the field. Go on, for God's sake, and shovel, you."

41 The man with the shovel suddenly ducked, grabbed his left arm with his right hand, and looked at his officer for orders. Lean picked the shovel from the ground. "Go to the rear," he said to the wounded man. He also addressed the other private. "You get under cover, too; I'll finish this business."

42 The wounded man scrambled hard still for the top of the ridge without devoting any glances to the direction from whence the bullets came, and the other man followed at an equal pace; but he was different, in that he looked back anxiously three times.

43 This is merely the way—often—of the hit and unhit.

44 Timothy Lean filled the shovel, hesitated, and then, in a movement which was like a gesture of abhorrence, he flung the dirt into the grave, and as it landed it made a sound—plop. Lean suddenly stopped and mopped his brow—a tired laborer.

45 "Perhaps we have been wrong," said the adjutant. His glance wavered stupidly. "It might have been better if we hadn't buried him just at this time. Of course, if we advance tomorrow the body would have been—"

46 "Damn you," said Lean, "shut your mouth." He was not the senior officer.

47 He again filled the shovel and flung the earth. Always the earth made that sound—plop. For a space Lean worked frantically, like a man digging himself out of danger.

48 Soon there was nothing to be seen but the chalk-blue face. Lean

filled the shovel. "Good God," he cried to the adjutant. "Why didn't you turn him somehow when you put him in? This—" Then Lean began to stutter.

49 The adjutant understood. He was pale to the lips. "Go on, man," he cried, beseechingly, almost in a shout.

50 Lean swung back the shovel. It went forward in a pendulum curve. When the earth landed it made a sound—plop. □

CHAPTER II

Narrative and Its Framework, Plot

"Tell me a story" is a request as old as language. Huddled around their fires at night, fearing the unknown concealed in the darkness, wanting their attention taken away from fear, primitive men probably turned to the most imaginative of their group and made this very suggestion. Then, caught up in his recounting of the cunning and strength of a great hunter, fighting and killing the hairy mammoth, they forgot their helpless fears, identifying themselves with the hero of the tale. Finally, satisfied with man's victory, they probably drifted off to sleep before reality returned to terrorize their soothed minds.

That first story probably began something like this: "Three moons journey toward the water lived a mighty hunter named Zed. He was the leader of his clan because he knew the ways of the mammoth and could track and slay it before it killed his men. One day when the sun had burned water to dust, when men were exhausted and children slept hungry. . . ." The primitive men forgot everything but Zed. What happened that drought-heavy day? How did Zed meet the challenges of despair and hunger? What happened next? Gone was the dark circle of fear outside the firelight. The gnawing hunger in the listeners' own bellies became less acute. They became Zed. Breathlessly, they waited to hear how he met the challenge, engaged in the conflict, and emerged victorious.

Primitive men, primitive needs, primitive tale. Yet no more primitive than the basic structure of the most sophisticated story you may read today. Basic to both is a man in conflict with something. Time passes as he meets his enemy (be it a mammoth or man's own loneliness) and defeats it—or is defeated by it.

Such is narrative. "The Book of Genesis" in the

Old Testament utilizes narrative at its simplest, best level. The enveloping action occupies seven days. Man's appearance begins the rising action. His conflict is established and suspense is generated as the reader hopes he will not eat of the forbidden fruit. Consequences are foreshadowed and suspense mounts as action continues to rise and he does eat it. What will God do? What will happen next? The climax is that shattering loss of Eden.

In neither the primitive tale of Zed nor Genesis is the focus of the story ever narrowed until a scene dominates that narrative. Each incident rises out the previous one until the conclusion is reached and, in the progress of incidents, each is as important as the one before or the one following.

Simple narrative is a recounting of an event or a series of events, usually in strict chronological order, leading to a meaningful conclusion. The action itself is the important element. Setting, characters, and dialog are necessary ingredients, but the focus is always on a larger element.

Panorama is the name of this larger element. It is the expository matter of a general nature with enough description and dialog to create a sketch but not enough to paint a picture. In it lie the answers to six questions: who, what, when, where, why, and how? A *scene* is a picture, a closer look at an incident enlarged and examined more carefully—one detail from panorama is focused on without the distractions of surrounding elements. A scene is specific reportage of a localized nature, and it usually requires about the same amount of time to report that it would to enact.

A newspaper account of an earthquake, for example, is a narrative. It details the action from the first tremor, through the severest quake, to the estimated damage to lives and property. The reporter's focus is on panorama rather than on scene in his account. But, later, he might write an account of a child separated from its parents. He would then detail the surroundings as they terrorized the child. He would try to recapture the child's incoherent babblings. He would assess the child's thoughts. The result would be a human interest story—narrative focused on character details. It would lack climax; it would lack narrative development through a progression of incidents. But it would be a narrowly focused examination of a scene enlarged out of panorama so that a character could be microscopically explored.

In the short story, one scene may comprise the total narration, or a series of scenes may be bound together by exposition which allows the author to span time, merely presenting a series of related facts and passing over the incidents he wishes to minimize. Panorama may also be used to join scenes and span time with a series of near-scenes which are not completely developed.

The simple narrative does not utilize the scene to any great degree—if at all. On the other hand, the short story employs the scene to reveal character or create *atmosphere* (which is merely another name for mood) through setting. To see the distinction, think of "The Book of Ruth" and "The Scythe" in Chapter 1. "The Book of Ruth" is almost exclusively panoramic narrative interrupted by a few near-scenes of limited dialog. "The Scythe" is a series of developed scenes bound together by panoramic narrative.

At the heart of the simple narrative, you will find the answers to the six panoramic questions and a general truth as the author sees it. That general truth is the *theme.* Who does what? When and where does he do it? Why does he do it? How does he go about doing it? What, of significance, does the narrative suggest? You could, if you desired, write a narrative. It might chronicle an actual situation from your own first-hand experience: John (who), a boy in your city (where), on the date you start writing (when), becomes a member of a street gang (what). He does this to achieve status which he has always lacked (why). As a result of a gang fight, a theft, and, finally, a mugging (how), he learns that status is one's vision of himself rather than the vision others have of him (theme). This realization causes him to "chicken out" of the mugging at the moment it is succeeding (climax).

And at the moment you achieved your outline (the material in the preceding paragraph), you would have your *plot,* the skeleton outline of narrative, the *identification* of a series of incidents which will lead to a climax and theme. While plot becomes the most important element of a story to the poor reader, it is the most inconsequential element to the author and the good reader. It is merely a device, a skeleton on which to hang the meaty matter of narrative: character revelation and theme exploration. Like the skeleton of the body, it should be substantial enough to support the total structure, but its function is not to present that which can be understandably observed.

Because character revelation and theme exploration would be your major concerns in your narrative, conflict would be central in at least three areas: in the gang brawls when John fights another boy (physical), in the theft as he challenges a moral code (social), and in his growing awareness that the mugging will be a violation of himself as well as of the victim (spiritual or psychological). At the implicit level, conflict would exist in John's mind throughout the narrative. However, as you would be writing a simple narrative, you would not explore that element of conflict for it would extend the narrative by adding a *character sketch* (a descriptive study of a character who is either a unique personality or a personality type; "The Squatter," pp. 130–133, is an excellent example). In "The Book of Ruth," you remember, the author remained objective, never entering a character's mind. He reported only what could be perceived with the five senses. Too, you might be tempted to describe a back alley in some detail, for the filth and gloom would provide powerful material for atmosphere. However, to do so would direct the reader's attention to the setting, and this would slow up your narrative flow. You would resist the temptation because narrative is panorama forging ahead, never pausing for scene which would slow it down.

To develop your narrative, you would concern yourself with *selection* (the choice of panoramic elements), *order* (arrangement of those elements in the best way so that unity will be apparent in the organization), *tone* (the overall effect of the story—that is, humorous, pathetic, sad, or ironic), *diction* (standard, acceptable language), and *idiom* (language used in such a personal way that it stamps the story with the author's personality so the narrative will reveal authorship to the reader).

Unity (completeness, containing everything necessary to create a sense of organic wholeness, and containing nothing that distracts from the total effect) and *coherence* (arrangement of all elements from words, phrases, and clauses to paragraphs and scenes so that their relationship to each other will be discernible and meaningful) would result if your presentation were systematic. And it would be systematic if: (1) the time span were brief, the chronology unbroken; (2) the geographical point of view remained clear and moved logically from incident to incident; (3) the narrative point of view remained constant. If you started the narrative in the first or third person, you would stay in first or third. If you started in the objective, the omniscient, or the limited omniscient point of view, you would stay in the one you chose. As this narrative would be John's story, you would probably choose a third person limited omniscient or a first person point of view which would make it imperative that you report only that which John could report if he were an actual person.

Further systematic controls you would find helpful are: (4) *transitions,* (5) *pace,* and (6) *proportion. Transitions* should transfer the reader's attention from one incident to the next without jarring his sensibilities. Satisfactory *pace* (the speed of narrative language) results from a careful attention to sentence length and patterns, vocabulary, and poetic devices which speed or slow the narrative flow. Vocabulary considerations are considerably more complex than "choosing the best word," a favored oversimplification in some English classes. Whether to prefer one near-synonym or another (*weary* or *exhausted* or *tired,* for example) is, certainly, included. So are levels of usage (*helpful* books in a school room become *functional* books if a teacher recommends they be purchased). In fiction, however, distinguishing between diction and idiom is probably more vital than either of the preceding. *Diction* is that body of standard, accepted language (free of trite phrases and slang) chosen by the careful person when he desires to communicate effectively without offending, startling, or overtaxing his hearer's intellect. *Idiom* is language at a more informal, colorful, or individual level of usage, designed to create fresh imagery, startling effect, or an impression of unique vitality. And two levels of idiom may appear in a work of fiction: (1) the author's distinctive language in description and exposition, and (2) the characters' distinctive speech in dialog. Should the author attempt to graft his idiom onto a character's speech, coherence could not survive the surgery.

Diction and idiom, then, increase or decrease the speed of narrative language as the author uses fast moving or slow moving words. *Inebriated* (diction) is slower in pace than *drunk* (idiom) which may be slower than *plowed* (distinctively personal idiom). Diction and idiom also contribute to such grammatical considerations as voice of verbs. Active voice verbs speed pace, passive voice verbs and verbs-of-being slow it. Notice the change of pace in the following statements: *The old man's neck* was *fragile in John's hands* (verb-of-being); *The old man's neck* was being *slowly* squeezed *in John's hands* (passive voice verb); *John slowly* squeezed *the fragile, old neck* (active voice verb). Contemporary idiom employs the verb-of-being and passive voice verb to suggest non-involvement or non-participation in an act by removing action from the subject.

If you are still unsure about the difference between diction and idiom, read the following newspaper item. The King James language is diction; the Scouse is idiom. The first paragraph of the account reveals the reporter's blending of diction and idiom. The last paragraph reveals an equally communicative melding by the vicar:

Scouse Bible

King James? Ee's a Bit Ard to Reed

KIRKDALE, England—(UPI)—The vicar here thinks the language barrier is keeping people away from church. The Rev. Richard Williams said Saturday that he intends to solve the problem by translating the Bible into "Scouse"—a Northwestern lingo that's almost English, but not quite.

A sample from the "Gospel According to Scousers": "Bein such a diddy feller ee'd ave ter get in the front row or see nowt. But ee wuz too late. The chap in frunt of im cud wind the liver clock. Thur wuz nowt for it but to climb a tree. Up ee went."

Which reads, in the King James version of the Bible, Zaccheus "sought to see Jesus who He was; and could not for the press because he was of little stature. And he ran before and climbed up a sycamore tree."

The King James version continues: Jesus "said unto Zaccheus, Make haste and come down, for today I must abide at thy house."

Scouse-speaking Christians will read: "Urry up and come down. I'm comin to yer ouse for tea."

Blasphemy? "Not at all," said the vicar. "I just wish I could get my tongue round the language as well."

Proportion is the space allotted to the beginning, middle, and end of a work. You concern yourself with it when you give a speech, write a composition, or construct the answer to an essay test question. As you make sure you have an introduction, body, and conclusion, you are checking proportion, for the first and last parts will be brief in comparison to the middle portion—if you have structured your paper well. Poor stories result when the author devotes too much space to the beginning of a story (the enveloping action), too little to the middle (generating circumstances and rising action) and end (climax and denouement, if there is one). However, some stories seem incomprehensible (as "The Book of Ruth" might if you did not understand the redemption custom) because enveloping action is slighted.

As you read the following narrative, concentrate on the controls employed by the author. Are diction and idiom in harmony with the action? Is the pace (both vocabulary and grammar) of the narrative flow (speed of narrative resulting from proportion in exposition, panorama, and scene) fast enough? Is the suspense high enough to make you want to keep reading to find out what happens next?

In twelve paragraphs, Mona Gardner narrates an incident that is scarcely more than an anecdote. As you read, observe the conversational flow of the narrative. It shares that quality of interest so often found in a well-told joke. Unusual in its use of the third person, present tense, the narrative could easily serve as the plot outline for a carefully constructed short story. As you read it, label the paragraphs of enveloping action, rising action, and the climax. Be prepared to identify the poetic devices and explain why they are effective. Read the story first by skipping the discussions.

The Dinner Party

by Mona Gardner

I first heard this story in India, where it is told as if true—though any naturalist would know it couldn't be. Later I learned that a magazine version of it appeared shortly before the First World War. This account, and its author, I have never been able to track down.

1The country is India. A colonial official and his wife are giving a large dinner party. They are seated with their guests—army officers and government attachés and their wives, and a visiting American naturalist—in their spacious dining room, which has a bare marble floor, open rafters, and wide glass doors opening onto a veranda.

2A spirited discussion springs up between a young girl who insists that women have outgrown the jumping-on-a-chair-at-the-sight-of-a-mouse era and a colonel who says that they haven't.

3"A woman's unfailing reaction in any crisis," the colonel says, "is to scream. And while a man may feel like it, he has that ounce more of nerve control than a woman has. And that last ounce is what counts."

Paragraphs 1–3 are enveloping action. The first sets the scene without elaborate detail. However, did you notice the author's inclusion of every detail pertinent to the story so none would have to be inserted or explained later? The second and third paragraphs generate interest in the tale, foreshadowing the direction the narrative will take. The characters lack distinguishing features because dwelling on them would take the focus away from narrative flow and misdirect it. The basic questions of who, where, when, and why are all answered in the first paragraph. Did you observe the way description is achieved in very few words in paragraph 1? How does the assonance of repeated *o*'s work in the last sentences of paragraphs 1 and 3?

4The American does not join in the argument but watches the other guests. As he looks, he sees a strange expression come over the face of the hostess. She is staring straight ahead, her muscles contracting slightly. With a slight gesture she summons the native boy standing behind her chair and whispers to him. The boy's eyes widen: he quickly leaves the room.

5Of the guests, none except the American notices this or sees the boy place a bowl of milk on the veranda just outside the open doors.

Paragraphs 4–5 are rising action. Suspense is generated as conflict enters the narrative. The reader is immediately aware of the cobra. The conflict becomes man against nature at this point. Notice the alliterative *s*'s in paragraph 4. They suggest a snake. Paragraph 5 utilizes the descriptive elements inserted in the first paragraph.

[6]The American comes to with a start. In India, milk in a bowl means only one thing—bait for a snake. He realizes there must be a cobra in the room. He looks up at the rafters—the likeliest place—but they are bare. Three corners of the room are empty, and in the fourth the servants are waiting to serve the next course. There is only one place left—under the table.

[7]His first impulse is to jump back and warn the others, but he knows the commotion would frighten the cobra into striking. He speaks quickly, the tone of his voice so arresting that it sobers everyone.

[8]"I want to know just what control everyone at this table has. I will count three hundred—that's five minutes—and not one of you is to move a muscle. Those who move will forfeit 50 rupees. Ready!"

[9]The 20 people sit like stone images while he counts. He is saying ". . . two hundred and eighty . . ." when, out of the corner of his eye, he sees the cobra emerge and make for the bowl of milk. Screams ring out as he jumps to slam the veranda doors safely shut.

Paragraphs 6–9 intensify the suspense with a time element. Will there be too little? Man against time is a complicating conflict here as the foreshadowing in paragraphs 2–3 is fully developed. Did you observe the point of view as a structural device? As it is third person limited, the focus is on the American for a definite reason. Were it on the hostess, there would be no story. Paragraph 6 returns to the brief description of paragraph 1. The final line of paragraph 7 hypnotizes the reader into an acceptance of the expository statement because poetic consonance of *s* sounds creates tension as tight as a cobra's coils. Paragraph 9 utilizes the simile "like stone images" for two reasons: description is vivid, brevity is achieved. How does the *s* alliteration in the last sentence of paragraph 9 contrast with its use in paragraph 4? The climax reaches its peak in this paragraph.

[10]"You were right, Colonel!" the host exclaims. "A man has just shown us an example of perfect control."

[11]"Just a minute," the American says, turning to his hostess. "Mrs. Wynnes, how did you know that cobra was in the room?"

[12]A faint smile lights up the woman's face as she replies: "Because it was crawling across my foot." □

Paragraphs 10–12 are carefully constructed denouement, made doubly effective by understatement in Mrs. Wynnes' answer. Denouement is effective only when it brings the unnoticed to the reader's attention. If it reveals anything an astute reader could not have known from the author's presentation, it is ineffective. In such a case, the author has probably withheld information unfairly. Mrs. Wynnes' answer was indicated in paragraph 4.

The pace of this narrative is rapid. The organization is careful. Elements are selected and introduced unobtrusively so that they will exist in the reader's memory when they are needed to forward the narrative. The proportion of the 3-6-3 paragraph structure is effective. You will notice that this is roughly the length of an essay you might be requested to write in class.

Unity results from interwoven conflicts: man against woman, man against nature, man against time. Allusion and symbol fuse throughout to unify the narrative as the juxtaposition of man, woman, and snake re-creates a subtle memory of the Garden of Eden. Reader sympathy is with the woman here for two reasons: the colonel is pompous and deserves to be proved wrong; Eve is somehow redeemed by Mrs. Wynnes.

The next simple narrative, "The Run on the Cherokee Strip," utilizes history as an element of interest. Suspense is generated through a time element once again. Told in the first person, the narrative utilizes third person limited point of view (in reference to Papa). All reported facts were passed from mother to son. Brief character illumination is employed throughout, but it never slows the pace of the narrative. Rather, it is inserted to intensify reader interest and generate greater sympathy for the father. Description is minimal since it would slow the pace. Exposition is inserted periodically, serving as time transition.

As you read, observe the generating circumstances (marked [1]), the rising action (marked [2]), and the climax (marked [3]). While this narrative is factual, poetic devices are frequently employed. Observe litotes in "This was no small tribute," understatement in "Papa wished him luck, and never saw the man again." Notice the frequency of such lines as "On a prairie experience is necessary to preserve a sense of direction"—a poetic immediacy pervades this and many other lines in the account. Is the ribbon simile effective in the Chisholm Trail description? It will be more vivid to those who have read and remembered Alfred Noyes' poem "The Highwayman." In the description of the draw, how does personification speed narrative flow? How much expository space is saved by such poetic devices?

Examine the diction and idiom of the narrative. Can you explain why the point of view is effective as a result of the retrospect of years and the experience of the narrator? Notice the pace of the narrative. Why does it slow up, speed forward, then slow up again?

Verisimilitude also pervades this narrative. The author doubtless did extensive research to achieve historical accuracy, but the facts seem to be a part of the fabric of recollection. Exposition in the narrative also serves to reinforce verisimilitude.

Unity rides with the horse in this narrative. The device is foreshadowed in the opening paragraph. Trees as symbols add a second unifying element. Justify proportion in this narrative as you read it.

The Run on the Cherokee Strip

by Marquis James

[1] [1] From my mother I learned of Papa's own part in the race. It was the kind of story that Mama, with her love of horses, would tell with relish.

[2] Especially for the Run, Papa had bought a race horse in El Reno. It was wind-broken but otherwise a sound and strong animal, capable of carrying my father's more than two hundred pounds.

[3] "In his young days your father was a real fancy rider," Mama would say. "And for a man of his size very easy on a horse."

[4] This was no small tribute. My mother was about as accomplished a judge of riding as any woman in our part of the country.

[5] The Run was a young man's undertaking. My father was crowding forty-nine, a good twenty years older than the average man who entered the race on horseback with serious intentions of reaching Enid in time to stake anything. A year and a half of law practice in Old Oklahoma and the Indian nations had made him fairly used to the saddle again. Nevertheless, he took three weeks to condition himself and to find out what he and his horse could do. He knew the ropes well enough to get himself the best possible place on the starting line—smack on the Chisholm Trail, just north of Hennessey, in Old Oklahoma.

[6] You could begin your race anywhere you could get to on one of the four borders of the Strip, which was about a hundred and sixty-five miles east and west by fifty-eight miles north and south. Papa picked the Hennessey section because it lay closest Enid, which he figured would be *the* town of the strip. There was also the Trail to follow. It made for easier riding and led straight to the desired townsite. On a prairie experience is necessary to preserve a sense of direction.

[7] Mama's understanding was that Papa spent about three days and nights on the line, holding his place. The wonder is the wait wasn't longer, considering the premium on places in the neighborhood of

the Trail. I have heard men tell of spending three weeks on the line. Probably they were with covered-wagon outfits, but, unless close to water, they must have got pretty tired of it. The sheets of some of the wagons were scrawled with notices of intention such as "Oklahoma or Bust." Substituting "Texas" or "Oregon," the phrase had been western usage for a good fifty years.

[8]The line was patrolled by soldiers to prevent anyone from crossing over before the opening gun. The country had been evacuated by the cattle outfits which formerly leased it from the Indians. Excepting land-office and post-office staffs and soldiers on the site of each county seat, the Strip was depopulated. That was the theory, and it came tolerably close to being the fact. Nobody knows how many sooners did manage to hide out in the promised land before the opening gun was fired, but probably not more than you would find trying to obtain their ends by illegal means in any collection of a hundred thousand persons. . . .

[9]After a man had staked a claim he had to "file" at the nearest land office. In order to file he was required to exhibit an evidence of registration permitting him to make the Run in the first place. Registration slips were issued from booths along the line. It was in no way difficult for a prospective sooner who knew the country to register a week before the Run and sneak up a draw through the thinly patrolled line. He could camp in the blackjacks west of Enid, for instance, and ride out with the first honest comers—as Mr. Wilcox suspected the man in light blue overalls had done. A cavalry troop encamped on the Enid site had reconnoitered the surrounding country for three weeks. Though the lieutenant in command was sure a number of sooners had eluded him they must have formed a minute proportion of the whole body of settlers.

[2] [10]The Hennessey stretch of the line broke five minutes before the official gun. Somebody may have discharged a firearm by accident. My father was in the saddle and ready. Waiting only to see that there was no turning back the tide, he, too, set off, keeping to the Chisholm Trail and reining his horse to a pace it could maintain for fifteen or sixteen miles and have a spurt left for an emergency.

[11]The Chisholm Trail was the name cowmen gave to the Oklahoma section of the Abilene Trail, greatest of the southwestern cattle thoroughfares. It ran from San Antonio, Texas, to the railway terminus at Abilene, Kansas, a distance of eighteen hundred miles. Though little used for cattle drives since the completion of the Rock Island Railroad through the Cherokee Strip in 1889, the famous prairie road was still distinct. Like a carelessly laid ribbon, which your eye would lose in the dips and pick up in the rises of the undulating plain, the Oklahoma part

stretched almost due north. On level places it was like several ribbons side by side. These markings were the Trail's core, made by the wheels of chuck wagons, calf wagons, freighters and stages. When wheels and hoofs wore through the sod, creating a "high center," teamsters would start a new road alongside the old. For two or three hundred yards on either side of these ruts the grass had been beaten down by the feet of the cattle. This on level stretches. To ford a stream or cross a draw the Trail narrowed.

12 The race was going well for my father. At first many riders and some drivers passed him; but this he had counted on. In the fullness of time, without increasing the pace of his horse, he began to pass them. When Papa calculated that he had gone about fifteen miles he was feeling the strain, and his horse was feeling it. Ahead of him were perhaps fifty riders in sight whom he doubted his ability to pass. (Fifty out of fifteen thousand starters from Hennessey.)

13 Glancing to the east my father saw the top of a distant string of trees. That meant a stream, an asset of great value to a claim: also an asset of great value to my father, who liked trees. They were the thing he missed most on the plains. Turning his horse from the Trail, he crossed the Rock Island track and the bed of a dry creek. He urged his tiring mount up the rise. On the other side he saw only a shallow draw, its naked sides exposing coarse sandy soil tinted from red to orange. Was this a wild-goose chase? Holding a northeast course he made for the next rise. He was traveling over short-grass prairie, knobby-surfaced and with washes of bare red soil: a good place for a horse, especially a tired, wind-broken horse, its breath coming in rasps, to stumble; and no good to grow anything. The crest of this second rise brought a welcome sight into view: the trees he had seen from the Trail; and beyond them more trees.

14 Watering the roots of the first trees was a disappointing stream, hardly more than a yard wide. (This was the driest season of the year.) But better trees were beyond; indeed, what seemed a veritable forest, in terms of the plains, with a noble green mass—surely the granddaddy of all the trees in the Cherokee Strip—dominating the whole. The first of these trees were soon reached. The creek was wider there: ten or twelve feet across. The illusion of a grove had been caused by the way the creek curved in the shape of an S. Papa followed the course of the stream in the direction of the Big Tree. He crossed the creek once and found that, to reach the Big Tree, he must cross again or double a loop. He started to double the loop and came upon a steep ravine. The ravine wouldn't have been much to head, but Papa didn't take the time. Precious minutes had been lost feeling his way toward the

trees. On the next fold of the prairie to the south other riders were in sight. Unseen riders might be coming up the draws. Papa wanted that creek, flowing in the shape of an S with good bottom land in the loops; and he wanted the Big Tree. His horse barely made the steep yonder side of the ravine. A few rods farther, at the high point on our pasture, luxuriant in red top, Papa dismounted and set his stake on what proved to be the Southeast Quarter of Section 17, Township 22, Range 6 West of the Indian Meridian.

15 It was 12:53 P.M., September 16, 1893. As the Hennessey line had broken at 11:55, my father had ridden seventeen miles in fifty-eight minutes without injuring his horse. A note of pride would touch Mama's tone as she spoke the last four words. Walter Cook covered eighteen miles in fifty to fifty-five minutes—he carried no watch and no one seems to have timed him exactly.

16 Something else my father had had to watch out for during the last part of his ride were the markers, designating section and certain quarter-section corners. Twenty years before, surveyors had checkerboarded the Strip with these little monuments. Where there were any, roughly cut sandstones sticking six or eight inches above the ground were used; elsewhere, "pits and mounds." A pit-and-mounds marker consisted of a hole about three feet deep, surrounded by four piles of earth and sod indicating the points of the compass. Virgin prairie sod is thick and durable. Except where beaten down by cattle, these mounds could still be picked up by a person who knew what to look for easier than the stones hidden by grass.

17 Before the Run much of the Strip had been burned over. I have heard this laid to sooners, in an effort to drive off rightful homesteaders. It appears, however, to have been the work of the troops—with the object of rendering markers more readily visible, of preventing prairie fires with possible serious consequences during the chaotic first days of settlement, and of smoking out sooners. The fires had been set too late. In areas they were burning on the day of the Run, and for some time after. I have heard men tell of riding through lines of flame, and of droves of rabbits, coyotes, and snakes fleeing the fires. Near North Town a woman was burned to death trying to save her team.

18 Streams, arid gulches, green bottom-land grass and so on stopped the fires in places. Where my father was had not been burned at all. Stone and pit-and-mounds markers were mixed in together, and all hard to see. Later examination disclosed the three designated corners of his quarter to be marked with stones—in all likelihood not visible more than a few yards away. As there was no time to search out these markers before he staked, my father had to estimate his boundaries by

eye—while in motion on horseback, taking his bearings from the last marker he had seen. In the matter of acquiring title to the Big Tree luck was with him, too. Only three corners of any quarter-section were marked. Lines had to be run to determine the fourth. [3] When they were run on our place the Big Tree was found to be less than a hundred yards from the Utsler boundary. Of course my father could have tried to make sure of the tree by setting his stake right under it. But he would have sacrificed the advantage of observation—for claim-jumpers and sooners—which his commanding position in the pasture afforded.

19 Having driven his stake, Papa set up a pup tent to which he affixed an American flag. I would like to know who gave him that flag, which was the last thing my father would ever have thought of taking along. From the tent he could see almost the entire claim, barring the East Draw and where the bluff hid the creek. He removed his saddle and, leading his horse so it would cool off gradually, began a tour of his estimated boundaries—probably looking for the markers. In the East Bottom he found a man preparing to set his stake. Cases of lead poisoning developed from a number of such meetings that day. But this man was no sooner or intentional claim-jumper. He rode with Papa to higher ground and took a look at the tent and the flag.

20 "You beat me out, stranger," said the man. "I'll strike eastward a piece."

21 Papa wished him luck, and never saw the man again. □

Simple narrative of another type is found in the fairy tale and the myth. Character, setting, and dialog are minimal in these forms. Recall "Cinderella," or read it if you have a copy at hand. Is Cinderella described in any detail? How about the kitchen or the palace? What can you tell about Cinderella from her dialog? As a reader, you have only a sketched setting, stock characters, foil characters, and a panoramic sweep of events. Yet out of that simple narrative emerges a satisfying experience. Movies employing narrative as their basic plots are almost as inattentive to detail. So is television.

Such charming accounts exist in all surviving literatures from the past. Thomas Bulfinch collected many of the Greek myths in *The Age of Fable,* from which the following narrative is taken. Enveloping action [1], rising action [2], and denouement [3] are marked. Observe proportion. In almost any narrative writing, whether it be the short story or the novel, major characters, setting (which includes time), and conflict are usually introduced as soon as possible. Authors know that the reader's imagination and interest must be captured rapidly or he will abandon the written material. To verify this statement, examine the beginnings of two or three short stories you like. You will notice the speed with which authors introduce the major elements.

As you read "Pyramus and Thisbe," make a brief, informal outline of the narrative. (Remember: that outline is the plot; plot is *not* narrative.) It will reveal proportion at a glance. As this is a working device, your outline need not be academically perfect. Also notice the many poetic devices Bulfinch employs. Much of the narrative will scan as easily as poetry.

Pyramus and Thisbe

[1] [1]Pyramus was the handsomest youth, and Thisbe the fairest maiden, in all Babylonia, where Semiramis reigned. Their parents occupied adjoining houses; and neighbourhood brought the young people together, and acquaintance ripened into love. They would gladly have married, but their parents forbade. One thing, however, they could not forbid—that love should glow with equal ardour in the bosoms of both. They conversed by signs and glances, and the fire burned more intensely for being covered up. [2] In the wall that parted the two houses there was a crack, caused by some fault in the structure. No one had remarked it before, but the lovers discovered it. What will not love discover! It afforded a passage to the voice; and tender messages used to pass backward and forward through the gap. As they stood, Pyramus on this side, Thisbe on that, their breaths would mingle. "Cruel wall," they said, "why do you keep two lovers apart? But we will not be ungrateful. We owe you, we confess, the privilege of transmitting loving words to willing ears." Such words they uttered on different sides of the wall; and when night came and they must say farewell, they pressed their lips upon the wall, she on her side, he on his, as they could come no nearer.

[2]Next morning, when Aurora had put out the stars, and the sun had melted the frost from the grass, they met at the accustomed spot. Then, after lamenting their hard fate, they agreed that next night, when all was still, they would slip away from the watchful eyes, leave their dwellings and walk out into the fields; and to insure a meeting, repair to a well-known edifice standing without the city's bounds, called the Tomb of Ninus, and that the one who came first should await the other at the foot of a certain tree. It was a white mulberry tree, and stood near a cool spring. All was agreed on, and they waited impatiently for

the sun to go down beneath the waters and night to rise up from them. Then cautiously Thisbe stole forth, unobserved by the family, her head covered with a veil, made her way to the monument and sat down under the tree. As she sat alone in the dim light of the evening she descried a lioness, her jaws reeking with recent slaughter, approaching the fountain to slake her thirst. Thisbe fled at the sight, and sought refuge in the hollow of a rock. As she fled she dropped her veil. The lioness after drinking at the spring turned to retreat to the woods, and seeing the veil on the ground, tossed and rent it with her bloody mouth.

[3] Pyramus, having been delayed, now approached the place of meeting. He saw in the sand the footsteps of the lion, and the colour fled from his cheeks at the sight. Presently he found the veil all rent and bloody. "O hapless girl," said he, "I have been the cause of thy death! Thou, more worthy of life than I, hast fallen the first victim. I will follow. I am the guilty cause, in tempting thee forth to a place of such peril, and not being myself on the spot to guard thee. Come forth, ye lions, from the rocks, and tear this guilty body with your teeth." He took up the veil, carried it with him to the appointed tree, and covered it with kisses and with tears. "*My* blood also shall stain your texture," said he, and drawing his sword plunged it into his heart. The blood spurted from the wound, and tinged the white mulberries of the tree all red; and sinking into the earth reached the roots, so that the red colour mounted through the trunk to the fruit.

[4] By this time Thisbe, still trembling with fear, yet wishing not to disappoint her lover, stepped cautiously forth, looking anxiously for the youth, eager to tell him the danger she had escaped. When she came to the spot and saw the changed colour of the mulberries she doubted whether it was the same place. While she hesitated she saw the form of one struggling in the agonies of death. She started back, a shudder ran through her frame as a ripple on the face of the still water when a sudden breeze sweeps over it. But as soon as she recognized her lover, she screamed and beat her breast, embracing the lifeless body, pouring tears into its wounds, and imprinting kisses on the cold lips. "O Pyramus," she cried, "what has done this? Answer me, Pyramus; it is your own Thisbe that speaks. Hear me, dearest, and lift that drooping head!" At the name of Thisbe, Pyramus opened his eyes, then closed them again. She saw her veil stained with blood and the scabbard empty of its sword. "Thy own hand has slain thee, and for my sake," she said. "I too can be brave for once, and my love is as strong as thine. I will follow thee in death, for I have been the cause; and

death which alone could part us shall not prevent my joining thee. And ye, unhappy parents of us both, deny us not our united request. As love and death have joined us, let one tomb contain us. And thou, tree, retain the marks of slaughter. Let thy berries still serve for memorials of our blood." So saying she plunged the sword into her breast. [3] Her parents ratified her wish, the gods also ratified it. The two bodies were buried in one sepulchre, and the tree ever after brought forth purple berries, as it does to this day. □

Your outline should look something like this:

I. Enveloping action
    A. Who: Pyramus and Thisbe.
    B. Where: Babylonia.
    C. When: Reign of Semiramis.
    D. What: Their love was thwarted.
    E. How: They were forbidden to speak to each other.
    F. Why: Their parents disapproved.
II. Rising action
    A. A wall separated them.
        1. They discovered a crack in the wall.
            a. They spoke through the crack.
            b. They arranged a tryst under a white mulberry tree.
    B. Thisbe arrived first.
        1. A lioness frightened her away.
        2. She dropped her veil.
        3. The lioness bloodied the veil.
    C. Pyramus arrived.
        1. He found the bloody veil.
        2. He thought Thisbe was dead.
        3. He killed himself with his sword.
        4. His blood changed the color of the mulberries.
    D. Thisbe returned.
        1. She noticed the changed color of the berries.
        2. She discovered the dying Pyramus.
        3. She killed herself with his sword.
        4. She asked for a single grave for herself and Pyramus.
III. Denouement
    A. Pyramus and Thisbe were buried together.
    B. The color of mulberries is their eternal memorial.

You doubtless can recognize the Romeo and Juliet story here. More recent retellings are *West Side Story* and *Fantasticks.* Such narratives retain their popularity with readers and, as they are adaptable to new forms, are constantly retold. Plots have pretty well been exhausted, but freshness of approach and treatment make the oldest material new once more. On the other hand, a dull, poorly proportioned, slow paced narrative of the most original ingredients is tiresome.

As the myth is a romantic, timeless form, the diction employed to recount it is also romantic and timeless. Would it be as effective had Pyramus been black-haired, six feet tall, with a cleft chin? Why is it unnecessary to know if the wall is brick, wood, or plaster? What is added by such a poetic line as "Cruel wall . . . we owe you, we confess, the privilege of transmitting loving words to willing ears"? How many poetic techniques can you detect? Five are employed.

The transitions are also worth noticing in this narrative of four paragraphs: "Next morning . . . ," "Pyramus having been delayed . . . ," "by this time. . . ." All three are definite time indicators, keeping the narrative flow steadily paced.

What is the theme? How does the denouement contribute to its effectiveness?

Theme is seldom ever stated as such in a literary work. It is usually revealed as the work unfolds and evidence of theme accrues. And the revelation of theme in a given work varies with its genre. For example, in the tunnel section of Hart Crane's *The Bridge* (a poem), Eudora Welty's "Death of a Travelling Salesman" (a short story), Arthur Miller's *The Death of a Salesman* (a play), and Sinclair Lewis' *Babbitt* (a novel), the theme is approximately the same; but it is revealed in a distinctive fashion in each form.

"Reveal or show rather than tell" is a constant rule with writers. Probably the only place they "tell" anything is in the simple narrative. To reveal or show requires space and time not available in the flow of narrative; yet the telling must be unobtrusive and casual. In Quentin Reynolds' "A Secret for Two," the author telegraphs the end of the story in the title. Throughout the narrative, he makes no attempt to conceal the secret. If the end comes as a surprise, the reader has been negligent indeed. As character, setting, and dialog are all secondary to narrative, the forward flow holds the reader's interest, and he is told many things which are not "shown." This is the device used in the detective story. The focus of narrative is elsewhere; the reader's attention is deliberately sidetracked so he will be unaware at the moment that he has been told something. Later he realizes he was not alert at the right moment. Notice the lines marked by asterisks, for they tell you—twenty different times—what the secret is.

A Secret for Two

by Quentin Reynolds

1 Montreal is a very large city, but it has some very small streets. Streets, for instance, like Prince Edward Street, which is only four blocks long. No one knew Prince Edward Street as well as did Pierre Dupin. Pierre had delivered milk to the families on the street for thirty years.

2 During the past fifteen years the horse which drew the milk
wagon used by Pierre was a large white horse named Joseph. When
the big white horse first came to the Provinçale Milk Company, he
didn't have a name. They told Pierre that he could use the white
horse. Pierre stroked the softness of the horse's neck and he looked
* into the eyes of the horse.

3 "This is a kind horse, a gentle and a faithful horse," Pierre said,
* "and I can see a beautiful spirit shining out of the eyes of the horse.
I will name him after good St. Joseph, who was also kind and gentle
and faithful and a beautiful spirit."

* 4 Within a year Joseph knew the milk route as well as Pierre. Pierre
used to boast that he didn't need reins—he never touched them. Each
morning Pierre arrived at the stables of the Provinçale Milk Company
at five o'clock. The wagon would be loaded and Joseph hitched to it.
* Pierre would call as he climbed into his seat and Joseph would turn
his head, and the other drivers would say that the horse would smile
at Pierre. Then Jacques, the foreman, would say, "All right, Pierre, go
on," and Pierre would call softly to Joseph, "Go on, my friend," and
this splendid combination would stalk proudly down the street.

* 5 The wagon, without any direction from Pierre, would roll three
blocks down St. Catherine Street, then turn right two blocks along
Roslyn Avenue; then left, for that was Prince Edward Street. The horse
would stop at the first house, allow Pierre perhaps thirty seconds to
get down from his seat and put a bottle of milk at the front door
and would then go on, skipping two houses and stopping at the
third. So down the length of the street. Then, Joseph would turn
* around and come back along the other side. Yes, Joseph was a smart
horse.

6 Pierre would boast at the stable of Joseph's skill. "I never touch the reins. He knows just where to stop. Why, a blind man could handle my route with Joseph pulling the wagon."

7 So it went on for years. Pierre and Joseph grew old together, but gradually, not suddenly. Pierre's huge walrus mustache was pure white now and Joseph didn't lift his knees so high. Jacques, the foreman of the stables, never noticed that they were both getting old until Pierre appeared one day carrying a heavy walking stick.

8 "Hey, Pierre," Jacques laughed. "Maybe you got the gout, hey?"

9 "But yes, Jacques," Pierre said uncertainly. "One grows old. One's legs get tired."

10 "You should teach the horse to carry the milk to the front door for you," Jacques told him. "He does everything else."

11 Pierre knew every one of the forty families he served on Prince Edward Street. The cooks knew that Pierre could neither read nor write, so they did not follow the usual custom of leaving a note in an empty bottle. If an additional quart of milk was needed, they would sing out when they heard his wagon wheels on the cobbled street, "Bring an extra quart this morning, Pierre."

12 Pierre had a remarkable memory. When he arrived at the stable he'd always remember to tell Jacques, "The Paquins took an extra quart this morning; the Lemoines bought a pint of cream."

13 Jacques would note these things in a little book he always carried. Most of the drivers had to make out the weekly bills and collect the money, but Jacques, liking Pierre, had always excused him from this task. All Pierre had to do was to arrive at five in the morning, walk to his wagon, which was always in the same spot at the curb, and deliver his milk.

14 One morning the president of the Provinçale Milk Company came to inspect the early morning deliveries. Jacques pointed Pierre out to him and said, "Watch how he talks to that horse. See how the horse listens and how he turns his head toward Pierre. See the look in that horse's eyes. You know, I think those two share a secret. It is as though they both sometimes chuckle at us as they go off on their route. Pierre is a good man, but he gets old. Would it be too bold of me to suggest that he be retired and be given a small pension?" he asked anxiously.

15 "But of course," the president laughed. "He has been on this route now for thirty years and never once has there been a complaint. Tell him it is time he rested. His salary will go on just the same."

16 But Pierre refused to retire. He was panic-stricken at the thought

of not driving Joseph every day. "We are two old men," he said to Jacques. "Let us wear out together. When Joseph is ready to retire—then I, too, will quit."

17 Jacques, who was a kind man, understood. There was something about Pierre and Joseph which made a man smile tenderly. It was as * though each drew some hidden strength from the other. When Pierre was sitting in his seat, and when Joseph was hitched to the wagon, neither seemed old. But when they finished their work, then Pierre would limp down the street slowly, seeming very old indeed. Then, the horse's head would drop and he would walk very wearily to his stall.

18 Then one morning Jacques had dreadful news for Pierre. The air was like iced wine that morning and the snow glistened like a million diamonds piled together.

19 Jacques said, "Pierre, your horse, Joseph did not wake this morning. He was very old, Pierre, he was twenty-five, and that is like seventy-five for a man."

20 "Yes," Pierre said, slowly. "Yes, I am seventy-five. And I cannot * see Joseph again."

21 "Of course you can," Jacques soothed. "He is over in his stall, looking very peaceful. Go over and see him."

* 22 Pierre took one step forward then turned. "No . . . you don't understand Jacques."

23 Jacques clapped him on the shoulder. "We'll find another horse just as good as Joseph. Why, in a month you'll teach him to know your route as well as Joseph did. We'll . . ."

* 24 The look in Pierre's eyes stopped him. For years Pierre had worn a heavy cap, the peak of which came low over his eyes. Now Jacques looked into Pierre's eyes and he saw something which startled him. * He saw a dead, lifeless look in them. The eyes were mirroring the grief that was in Pierre's heart and his soul. It was as though his heart and soul had died.

25 "Take today off, Pierre," Jacques said, but already Pierre was hobbling off down the street, and had one been near one would have seen tears streaming down his cheeks and have heard half-smothered sobs. Pierre walked to the corner and stepped into the street. There was a warning yell from the driver of a huge truck that was coming fast and there was the scream of brakes, but Pierre apparently heard neither.

26 Five minutes later an ambulance driver said, "He's dead. Was killed instantly."

[27]Jacques and several of the milk-wagon drivers had arrived, and they looked down at the still figure.

[28]"I couldn't help it," the driver of the truck protested, "he walked
* right into my truck. He never saw it, I guess. Why, he walked into it as though he was blind."

[29]The ambulance doctor bent down. "Blind? Of course the man
* was blind. See those cataracts? This man has been blind for five years." He turned to Jacques, "You say he worked for you? Didn't you know he was blind?"

[30]"No . . . no . . ." Jacques said softly. "None of us knew. Only one knew—a friend of his named Joseph. . . . It was a secret, I think, just between those two." □

Did you notice the author's skill in focusing your attention on the narrative flow and on the "friendship" between Pierre and Joseph? Check back now for all of the transitions. They are not words such as *next* and *then*. More subtle transitions are employed. Time passage is marked; names are repeated; one half of the Pierre-Joseph combination will mark the end of one section, the other serving as transition into the next.

Allusion makes the naming of the horse a sharply focused feature of the story. St. Joseph was one who "saw" truth and acted on it. (Why would "Christopher" have been a poor choice of names?) In this narrative, the character of Pierre is as undeveloped as that of Mrs. Wynnes in "The Dinner Party," though you know more about Pierre. However, did you notice *where* and *how* you know him? Only at work. The narrative is concerned with the bond between man and horse. What happens to Pierre away from his job is of little consequence. The author is interested in Pierre only as a component of the immediate narrative. While character, dialog, and description are elements of narrative, and each narrative you have thus far studied utilizes them, the focus is away from them and on the panoramic sweep of events.

In the next story, "Our Lady's Juggler," greater attention is given to description, for it is necessary to the flow of narrative. Anatole France divided the narrative into three sections. As you read it, decide why he divided it that way. Observe the function of description as a narrative device. Notice the transitions. The tone is reverent, the mood promising. In section II, notice the skillful interweaving of expository and poetic construction. The time spans and pace of the work are carefully synchronized. See if you can discover how. Examine the diction and verb usage for their contributions to the total effect.

Our Lady's Juggler

by Anatole France

1In the days of King Louis there was a poor juggler in France, a native of Compiègne, Barnaby by name, who went about from town to town performing feats of skill and strength.

2On fair days he would unfold an old worn-out carpet in the public square, and when by means of a jovial address, which he had learned of a very ancient juggler, and which he never varied in the least, he had drawn together the children and loafers, he assumed extraordinary attitudes, and balanced a tin plate on the tip of his nose. At first the crowd would feign indifference.

3But when, supporting himself on his hands face downwards, he threw into the air six copper balls, which glittered in the sunshine, and caught them again with his feet; or when throwing himself backwards until his heels and the nape of the neck met, giving his body the form of a perfect wheel, he would juggle in this posture with a dozen knives, a murmur of admiration would escape the spectators, and pieces of money rain down upon the carpet.

4Nevertheless, like the majority of these who live by their wits, Barnaby of Compiègne had a great struggle to make a living.

5Earning his bread in the sweat of his brow, he bore rather more than his share of the penalties consequent upon the misdoings of our father Adam.

6Again, he was unable to work as constantly as he would have been willing to do. The warmth of the sun and the broad daylight were as necessary to enable him to display his brilliant parts as to the trees if flower and fruit should be expected of them. In winter time he was nothing more than a tree stripped of its leaves, and as it were dead. The frozen ground was hard to the juggler, and, like the grasshopper of which Marie de France tells us, the inclement season caused him to suffer both cold and hunger. But as he was simple-natured he bore his ills patiently.

7He had never meditated on the origin of wealth, nor upon the inequality of human conditions. He believed firmly that if this life should prove hard, the life to come could not fail to redress the balance, and this hope upheld him. He did not resemble those thievish and miscreant Merry Andrews who sell their souls to the devil. He never blasphemed God's name; he lived uprightly, and although he had no wife of his own, he did not covet his neighbour's, since woman is ever the enemy of the strong man, as it appears by the history of Samson recorded in the Scriptures.

8In truth, his was not a nature much disposed to carnal delights, and it was a greater deprivation to him to forsake the tankard than the Hebe who bore it. For whilst not wanting in sobriety, he was fond of a drink when the weather waxed hot. He was a worthy man who feared God, and was very devoted to the Blessed Virgin.

[9]Never did he fail on entering a church to fall upon his knees before the image of the Mother of God, and offer up this prayer to her:

[10]"Blessed Lady, keep watch over my life until it shall please God that I die, and when I am dead, ensure to me the possession of the joys of paradise."

Section I is enveloping action. Ten paragraphs chronicle many years of Barnaby's life as his character, beliefs, and needs are stated. To show or reveal them would require more space than the author wishes to allot.

II

[11]Now on a certain evening after a dreary wet day, as Barnaby pursued his road, sad and bent, carrying under his arm his balls and knives wrapped up in his old carpet, on the watch for some barn where, though he might not sup, he might sleep, he perceived on the road, going in the same direction as himself, a monk, whom he saluted courteously. And as they walked at the same rate they fell into conversation with one another.

[12]"Fellow traveller," said the monk, "how comes it about that you are clothed all in green? Is it perhaps in order to take the part of a jester in some mystery play?"

[13]"Not at all, good father," replied Barnaby. "Such as you see me, I am called Barnaby, and for my calling I am a juggler. There would be no pleasanter calling in the world if it would always provide one with daily bread."

[14]"Friend Barnaby," returned the monk, "be careful what you say. There is no calling more pleasant than the monastic life. Those who lead it are occupied with the praises of God, the Blessed Virgin, and the saints; and, indeed, the religious life is one ceaseless hymn to the Lord."

[15]Barnaby replied—

[16]"Good father, I own that I spoke like an ignorant man. Your calling cannot be in any respect compared to mine, and although there may be some merit in dancing with a penny balanced on a stick on the tip of one's nose, it is not a merit which comes within hail of your own. Gladly would I, like you, good father, sing my office day by day, and specially the office of the most Holy Virgin, to whom I have vowed a singular devotion. In order to embrace the monastic life I would willingly abandon the art by which from Soissons to Beauvais I am well known in upwards of six hundred towns and villages."

[17]The monk was touched by the juggler's simplicity, and as he was not lacking in discernment, he at once recognized in Barnaby one of those men of whom it is said in the Scriptures: Peace on earth to men of good will. And for this reason he replied—

[18]"Friend Barnaby, come with me, and I will have you admitted into the mon-

astery of which I am Prior. He who guided St. Mary of Egypt in the desert set me upon your path to lead you into the way of salvation."

[19]It was in this manner, then, that Barnaby became a monk. In the monastery into which he was received the religious vied with one another in the worship of the Blessed Virgin, and in her honour each employed all the knowledge and all the skill which God had given him.

[20]The prior on his part wrote books dealing according to the rules of scholarship with the virtues of the Mother of God.

[21]Brother Maurice, with a deft hand, copied out these treatises upon sheets of vellum.

[22]Brother Alexander adorned the leaves with delicate miniature paintings. Here were displayed the Queen of Heaven seated upon Solomon's throne, and while four lions were on guard at her feet, around the nimbus which encircled her head hovered seven doves, which are the seven gifts of the Holy Spirit, the gifts, namely, of Fear, Piety, Knowledge, Strength, Counsel, Understanding, and Wisdom. For her companions she had six virgins with hair of gold, namely, Humility, Prudence, Seclusion, Submission, Virginity, and Obedience.

[23]At her feet were two little naked figures, perfectly white, in an attitude of supplication. These were souls imploring her all-powerful intercession for their soul's health, and we may be sure not imploring in vain.

[24]Upon another page facing this, Brother Alexander represented Eve, so that the Fall and the Redemption could be perceived at one and the same time—Eve the Wife abased, and Mary the Virgin exalted.

[25]Furthermore, to the marvel of the beholder, this book contained presentments of the Well of Living Waters, the Fountain, the Lily, the Moon, the Sun, and the Garden Enclosed of which the Song of Songs tells us, the Gate of Heaven and the City of God, and all these things were symbols of the Blessed Virgin.

[26]Brother Marbode was likewise one of the most loving children of Mary.

[27]He spent all his days carving images in stone, so that his beard, his eyebrows, and his hair were white with dust, and his eyes continually swollen and weeping; but his strength and cheerfulness were not diminished, although he was now well gone in years, and it was clear that the Queen of Paradise still cherished her servant in his old age. Marbode represented her seated upon a throne, her brow encircled with an orb-shaped nimbus set with pearls. And he took care that the folds of her dress should cover the feet of her, concerning whom the prophet declared: My beloved is as a garden enclosed.

[28]Sometimes, too, he depicted her in the semblance of a child full of grace, and appearing to say, "Thou art my God, even from my mother's womb."

[29]In the priory, moreover, were poets who composed hymns in Latin, both in prose and verse, in honour of the Blessed Virgin Mary, and amongst the company was even a brother from Picardy who sang the miracles of Our Lady in rhymed verse and in the vulgar tongue.

Section II is generating circumstances (paragraphs 11–18) and rising action. The time span is considerably shorter than it was in section I, though nineteen paragraphs are devoted to the section. Description occupies nine of them as monk after monk is described at his work. Each serves as a foil to Barnaby and his lack of talent as rising action occupies paragraphs 19–29. "Rhymed verse" in paragraph 29 is synonymous with *diction;* "the vulgar tongue" with *idiom.*

III

30 Being a witness of this emulation in praise and the glorious harvest of their labours, Barnaby mourned his own ignorance and simplicity.

31 "Alas!" he sighed, as he took his solitary walk in the little shelterless garden of the monastery, "wretched wight that I am, to be unable, like my brothers, worthily to praise the Holy Mother of God, to whom I have vowed my whole heart's affection. Alas! alas! I am but a rough man and unskilled in the arts, and I can render you in service, blessed Lady, neither edifying sermons, nor treatises set out in order according to rule, nor ingenious paintings, nor statues truthfully sculptured, nor verses whose march is measured to the beat of feet. No gift have I, alas!"

32 After this fashion he groaned and gave himself up to sorrow. But one evening, when the monks were spending their hour of liberty in conversation, he heard one of them tell the tale of a religious man who could repeat nothing other than the Ave Maria. This poor man was despised for his ignorance; but after his death there issued forth from his mouth five roses in honour of the five letters of the name Mary (Marie), and thus his sanctity was made manifest.

33 Whilst he listened to this narrative Barnaby marvelled yet once again at the loving kindness of the Virgin; but the lesson of that blessed death did not avail to console him, for his heart overflowed with zeal, and he longed to advance the glory of his Lady, who is in heaven.

34 How to compass this he sought but could find no way, and day by day he became the more cast down, when one morning he awakened filled full with joy, hastened to the chapel, and remained there alone for more than an hour. After dinner he returned to the chapel once more.

35 And, starting from that moment, he repaired daily to the chapel at such hours as it was deserted, and spent within it a good part of the time which the other monks devoted to the liberal and mechanical arts. His sadness vanished, nor did he any longer groan.

36 A demeanour so strange awakened the curiosity of the monks.

37 These began to ask one another for what purpose Brother Barnaby could be indulging so persistently in retreat.

38 The prior, whose duty it is to let nothing escape him in the behaviour of his children in religion, resolved to keep a watch over Barnaby during his withdrawals

to the chapel. One day, then, when he was shut up there after his custom, the prior, accompanied by two of the older monks, went to discover through the chinks in the door what was going on within the chapel.

39 They saw Barnaby before the altar of the Blessed Virgin, head downwards, with his feet in the air, and he was juggling with six balls of copper and a dozen knives. In honour of the Holy Mother of God he was performing those feats, which aforetime had won him most renown. Not recognizing that the simple fellow was thus placing at the service of the Blessed Virgin his knowledge and skill, the two old monks exclaimed against the sacrilege.

40 The prior was aware how stainless was Barnaby's soul, but he concluded that he had been seized with madness. They were all three preparing to lead him swiftly from the chapel, when they saw the Blessed Virgin descend the steps of the altar and advance to wipe away with a fold of her azure robe the sweat which was dropping from her juggler's forehead.

41 Then the prior, falling upon his face upon the pavement, uttered these words—

42 "Blessed are the simple-hearted, for they shall see God."

43 "Amen!" responded the old brethren, and kissed the ground. □

Section III focuses on Barnaby in his time of greatest conflict. The focus narrows further until, in the last five paragraphs, a scene is presented—but still in panoramic fashion. Details are merely sketched in, not carefully drawn.

Because of the panoramic treatment and one scene presented in outline, the pace of the narrative is rapid, hurrying over everything but the careful and elaborate details of the brother monks' holy labors. As a result, the narrative seems to resemble a large religious canvas, illuminated at essential points. Structurally, the narrative emulates a triptych, the center panel alive with color, the sides hazy and blurred in detail. Such experimentation lends greatness to the simple narrative. The moral lesson so obvious at the end is, of course, the theme of the work. As such, this narrative is *didactic* (in poetry or prose, a work which has instruction—usually moral—as its primary purpose).

Suggested Activities. 1. Reread "The Dinner Party" (p. 49). Using the same number of paragraphs of approximately the same length, recount an interesting incident from your own experience. Make sure you have a stateable theme to work from. Strive for narrative flow built on suspense. Remember time as an aid. Pay careful attention to the diction and idiom of your narrative, making sure it creates the tone, mood, and atmosphere you wish to convey. Do not conceal essential information; reveal it, but focus away from it so that your reader's attention will be diverted. Write it in third person limited omniscient point of view (see pp. 20 and 202).

2. In a brief narrative, recount an incident from history. Be sure you choose one that suggests suspense. If you are unfamiliar with the setting, do a little research to lend verisimilitude to your narrative. Assume you were a child at the time of the incident and you are telling it years later when you are old enough to be selective in what you choose to tell. Pay particular attention to the organization of the details you select. Make sure each is pertinent to the narrative. If its absence would not do damage to the narrative flow, cut it out. Use third person limited omniscient or first person point of view. As you are merely reporting an incident you observed without taking part in it, your opening, as in "The Run on the Cherokee Strip" (p. 52), will have to be first person. Ordinarily, switching point of view (called *violating point of view*) is a weakness in prose fiction. In such accounts as this, it is effective because it gives immediacy to incidents out of the past.

3. Using the basic narrative of "Pyramus and Thisbe," update the material to your time and geographical location. You might use religion, national background, economic circumstances or some such as the reason for parental disapproval. Your Louisa and Timothy or Bonnie and Jimmy will not encounter lions, but there are any number of romantic ways to dispose of lovers. Attempt this narrative in poetic prose, modeling it on Bulfinch's structure of four paragraphs in the same proportion and pace as his work. The mulberry element will challenge your ingenuity. You will probably be irritated as your first efforts seem too sweet, thoroughly unbelievable, or overly romantic in a bad movie fashion. Keep working at it, noticing how a sharpening of your poetic prose diction can make it more acceptable as you improve that ingredient.

Suggested Assignments. 1. Read the following narrative and write a three-paragraph analysis. Discuss proportion and pace, foreshadowing, and conflict as they are employed by the author.

2. In a brief paper, discuss the diction and two levels of idiom (the author's and the characters') of this work. Pay particular attention to pace and proportion in your own paper. If you have learned all the rules of composition, you may be able to accomplish this assignment in three paragraphs. A more workable outline would include one paragraph introducing the subject, three paragraphs exploring the three language levels, and a final paragraph summarizing your conclusions. Or you might be able to include both levels of idiom in one paragraph if you are constantly aware of proportion in the middle of your paper.

A Question of Blood

by Ernest Haycox

[1]That fall of 1869 when Frank Isabel settled in the Yellow Hills the nearest town was a four-day ride to the north and his closest white neighbor lived at the newly established Hat ranch, seventy miles over in Two Dance Valley. The Indians were on reservation but it was still risky for a man to be alone in the country.

[2]It made no difference to Isabel. He was young and self-willed. The land was free, well grassed and watered and ideal for a poor man who had ambition. This was why he had come.

[3]Yet, cool and smart as he was, he had made no calculation for the imperious hungers that soon or late come to a lonely man. And presently, seeing no hope of a white woman in the land for many years, he went down to the reservation and took unto himself a Crow girl, the bargain being sealed by the payment to her father of one horse and a quart of whisky.

[4]She was more than he had expected in an Indian woman: quick to perceive the way his mind ran, showing him sudden streaks of gay mischief-making calm, and sometimes an odd flash of affection. Before the boy baby was born he drove her three hundred miles to Cheyenne and married her in the white way.

[5]It was a sense of justice in him rather than any need in her eyes that impelled him to do this. For he was learning that though an Indian woman was a dutiful woman immemorial customs guided her in a way he could not hope to touch or change.

[6]Often at night, smoking before the fire and watching his boy crawl so awkwardly across the floor, he felt a strangeness at seeing her darkly crouched in a corner, lost in thoughts he could never reach. He talked her tongue poorly and she would speak no English; and so silence lay between them.

[7]Meanwhile Two Dance town grew out of the empty prairie sixty miles away and the valley below him began to fill up with cattlemen long before he had thought they would come.

[8]One by one the few trappers who had pioneered the Yellows began to send their squaws and their half-breed children back to the reservation as a shame-faced gesture of a mistake that had to be righted. He said nothing of this to the Crow woman, yet when fear showed in her eyes he knew she had heard. He said then: "Those men are fools. I am not ashamed of you." And was happy to see the fear die.

[9]This was why he took her to Two Dance. It pleased him to have

her be seen in that drumming little cattle town, for she was a pretty woman with her black hair braided and her clothes neat and colorful under the sun. But he had forgotten her customs and when they walked up the street she followed behind him as a squaw always did, obediently and with her head faintly lowered. He knew how Two Dance would see that and anger colored his talk to her on the way home. "A white man's wife walks beside him, not behind."

10 He saw that dark fear in her eyes again, and had no way of softening it. Never afterward did she come to town.

11 He knew then how it was to be. At hay time, when he went down to help out on Hat, he could feel that faint line drawn between him and the others; at the roundup fire he sat apart, with the strangeness there—a white man who was yet not quite white. One fall night at town he stepped in to watch a dance at the Army post; fair, pleasant girls went by and he saw their eyes touch him and pass on. He was a squaw man. . . .

12 He went home late that night quite drunk. In the morning the Crow girl was gone with her boy.

13 He didn't follow, for he knew that either she would return or wouldn't, and that nothing he did could change her mind. Late in the third day she came back without a word. When he went in to supper that night he sat down to a single plate on the table. Her own plate and that of the boy's were on a floor blanket in a corner of the room.

14 It was, he saw, her decision. He was white and might eat at his table. But she was Indian and so was the boy, and the table was not for them.

15 There was a kindness in Frank Isabel that governed the coolest and longest of his thoughts and this was what held him still as the days went on. He could see the depth and the length of his mistake now. For himself, Frank Isabel thought, there was no help. For the girl, none. It was the boy he kept weighing in his mind, so slowly and so painfully.

16 One winter night, at mealtime, Jim Benbow of Hat dropped in for a cup of coffee. There was a little talk of cattle snowed into the timber and afterward Benbow put on his hat and went to the door. As he left, his glance crossed to the Crow woman and to the boy crouched in the corner and he said briefly, "Your youngster's growin' up, Frank," and left.

17 There was the rush of wind along the cabin eaves and deep silence inside. Isabel sat with his long arms idle on the table, remembering Benbow's words, which had contained a note of judgment. Presently he rose and brought another chair to the table and went over to where

the Crow girl crouched mutely in the corner. He lifted the boy and put him in the chair at the table and stood there a moment. He said: "Hereafter he eats at the table."

18 She drew farther and farther back into the corner, like a shadow vanishing. And then, with his face turned suddenly away, he heard her stifled and terrible crying tremble the room's silence. □

CHAPTER III

Description—The Appeal to the Senses

In *The Seagull,* Anton Chekhov defines description tersely and completely, incorporating descriptive aids within his definition: "The broken bottleneck glitters on the dam and the mill-wheel casts a black shadow—and there you have the moonlight night."

The same perceptive selectivity and presentation that characterize the best poetry are nowhere more valuable to the prose writer than in his descriptive passages, for there he must capture an impression in a few sensitively chosen words and communicate it to one or more of the reader's five senses. You, the reader, may be unfamiliar with the canals of Venice or the prairies of Kansas, but you have a concept of water and boats, old houses and song, or of grass and flat land, wheat and corn. If the author can synthesize his concepts into a pattern that will awaken your memory, you will supply many details from your personal experience, combine them with his details, and create the canals of Venice or the Kansas prairie.

Good description, then, is not a tedious, photographic cataloguing of every element of a picture. It is a sharp focusing on key details which will trigger your memory and enable you to arrange the stored components into a pattern. In Chekhov's description (which ends with the word *shadow*), neither moonlight nor night is mentioned; yet a sharp, clear picture emerges. In the visual art of painting, the same idea is suggested by Heinrich Wölfflin who says of painting a turning wheel: ". . . only when the wheel has been made indistinct does it begin to turn."*

Two images are contrasted in Chekhov's description; one abstract and three concrete nouns are juxtaposed; two active voice verbs are employed; two apt adjectives are placed in parallel construction,

* *Principles of Art History,* tr. M. D. Hottinger (New York, n.d.), p. 22.

as are the two clauses of the compound sentence. Alliteration in *b*'s, assonance in *a*'s and *o*'s, consonance in *l*'s, *t*'s, and *k*'s refine the symbols of light and darkness as the moon reflects on glass and projects the mill-wheel shadow. The reader may supply any number of details: the lake formed by the dam, the stream sluiced in to turn the wheel and run away through lush meadows. Do willows rim the lake? Is this a picnic spot? Why is there a broken bottleneck on the dam, and what kind of bottle was it? Is the dam a concrete structure, an earthen barrier, a beavers' weir? Why is the word *shadow* intensified by the adjective *black?* Is there another color for shadow? Can you smell the water? Or feel the jagged edges of glass? Or hear the creak of the mill-wheel? Is it turning or still? Do nightbirds call? Is there dew underfoot? Did you notice the space order of details? Moon shines *down* on glass, on dam, reflects *down* from dam to mill-wheel; the wheel casts a shadow *down* on the ground.

Compare the picture you have created with one created by a classmate. Involved in your reactions are the individual stored memories and unique connotations the words hold for you; therefore, the pictorial details probably will not be remarkably similar. The haiku in prose—for such this sentence is—has worked its magic for you, the reader.

What general rules of good description can you extract from Chekhov's sentence? First, the writer considers the scene he wishes to create. He decides what mood, tone, and atmosphere it should convey. Second, selecting the ingredients that most appeal to the five senses, he activates them subtly without *direct* reference to them. Third, he then arranges the details in their best possible order to lead the reader's senses through a pattern of logical progression. Fourth, he uses adjectives sparingly and then only if they are vital to the description, as *black* is to *shadow.* (Was the bottle green or white or brown? Chekhov allowed you to supply that color. Check your picture. You *did* see a color he didn't mention. Had he chosen one, it might have interfered with your memory.) Fifth, he uses active voice verbs! Good description may employ static elements (*bottleneck, dam, mill-wheel* are fixed in space), but the picture is alive with movement as moonlight *glitters* and mill-wheel *casts.* Suddenly water runs, wind sighs, grass moves in your mental picture as change and action pervade the description. Sixth, he then refines his language, using any helpful poetic devices, but being careful not to overuse them. If they become obtrusive, he may destroy the mood, tone, and atmosphere he wishes to achieve. The minute the reader becomes aware of "precious" language rather than of the imagery created by language, the writer has failed.

The following paragraph is a rephrased passage from the writings of Samuel L. Clemens. Read it, noticing its dull, uninteresting description, the trite phrases which indicate an insensitivity to detail, the falsity of the pseudo-scientific ending:

The sky grew dark. Thunder rolled and lightning flashed. The birds had assessed the situation correctly. It started to rain cats and dogs and the wind blew a gale. The day turned black as night and it rained so hard you could hardly see the nearby trees. Then a gust of wind would bend the trees until they almost touched the ground before they snapped back up. Lightning would suddenly light up the whole landscape and then darkness would fall again. In a minute, thunder would follow the lightning, for it is the sound electricity makes as it breaks the sound barrier.

Not all the excellence leaves the passage even in its poorly written form, of course, for Mark Twain's selection of details and their order have been retained. Furthermore, the verbs running through the paragraph keep it from becoming static. But the paragraph lacks mood, tone, and atmosphere. It has been reduced to dullness.

In *The Adventures of Huckleberry Finn,* Twain incorporated this description into the part of the narrative where Huck is running away with the slave Jim. Predicting rain by watching the behavior of some young birds, Jim suggests that he and Huck take refuge in a cave. From that vantage point, Huck describes the storm, revealing his religious background, his affinity with nature, and his lack of formal education. As you read the actual description below, notice the selection and arrangement of details, the strong action verbs, the verbals, and the numerous poetic devices. Notice the use of the words *underside* and *under side* and see if you can detect the sound, technical reason for the two uses:

Pretty soon it darkened up, and begun to thunder and lighten; so the birds was right about it. Directly it begun to rain, and it rained like all fury, too, and I never see the wind blow so. It was one of these regular summer storms. It would get so dark that it looked all blue-black outside, and lovely; and the rain would thrash along by so thick that the trees off a little ways looked dim and spider-webby; and here would come a blast of wind that would bend the trees down and turn up the pale underside of the leaves; and then a perfect ripper of a gust would follow along and set the branches to tossing their arms as if they was just wild; and next, when it was just about the bluest and blackest—*fst!* it was as bright as glory, and you'd have a little glimpse of tree-tops a-plunging about away off yonder in the storm, hundreds of yards further than you could see before; dark as sin again in a second, and now you'd hear the thunder let go with an awful crash, and then go rumbling, grumbling, tumbling down the sky towards the under side of the world, like rolling empty barrels down-stairs—where it's long stairs and they bounce a good deal, you know.

The diction and idiom of the description reveal Huck's varied background as he sensitively reacts to nature and alludes to the religious attitudes of the Mississippi River dwellers. Active voice verbs sweep the description along as rapidly as gusts of wind. Transitional words give unity to the passage and indicate a time progression. Beginning with *pretty soon,* the passage runs smoothly along on the words *directly, and then, and next, again, and now,* and *and then* as they bind the active voice verbs into one continuous motion. Abstract words are placed in tension with concrete ones in such combinations as *dim and spider-webby* to create atmosphere so real you can almost feel the misted air of the cave.

Poetic devices abound in the passage, giving it reality and effectiveness. Notice such similes as "like all fury," "as bright as glory," "dark as sin." Lightning becomes electric in the onomatopoetic *fst!* prefacing *glory* which, metaphorically, is endowed with brilliance. *Rumbling, grumbling, tumbling* are onomatopoetic as feminine rhyme is employed in the three words to create thunder, a description extended poetically into the empty barrels simile. Contrast and emotional foreshadowing are brilliantly employed in *underside* (immediate, concrete) and *under side* (distant, abstract). A less perceptive writer might have used a trite phrase such as "towards China," and the effect would be lost. Static adjectives are almost absent. Sharp contrasts are created in the progressive darkening through *blue-black, dim and spider-webby, pale, bluest and blackest, bright,* and *dark.* The darkness is intensified by the cave context which you probably see illuminated by the lightning flashes. And you probably also see the contrast in Huck's white skin and Jim's black. Much of what you see, feel, and hear is not actually in the words of the description. As it is selective, well-organized, unified, and coherent, the paragraph enlists your cooperation—and you give it.

Did you notice how *wet* the atmosphere is?

In context, a subtle undercurrent of guilt is established in the passage. Huck is placed in a difficult situation. He feels he should help Jim, a fellow prisoner, escape. But, a victim of the slave-holding times, he feels he is aiding and abetting a theft. The light-dark contrasts in the storm, sin, and redemption reveal a great deal about his ambivalence. The passage is not employed for its own sake, however excellent the description. More important, it allows you to recognize many things about Huck that you would have rejected had Twain detailed them in exposition.

At this point, turn back to "The Scythe" (p. 22) and examine a paragraph that you think is excellent description—there are many. Isolate as many of the techniques as you can. Why are they effective? How do they work within the framework of the total story? Is the descriptive passage merely inserted because it is a good description or has it a greater function? To how many areas of the story does it contribute? What does it reveal about character? Does it establish mood, tone, or atmosphere? How does it relate them to the theme?

Careful authors do not employ description unless it has a definite function in the story. To stop the narrative flow and describe a sunset or a storm, a flower, or a dog—such would remove focus from the progress of the narrative. If, on the other hand, the description reveals character or the inserted details are essential, it has validity.

Two of the best uses of description in narrative lie in character revelation and narrative progression. Description may "show" something about a character that narrative could not "tell" without violating point of view. Have you noticed in your reading that nature often seems to reflect a character's attitudes? Objectively, such a possibility is ridiculous. Nature reflects nothing but nature. It may influence a person's attitude, but his attitudes certainly can't change it. Sunshine is the same sunshine in the following sentences, but observe the change as description is applied to it:

> The sun shone.
>
> On the lake, the sun skated from ripple to ripple.
>
> Inquisitively, the sun poked long fingers into the fern bed.
>
> The sun herded shadows before it.
>
> The sun honed edges of the dust.
>
> With its mobile advantage, the sun dispersed the dark.

Each of the descriptions reveals a different attitude, not a different sun. The focus seems to be on one thing, but a subtle insinuation emerges, and the reader's concepts are changed without his knowledge.

You have, doubtless, read Edgar Allan Poe's "The Cask of Amontillado." As Montressor leads Fortunato to his tomb, description of the catacombs is palpable and eloquent. Physical details are established; the narrative progresses as focus shifts from one component to the next, and Montressor's methodical mind is revealed. Had Poe allowed Montressor to tell us he was methodical and precise, the statement would mean little; whereas his attention to detail reveals the order and precision which allow him to plan and execute his revenge:

[1]. . . [1] We passed through a range of low arches, descended, passed on, and descending again, arrived at a deep crypt, in which the foulness of the air caused our flambeaux rather to glow than flame.

[2][2] At the most remote end of the crypt there appeared another less spacious. Its walls had been lined with human remains, piled to the vault overhead, in the fashion of the great catacombs of Paris. Three sides of this interior crypt were still ornamented in this manner. [3] From the fourth the bones had been thrown down, and lay promiscuously upon the earth, forming at one point a mound of some size. Within the wall thus exposed by the displacing of the bones, we perceived a still interior crypt or recess, in depth about four feet, in width three, in height six or seven. [4] It seemed to have been constructed for no especial use within itself, but formed merely the interval between two of the colossal supports of the roof of the catacombs, and was backed by one of their circumscribing walls of solid granite.

[3]It was in vain that Fortunato, uplifting his dull torch, endeavoured to pry into the depth of the recess. Its termination the feeble light did not enable us to see.

The range of arches [1] suggests gothic architecture and movement—one follows another. The verb series *descended, passed on,* and *arrived,* reinforced by the participle *descending,* ties the narrative progression to the descriptive. The "foulness of the air" is insinuated into the skeletons [2] which are *piled,* serving as *lining* and *ornamentation.* The casual *thrown down* [3] leads into *lay promiscuously,* and Montressor's cold detachment is revealed. The expository statement [4] would be meaningless had Poe not revealed Montressor's character through focus on descriptive elements chosen by Montressor.

Poe's contemporary, Nathaniel Hawthorne, utilizes description and narrative to tell the reader what he needs to know in the opening paragraphs of "The Minister's Black Veil":

[1]The sexton stood in the porch of Milford meeting-house, pulling busily at the bell-rope. The old people of the village came stooping along the street. Children, with bright faces, tripped merrily beside their parents, or mimicked a graver gait, in the conscious dignity of their Sunday clothes. Spruce bachelors looked sidelong at the pretty maidens, and fancied that the Sabbath sunshine made them prettier than on week days. When the throng had mostly streamed into the porch, the sexton began to toll the bell, keeping his eye on the Reverend Mr. Hooper's door. The first glimpse of the clergyman's figure was the signal for the bell to cease its summons.

[2]"But what has good Parson Hooper got upon his face?" cried the sexton in astonishment.

[3]All within hearing immediately turned about, and beheld the semblance of Mr. Hooper, pacing slowly his meditative way towards the meeting-house. With one

accord they started, expressing more wonder than if some strange minister were coming to dust the cushions of Mr. Hooper's pulpit.

4"Are you sure it is our parson?" inquired Goodman Gray of the sexton.

5"Of a certainty it is good Mr. Hooper," replied the sexton. "He was to have exchanged pulpits with Parson Shute, of Westbury; but Parson Shute sent to excuse himself yesterday, being to preach a funeral sermon."

6The cause of so much amazement may appear sufficiently slight. Mr. Hooper, a gentlemanly person, of about thirty, though still a bachelor, was dressed with due clerical neatness, as if a careful wife had starched his band, and brushed the weekly dust from his Sunday's garb. There was but one thing remarkable in his appearance. Swathed about his forehead, and hanging down over his face, so low as to be shaken by his breath, Mr. Hooper had on a black veil. On a nearer view it seemed to consist of two folds of crape, which entirely concealed his features, except the mouth and chin, but probably did not intercept his sight, further than to give a darkened aspect to all living and inanimate things. With this gloomy shade before him, good Mr. Hooper walked onward, at a slow and quiet pace, stooping somewhat, and looking on the ground, as is customary with abstracted men, yet nodding kindly to those of his parishioners who still waited on the meeting-house steps. But so wonder-struck were they that his greeting hardly met with a return.

7"I can't really feel as if good Mr. Hooper's face was behind that piece of crape," said the sexton.

8"I don't like it," muttered an old woman, as she hobbled into the meeting-house. "He has changed himself into something awful, only by hiding his face."*

Did you notice such phrases as "pulling busily" or "stooping along the street" or "to dust the cushions"? Why is "graver gait" effective? There is more than one reason! Examine such sentences as "The cause of so much amazement may appear sufficiently slight" and "But so wonder-struck were they that his greeting hardly met with a return." How much of their effectiveness lies in poetic techniques? How many poetic techniques can you detect? Do not overlook understatement in both sentences—it is frequently an author's most dramatic and useful tool. Can you explain why, using these two sentences as examples? How is symbol introduced in these paragraphs? How is it developed? Is its insertion a jarring element? How does description serve narra-

* "Another clergyman in New England, Mr. Joseph Moody, of York, Maine, who died about eighty years since, made himself remarkable by the same eccentricity that is here related of the Reverend Mr. Hooper. In his case, however, the symbol had a different import. In early life he had accidentally killed a beloved friend; and from that day till the hour of his own death, he hid his face from men."—From Hawthorne's *Journals*

tive? The remainder of "the parable" (for so Hawthorne subtitled this story) is worth examination. You can find it in many anthologies.

Narrative and description may, of course, be independent forms, interesting, complete, and artistically valuable alone or in combination. In prose fiction, they should be a part of and essential to the progression of the story. Readers are interested, actually, in one thing: themselves. The broader view that many people are interested in the human race begins with an interest in Self. They read, then, about human beings—which are extensions of themselves. Their concern with factual matter about gardening or dogs is related to their own interest in those subjects as they are related to human beings. A description of a sunrise, a flock of geese flying south, a colt in spring pasture—all interest the reader as a human being. He sees things as they are related to him. Description serves as a backdrop or interpretative element for a closer look at himself. You would not care to live in a bare room; it is not the dramatic background your life deserves. A flock of geese flying south is of scientific interest alone until a sensitive human observes the flight. It then becomes personally meaningful as it causes him to reflect on changing seasons, his own passing life, the complexities of "God's plan." The descriptive passage will reveal his mood as sorrowful, joyous, pensive, or indifferent. It is the same flight of geese; its importance lies in what it reveals to or about the observer.

That poetic devices are basic to effective description becomes an obvious truth as you examine good description analytically. Successful writers employ such devices extensively and well. Notice the welding of narrative and description in Chapter I of *Peyton Place* by Grace Metalious. As a novel, *Peyton Place* is poorly developed and sensational. But Chapter I suffers no such criticism—it is descriptive narrative at its best. A sultry, brooding, explosive passion (atmosphere) pervades this chapter and sets the tone for the rest of the novel. Read the chapter first by skipping the discussion between paragraphs; then come back; read each paragraph; isolate the techniques as you see them; then read the discussion sections:

1 Indian summer is like a woman. Ripe, hotly passionate, but fickle, she comes and goes as she pleases so that one is never sure whether she will come at all, nor for how long she will stay. In northern New England, Indian summer puts up a scarlet-tipped hand to hold winter back for a little while. She brings with her the time of the last warm spell, an unchartered season which lives until Winter moves in with its backbone of ice and accoutrements of leafless trees and hard frozen ground. Those grown old, who have had the youth bled from them by the jagged-edged winds of winter, know sorrowfully that Indian summer is a sham to be

met with hard-eyed cynicism. But the young wait anxiously, scanning the chill autumn skies for a sign of her coming. And sometimes the old, against all the warnings of better judgment, wait with the young and hopeful, their tired, winter eyes turned heavenward to seek the first traces of a false softening.

The opening sentence is a simile. In the course of the chapter it becomes an extended metaphor, thoroughly developed as narrative and description flow together. Notice the comparative points in this paragraph: the transience of Indian summer and woman, the painted fingernails (abstract-concrete). A second contrast is offered in the reception by the young and the old. Beginning in this paragraph and extending to the end of the book, conflict between youth and age is a plot device in *Peyton Place.*

[2]One year, early in October, Indian summer came to a town called Peyton Place. Like a laughing, lovely woman Indian summer came and spread herself over the countryside and made everything hurtfully beautiful to the eye.

Narrative transition (*One year*) welds this paragraph to the first one. The simile is extended in voluptuousness. Notice the poetic *hurtfully.* Try to explain what it means. If you have difficulty, you might read Edna St. Vinçent Millay's poem "God's World."

[3]The sky was low, of a solidly unbroken blue. The maples and oaks and ashes, all dark red and brown and yellow, preened themselves in the unseasonably hot light, under the Indian summer sun. The conifers stood like disapproving old men on all the hills around Peyton Place and gave off a greenish yellow light. On the roads and sidewalks of the town there were fallen leaves which made such a gay crackling when stepped upon and sent up such a sweet scent when crushed that it was only the very old who walked over them and thought of death and decay.

A distinct appeal to the senses appears in this paragraph. Blue *exists* everywhere in the verb-of-being of sentence 1. The youth-age contrast is reduced to personification as the deciduous trees become the young and the evergreens become the old—vibrant colors characterize the first; a sickly color, the second. The ear hears dead leaves underfoot. The feel of crunching is palpable; the nose smells their sweet scent. The youth-age contrast is sharpened in the last three clauses of the final sentence, and it is sharpened in the reader's awareness. An atmosphere of "between times" pervades the first three paragraphs. Did you notice the alliteration, consonance, assonance, onomatopoeia, and simile in paragraph 3?

[4]The town lay still in the Indian summer sun. On Elm Street, the main thoroughfare, nothing moved. The shopkeepers, who had rolled protective canvas awnings down over their front windows, took the lack of trade philosophically and retired to the back rooms of their stores where they alternately dozed, glanced at the *Peyton Place Times*, and listened to the broadcast of a baseball game.

The waiting atmosphere has been built to this point, and this paragraph intensifies it, serving as a transition to pivot the reader into the next paragraph. The heavy drowsiness of the day is created in the paragraph as *r, s,* and *t* combinations lull the reader gently into the atmosphere of the afternoon. The alliterative *b*'s of "broadcast of a baseball game" add a raucousness to the paragraph as it pivots into the description of competitive churches.

[5]To the east on Elm Street, beyond the six blocks occupied by the business section of the town, rose the steeple of the Congregational church. The pointed structure pierced through the leaves of the surrounding trees and shone, dazzlingly white, against the blue sky. At the opposite end of the business district stood another steepled structure. This was St. Joseph's Catholic Church, and its spire far outshone that of the Congregationalists, for it was topped with a cross of gold.

Did you notice the repetition of *town* in sentence 1? It effectively bridges the paragraphs. Contrasts appear again. The inactivity of the town is contrasted with the upward thrust of the two steeples, one white, one gold. The conservative religious element of the first church is contrasted with the exotic facade of the second. An emotional response is generated, and religious conflict is added in understatement.

[6]Seth Buswell, the owner and editor of the *Peyton Place Times*, had once written, rather poetically, that the two churches bracketed and held the town like a pair of gigantic book ends, an observation which had set off a series of minor explosions in Peyton Place. There were few Catholics in town who cared to be associated in any partnership with the Protestants, while the Congregationalists had as little desire to be paired off with the Papists. If imaginary book ends were to exist in Peyton Place they would both have to be of the same religious denomination.

The first named character is introduced seemingly effortlessly; a similar transition was employed in paragraph 4 with the first mention of the newspaper. Paragraph 5, in turn, serves as a transition into the flashback of this paragraph. "Rather poetically" is interesting, for Metalious seems to enjoy here the technique she details in recounting Seth's "fun." Poetic device within poetic device leads into ironic hyperbole—another contrast.

[7]Seth had laughed at the arguments heard all over town that week, and in his next edition he reclassified the two churches as tall, protective mountains guarding the peaceful business valley. Both Catholics and Protestants scanned this second article carefully for a trace of sarcasm or facetiousness, but in the end everyone had taken the story at its face value and Seth laughed harder than before.

The simile of paragraph 6 becomes a metaphor in this paragraph, and "at its face value" is a cliché deliberately and effectively used to indicate the weak perceptiveness of the townspeople. Their petty attention to unimportant matters is casually established without obviousness as Metalious focuses away from the facts she wishes to convey to the reader. Her focal point achieves by indirection what would have been offensive to the reader if stated directly.

[8]Dr. Matthew Swain, Seth's best friend and oldest crony, grunted, "Mountains, eh? More like a pair of goddamned volcanoes."

[9]"Both of 'em breathin' brimstone and fire," Seth added, still laughing as he poured two more drinks.

[10]But the doctor would not laugh with his friend. There were three things which he hated in this world, he said often and angrily: death, venereal disease and organized religion.

[11]"In that order," the doctor always amended. "And the story, clean or otherwise, that can make me laugh at one of these has never been thought up."

Mountains repeated serves as the transition into the four paragraphs of dialog employed here for their narrative value in informing the reader of Matthew Swain's biases. The poetic extension of *mountains* to *volcanoes* is also used transitionally, metaphorically, and symbolically. Did you notice the allusion to Hell in "brimstone and fire"? And were you aware that the volcanoes are "goddamned"? The word is used denotatively and connotatively.

[12]But on this hot October afternoon Seth was not thinking of opposing religious factions or, for that matter, of anything in particular. He sat at his desk behind the plate glass window of his street floor office, sipping at a cold drink, and listened desultorily to the baseball game.

A transitional *but* removes the focus entirely from Mat and fixes it on Seth as paragraph 4 is alluded to, bringing the narrative back to the present.

[13]In front of the courthouse, a large white stone building with a verdigris-colored dome, a few old men lounged on the wooden benches which seem to be part of every municipal building in America's small towns. The men leaned back against the warm sides of the courthouse, their tired eyes shaded by battered felt hats, and let the Indian summer sun warm their cold, old bones. They were as still as the trees for which the main street had been named.

Symbolism is employed as the white (pure) walls (recalling the Congregational church spire) are contrasted to the verdigris (tarnished) dome (recalling the Catholic Church spire) of the courthouse. Is legal intent (walls) also capped by a crust of poisonous compound? Conflict is suggested as civic law and moral law are contrasted. Decay is recalled from paragraph 3 and reinforced as Indian summer, trees, and the old men are reinjected into the narrative flow.

[14]Under the elms the black tarred sidewalks, ruffled in many places by the pushing roots of the giant trees, were empty. The chime clock set into the red brick front of the Citizens' National Bank, across the street from the courthouse, struck once. It was two-thirty on a Friday afternoon. □

The trees of paragraph 13 are named by way of transition; they are in conflict with man's "tarred sidewalks." The final conflicting social element, the bank, is introduced. Time goes from an abstraction (Indian summer) to a specific point (2:30 P.M. on Friday).

Had the remainder of *Peyton Place* been as brilliantly conceived and executed as its first chapter, the book would probably be as critically successful as it has been monetarily—and it has become the best selling novel of all time.

Far removed, critically, from Grace Metalious, John Steinbeck has received countless accolades for his novel *The Grapes of Wrath.* It is structured in chapters alternating between plot and social comment. Chapter III is "The Turtle," an allegory in which the turtle symbolizes the Okies. Read it in the same way you read Chapter I of *Peyton Place:*

[1]The concrete highway was edged with a mat of tangled, broken, dry grass, and the grass heads were heavy with oat beards to catch on a dog's coat, and foxtails to tangle in a horse's fetlocks, and clover burrs to fasten in sheep's wool; sleeping life waiting to be spread and dispersed, every seed armed with an appliance of dispersal, twisting darts and parachutes for the wind, little spears and balls of tiny thorns, and all waiting for animals and for the wind, for a man's trouser cuff or the hem of a woman's skirt, all passive but armed with appliances of activity, still, but each possessed of the anlage of movement.

Steinbeck's powers of observation are acute. Each detail in this chapter is sharply defined under the microscopic vision of the author. Conflict opens the description as a man-made highway cuts across nature's path of growth. Seeds are personified as waiting, anticipating conveyance. Concrete imagery exists in the careful selection of concrete nouns: *highway, mat, grass heads, beards, coat, foxtails, fetlocks, burrs, wool, seed, appliance, darts, parachutes, spears, balls, thorns, wind, cuff, hem, anlage.* Repetition strengthens the paragraph throughout, but it is repetition of ideas, not of words. Nature and technology are combined and contrasted in the language, and a poetic tone runs through the lines. Notice the verbs and verbals as movement stirs throughout the paragraph. What might be static description seethes with life, yet an atmosphere of waiting hovers over everything—life will not be halted.

2 The sun lay on the grass and warmed it, and in the shade under the grass the insects moved, ants and ant lions to set traps for them, grasshoppers to jump into the air and flick their yellow wings for a second, sow bugs like little armadillos, plodding restlessly on many tender feet. And over the grass at the roadside a land turtle crawled, turning aside for nothing, dragging his high-domed shell over the grass. His hard legs and yellow-nailed feet threshed slowly through the grass, not really walking, but boosting and dragging his shell along. The barley beards slid off his shell, and the clover burrs fell on him and rolled to the ground. His horny beak was partly open, and his fierce, humorous eyes, under brows like fingernails, stared straight ahead. He came over the grass leaving a beaten trail behind him, and the hill, which was the highway embankment, reared up ahead of him. For a moment he stopped, his head held high. He blinked and looked up and down. At last he started to climb the embankment. Front clawed feet reached forward but did not touch. The hind feet kicked his shell along, and it scraped on the grass, and on the gravel. As the embankment grew steeper and steeper, the more frantic were the efforts of the land turtle. Pushing hind legs strained and slipped, boosting the shell along, and the horny head protruded as far as the neck could stretch. Little by little the shell slid up the embankment until at last a parapet cut straight across its line of march, the shoulder of the road, a concrete wall four inches high. As though they worked independently the hind legs pushed the shell against the wall. The head upraised and peered over the wall to the broad smooth plain of cement. Now the hands, braced on top of the wall, strained and lifted, and the shell came slowly up and rested its front end on the wall. For a moment the turtle rested. A red ant ran into the shell, into the soft skin inside the shell, and suddenly head and legs snapped in, and the armored tail clamped in sideways. The red ant was crushed between body and legs. And one head of wild oats was clamped into the shell by a front leg. For a long moment the turtle lay still, and then the neck crept out and the old humorous frowning eyes looked about and the legs and tail came out. The back legs

went to work, straining like elephant legs, and the shell tipped to an angle so that the front legs could not reach the level cement plain. But higher and higher the hind legs boosted it, until at last the center of balance was reached, the front tipped down, the front legs scratched at the pavement, and it was up. But the head of wild oats was held by its stem around the front legs.

This paragraph opens with an active voice verb that connotation weakens almost to a verb of being. A verb of slightly greater intensity follows, and motion builds steadily then as the description moves from one verb or verbal to the next until the turtle crawls into the description, and narrative is welded to description to create this mighty miniature of fiction.

Conflict in nature is introduced with ants and ant lions. Color and heat are introduced with sun and grasshoppers. The turtle's appearance is foreshadowed by sow bugs "like little armadillos." The turtle, dragging his shell (notice how *high-domed* suggests "home") appears, and his nails are yellow as were the sun and grasshoppers' wings. The grasshoppers jumped free of the earth; the turtle is almost chained to it. Sow bugs had *tender* feet; the turtle has *nailed* feet. Seeds shower over him. His eyebrows are like fingernails; his beak is horny. Exterior hardness and protectiveness characterize him. But his eyes are humorous.

One of the most basic of all prose forms, the *process theme,* is utilized at this point. Every minute detail of the turtle's assault on the highway embankment is detailed in exact chronological order. Self-protection is emphasized again as the red ant appears. And life force (the wild oats head) attaches itself to him. This moment was foreshadowed in the first paragraph. Notice the rhyme in *out-about-out* in the sentence beginning "For a long moment." Did you observe the strength image growing into the "elephant legs" simile?

3 Now the going was easy, and all the legs worked, and the shell boosted along, waggling from side to side. A sedan driven by a forty-year old woman approached. She saw the turtle and swung to the right, off the highway, the wheels screamed and a cloud of dust boiled up. Two wheels lifted for a moment and then settled. The car skidded back onto the road, and went on, but more slowly. The turtle had jerked into its shell, but now it hurried on, for the highway was burning hot.

The time transition is made with *now.* The elephant legs simile is extended into "waggling from side to side," a *poetic license* (a writer's privilege to depart from normal standards), for turtles don't "waggle" —but elephants do. Contrasts are introduced as a woman driver swerves to avoid the turtle. A subtle implication is that women are givers of life, not takers. Can wheels scream? If personification is used, they can.

[4]And now a light truck approached, and as it came near, the driver saw the turtle and swerved to hit it. His front wheel struck the edge of the shell, flipped the turtle like a tiddly-wink, spun it like a coin, and rolled it off the highway. The truck went back to its course along the right side. Lying on its back, the turtle was tight in its shell for a long time. But at last its legs waved in the air, reaching for something to pull it over. Its front foot caught a piece of quartz and little by little the shell pulled over and flopped upright. The wild oat head fell out and three of the spearhead seeds stuck in the ground. And as the turtle crawled on down the embankment, its shell dragged dirt over the seeds. The turtle entered a dust road and jerked itself along, drawing a wavy shallow trench in the dust with its shell. The old humorous eyes looked ahead, and the horny beak opened a little. His yellow toe nails slipped a fraction in the dust. □

The time transition is made with *And now.* A man (taker of life?) swerves to hit the turtle. Simile follows simile as the picture is vividly created. Language creates emotional tightness as *l*'s and *t*'s work alliteratively and consonantly in "Lying on its back, the turtle was tight in its shell for a long time." The verb *flopped* is onomatopoetically right. Alliteration is vivid in "spearhead seeds stuck" and "dragged dirt." Life achieves its transplanting as the turtle refuses to be defeated. *Nails, yellow,* and heat (*dust*) bring the progression full circle.

"The Turtle" is a complete work in itself. Had it not been incorporated into *The Grapes of Wrath,* it would be a great minor work of fiction. As it is, it represents certain truths about all fiction. Whether that fiction is prose or poetry, a novel, a short story, a myth, a fable, or a fairy tale, it will chronicle the efforts of a character to meet a situation involving problems and difficulties. That situation will result from an obstacle's being placed in the character's path. In finding a way to remove or get around that obstacle, the character becomes the focal point of fiction.

Suggested Activities. 1. Select the most static thing you can find (a crack in a sidewalk is an excellent choice) and write a descriptive paragraph, focusing on the static element. You may *not* use one verb-of-being or one verb in the passive voice. Every verb must be an *action* verb in the *active* voice. Make your paragraph at least ten sentences in length with careful attention given to proportion in types of sentences (simple, compound, complex, compound-complex). Use the simple sentence to focus the reader's attention sharply and suddenly on startling details. Use the complex or the compound-complex sentence to extend descriptive elements into each other. Allow yourself no more than one compound sentence and it may *not* be compounded by *and, or,* or *but.*

In completing this assignment, find your subject; study it; make notes. If people find it a little strange that you are sitting on a sidewalk, taking notes on a crack, ignore them. Writers are seldom really eccentric—their behavior is just a little strange as they go to extremes to perceive in a fresh fashion.

2. Choose a very ordinary room. Write three different paragraphs of description, concentrating on mood, tone, and atmosphere. For instance, imagine it is cheerful, unfriendly, or hostile. Or imagine it conducive to study, or lethargy, or terror. Your focus will change as you write the various paragraphs. Be sparing of adjectives and adverbs. Try to replace them with verbals. Remember proportion in sentence structure. Pace will certainly change as you choose language to reveal happiness and sadness.

3. Choose a vista that you like. Describe it in two ways. In one, start by focusing on details at your feet. Raising your eyes slowly, describe things at a little distance, greater distance, long distance. You will go from a focus on limited scene to panoramic description. In the second, reverse the progression and start with panorama. Avoid verbs-of-being. Concentrate on all five senses. See how unobtrusively you can include appeal to them.

4. Depending on the weather at the time of this exercise, describe a storm, a sunset, a moonlit night, or the fifteen-minute period before sunrise. Be especially cautious here as this exercise will invite the trite phrase. Use adjectives sparingly, concentrating on exactness in the ones you do use. There are many shades of red, green, blue, and purple—be specific. Do *not* use the words *blend, melt,* or *flow* in any tense. Poetic devices will be helpful, but remember that moons and suns as ghostly galleons, canoes, pumpkin pies, oranges, balls of fire, and egg yolks have been discovered by a plethora of writers! In your progression, you might try to go from understatement to hyperbole or from hyperbole to understatement. Such progression can teach you a great deal about special effects in description.

Suggested Assignments. 1. Read the following stories by Stephen Vincent Benét and Graham Greene. In a well-organized paper, compare the descriptive effects of the two writers. As the stories are so similar in plot and theme, they offer excellent comparative possibilities. Notice also the narrative features that are similar and dissimilar.

2. Compare the uses of point of view as the two authors employ it in these two stories. Why has each chosen as he has? Discuss their use in a brief paper.

3. The uses of language distinguish the prose of these two authors.

Compare their stories for vocabulary choice and poetic devices. Which seems to owe a greater debt to poetry? Defend your decision in a three-paragraph paper.

By the Waters of Babylon

by Stephen Vincent Benét

1 The north and the west and the south are good hunting ground, but it is forbidden to go east. It is forbidden to go to any of the Dead Places except to search for metal and then he who touches the metal must be a priest or the son of a priest. Afterwards, both the man and the metal must be purified. These are the rules and the laws; they are well made. It is forbidden to cross the great river and look upon the place that was the Place of the Gods—this is most strictly forbidden. We do not even say its name though we know its name. It is there that spirits live, and demons—it is there that there are the ashes of the Great Burning. These things are forbidden—they have been forbidden since the beginning of time.

2 My father is a priest; I am the son of a priest. I have been in the Dead Places near us, with my father—at first, I was afraid. When my father went into the house to search for the metal, I stood by the door and my heart felt small and weak. It was a dead man's house, a spirit house. It did not have the smell of man, though there were old bones in a corner. But it is not fitting that a priest's son should show fear. I looked at the bones in the shadow and kept my voice still.

3 Then my father came out with the metal—a good, strong piece. He looked at me with both eyes but I had not run away. He gave me the metal to hold—I took it and did not die. So he knew that I was truly his son and would be a priest in my time. That was when I was very young—nevertheless, my brothers would not have done it, though they are good hunters. After that, they gave me the good piece of meat and the warm corner of the fire. My father watched over me—he was glad that I should be a priest. But when I boasted or wept without a reason, he punished me more strictly than my brothers. That was right.

4 After a time, I myself was allowed to go into the dead houses and search for metal. So I learned the ways of those houses—and if I saw bones, I was no longer afraid. The bones are light and old—sometimes they will fall into dust if you touch them. But that is a great sin.

[5] I was taught the chants and the spells—I was taught how to stop the running of blood from a wound and many secrets. A priest must know many secrets—that was what my father said.

[6] If the hunters think we do all things by chants and spells, they may believe so—it does not hurt them. I was taught how to read in the old books and how to make the old writings—that was hard and took a long time. My knowledge made me happy—it was like a fire in my heart. Most of all, I liked to hear of the Old Days and the stories of the gods. I asked myself many questions that I could not answer, but it was good to ask them. At night, I would lie awake and listen to the wind—it seemed to me that it was the voice of the gods as they flew through the air.

[7] We are not ignorant like the Forest People—our women spin wool on the wheel, our priests wear a white robe. We do not eat grubs from the trees, we have not forgotten the old writings, although they are hard to understand. Nevertheless, my knowledge and my lack of knowledge burned in me—I wished to know more. When I was a man at last, I came to my father and said, "It is time for me to go on my journey. Give me your leave."

[8] He looked at me for a long time, stroking his beard, then he said at last, "Yes. It is time." That night, in the house of the priesthood, I asked for and received purification. My body hurt but my spirit was a cool stone. It was my father himself who questioned me about my dreams.

[9] He bade me look into the smoke of the fire and see—I saw and told what I saw. It was what I have always seen—a river, and, beyond it, a great Dead Place and in it the gods walking. I have always thought about that. His eyes were stern when I told him—he was no longer my father but a priest. He said, "This is a strong dream."

[10] "It is mine," I said, while the smoke waved and my head felt light. They were singing the Star song in the outer chamber and it was like the buzzing of bees in my head.

[11] He asked me how the gods were dressed and I told him how they were dressed. We know how they were dressed from the book, but I saw them as if they were before me. When I had finished, he threw the sticks three times and studied them as they fell.

[12] "This is a very strong dream," he said. "It may eat you up."

[13] "I am not afraid," I said and looked at him with both eyes. My voice sounded thin in my ears but that was because of the smoke.

[14] He touched me on the breast and the forehead. He gave me the bow and the three arrows.

[15] "Take them," he said. "It is forbidden to travel east. It is forbidden

to cross the river. It is forbidden to go to the Place of the Gods. All these things are forbidden."

16 "All these things are forbidden," I said, but it was my voice that spoke and not my spirit. He looked at me again.

17 "My son," he said. "Once I had young dreams. If your dreams do not eat you up, you may be a great priest. If they eat you, you are still my son. Now go on your journey."

18 I went fasting, as is the law. My body hurt but not my heart. When the dawn came, I was out of sight of the village. I prayed and purified myself, waiting for a sign. The sign was an eagle. It flew east.

19 Sometimes signs are sent by bad spirits. I waited again on the flat rock, fasting, taking no food. I was very still—I could feel the sky above me and the earth beneath. I waited till the sun was beginning to sink. Then three deer passed in the valley going east—they did not mind me or see me. There was a white fawn with them—a very great sign.

20 I followed them, at a distance, waiting for what would happen. My heart was troubled about going east, yet I knew that I must go. My head hummed with my fasting—I did not even see the panther spring upon the white fawn. But, before I knew it, the bow was in my hand. I shouted and the panther lifted his head from the fawn. It is not easy to kill a panther with one arrow but the arrow went through his eye and into his brain. He died as he tried to spring—he rolled over, tearing at the ground. Then I knew I was meant to go east—I knew that was my journey. When the night came, I made my fire and roasted meat.

21 It is eight suns' journey to the east and a man passes by many Dead Places. The Forest People are afraid of them but I am not. Once I made my fire on the edge of a Dead Place at night and, next morning, in the dead house, I found a good knife, little rusted. That was small to what came afterward but it made my heart feel big. Always when I looked for game, it was in front of my arrow, and twice I passed hunting parties of the Forest People without their knowing. So I knew my magic was strong and my journey clean, in spite of the law.

22 Toward the setting of the eighth sun, I came to the banks of the great river. It was half-a-day's journey after I had left the god-road—we do not use the god-roads now for they are falling apart into great blocks of stone, and the forest is safer going. A long way off, I had seen the water through trees but the trees were thick. At last, I came out upon an open place at the top of a cliff. There was the great river below, like a giant in the sun. It is very long, very wide. It could eat all the streams we know and still be thirsty. Its name is Ou-dis-sun, the Sacred,

the Long. No man of my tribe had seen it, not even my father, the priest. It was magic and I prayed.

23 Then I raised my eyes and looked south. It was there, the Place of the Gods.

24 How can I tell what it was like—you do not know. It was there, in the red light, and they were too big to be houses. It was there with the red light upon it, mighty and ruined. I knew that in another moment the gods would see me. I covered my eyes with my hands and crept back into the forest.

25 Surely, that was enough to do, and live. Surely it was enough to spend the night upon the cliff. The Forest People themselves do not come near. Yet, all through the night, I knew that I should have to cross the river and walk in the places of the gods, although the gods ate me up. My magic did not help me at all and yet there was a fire in my bowels, a fire in my mind. When the sun rose, I thought, "My journey has been clean. Now I will go home from my journey." But, even as I thought so, I knew I could not. If I went to the Place of the Gods, I would surely die, but, if I did not go, I could never be at peace with my spirit again. It is better to lose one's life than one's spirit, if one is a priest and the son of a priest.

26 Nevertheless, as I made the raft, the tears ran out of my eyes. The Forest People could have killed me without fight, if they had come upon me then, but they did not come. When the raft was made, I said the sayings for the dead and painted myself for death. My heart was cold as a frog and my knees like water, but the burning in my mind would not let me have peace. As I pushed the raft from the shore, I began my death song—I had the right. It was a fine song.

27 "I am John, son of John," I sang. "My people are the Hill People.
They are the men.
I go into the Dead Places but I am not slain.
I take the metal from the Dead Places but I am not blasted.
I travel upon the god-roads and am not afraid. E-yah! I have killed the panther, I have killed the fawn!
E-yah! I have come to the great river. No man has come there before.
It is forbidden to go east, but I have gone, forbidden to go on the great river, but I am there.
Open your hearts, you spirits, and hear my song. Now I go to the Place of the Gods, I shall not return.
My body is painted for death and my limbs weak, but my heart is big as I go to the Place of the Gods!"

28 All the same, when I came to the Place of the Gods, I was afraid, afraid. The current of the great river is very strong—it gripped my raft with its hands. That was magic, for the river itself is wide and calm. I could feel evil spirits about me, in the bright morning; I could feel their breath on my neck as I was swept down the stream. Never have I been so much alone—I tried to think of my knowledge, but it was a squirrel's heap of winter nuts. There was no strength in my knowledge any more and I felt small and naked as a new-hatched bird—alone upon the great river, the servant of the gods.

29 Yet, after a while, my eyes were opened and I saw. I saw both banks of the river—I saw that once there had been god-roads across it, though now they were broken and fallen like broken vines. Very great they were, and wonderful and broken—broken in the time of the Great Burning when the fire fell out of the sky. And always the current took me nearer to the Place of the Gods, and the huge ruins rose before my eyes.

30 I do not know the customs of rivers—we are the People of the Hills. I tried to guide my raft with the pole but it spun around. I thought the river meant to take me past the Place of the Gods and out into the Bitter Water of the legends. I grew angry then—my heart felt strong. I said aloud, "I am a priest and the son of a priest!" The gods heard me—they showed me how to paddle with the pole on one side of the raft. The current changed itself—I drew near to the Place of the Gods.

31 When I was very near, my raft struck and turned over. I can swim in our lakes—I swam to the shore. There was a great spike of rusted metal sticking out into the river—I hauled myself up upon it and sat there, panting. I had saved my bow and two arrows and the knife I found in the Dead Place but that was all. My raft went whirling downstream toward the Bitter Water. I looked after it, and thought if it had trod me under, at least I would be safely dead. Nevertheless, when I had dried my bowstring and re-strung it, I walked forward to the Place of the Gods.

32 It felt like ground underfoot; it did not burn me. It is not true what some of the tales say, that the ground there burns forever, for I have been there. Here and there were the marks and stains of the Great Burning, on the ruins, that is true. But they were old marks and old stains. It is not true either, what some of our priests say, that it is an island covered with fogs and enchantments. It is not. It is a great Dead Place—greater than any Dead Place we know. Everywhere in it there are god-roads, though most are cracked and broken. Everywhere there are the ruins of the high towers of the gods.

33 How shall I tell what I saw? I went carefully, my strung bow in my hand, my skin ready for danger. There should have been the wailings of spirits and the shrieks of demons, but there were not. It was very silent and sunny where I had landed—the wind and the rain and the birds that drop seeds had done their work—the grass grew in the cracks of the broken stone. It is a fair island—no wonder the gods built there. If I had come there, a god, I also would have built.

34 How shall I tell what I saw? The towers are not all broken—here and there one still stands, like a great tree in the forest, and the birds nest high. But the towers themselves look blind, for the gods are gone. I saw a fish-hawk, catching fish in the river. I saw a little dance of white butterflies over a great heap of broken stones and columns. I went there and looked about me—there was a carved stone with cut-letters, broken in half. I can read letters but I could not understand these. They said UBTREAS. There was also the shattered image of a man or a god. It had been made of white stone and he wore his hair tied back like a woman's. His name was ASHING, as I read on the cracked half of a stone. I thought it wise to pray to ASHING, though I do not know that god.

35 How shall I tell what I saw? There was no smell of man left, on stone or metal. Nor were there many trees in that wilderness of stone. There are many pigeons, nesting and dropping in the towers—the gods must have loved them, or, perhaps, they used them for sacrifices. There are wild cats that roam the god-roads, green-eyed, unafraid of man. At night they wail like demons but they are not demons. The wild dogs are more dangerous, for they hunt in a pack, but them I did not meet till later. Everywhere there are the carved stones, carved with magical numbers or words.

36 I went north—I did not try to hide myself. When a god or a demon saw me, then I would die, but meanwhile I was no longer afraid. My hunger for knowledge burned in me—there was so much that I could not understand. After a while, I knew that my belly was hungry. I could have hunted for my meat, but I did not hunt. It is known that the gods did not hunt as we do—they got their food from enchanted boxes and jars. Sometimes these are still found in the Dead Places—once, when I was a child and foolish, I opened such a jar and tasted it and found the food sweet. But my father found out and punished me for it strictly, for, often, that food is death. Now, though, I had long gone past what was forbidden, and I entered the likeliest towers, looking for the food of the gods.

37 I found it at last in the ruins of a great temple in the mid-city. A mighty temple it must have been, for the roof was painted like the

sky at night with its stars—that much I could see, though the colors were faint and dim. It went down into great caves and tunnels—perhaps they kept their slaves there. But when I started to climb down, I heard the squeaking of rats, so I did not go—rats are unclean, and there must have been many tribes of them, from the squeaking. But near there, I found food, in the heart of a ruin, behind a door that still opened. I ate only the fruits from the jars—they had a very sweet taste. There was drink, too, in bottles of glass—the drink of the gods was strong and made my head swim. After I had eaten and drunk, I slept on the top of a stone, my bow at my side.

38 When I woke, the sun was low. Looking down from where I lay, I saw a dog sitting on his haunches. His tongue was hanging out of his mouth; he looked as if he were laughing. He was a big dog, with a gray-brown coat, as big as a wolf. I sprang up and shouted at him but he did not move—he just sat there as if he were laughing. I did not like that. When I reached for a stone to throw, he moved swiftly out of the way of the stone. He was not afraid of me; he looked at me as if I were meat. No doubt I could have killed him with an arrow, but I did not know if there were others. Moreover, night was falling.

39 I looked about me—not far away there was a great, broken god-road, leading north. The towers were high enough, but not so high, and while many of the dead-houses were wrecked, there were some that stood. I went toward this god-road, keeping to the heights of the ruins, while the dog followed. When I had reached the god-road, I saw that there were others behind him. If I had slept later, they would have come upon me asleep and torn out my throat. As it was, they were sure enough of me; they did not hurry. When I went into the dead-house, they kept watch at the entrance—doubtless they thought they would have a fine hunt. But a dog cannot open a door and I knew, from the books, that the gods did not like to live on the ground but on high.

40 I had just found a door I could open when the dogs decided to rush. Ha! They were surprised when I shut the door in their faces—it was a good door, of strong metal. I could hear their foolish baying beyond it but I did not stop to answer them. I was in darkness—I found stairs and climbed. There were many stairs, turning around till my head was dizzy. At the top was another door—I found the knob and opened it. I was in a long small chamber—on one side of it was a bronze door that could not be opened, for it had no handle. Perhaps there was a magic word to open it but I did not have the word. I turned to the door in the opposite side of the wall. The lock of it was broken and I opened it and went in.

[41] Within, there was a place of great riches. The god who lived there must have been a powerful god. The first room was a small ante-room—I waited there for some time, telling the spirits of the place that I came in peace and not as a robber. When it seemed to me that they had had time to hear me, I went on. Ah, what riches! Few, even, of the windows had been broken—it was all as it had been. The great windows that looked over the city had not been broken at all though they were dusty and streaked with many years. There were coverings on the floors, the colors not greatly faded, and the chairs were soft and deep. There were pictures upon the walls, very strange, very wonderful—I remember one of a bunch of flowers in a jar—if you came close to it, you could see nothing but bits of color, but if you stood away from it, the flowers might have been picked yesterday. It made my heart feel strange to look at this picture—and to look at the figure of a bird, in some hard clay, on a table and see it so like our birds. Everywhere there were books and writings, many in tongues that I could not read. The god who lived there must have been a wise god and full of knowledge. I felt I had right there, as I sought knowledge also.

[42] Nevertheless, it was strange. There was a washing-place but no water—perhaps the gods washed in air. There was a cooking place but no wood, and though there was a machine to cook food, there was no place to put fire in it. Nor were there candles or lamps—there were things that looked like lamps but they had neither oil nor wick. All these things were magic, but I touched them and lived—the magic had gone out of them. Let me tell one thing to show. In the washing-place, a thing said "Hot" but it was not hot to the touch—another thing said "Cold" but it was not cold. This must have been a strong magic but the magic was gone. I do not understand—they had ways—I wish that I knew.

[43] It was close and dry and dusty in their house of the gods. I have said the magic was gone but that is not true—it had gone from the magic things but it had not gone from the place. I felt the spirits about me, weighing upon me. Nor had I ever slept in a Dead Place before—and yet, tonight, I must sleep there. When I thought of it, my tongue felt dry in my throat, in spite of my wish for knowledge. Almost I would have gone down again and faced the dogs, but I did not.

[44] I had not gone through all the rooms when the darkness fell. When it fell, I went back to the big room looking over the city and made fire. There was a place to make fire and a box with wood in it, though I do not think they cooked there. I wrapped myself in a floor-covering and slept in front of the fire—I was very tired.

[45] Now I tell what is very strong magic. I woke in the midst of the night. When I woke, the fire had gone out and I was cold. It seemed to me that all around me there were whisperings and voices. I closed my eyes to shut them out. Some will say that I slept again, but I do not think that I slept. I could feel the spirits drawing my spirit out of my body as a fish is drawn on a line.

[46] Why should I lie about it? I am a priest and the son of a priest. If there are spirits, as they say, in the small Dead Places near us, what spirits must there not be in that great Place of the Gods? And would not they wish to speak? After such long years? I know that I felt myself drawn as a fish is drawn on a line. I had stepped out of my body—I could see my body asleep in front of the cold fire, but it was not I. I was drawn to look out upon the city of the gods.

[47] It should have been dark, for it was night, but it was not dark. Everywhere there were lights—lines of light—circles and blurs of light—ten thousand torches would not have been the same. The sky itself was alight—you could barely see the stars for the glow in the sky. I thought to myself "This is strong magic" and trembled. There was a roaring in my ears like the rushing of rivers. Then my eyes grew used to the light and my ears to the sound. I knew that I was seeing the city as it had been when the gods were alive.

[48] That was a sight indeed—yes, that was a sight: I could not have seen it in the body—my body would have died. Everywhere went the gods, on foot and in chariots—there were gods beyond number and counting and their chariots blocked the streets. They had turned night to day for their pleasure—they did not sleep with the sun. The noise of their coming and going was the noise of the many waters. It was magic what they could do—it was magic what they did.

[49] I looked out of another window—the great vines of their bridges were mended and the god-roads went east and west. Restless, restless, were the gods and always in motion! They burrowed tunnels under rivers—they flew in the air. With unbelievable tools they did giant works—no part of the earth was safe from them, for, if they wished for a thing, they summoned it from the other side of the world. And always, as they labored and rested, as they feasted and made love, there was a drum in their ears—the pulse of the giant city, beating and beating like a man's heart.

[50] Were they happy? What is happiness to the gods? They were great, they were mighty, they were wonderful and terrible. As I looked upon them and their magic, I felt like a child—but a little more, it seemed to me, and they would pull down the moon from the sky. I saw them with wisdom beyond wisdom and knowledge beyond knowl-

edge. And yet not all they did was well done—even I could see that—and yet their wisdom could not but grow until all was peace.

51 Then I saw their fate come upon them and that was terrible past speech. It came upon them as they walked the streets of their city. I have been in the fights with the Forest People—I have seen men die. But this was not like that. When gods war with gods, they use weapons we do not know. It was fire falling out of the sky and a mist that poisoned. It was the time of the Great Burning and the Destruction. They ran about like ants in the streets of their city—poor gods, poor gods! Then the towers began to fall. A few escaped—yes, a few. The legends tell it. But, even after the city had become a Dead Place, for many years the poison was still in the ground. I saw it happen, I saw the last of them die. It was darkness over the broken city and I wept.

52 All this, I saw. I saw it as I have told it, though not in the body. When I woke in the morning, I was hungry, but I did not think first of my hunger for my heart was perplexed and confused. I knew the reason for the Dead Places but I did not see why it had happened. It seemed to me it should not have happened, with all the magic they had. I went through the house looking for an answer. There was so much in the house I could not understand—and yet I am a priest and the son of a priest. It was like being on one side of the great river, at night, with no light to show the way.

53 Then I saw the dead god. He was sitting in his chair, by the window, in a room I had not entered before and, for the first moment, I thought that he was alive. Then I saw the skin on the back of his hand—it was like dry leather. The room was shut, hot and dry—no doubt that had kept him as he was. At first I was afraid to approach him—then the fear left me. He was sitting looking out over the city—he was dressed in the clothes of the gods. His age was neither young nor old—I could not tell his age. But there was wisdom in his face and great sadness. You could see that he would have not run away. He had sat at his window, watching his city die—then he himself had died. But it is better to lose one's life than one's spirit—and you could see from the face that his spirit had not been lost. I knew, that, if I touched him, he would fall into dust—and yet, there was something unconquered in the face.

54 That is all of my story, for then I knew he was a man—I knew then that they had been men, neither gods nor demons. It is a great knowledge, hard to tell and believe. They were men—they went a dark road, but they were men. I had no fear after that—I had no fear going home, though twice I fought off the dogs and once I was hunted for two days by the Forest People. When I saw my father again, I prayed

and was purified. He touched my lips and my breast, he said, "You went away a boy. You come back a man and a priest." I said, "Father, they were men! I have been in the Place of the Gods and seen it! Now slay me, if it is the law—but still I know they were men."

55 He looked at me out of both eyes. He said, "The law is not always the same shape—you have done what you have done. I could not have done it my time, but you come after me. Tell!"

56 I told and he listened. After that, I wished to tell all the people but he showed me otherwise. He said, "Truth is a hard deer to hunt. If you eat too much truth at once, you may die of the truth. It was not idly that our fathers forbade the Dead Places." He was right—it is better the truth should come little by little. I have learned that, being a priest. Perhaps, in the old days, they ate knowledge too fast.

57 Nevertheless, we make a beginning. It is not for the metal alone we go to the Dead Places now—there are the books and the writings. They are hard to learn. And the magic tools are broken—but we can look at them and wonder. At least, we make a beginning. And, when I am chief priest we shall go beyond the great river. We shall go to the Place of the Gods—the place newyork—not one man but a company. We shall look for the images of the gods and find the god ASHING and the others—the gods Lincoln and Biltmore and Moses. But they were men who built the city, not gods or demons. They were men. I remember the dead man's face. They were men who were here before us. We must build again. □

A Discovery in the Woods

by Graham Greene

1 The village lay among the great red rocks about a thousand feet up and five miles from the sea, which was reached by a path that wound along the contours of the hills. No one in Pete's village had ever travelled further, though Pete's father had once, while fishing, encountered men from another small village beyond the headland, which stabbed the sea twenty miles to the east. The children, when they didn't accompany their fathers to the shingled cove in which the boats lay, would climb up higher for their games—of "Old Noh" and "Ware that Cloud"—below the red rocks that dominated their home. Low scrub a few hundred feet up gave place to woodland: trees clung to the rock-face like climbers caught in an impossible situation, and among the trees were the bushes of blackberry, the biggest fruits always sheltered

from the sun. In the right season the berries formed a tasty sharp dessert to the invariable diet of fish. It was, taking it all in all, a sparse and simple yet a happy life.

2 Pete's mother was a little under five feet tall; she had a squint and she was inclined to stumble when she walked, but her movements to Pete seemed at their most uncertain the height of human grace, and when she told him stories, as she often did on the fifth day of the week, her stammer had for him the magical effect of music. There was one word in particular "t-t-t-tree" which fascinated him. "What is it?" he would ask, and she would try to explain. "You mean an oak?" "A t-tree is not an oak. But an oak is a t-t-tree, and so is a b-birch." "But a birch is quite different from an oak. Anyone can tell they are not the same, even a long way off, like a dog and a cat." "A dog and a c-cat are both animals." She had from some past generation inherited this ability to generalise, of which he and his father were quite incapable.

3 Not that he was a stupid child unable to learn from experience. He could even with some difficulty look back into the past for four winters, but the furthest time he could remember was very like a sea-fog, which the wind may disperse for a moment from a rock or a group of trees, but it closes down again. His mother claimed that he was seven years old, but his father said that he was nine and that after one more winter he would be old enough to join the crew of the boat which his father shared with a relation (everybody in the village was in some way related). Perhaps his mother had deliberately distorted his age to postpone the time when he would have to go fishing with the men. It was not only the question of danger—though every winter brought a mortal casualty along with it, so that the size of the village hardly increased more than a colony of ants; it was also the fact that he was the only child. (There were two sets of parents in the village, the Torts and the Foxes, who had more than one child, and the Torts had triplets.) When the time came for Pete to join his father, his mother would have to depend on other people's children for blackberries in the autumn, or just go without, and there was nothing she loved better than blackberries with a splash of goat's milk.

4 So this, he believed, was to be the last autumn on land, and he was not much concerned about it. Perhaps his father was in the right about his age, for he had become aware that his position as leader of a special gang was now too incontestable: his muscles felt the need of strengthening against an opponent greater than himself. His gang consisted this October of four children, to three of whom he had allotted numbers, for this made his commands sound more abrupt and discipline

so much the easier. The fourth member was a seven-year-old girl called Liz, unwillingly introduced for reasons of utility.

5 They met among the ruins at the edge of the village. The ruins had always been there, and at night the children, if not the adults too, believed them to be haunted by giants. Pete's mother, who was far superior in knowledge to all the other women in the village, nobody knew why, said that her grandmother had spoken of a great catastrophe which thousands of years ago had involved a man called Noh—perhaps it was a thunderbolt from the sky, a huge wave (it would have needed a wave at least a thousand feet high to have extinguished this village), or maybe a plague, so some of the legends went, that had killed the inhabitants and left these ruins to the slow destruction of time. Whether the giants were the phantoms of the slayers or of the slain the children were never quite clear.

6 The blackberries this particular autumn were nearly over and in any case the bushes that grew within a mile of the village—which was called Bottom, perhaps because it lay at the foot of the red rocks—had been stripped bone-bare. When the gang had gathered at the rendezvous Pete made a revolutionary proposal—that they should enter a new territory in search of fruit.

7 Number One said disapprovingly, "We've never done that before." He was in all ways a conservative child. He had small deep-sunk eyes like holes in stone made by the dropping of water, and there was practically no hair on his head and that gave him the air of a shrivelled old man.

8 "We'll get into trouble," Liz said, "if we do."

9 "Nobody need know," Pete said, "so long as we take the oath."

10 The village by long custom claimed that the land belonging to it extended in a semi-circle three miles deep from the last cottage—even though the last cottage was a ruin of which only the foundations remained. Of the sea too they reckoned to own the water for a larger, more ill-defined area that extended some twelve miles out to sea. This claim, on the occasion when they encountered the boats from beyond the headland, nearly caused a conflict. It was Pete's father who made peace by pointing towards the clouds which had begun to mass over the horizon, one cloud in particular of enormous black menace, so that both parties turned in agreement towards the land, and the fishermen from the village beyond the headland never sailed again so far from their home. (Fishing was always done in grey overcast weather or in fine blue clear weather, or even during moonless nights, when the stars were sufficiently obscured; it was only when the shape of the clouds could be discerned that by general consent fishing stopped.)

11 "But suppose we meet someone?" Number Two asked.

12 "How could we?" Pete said.

13 "There must be a reason," Liz said, "why they don't want us to go."

14 "There's no reason," Pete said, "except the law."

15 "Oh, if it's only the law," Number Three said, and he kicked a stone to show how little he thought of the law.

16 "Who does the land belong to?" Liz asked.

17 "To nobody," Pete said. "There's no one there at all."

18 "All the same nobody has rights," Number One said sententiously, looking inwards, with his watery sunk eyes.

19 "You are right there," Pete said. "Nobody has."

20 "But I didn't mean what you mean," Number One replied.

21 "You think there are blackberries there, further up?" Number Two asked. He was a reasonable child who only wanted to be assured that a risk was worth while.

22 "There are bushes all the way up through the woods," Pete said.

23 "How do you know?"

24 "It stands to reason."

25 It seemed odd to him that day how reluctant they were to take his advice. Why should the blackberry-bushes abruptly stop their growth on the border of their own territory? Blackberries were not created for the special use of Bottom. Pete said, "Don't you want to pick them one time more before the winter comes?" and they hung their heads, as though they were seeking a reply in the red earth where the ants made roads from stone to stone. At last Number One said, "Nobody's been there before," as if that was the worst thing he could think of to say.

26 "All the better blackberries," Pete replied.

27 Number Two said after consideration, "The wood looks deeper up there and blackberries like the shade."

28 Number Three yawned. "Who cares about blackberries anyway? There's other things to do than pick. It's new ground, isn't it? Let's go and see. Who knows . . . ?"

29 "Who knows?" Liz repeated in a frightened way and looked first at Pete and then at Number Three as though it were possible that perhaps *they* might.

30 "Hold up your hands and vote," Pete said. He shot his own arm commandingly up and Number Three was only a second behind. After a little hesitation Number Two followed suit; then, seeing that there was a majority anyway for going further, Liz raised a cautious hand but with a backward glance at Number One. "So you're for home?" Pete said to Number One with scorn and relief.

31 "He'll have to take the oath anyway," Number Three said, "or else . . ."

32 "I don't have to take the oath if I'm going home."

33 "Of course you have to or else you'll tell."

34 "What do I care about your silly oath? It doesn't mean a thing. I can take it and tell just the same."

35 There was a silence: the other three looked at Pete. The whole foundation of their mutual trust seemed to be endangered. No one had ever suggested breaking the oath before. At last Number Three said, "Let's bash him."

36 "No," Pete said. Violence, he knew, was not the answer. Number One would run home just the same and tell everything. The whole blackberry-picking would be spoilt by the thought of the punishment to come.

37 "Oh hell," Number Two said. "Let's forget the blackberries and play Old Noh."

38 Liz, like the girl she was, began to weep. "I want to pick blackberries."

39 But Pete had been given time to reach his decision. He said, "He's going to take the oath and he's going to pick blackberries too. Tie his hands."

40 Number One tried to escape, but Number Two tripped him up. Liz bound his wrists with her hair-ribbon, pulling a hard knot which only she knew—it was for such special skills as this that she had gained her entry into the gang. Number One sat on a chunk of ruin and sneered at them. "How do I pick blackberries with my hands tied?"

41 "You were greedy and ate them all. You brought none home. They'll find the stains all over your clothes."

42 "Oh, he'll get such a beating," Liz said with admiration. "I bet they'll beat him bare."

43 "Four against one."

44 "Now you are going to take the oath," Pete said. He broke off two twigs and held them in the shape of a cross. Each of the other three members of the gang gathered saliva in the mouth and smeared the four ends of the cross. Then Pete thrust the sticky points of wood between the lips of Number One. Words were unnecessary: the same thought came inevitably to the mind of everyone with the act: "Strike me dead if I tell." After they had dealt forcibly with Number One each followed the same ritual. (Not one of them knew the origin of the oath; it had passed down through generations of such gangs. Once Pete, and perhaps all the others at one time or another had done the same in the darkness of bed, tried to explain to himself the ceremony of

the oath: in sharing the spittle maybe they were sharing each other's lives, like mixing blood, and the act was solemnised upon a cross because for some reason a cross always signified shameful death.)

45 "Who's got a bit of string?" Pete said.

46 They tied the string to Liz's hair-ribbon and jerked Number One to his feet. Number Two pulled the string and Number Three pushed from behind. Pete led the way, upwards and into the wood, while Liz trailed alone behind; she couldn't move quickly because she had very bandy legs. Now that he realised there was nothing to be done about it, Number One made little trouble; he contented himself with an occasional sneer and lagged enough to keep the cord stretched tight, so that their march was delayed, and nearly two hours passed before they came to the edge of the known territory, emerging from the woods of Bottom on to the edge of a shallow ravine. On the other side the rocks rose again in exactly the same way, with the birch-trees lodged in every crevice up to the sky-line, to which no one from the village of Bottom had ever climbed; in all the interstices of roots and rocks the blackberries grew. From where they stood they could imagine they saw a blue haze like autumn smoke from the great luscious untouched fruit dangling in the shade.

2

47 All the same they hesitated a while before they started going down; it was as though Number One retained a certain malevolent influence and they had bound themselves to it by the cord. He squatted on the ground and sneered up at them. "You see you don't dare . . ."

48 "Dare what?" Pete asked, trying to brush his words away before any doubts could settle on Two or Three or Liz and sap the uncertain power he still possessed.

49 "Those blackberries don't belong to us," One said.

50 "Then who do they belong to?" Pete asked him, noting how Number Two looked at Number One as though he expected an answer.

51 Three said with scorn, "Finding's keeping," and kicked a stone down into the ravine.

52 "They belong to the next village. You know that as well as I do."

53 "And where's the next village?" Pete asked.

54 "Somewhere."

55 "For all you know there isn't another village."

56 "There must be. It's common sense. We can't be the only ones—we and Two Rivers." That was what they called the village which lay beyond the headland.

57 "But how do you *know?*" Pete said. His thoughts took wing.

"Perhaps we *are* the only ones. Perhaps we could climb up there and go on for ever and ever. Perhaps the world's empty." He could feel that Number Two and Liz were half-way with him—as for Number Three he was a hopeless case; he cared for nothing. But all the same, if he had to choose his successor, he would prefer Number Three's care-for-nothing character than the elderly inherited rules of Number One or the unadventurous reliability of Number Two.

58 Number One said, "You are just crazy," and spat down into the ravine. "We couldn't be the only ones alive. It's common sense."

59 "Why not?" Pete said. "Who knows?"

60 "Perhaps the blackberries are poisoned," Liz said. "Perhaps we'll get the gripes. Perhaps there's savages there. Perhaps there's giants."

61 "I'll believe in giants when I see them," Pete said. He knew how shallow her fear was; she only wanted to be reassured by someone stronger.

62 "You talk a lot," Number One said, "but you can't even organise. Why didn't you tell us to bring baskets if we were going to pick things?"

63 "We don't need baskets. We've got Liz's skirt."

64 "And it's Liz who'll be thrashed when her skirt's all stained."

65 "Not if it's full of blackberries she won't. Tie up your skirt, Liz."

66 Liz tied it up, making it into a pannier in front, with a knot behind just above the opening of her small plump buttocks. The boys watched her with interest to see how she fixed it. "They'll all fall out," Number One said. "You ought to have taken the whole thing off an' made a sack."

67 "How could I climb holding a sack? You don't know a thing, Number One. I can fix this easy." She squatted on the ground with a bare buttock on each heel and tied and retied the knot till she was quite satisfied that it was firm.

68 "So now we go down," Number Three said.

69 "Not till I give the order. Number One, I'll release you if you promise to give no trouble."

70 "I'll give plenty of trouble."

71 "Number Two and Three, you take charge of Number One. You're the rear-guard, see. If we have to retreat in a hurry, you just leave the prisoner behind. Liz and I go ahead to reconnoitre."

72 "Why Liz?" Number Three said. "What good's a girl?"

73 "In case we have to use a spy. Girl spies are always best. Anyway they wouldn't bash a girl."

74 "Pa does," Liz said, twitching her buttocks.

75 "But I want to be in the van," Three said.

76 "We don't know which is the van yet. They may be watching us now while we talk. They may be luring us on, and then they'll attack in the rear."

77 "You're afraid," Number One said. "Fainty goose! Fainty goose!"

78 "I'm not afraid, but I'm boss, I'm responsible for the gang. Listen all of you, in case of danger we give one short whistle. Stay where you are. Don't move. Don't breathe. Two short whistles mean abandon the prisoner and retreat double-quick. One long whistle means treasure discovered, all well, come as quick as you can. Everybody got that clear?"

79 "Yah," said Number Two. "But suppose we're just lost?"

80 "Stay where you are and wait for a whistle."

81 "Suppose *he* whistles—to confuse?" Number Two asked, digging at Number One with his toe.

82 "If he does gag him. Gag him hard, so his teeth squeak."

83 Pete went to the edge of the plateau and gazed down, to choose his path through the scrub; the rocks descended some thirty feet. Liz stood close behind him and held the edge of his shirt. "Who are *They?*" she whispered.

84 "Strangers."

85 "You don't believe in giants?"

86 "No."

87 "When I think of giants, I shiver—here," and she laid her hand on the little bare mount of Venus below her panniered skirt.

88 Pete said, "We'll start down there between those clumps of gorse. Be careful. The stones are loose and we don't want to make any noise at all." He turned back to the others, who watched him with admiration, envy and hate (that was Number One). "Wait till you see us start climbing up the other side and then you come on down." He looked at the sky. "The invasion began at noon," he announced with the precision of an historian recording an event in the past which had altered the shape of the world.

3

89 "We could whistle now," Liz suggested. They were half-way up the slope of the ravine by this time, out of breath from the scramble. She put a blackberry in her mouth and added, "They're sweet. Sweeter than ours. Shall I start picking?" Her thighs and bottom were scratched with briars and smeared with blood the colour of blackberry juice.

90 Pete said, "Why, I've seen better than these in our territory. Liz, don't you notice, not one of them's been picked. No one's ever come here. These ones are nothing to what we'll find later. They've been growing for years and years and years—why, I wouldn't be surprised

if we came on a whole forest of them with bushes as high as trees and berries as big as apples. We'll leave the little ones for the others if they want to pick them. You and I will climb up higher and find real treasure." As he spoke he could hear the scrape of the others' shoes and the roll of a loose stone, but they could see nothing because the bushes grew so thick around the trees. "Come on. If we find treasure first, it's ours."

91 "I wish it was real treasure, not just blackberries."

92 "It might be real treasure. No one's ever explored here before us."

93 "Giants?" Liz asked him with a shiver.

94 "Those are stories they tell children. Like Old Noh and his ship. There never were giants."

95 "Not Noh?"

96 "What a baby you are."

97 They climbed up and up among the birches and bushes, and the sound of the others diminished below them. There was a different smell here: hot and moist and metallic, far away from the salt of the sea. Then the trees and bushes thinned and they were at the summit of the hills. When they looked backwards, Bottom was hidden by the ridge between, but through the trees they could see a line of blue as though the sea had been lifted up almost to their level by some gigantic convulsion. They turned nervously away from it and stared into the unknown land ahead.

4

98 "It's a house," Liz said. "It's a huge house."

99 "It can't be. You've never seen a house that size—or that shape," but he knew that Liz was right. This had been made by men and not by nature. It was something in which people had once lived.

100 "A house for giants," Liz said fearfully.

101 Pete lay on his stomach and peered over the edge of the ravine. A hundred feet down among the red rocks lay a long structure glinting here and there among the bushes and moss which overgrew it—it stretched beyond their sight, trees climbed along its sides, trees had seeded on the roof, and up the length of two enormous chimneys ivy twined and flowering plants with trumpet-mouths. There was no smoke, no sign of any occupant; only the birds, perhaps disturbed by their voices, called warnings among the trees, and a colony of starlings rose from one of the chimneys and dispersed.

102 "Let's go back," Liz whispered.

103 "We can't now," Pete said. "Don't be afraid. It's only another ruin. What's wrong with ruins? We've always played in them."

104 "It's scary. It's not like the ruins at Bottom."

105 "Bottom's not the world," Pete said. It was the expression of a profound belief he shared with no one else.

106 The huge structure was tilted at an angle, so that they could almost see down one of the enormous chimneys, which gaped like a hole in the world. "I'm going down to look," Pete said, "but I'll spy out the land first."

107 "Shall I whistle?"

108 "Not yet. Stay where you are in case the others come."

109 He moved with caution along the ridge. Behind him the strange thing—not built of stone or wood—extended a hundred yards or more, sometimes hidden, sometimes obscured by trees, but in the direction he now took the cliff was bare of vegetation, and he was able to peer down at the great wall of the house, not straight but oddly curved, like the belly of a fish or . . . He stood still for a moment, looking hard at it: the curve was the enormous magnification of something that was familiar to him. He went thoughtfully on, pondering on the old legend which had been the subject of their games. Nearly a hundred yards further he stopped again. It was as though at this point some enormous hand had taken the house and split it in two. He could look down between the two portions and see the house exposed floor by floor—there must be five, six, seven of them, with nothing stirring inside, except where the bushes had found a lodging and a wing flickered. He could imagine the great halls receding into the dark, and he thought how all the inhabitants of Bottom could have lived in a single room on a single floor and still have found space for their animals and their gear. How many thousand people, he wondered, had once lived in this enormous house? He hadn't realised the world contained so many.

110 When the house was broken—how?—one portion had been flung upwards at an angle, and only fifty yards from where he stood he could see where the end of it penetrated the ridge, so that if he wished to explore further he had only to drop a few yards to find himself upon the roof. There trees grew again and made an easy descent. He had no excuse to stay, and suddenly aware of loneliness and ignorance and the mystery of the great house he put his fingers to his mouth and gave one long whistle to summon all the others.

5

111 They were overawed too, and if Number One had not so jeered at them, perhaps they would have decided to go home with the secret of the house locked in their minds with a dream of one day returning. But when Number One said, "Softies, Fainties . . ." and shot his spittle

down towards the house, Number Three broke silence. "What are we waiting for?" Then Pete had to act, if he was to guard his leadership. Scrambling from branch to branch of a tree that grew from a plateau of rock below the ridge, he got within six feet of the roof and dropped. He landed on his knees upon a surface cold and smooth as an egg-shell. The four children looked down at him and waited.

112 The slope of the roof was such that he had to slide cautiously downwards on his bottom. At the end of the descent there was another house which had been built upon the roof, and he realised from where he sat that the whole structure was not one house but a succession of houses built one over the other, and above the topmost house loomed the tip of the enormous chimney. Remembering how the whole thing had been torn apart, he was careful not to slide too fast for fear that he should plunge into the gap between. None of the others had followed him; he was alone.

113 Ahead of him was a great arch of some unknown material, and below the arch a red rock rose and split it in two. This was like a victory for the mountains; however hard the material men had used in making the house, the mountains remained the stronger. He came to rest with his feet against a rock and looked down into the wide gap where the rock had come up and split the houses; the gap was many yards across; it was bridged by a fallen tree, and although he could see but a little way down, he had the same sense which he had received above that he was looking into something as deep as the sea. Why was it he half expected to see fishes moving there?

114 With his hand pressed on the needle of red rock he stood upright and, looking up, was startled to see two unwinking eyes regarding him from a few feet away. Then as he moved again he saw that they belonged to a squirrel, the colour of the rock: it turned without hurry or fear, lifted a plumy tail and neatly evacuated before it leapt into the hall ahead of him.

115 The hall—it was indeed a hall, he realised, making his way towards it astride the fallen tree, and yet the first impression he had was of a forest, with the trees regularly spaced as in a plantation made by men. It was possible to walk there on a level, though the ground was hummocked with red rock which here and there had burst through the hard paving. The trees were not trees at all but pillars of wood, which still showed in patches a smooth surface, but pitted for most of their length with worm-holes and draped with ivy that climbed to the roof fifty feet up to escape through a great tear in the ceiling. There was a smell of vegetation and damp, and all down the hall were dozens of small green tumuli like woodland-graves.

116 He kicked one of the mounds with a foot and it disintegrated immediately below the thick damp moss that covered it. Gingerly he thrust his hand into the soggy greenery and pulled out a strut of rotting wood. He moved on and tried again a long curved hump of green which stood more than breast-high—not like a common grave—and this time he stubbed his toes and winced with the pain. The greenery had taken no root here, but had spread from tumulus to hump across the floor, and he was able to pluck away without difficulty the leaves and tendrils. Underneath lay a stone slab in many beautiful colours, green and rose-pink and red the colour of blood. He moved around it, cleaning the surface as he went, and here at last he came on real treasure. For a moment he did not realise what purpose those half-translucent objects could have served; they stood in rows behind a smashed panel, most broken into green rubble, but a few intact, except for the discoloration of age. It was from their shape he realised that they must once have been drinking pots, made of a material quite different from the rough clay to which he was accustomed. Scattered on the floor below were hundreds of hard round objects stamped with the image of a human head like those his grandparents had dug up in the ruins of Bottom—objects useless except that with their help it was possible to draw a perfect circle and they could be used as forfeits, in place of pebbles, in the game of "Ware that Cloud." They were more interesting than pebbles. They had dignity and rareness which belonged to all old things made by man—there was so little to be seen in the world older than an old man. He was tempted momentarily to keep the discovery to himself, but what purpose would they serve if they were not employed? A forfeit was of no value kept secret in a hole, so, putting his fingers to his mouth, he blew the long whistle again.

117 While waiting for the others to join him, he sat on the stone slab deep in thought and pondered all he had seen, especially that great wall like a fish's belly. The whole huge house, it seemed to him, was like a monstrous fish thrown up among the rocks to die, but what a fish and what a wave to carry it so high.

118 The children came sliding down the roof, Number One still in tow between them; they gave little cries of excitement and delight; they were quite forgetful of their fear, as though it were the season of snow. Then they picked themselves up by the red rock, as he had done, straddled the fallen tree, and hobbled across the vast space of the hall, like insects caught under a cup.

119 "There's treasure for you," Pete said with pride and he was glad to see them surprised into silence at the spectacle; even Number One forgot to sneer, and the cord by which they held him trailed neglected

on the ground. At last Number Two said, "Coo! It's better than blackberries."

120 "Put the forfeits into Liz's skirt. We'll divide them later."

121 "Does Number One get any?" Liz asked.

122 "There's enough for all," Pete said. "Let him go." It seemed the moment for generosity, and in any case they needed all their hands. While they were gathering up the forfeits he went to one of the great gaps in the wall that must once have been windows, covered perhaps like the windows of Bottom with straw mats at night, and leant far out. The hills rose and fell, a brown and choppy sea; there was no sign of a village anywhere, not even of a ruin. Below him the great black wall curved out of sight; the place where it touched the ground was hidden by the tops of trees that grew in the valley below. He remembered the old legend, and the game they played among the ruins of Bottom. "Noh built a boat. What kind of a boat? A boat for all the beasts and Brigit too. What kind of beasts? Big beasts like bears and beavers and Brigit too . . ."

123 Something went twang with a high musical sound and then there was a sigh which faded into silence. He turned and saw that Number Three was busy at yet another mound—the second biggest mound in the hall. He had unearthed a long box full of the oblongs they called dominoes, but every time he touched a piece a sound came, each a little different, and when he touched one a second time it remained silent. Number Two, in the hope of further treasure, groped in the mound and found only rusty wires which scratched his hands. No more sounds were to be coaxed out of the box, and no one ever discovered why at the beginning it seemed to sing to them.

6

124 Had they ever experienced a longer day even at the height of mid-summer? The sun, of course, stayed longer on the high plateau, and they could not tell how far night was already encroaching on the woods and valleys below them. There were two long narrow passages in the house down which they raced, tripping sometimes on the broken floor—Liz kept to the rear, unable to run fast for fear of spilling the forfeits from her skirt. The passages were lined with rooms, each one large enough to contain a family from Bottom, with strange tarnished twisted fixtures of which the purpose remained a mystery. There was another great hall, this one without pillars, which had a great square sunk in the floor lined with coloured stone; it shelved upwards, so that at one end it was ten feet deep and at the other so shallow that they could drop down to the drift of dead leaves and the scraps of

twigs blown there by winter winds, and everywhere the droppings of birds like splashes of soiled snow.

125 At the end of yet a third hall they came, all of them, to a halt, for there in front of them, in bits and pieces, were five children staring back, a half-face, a head cut in two as though by a butcher's hatchet, a knee severed from a foot. They stared at the strangers and one of them defiantly raised a fist—it was Number Three. At once one of the strange flat children lifted his fist in reply. Battle was about to be joined; it was a relief in this empty world to find real enemies to fight, so they advanced slowly like suspicious cats, Liz, a little in the rear, and there on the other side was another girl with skirts drawn up in the same fashion as hers to hold the same forfeits, with a similar little crack under the mount below the belly, but her face obscured with a green rash, one eye missing. The strangers moved their legs and arms, and yet remained flat against the wall, and suddenly they were touching nose to nose, and there was nothing there at all but the cold smooth wall. They backed away and approached and backed away: this was something not one of them could understand. So without saying anything to each other, in a private awe, they moved away to where steps led down to the floor below; there they hesitated again, listening and peering, their voices twittering against the unbroken silence, but they were afraid of the darkness, where the side of the mountain cut off all light, so they ran away and screamed defiantly down the long passages, where the late sun slanted in, until they came to rest at last in a group on the great stairs which led upwards into brighter daylight where the enormous chimneys stood.

126 "Let's go home," Number One said. "If we don't go, soon it will be dark."

127 "Who's a Faintie now?" Number Three said.

128 "It's only a house. It's a big house, but it's only a house."

129 Pete said, "It's not a house," and they all turned and looked their questions at him.

130 "What do you mean, not a house?" Number Two asked.

131 "It's a boat," Pete said.

132 "You are crazy. Whoever saw a boat as big as this?"

133 "Whoever saw a house as big as this?" Liz asked.

134 "What's a boat doing on top of a mountain? Why would a boat have chimneys? What would a boat have forfeits for? When did a boat have rooms and passages?" They threw their sharp objections at him, like handfuls of gravel to sting him into sense.

135 "It's Noh's boat," Pete said.

136 "You're nuts," Number One said. "Noh's a game. There was never anyone called Noh."

137 "How can we tell? Maybe he did live hundreds of years ago. And if he had all the beasts with him, what could he do without lots of cages? Perhaps those aren't rooms along the passage there; perhaps they are cages."

138 "And that hole in the floor?" Liz asked. "What's that for?"

139 "I've been thinking about it. It might be a tank for water. Don't you see, he'd have to have somewhere to keep the water-rats and the tadpoles."

140 "I don't believe it," Number One said. "How would a boat get up here?"

141 "How would a house as big as this get up here? You know the story. It floated here, and then the waters went down again and left it."

142 "Then Bottom was at the bottom of the sea once?" Liz asked. Her mouth fell open and she scratched her buttocks stung with briars and scraped with rock and smeared with bird-droppings.

143 "Bottom didn't exist then. It was all so long ago . . ."

144 "He might be right," Number Two said. Number Three made no comment: he began to mount the stairs towards the roof, and Pete followed quickly and overtook him. The sun lay flat across the tops of the hills which looked like waves, and in all the world there seemed to be nobody but themselves. The great chimney high above shot out a shadow like a wide black road. They stood silent, awed by its size and power, where it tilted towards the cliff above them. Then Number Three said, "Do you really believe it?"

145 "I think so."

146 "What about all our other games? 'Ware that Cloud.' "

147 "It may have been the cloud which frightened Noh."

148 "But where did everybody go? There aren't any corpses."

149 "There wouldn't be. Remember the game. When the water went down, they all climbed off the boat two by two."

150 "Except the water-rats. The water went down too quickly and one of them was stranded. We ought to find *his* corpse."

151 "It was hundreds of years ago. The ants would have eaten him."

152 "Not the bones, they couldn't eat those."

153 "I'll tell you something I saw—in those cages. I didn't say anything to the others because Liz would have been scared."

154 "What did you see?"

155 "I saw snakes."

156 "No!"

157 "Yes, I did. And they're all turned to stone. They curled along the floor, and I kicked one and it was hard like one of those stone fish they found above Bottom."

158 "Well," Number Three said, "that seems to prove it," and they

were silent again, weighed down by the magnitude of their discovery. Above their heads, between them and the great chimney, rose yet another house in this nest of houses, and a ladder went up to it from a spot close to where they stood. On the front of the house twenty feet up was a meaningless design in tarnished yellow. Pete memorised the shape, to draw it later in the dust for his father who would never, he knew, believe their story, who would think they had dug the forfeits—their only proof—up in the ruins at the edge of Bottom. The design was like this:

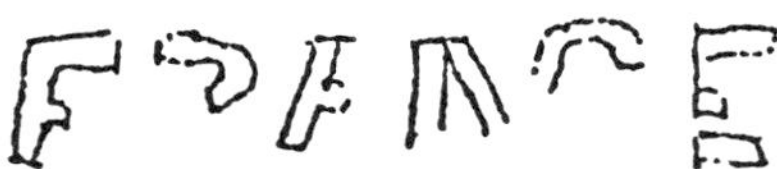

159 "Perhaps that's where Noh lived," Number Three whispered, gazing at the design as if it contained a clue to the time of legends, and without another word they both began to climb the ladder, just as the other children came on to the roof below them.

160 "Where are you going?" Liz called, but they didn't bother to answer her. The thick yellow rust came off on their hands as they climbed and climbed.

161 The other children came chattering up the stairs and then they saw the man too and were silent.

162 "Noh," Pete said.

163 "A giant," Liz said.

164 He was a white clean skeleton, and his skull had rolled on to the shoulder-bone and rested there as though it had been laid on a shelf. All round him lay forfeits brighter and thicker than the forfeits in the hall, and the leaves had drifted against the skeleton, so that they had the impression that he was lying stretched in sleep in a green field. A shred of faded blue material, which the birds had somehow neglected to take at nesting-time, still lay, as though for modesty, across the loins, but when Liz took it up in her fingers it crumbled away to a little powder. Number Three paced the length of the skeleton. He said, "He was nearly six feet tall."

165 "So there *were* giants," Liz said.

166 "And they played forfeits," Number Two said, as though that reassured him of their human nature.

167 "Moon ought to see him," Number One said; "that would take him down a peg." Moon was the tallest man ever known in Bottom, but he was more than a foot shorter than this length of white bone.

They stood around the skeleton with eyes lowered as though they were ashamed of something.

168 At last Number Two said suddenly, "It's late. I'm going home," and he made his hop-and-skip way to the ladder, and after a moment's hesitation Number One and Number Three limped after him. A forfeit went crunch under a foot. No one had picked these forfeits up, nor any other of the strange objects which lay gleaming among the leaves. Nothing here was treasure-trove; everything belonged to the dead giant.

169 At the top of the ladder Pete turned to see what Liz was up to. She sat squatting on the thigh-bones of the skeleton, her naked buttocks rocking to and fro as though in the act of possession. When he went back to her he found that she was weeping.

170 "What is it, Liz?" he asked.

171 She leant forward towards the gaping mouth. "He's beautiful," she said, "he's so beautiful. And he's a giant. Why aren't there giants now?" She began to keen over him like a little old woman at a funeral. "He's six feet tall," she cried, exaggerating a little, "and he has beautiful straight legs. No one has straight legs in Bottom. Why aren't there giants now? Look at his lovely mouth with all the teeth. Who has teeth like that in Bottom?"

172 "*You* are pretty, Liz," Pete said, shuffling around in front of her, trying in vain to straighten his own spine like the skeleton's, beseeching her to notice him, feeling jealousy for those straight white bones upon the floor and for the first time a sensation of love for the little bandy-legged creature bucketing to and fro.

173 "Why aren't there any giants now?" she repeated for the third time, with her tears falling among the bird-droppings. He went sadly to the window and looked out. Below him the red rock split the floor, and up the long slope of the roof he could see the three children scrambling towards the cliff; awkward, with short uneven limbs, they moved like little crabs. He looked down at his own stunted and uneven legs and heard her begin to keen again for a whole world lost.

174 "He's six feet tall and he has beautiful straight legs." □

CHAPTER IV

Character and Dialog—Focal Points of Fiction

Answering his own question, "What is man?", Pepin, the eldest son of Charlemagne, said, "The slave of death, the guest of an inn, a wayfarer passing." Metaphorically, man doesn't seem to be much more. Alphonse de Lamartine said man is a "fallen god who remembers the heavens." Perhaps that explains man's dissatisfaction with the world. Blaise Pascal decided: "What a chimera then is man! What a novelty! What a monster, what a chaos, what a contradiction, what a prodigy! Judge of all things, feeble worm of the earth, depository of truth, a sink of uncertainty and error, the glory and the shame of the universe." Perhaps that explains man's dissatisfaction with himself.

Regardless of what man is, his state is one of constant unrest. He is in constant conflict, for he is afraid of both life and death. But since conflict and fear move him to act, they make man fictionally interesting. What man is content with life or wants no change? What man has attained his ambition, or is not in conflict with anyone or with himself, or is happy to grow old and to die? What man is unafraid? If you know such a person, he is either a figment of your imagination or a frontal lobotomy success. He is not a person with blood and life and interest!

What about the woman who panics at a wrinkle, thinks herself unattractive, knows she will never bear children, and fears the empty years ahead? Or the woman who thinks her husband is tired of her, who feels her children have outgrown her, and who finds her friends avoiding her? What of the woman whose husband develops cancer, whose child is afraid of her, who sees financial ruin coming, and who knows she will die before her duties as wife and mother are accomplished?

Now, *there's* a woman! *She* has areas of conflict!

And, if you meet her in fiction, you can become very interested in her because her problems are yours—or might be in some varied form.

And what about the man who fears the male climacteric, who wants a promotion he fears he can't have, and suddenly finds himself a victim of young hoods? Or the teenager who is disfigured by acne, perplexed by contemporary morality, and faces the possibility of war?

Ah, *those* people are very real characters!

Is Hamlet interesting because he's a prince without financial worry? Of course not. He's a young man in a quandary. What is the best thing to do? And when? Well, those questions make him interesting. He has problems. As he works them out, he gets more interesting. He ceases to be a creation of one William Shakespeare and becomes the Edwards' kid, John, who thinks his mother made a mistake in remarrying. His stepfather doesn't love her. He wants the business, the house, and he wants John to go back to military school. At least he'll be out of the way for a while. John has a conflict! And so has Hamlet. Somehow they become one person. That's character. And that's fiction.

Where, then, does an author find characters, and how does he bring them alive in words so that you, the reader, can know them, sympathize with them, understand them, and identify with them?

Actually, you, as well as authors, already know many such people. They are your family, friends, and acquaintances. If you examine them coldly, objectively, and critically, you may be surprised how perfect they are for fictional purposes. It is probable an author would not use them exactly as they exist, however, for he would not want to offend them on recognition, and they would probably require modification to suit the demands of plot. As a result, the author might change their appearances, some of their behavior patterns, or their mannerisms. He might borrow a defect from one and give it to another. Or he might create a peculiarity for one. Other characters might be a composite of several people.

A second source of characters is the daily world that surrounds both you and authors. For example, the following entry is from a student writer's notebook:

I was in a dimestore luncheonette. Attractive woman, well-dressed, wedding ring. Watching for someone and drinking coffee. Man joined her and explained, "Janet called just as I was leaving the apartment. Tim's having trouble with one of his teachers. . . ." Woman, irritated, answered, "I'll bet. She manufactures situations to get you out to the house. She uses the kids to make you feel guilty." He started to fidget and suggested she lower her voice. She was angry, but she changed the subject. Started talking about his apartment and what she wanted to do about some furniture for it. "If that wing chair were moved over by the window and the desk. . . ." He hadn't seemed to be listening, but he was, for he suddenly snapped, "Damn it, you rearrange my life and my furniture without even changing your expression . . . !"

It is only an incident, but the student had an ear for the interesting. The possibilities of the brief exchange are obvious—and numerous. "It seemed mean to listen," the student said. "There was something so . . . *furtive* about it. The man kept looking around like he was afraid someone would see them. And they were so out of place in that dime-store. They should have been in a very expensive lounge or restaurant. I bet they never got married. It was pretty obvious he wanted to go back to his wife, but he was too involved with the woman. . . ."

Another notebook entry:

I was making a phone call from the open booths in the student union. A woman—older than most students—was talking on the phone in the next stall. She said, "I held the door open with my foot while I kissed them goodbye. Honestly, Mother, if I'd let that house close on me, I'd never have been able to go back inside. All of a sudden I hated everything about my life." She listened a minute. Then, "You know Chuck better than that. If Billy called from the airport today, Chuck would insist he spend the weekend at our house. He thinks I can't be unfaithful!"

Melodramatic? Possibly. But it is interesting. And did you notice the line, "Honestly, Mother, if I'd let that house close on me, I'd never have been able to go back inside"? It's the kind of dialog that creates verisimilitude with its originality. *And* it reveals character! The student said, "That woman *wanted* to be a prisoner in that house. She wasn't nearly as secure as she sounded. She's the kind of woman who's afraid of life. She wants her husband to be jealous and worry, but she'll never give him reason because she can't let that house shut her out. But she'll resent his not knowing she wants glamour and excitement. And one day, it'll catch up with her."

These notebook entries contain plot suggestions. Creative writing students frequently lament, "But I can't find a plot!" not realizing their main problem lies in not having a character. Plot is what happens to a character, and, until the author has an interesting person, plot won't suggest itself. What the characters looked like isn't in the note-book entries given above—nor should such descriptions be there ordinarily. True, the final plot will indicate physical character description. But a character's importance lies on the inside of the human shell. Only when physical features affect his attitudes and behavior do they become important.

Turn to p. 299 and read "On the Genesis of *The Real Thing*" by Henry James. As you will learn later in the chapter, James is not completely truthful, but you can see beginnings for the story. Also reread Hawthorne's notebook entry in the footnote on p. 81.

"But doesn't the author have to say *exactly* what a character looks like?" you may ask. By no means. Probably the "most beautiful woman the world has ever known" was Helen of Troy—and that on Homer's authority. History did not record her physical features, only her weaknesses and romantic notions which precipitated the Trojan War. Homer, who might have described her, preferred to describe her effect on old men long past sexual lust who turned their attention from the battle below and stared after her as she walked on the walls of Troy. Her beauty becomes immediately apparent in the old men's reactions to her:

They reacht the Scæan towrs,
Where Priam sat to see the fight with all his Counsellours,
Panthous, Lampus, Clytius and stout Hicetaon,
Thimœtes, wise Antenor and profound Ucalegon—
All grave old men, and souldiers they had bene, but for age
Now left the warres; yet Counsellors they were exceeding sage.
And as in well-growne woods, on trees, cold spinie Grashoppers
Sit chirping and send voices out that scarce can pierce our eares
For softnesse and their weake faint sounds; so (talking on the towre)
These Seniors of the people sate, who, when they saw the powre
Of beautie in the Queene ascend, even those cold-spirited Peeres,
Those wise and almost witherd men, found this heate in their yeares
That they were forc't (though whispering) to say: 'What man can blame
The Greekes and Troyans to endure, for so admir'd a Dame,
So many miseries, and so long? In her sweet countenance shine
Lookes like the Goddesses'. And yet (though never so divine)
Before we boast, unjustly still, of her enforced prise
And justly suffer for her sake, with all our progenies,
Labor and ruine, let her go: the profit of our land
Must passe the beautie.' Thus, though these could beare so fit a hand
On their affections, yet when all their gravest powers were usde
They could not chuse but welcome her, and rather they accusde
The gods than beautie.

Chapman's Homer, Bk. III, ll. 155–177°

° Ed. Allardyce Nicoll (New York, 1956), pp. 78–79.

In fact, there are many ways an author can reveal character. He may prefer to draw a *static portrait,* one wherein the reader is merely told what the author wishes him to know. Such a passage suffers, usually, from length that destroys proportion in a short story. Too, it may be detrimental to the pace of the story since all forward flow must stop and the description be inserted. Such passages, obviously, lend themselves to longer works, but they are also encountered in the short story.

Closely allied to the static portrait is *author analysis.* It examines the behavior of the character, offering judgments of a clinical nature. If a character is a compulsive gum-chewer, the author may suggest it is silent speech. This approach may lead to a sort of psychologist's casebook wherein the analysis becomes more important than the character.

The *stream-of-consciousness* technique may reveal a great deal about a character if it is cleverly manipulated. Actually, the human animal isn't particularly ordered in his thinking. Even when he sets about consciously to think, various ideas intrude. As he broods on a slight by a friend, he may be simultaneously aware of the beauty of an automobile. As he examines an automobile, he may be reminded of the bell on his first bicycle. If a stream-of-consciousness passage is patterned in such a fashion that the character confines himself to the subject at hand, organizes it, and examines it logically, it may sound contrived and false. On the other hand, if he jumps from one seemingly unrelated subject to another as actuality suggests, a meaningless jumble results, for short story material must be *selected* rather than indiscriminately repeated in imitation of reality. Thus, the use of stream-of-consciousness must be skillfully handled.

Environment may also be employed to reveal a character. At the simplest level, a woman who has an overdecorated bedroom dripping with flounced and ruffled furniture may be a featherbrained creature. She may also, however, be an ugly woman compensating by using a "beautiful" background. Notice the many things such a situation would betray about a woman. If a very mannish woman is established in such a guest room for the night, her mannish qualities are intensified. If a fragile, dainty creature inhabits the room, it may serve as a backdrop for her *or* she may fade into the picture. Furthermore, her reaction to her environment will certainly be revealing. The featherbrained creature, on first beholding such a room, might be expected to say, "Oh, it's lovely. And I just adore Priscilla curtains. They're so Miles Standish." By mutilating the metaphor, she reveals an incapacity for ordered thought. But did you notice that she reveals her powers of observation, her education, and her mental associations? The ugly woman might say, "I feel so beautiful in such a room," betraying her knowledge of personal ugliness. Or, bitterly, she might say, "I hate rooms like this. All these lovely ruffles offer me nowhere to hide." If she designed the room, she might apologize, "I like beauty around me. I think it reflects in people." Do you detect pathos in her? The extremely mannish woman might merely say, "Ugh!" or "Really!" or "Where the hell's the john?" She might say, "I'll probably strangle in those damned ruffles," or "How do you find the bed under all those discarded tutus?" Each reaction reveals something.

The reaction of other characters in the story or a character's reaction to them will reveal a great deal also. Do they like each other? How do they show their affinity? If a character says, "John's a charming boy, but he does toady to people," character is revealed doubly. When a fictional wife observes, "My husband isn't a wildly exciting lover," does she reveal anything about herself? What does she reveal about her husband? If a character winces as he shakes hands with another man, what is revealed about both of them? Or if a man says, "I didn't know whether to kiss her hand or shake it" of a female character, what is revealed about each? What if he makes the same statement after being introduced to another man? Don't jump to conclusions! The statement reveals something about *both* characters.

Events occur in a story, and characters react to those events. Their reaction tells the reader a great deal. If two characters read an account of an earthquake and one comments on the "dreadful loss of life" while the second sympathizes, "Pity the poor insurance companies!" you know something about each. When a husband and wife set out for a social call, he may "hope they don't play that dreary chamber music all evening" while she may "hope nobody suggests dancing because Mr. Cord holds me too tight."

In other words, almost every character indication rests on some *dialog* (the speech of characters). Static descriptions, of course, do not. However, a sense of dialog is essential to character studies. In the notebook examples, what the people said revealed their character as well as something about the people they discussed. What they did *not* say also subtly indicated a great deal.

Characters in fiction are, generally, of three types: *rounded* or *main characters, stock characters* or ones who are mere *stereotypes,* and *foil characters,* who are designed to illuminate main characters. A stock character acts, thinks, and behaves as the reader expects him to. The precious little girl modeled after Shirley Temple, the Uncle Tom Negro character, the Jewish Shylock character—all are stock and, usually, as far removed from real life as characters can be. They fill a need in stories and can be sketched in with relatively little effort, for the author has a great deal of reader help. If the prostitute has a "heart of gold," the reader recognizes her from his preconceptions. The wicked stepmother was long ago established in the fairy tale. As stereotypes, they are said to be *flat* (not fully developed), for narrative focus seldom remains on them. Foil characters may be either flat or moderately rounded depending on their importance in the story, but main characters must be rounded enough to *seem* fully developed. All generalizations have their exceptions, however, and you will find the stock character fully rounded in Jack London's *All Gold Cañon* (pp. 431–452). Stock and foil characters are often called *static* (unchanging); rounded characters are said to be *dynamic* (changing in the course of the story).

One distinguishing characteristic often is enough to establish stock and foil characters. Who does not think of pirates as wooden-legged? If a character blinks his eyes constantly, he seems a little defective. A man who clears his throat constantly is either pompous or mousy. A woman who flutters her hands is featherheaded. What of the teenager who ends every sentence with "You know what I mean?" Or the adult who regularly inserts a negative statement into his speech: "I don't believe in spreading rumor, but. . . ."? The list goes on and on.

If you examine yourself, your friends, and your family—objectively, making notes—you will find every person favors certain words and phrases which he overuses. They may represent limited vocabulary, preoccupation with a subject, or outright poverty of intellect. But they also characterize him. Think of a teacher you like and of one you dislike. List the distinguishing speech repetitions of each. You will find it relatively easy. What phrase does a close friend or family member use so often you can predict its usage?

Extending your notes, you will find that most people have some peculiar mannerism. Some gulp air, some laugh too heartily, some walk mincingly. The nose-twitcher and the knuckle-popper both reveal distinctive traits about themselves.

As dialog is such an integral part of character, the author trains his ear to detect definite speech patterns. He listens to inflections, notes pauses, or observes hand movements in conjunction with speech. Dialog in stories will not, of course, be completely imitative—pages of meaningless conversation would result from such a re-creation. Dialog must be true-sounding, however. And it must be sharply defined enough to indicate body movement and inflection as the reader *hears* it in the story. In short, it must create a sense of scene.

The writer, then, as he works with character and dialog, observes and listens carefully, identifies useful elements, chooses the ones most pertinent to his purpose, and, finally, arranges them in the most revealing possible pattern.

For example, writing in the *Yale Review* on "*Noon Wine:* The Sources," Katherine Anne Porter once said:

> By the time a writer has reached the end of a story, he has lived it at least three times over—first in the series of actual events that, directly or indirectly, have combined to set up that commotion in his mind and senses that causes him to write the story; second, in memory; and third in the re-creation of this chaotic stuff. . . .
>
> . . . the story is fiction; but it is made up of thousands of things that did happen to living human beings in a certain part of the country, at a certain time of my life, things that are still remembered by others as single incidents; not as I remembered them, floating and moving with their separate life and reality, meeting and parting and mingling in my thoughts until they established their relationship and meaning to me. I could see and feel very clearly that all these events, episodes—hardly that, sometimes, but just mere glimpses and flashes here and there of lives strange or moving or astonishing to me—were forming a story, almost of themselves, it seemed; out of their apparent incoherence, unrelatedness, they grouped and clung in my mind in a form that gave a meaning to the whole that the individual parts had lacked. So I feel that this story is "true" in the way that a work of fiction should be true, created out of all the scattered particles of life I was able to absorb and combine and to shape into a living new being. . . .
>
> Someone asked me once where I had ever heard that conversation in "Noon Wine" between two men about chewing tobacco—that apparently aimless talk between Mr. Hatch and Mr. Thompson which barely masks hatred and is leading toward a murder. It seems that I *must* have heard something of the sort somewhere, sometime or another; I do not in the least remember it. But that whole countryside was full of tobacco-chewing men, whittling men, hard-working farming men perched on fences with their high heels caught on a rail, or squatting on their toes, gossiping idly and comfortably for hours at a time. . . .
>
> There is an early memory, not the first, but certainly before my third year, always connected with this story, "Noon Wine"; it is the source, if there could be only one. I was a very small child. I know this by the remembered vastness of the world around me, the giant heights of grown-up people; a chair something to be scaled like a mountain; a table top to be peered over on tiptoe. It was late summer and near sunset, for the sky was a clear green-blue with long streaks of burning rose in it, and the air was full of the mournful sound of swooping bats. I was all alone in a wide grassy plain—it was the lawn on the east side of the house—and I was in that state of instinctive bliss which children only know, when there came like a blow of thunder echoing and rolling in that green sky, the explosion of a shotgun, not very far away; for it shook the air. There followed at once a high,

thin, long-drawn scream, a sound I had never heard, but I knew what it was—it was the sound of death in the voice of a man. How did I know it was a shotgun? How should I not have known? How did I know it was death? We are born knowing death. . . .

[When Katherine Anne Porter was nine years old, the family had callers.] Then I saw first a poor sad pale beaten-looking woman in a faded cotton print dress and a wretched little straw hat with a wreath of wilted forgetmenots. She looked as if she had never eaten a good dinner, or slept in a comfortable bed, or felt a gentle touch; the mark of life-starvation was all over her. Her hands were twisted tight in her lap and she was looking down at them in shame. Her eyes were covered with dark glasses. While I stared at her, I heard the man sitting near her almost shouting in a coarse, roughened voice: "I swear, it was in self-defense! His life or mine! If you don't believe me, ask my wife here. She saw it. My wife won't lie!" Every time he repeated these words, without lifting her head or moving, she would say in a low voice, "Yes, that's right. I saw it. . . ."

I used this scene in "Noon Wine," but the man in real life was not lean and gaunt and blindly, foolishly proud, like Mr. Thompson; no, he was just a great loose-faced, blabbing man full of guilt and fear, and he was bawling at my grandmother, his eyes bloodshot with drink and tears, "Lady, if you don't believe me, ask my wife! She won't lie!"

Out of these "glimpses and flashes" came Miss Porter's short novel *Noon Wine,* a sensitive, beautiful work of flawless prose. The pattern she chose utilized these memories, but they were refined through the spirit of her remarkable talent.

Real life dialog is usually less dramatic than that remembered by Miss Porter, for people seldom really converse. They carry on simultaneous monologs while their minds are fixed on utterly different things. In daily life, you may say, "I have such a headache!" only to have a friend respond, "I wonder what's for lunch?" Such an exchange might occur in a story, but it would be designed to show rudeness or disinterest or preoccupation in the second speaker. Used as heard in life, it would be dull and meaningless.

If it is convenient, try switching on a tape recorder at some gathering of people. Later, listen to the tape, noting the disjointed speech, the obvious lack of attention, the disregard for grammatical correctness. Written dialog should have some of that quality, but, unfortunately, many writers become so acutely aware of grammar and syntax in dialog that they create stilted, unnatural conversation.

Writers have created characters from many approaches. Examine the following ones, isolating the devices of poetry and prose that contribute to their success.

In Henry Fielding's *The History of the Life of the Late Mr. Jonathan Wild,* the central character is a "fence." Arranging robberies, he receives and disposes of the stolen goods by selling them back to their original owners. He splits the profits—with great reluctance—with the thieves and is not above acting as a "stool pigeon" if he can sell the thief to the police at a profit. Fielding's character sketch is static, containing no direct dialog. The tone is ironic, the development reliant on understatement:

Jonathan Wild had every qualification necessary to form a great man. As his most powerful and predominant passion was ambition, so nature had, with consummate propriety, adapted all his faculties to the attaining those glorious ends to which this passion directed him. He was extremely ingenious in inventing designs, artful in contriving the means to accomplish his purposes, and resolute in executing them: for as the most exquisite cunning and most undaunted boldness qualified him for any undertaking, so was he not restrained by any of those weaknesses which disappoint the views of mean and vulgar souls, and which are comprehended in one general term of honesty, which is a corruption of HONOSTY, a word derived from what the Greeks call an ass. He was entirely free from those low vices of modesty and good-nature, which, as he said, implied a total negation of human greatness, and were the only qualities which absolutely rendered a man incapable of making a considerable figure in the world. His lust was inferior only to his ambition; but, as for what simple people call love, he knew not what it was. His avarice was immense, but it was of the rapacious, not of the tenacious kind; his rapaciousness was indeed so violent, that nothing ever contented him but the whole; for, however considerable the share was which his coadjutors allowed him of a booty, he was restless in inventing means to make himself master of the smallest pittance reserved by them. He said laws were made for the use of *prigs* only, and to secure their property; they were never therefore more perverted than when their edge was turned against these; but that this generally happened through their want of sufficient dexterity. The character which he most valued himself upon, and which he principally honoured in others, was that of hypocrisy. His opinion was, that no one could carry *priggism* very far without it; for which reason, he said, there was little greatness to be expected in a man who acknowledged his vices, but always much to be hoped from him who professed great virtues: wherefore, though he would always shun the person whom he discovered guilty of a good action, yet he was never deterred by a good character, which was more commonly the effect of profession than of action: for which reason, he himself was always very liberal of honest professions, and had as much virtue and goodness in his mouth as a saint; never in the least scrupling to swear by his honour, even to those who knew him the best; nay, though he held good-nature and modesty in the highest contempt, he constantly practised the affectation of both, and recommended this to others, whose welfare, on his own account, he wished well to.

Clearly, the author does not have to like a character to reveal him. Often, in fact, an unlikable one is easier to create than a personable one, an evil one easier than a good one. Lucifer, for instance, in Milton's *Paradise Lost,* is far more interesting than God. The author must, however, see such characters more completely than the ones he likes. To attack such a character would be to destroy him as a creation. The author's moral judgments must be restrained and implicit rather than direct and explicit.

Did you notice the narrative quality of Fielding's character study? How much is shown? How much is stated? Had Fielding wished, he could have given this passage a basic expository treatment. It is saved from that dull form, however, by the restrained humor of irony. The details are sharp and clear; their selection is careful; their arrangement, precise. And the passage builds from an introductory sentence to a firm conclusion.

Washington Irving, in "The Legend of Sleepy Hollow," combines narrative and description to create the unforgettable Ichabod Crane and provide historical foundation for a contempt of teachers that is unique in America:

In this by-place of nature, there abode, in a remote period of American history, that is to say, some thirty years since, a worthy wight of the name of Ichabod Crane; who sojourned, or, as he expressed it, "tarried," in Sleepy Hollow, for the purpose of instructing the children of the vicinity. He was a native of Connecticut, a State which supplies the Union with pioneers for the mind as well as for the forest, and sends forth yearly its legions of frontier woodsmen and country school-masters. The cognomen of Crane was not inapplicable to his person. He was tall, but exceedingly lank, with narrow shoulders, long arms and legs, hands that dangled a mile out of his sleeves, feet that might have served for shovels, and his whole frame most loosely hung together. His head was small, and flat at top, with huge ears, large green glassy eyes, and a long snipe nose, so that it looked like a weather-cock perched upon his spindle neck, to tell which way the wind blew. To see him striding along the profile of a hill on a windy day, with his clothes bagging and fluttering about him, one might have mistaken him for the genius of famine descending upon the earth, or some scarecrow eloped from a corn-field.

His school-house was a low building of one large room, rudely constructed of logs; the windows partly glazed, and partly patched with leaves of old copy-books. It was most ingeniously secured at vacant hours by a withe twisted in the handle of the door, and stakes set against the window-shutters; so that, though a thief might get in with perfect ease, he would find some embarrassment in getting out: an idea most probably borrowed by the architect, Yost Van Houten, from the mystery of an eel-pot. The school-house stood in a rather lonely but pleasant situation, just at the foot of a woody hill, with a brook running close by, and a formidable birch-tree growing at one end of it. From hence the low murmur of his pupils' voices, conning over their lessons, might be heard on a drowsy summer's day, like the hum of a bee-hive; interrupted now and then by the authoritative voice of the master, in the tone of menace or command; or, peradventure, by the appalling sound of the birch, as he urged some tardy loiterer along the flowery path of knowledge. Truth to say, he was a conscientious man, and ever bore in mind the golden maxim, "Spare the rod and spoil the child."—Ichabod Crane's scholars certainly were not spoiled.

The diction of this excerpt is deliberately pompous, supplying a humorous tone. Such words as *wight* (a person), *tarried* and *cognomen* clearly indicate the gentle spoofing. Hyperbole in "hands that dangled a mile out of his sleeves" is structurally balanced against litotes in "Ichabod Crane's scholars certainly were not spoiled." Simile and metaphor are skillfully chosen, painting instant pictures for the reader. The schoolhouse description serves not only as setting but almost as a foil for Crane, for it is as complex in structure as he—and as ludicrous. Poetry pervades the two paragraphs as the prose flows rhythmically along. Comparisons and contrasts abound. Crane is compared to a genius of famine, a scarecrow, and the schoolhouse. The schoolhouse, as ugly as Crane, is a perfect setting for him, and the combined ugliness is contrasted sharply with the natural beauty of the geographic setting and the implied charm of the children. Their drowsy study noises contrast with Crane's authoritative voice and birch. The diction reflects these contrasts in the first sentence as "a remote period of American history" is reduced to "that is to say, some thirty years since."

The clever combination of straight narrative in tension with hyperbole and understatement creates the wonderfully humorous tone of the piece and overlays the whole with the distant charm of a fairy tale. A quite different treatment of character, however, is the clinical analysis of Jenny Petherbridge in Djuna Barnes' *Nightwood.* The casebook approach is avoided as specific illustrations reinforce the analyzed characteristics of Jenny, who is "The Squatter." In a short story, an author can usually ill afford as much space for character analysis as is given to Jenny Petherbridge in this novel. However, because your aim now is to learn how an author's use of detail can reveal a character completely, this is an excellent example. Read the selection first by skipping over the discussion passages.

[1] Jenny Petherbridge was a widow, a middle-aged woman who had been married four times. Each husband had wasted away and died; she had been like a squirrel racing a wheel day and night in an endeavour to make them historical; they could not survive it.

Paragraph 1 establishes the necessary knowledge of Jenny's past. How effective is the simile since it ends in understatement? How does the structure of the second sentence make the description acceptable in spite of the extreme cruelty?

[2]She had a beaked head and the body, small, feeble, and ferocious, that somehow made one associate her with Judy; they did not go together. Only severed could any part of her have been called "right." There was a trembling ardour in her wrists and fingers as if she were suffering from some elaborate denial. She looked old, yet expectant of age; she seemed to be steaming in the vapours of someone else about to die; still she gave off an odour to the mind (for there are purely mental smells that have no reality) of a woman about to be *accouchée*. Her body suffered from its fare, laughter and crumbs, abuse and indulgence. But put out a hand to touch her, and her head moved perceptibly with the broken arc of two instincts, recoil and advance, so that the head rocked timidly and aggressively at the same moment, giving her a slightly shuddering and expectant rhythm.

Paragraph 2 is built on the allusion to the female puppet of Punch and Judy shows. The metaphor is controlled throughout, constantly recalling the laughable but pathetic clumsiness of the marionette.

[3]She writhed under the necessity of being unable to wear anything becoming, being one of those panicky little women who, no matter what they put on, look like a child under penance.

[4]She had a fancy for tiny ivory or jade elephants; she said they were luck; she left a trail of tiny elephants wherever she went; and she went hurriedly and gasping.

Paragraphs 3–4 establish size, both physical and mental. Note the effect of the simile in paragraph 3, the verbs and verbals in both 3 and 4. Why are *hurriedly* and *gasping* so effective? Do they refer to "a child under penance" in any way?

[5]Her walls, her cupboards, her bureaux, were teeming with second-hand dealings with life. It takes a bold and authentic robber to get first-hand plunder. Someone else's marriage ring was on her finger; the photograph taken of Robin for Nora sat upon her table. The books in her library were other people's selections. She lived among her own things like a visitor to a room kept "exactly as it was when—" She tiptoed, even when she went to draw a bath, nervous and *andante*. She stopped, fluttering and febrile, before every object in her house. She had no sense of humour or peace or rest, and her own quivering uncertainty made even the objects which she pointed out to the company, as, "My virgin from Palma," or, "The left-hand glove of La Duse," recede into a distance of uncertainty, so that it was almost impossible for the onlooker to see them at all. When anyone was witty about a

contemporary event, she would look perplexed and a little dismayed, as if someone had done something that really should not have been done; therefore her attention had been narrowed down to listening for *faux pas.* She frequently talked about something being the "death of her," and certainly anything could have been had she been the first to suffer it. The words that fell from her mouth seemed to have been lent to her; had she been forced to invent a vocabulary for herself, it would have been a vocabulary of two words, "ah" and "oh." Hovering, trembling, tiptoeing, she would unwind anecdote after anecdote in a light rapid lisping voice which one always expected to change, to drop and to become the "every day" voice; but it never did. The stories were humorous, well told. She would smile, toss her hands up, widen her eyes; immediately everyone in the room had a certain feeling of something lost, sensing that there was one person who was missing the importance of the moment, who had not heard the story; the teller herself.

Paragraph 5 extends the child imagery with examples. While dialog is absent, it seems to be a component. Could such speech have been created in dialog?

6 She had endless cuttings and scraps from journals and old theatre programmes, haunted the *Comédie Française,* spoke of Molière, Racine and *La Dame aux Camélias.* She was generous with money. She made gifts lavishly and spontaneously. She was the worst recipient of presents in the world. She sent bushel baskets of camellias to actresses because she had a passion for the characters they portrayed. The flowers were tied with yards of satin ribbon, and a note accompanied them, effusive and gentle. To men she sent books by the dozen; the general feeling was that she was a well-read woman, though she had read perhaps ten books in her life.

7 She had a continual rapacity for other people's facts; absorbing time, she held herself responsible for historic characters. She was avid and disorderly in her heart. She defiled the very meaning of personality in her passion to be a person; somewhere about her was the tension of the accident that made the beast the human endeavour.

Paragraphs 6–7 extend the "second-hand dealings with life" and explore Jenny's intellect and personality.

8 She was nervous about the future; it made her indelicate. She was one of the most unimportantly wicked women of her time—because she could not let her time alone, and yet could never be a part of it. She wanted to be the reason for everything and so was the cause of nothing. She had the fluency of tongue and action meted out by divine providence to those who cannot think for themselves. She was master of the over-sweet phrase, the over-tight embrace.

In paragraph 8, words or ideas are linked with two unrelated words or ideas to create comparisons not otherwise possible (*unimportantly wicked*, for example). Called *syllepsis*, this poetic device is effective in achieving invective. The author *seems* thoroughly objective, however, as the tone remains clinical and detached. Point out other examples of this device.

[9]One inevitably thought of her in the act of love emitting florid *commedia dell' arte* ejaculations; one should not have thought of her in the act of love at all. She thought of little else, and though always submitting to the act, spoke of and desired the spirit of love; yet was unable to attain it.

[10]No one could intrude upon her because there was no place for intrusion. This inadequacy made her insubordinate—she could not participate in a great love, she could only report it. Since her emotional reactions were without distinction, she had to fall back on the emotions of the past, great loves already lived and related, and over those she seemed to suffer and grow glad.

[11]When she fell in love it was with a perfect fury of accumulated dishonesty; she became instantly a dealer in second-hand and therefore incalculable emotions. As, from the solid archives of usage, she had stolen or appropriated the dignity of speech, so she appropriated the most passionate love that she knew, Nora's for Robin. She was a "squatter" by instinct. □

Paragraphs 9–11 search out her capacity for love and create her role in the story. The description becomes a circle as the reader realizes why the four husbands of paragraph 1 "could not survive it."

Miss Barnes' detailed analysis is necessary here. Certainly paragraphs 9, 10, and 11 contain the information the reader needs, but read them without the first eight paragraphs and you will understand the need of the earlier ones.

In writing such passages, the author may be tempted to overwrite, diverting the reader's attention by poetic devices, by clinical observation, by artful (rather than functional) syntax. The passage then becomes important as an entity rather than as a component of the larger unit. Such attention creates what are called *purple patches* because the passage "stands out" as a self-conscious literary effort, dwarfing the sections around it. Not always a vice, overwriting sometimes creates such passages as the brilliant description of Queen Mab's chariot in Shakespeare's *Romeo and Juliet.* You should be aware at all times of the *effectiveness* of whatever device the author employs.

In his novel *Babbitt,* Sinclair Lewis combines narrative flow, description, character, and dialog to create a scene fairly throbbing with verisimilitude. Tone, mood, and atmosphere are achieved through careful attention to idiom superimposed on diction as Babbitt and Chum Frink are superimposed on the geographic setting. The contrasts in Eathorne, Babbitt, and Frink serve to vitalize the three characters. Eathorne and Babbitt are fully rounded (if they seem stock, it is because innumerable imitations have been made of them since their creation), while Frink is a foil for Babbitt, being a mirror-image of him. And here, even fully rounded characters serve as foils as Babbitt and Eathorne intensify each other through comparison and contrast:

Chapter XVII

I

1 There are but three or four old houses in Floral Heights, and in Floral Heights an old house is one which was built before 1880. The largest of these is the residence of William Washington Eathorne, president of the First State Bank.

2 The Eathorne Mansion preserves the memory of the "nice parts" of Zenith as they appeared from 1860 to 1900. It is a red brick immensity with gray sandstone lintels and a roof of slate in courses of red, green, and dyspeptic yellow. There are two anemic towers, one roofed with copper, the other crowned with castiron ferns. The porch is like an open tomb; it is supported by squat granite pillars above which hang frozen cascades of brick. At one side of the house is a huge stained-glass window in the shape of a keyhole.

3 But the house has an effect not at all humorous. It embodies the heavy dignity of those Victorian financiers who ruled the generation between the pioneers and the brisk "sales-engineers" and created a somber oligarchy by gaining control of banks, mills, land, railroads, mines. Out of the dozen contradictory Zeniths which together make up the true and complete Zenith, none is so powerful and enduring yet none so unfamiliar to the citizens as the small, still, dry, polite, cruel Zenith of the William Eathornes; and for that tiny hierarchy the other Zeniths unwittingly labor and insignificantly die.

4 Most of the castles of the testy Victorian tetrarchs are gone now or decayed into boarding-houses, but the Eathorne Mansion remains virtuous and aloof, reminiscent of London, Back Bay, Rittenhouse Square. Its marble steps are scrubbed daily, the brass plate is reverently polished, and the lace curtains are as prim and superior as William Washington Eathorne himself.

5 With a certain awe Babbitt and Chum Frink called on Eathorne for a meeting of the Sunday School Advisory Committee; with uneasy

stillness they followed a uniformed maid through catacombs of reception-rooms to the library. It was as unmistakably the library of a solid old banker as Eathorne's side-whiskers were the side-whiskers of a solid old banker. The books were most of them Standard Sets, with the correct and traditional touch of dim blue, dim gold, and glossy calf-skin. The fire was exactly correct and traditional; a small, quiet, steady fire, reflected by polished fire-irons. The oak desk was dark and old and altogether perfect; the chairs were gently supercilious.

6 Eathorne's inquiries as to the healths of Mrs. Babbitt, Miss Babbitt, and the Other Children were softly paternal, but Babbitt had nothing with which to answer him. It was indecent to think of using the "How's tricks, ole socks?" which gratified Vergil Gunch and Frink and Howard Littlefield—men who till now had seemed successful and urbane. Babbitt and Frink sat politely, and politely did Eathorne observe, opening his thin lips just wide enough to dismiss the words, "Gentlemen, before we begin our conference—you may have felt the cold in coming here—so good of you to save an old man the journey—shall we perhaps have a whisky toddy?"

7 So well trained was Babbitt in all the conversation that befits a Good Fellow that he almost disgraced himself with "Rather than make trouble, and always providin' there ain't any enforcement officers hiding in the waste-basket—" The words died choking in his throat. He bowed in flustered obedience. So did Chum Frink.

8 Eathorne rang for the maid.

9 The modern and luxurious Babbitt had never seen any one ring for a servant in a private house, except during meals. Himself, in hotels, had rung for bell-boys, but in the house you didn't hurt Matilda's feelings; you went out in the hall and shouted for her. Nor had he, since prohibition, known any one to be casual about drinking. It was extraordinary merely to sip his toddy and not cry, "Oh, maaaaan, this hits me right where I live!" And always, with the ecstasy of youth meeting greatness, he marveled, "That little fuzzy-face there, why, he could make me or break me! If he told my banker to call my loans—! Gosh! That quarter-sized squirt! And looking like he hadn't got a single bit of hustle to him! I wonder—Do we Boosters throw too many fits about pep?"

10 From this thought he shuddered away, and listened devoutly to Eathorne's ideas on the advancement of the Sunday School, which were very clear and very bad.

11 Diffidently Babbitt outlined his own suggestions:

12 "I think if you analyze the needs of the school, in fact, going right at it as if it was a merchandizing problem, of course the one

basic and fundamental need is growth. I presume we're all agreed we won't be satisfied till we build up the biggest darn Sunday School in the whole state, so the Chatham Road Presbyterian won't have to take anything off anybody. Now about jazzing up the campaign for prospects: they've already used contesting teams, and given prizes to the kids that bring in the most members. And they made a mistake there: the prizes were a lot of folderols and doodads like poetry books and illustrated Testaments, instead of something a real live kid would want to work for, like real cash or a speedometer for his motor cycle. Course I suppose it's all fine and dandy to illustrate the lessons with these decorated book-marks and blackboard drawings and so on, but when it comes down to real he-hustling, getting out and drumming up customers—or members, I mean, why, you got to make it worth a fellow's while.

13 "Now, I want to propose two stunts: First, divide the Sunday School into four armies, depending on age. Everybody gets a military rank in his own army according to how many members he brings in, and the duffers that lie down on us and don't bring in any, they remain privates. The pastor and superintendent rank as generals. And everybody has got to give salutes and all the rest of that junk, just like a regular army, to make 'em feel it's worth while to get rank.

14 "Then, second: Course the school has its advertising committee, but, Lord, nobody ever really works good—nobody works well just for the love of it. The thing to do is to be practical and up-to-date, and hire a real paid press-agent for the Sunday School—some newspaper fellow who can give part of his time."

15 "Sure, you bet!" said Chum Frink.

16 "Think of the nice juicy bits he could get in!" Babbitt crowed. "Not only the big, salient, vital facts, about how fast the Sunday School—and the collection—is growing, but a lot of humorous gossip and kidding: about how some blowhard fell down on his pledge to get new members, or the good time the Sacred Trinity class of girls had at their wieniewurst party. And on the side, if he had time, the press-agent might even boost the lessons themselves—do a little advertising for all the Sunday Schools in town, in fact. No use being hoggish toward the rest of 'em, providing we can keep the bulge on 'em in membership. Frinstance, he might get the papers to—Course I haven't got a literary training like Frink here, and I'm just guessing how the pieces ought to be written, but take frinstance, suppose the week's lesson is about Jacob; well, the press-agent might get in something that would have a fine moral, and yet with a trick headline that'd get folks to read it—say like: *Jake Fools the Old Man; Makes Getaway with Girl and Bankroll.*

See how I mean? That'd get their interest! Now, course, Mr. Eathorne, you're conservative, and maybe you feel these stunts would be undignified, but honestly, I believe they'd bring home the bacon."

17 Eathorne folded his hands on his comfortable little belly and purred like an aged pussy:

18 "May I say, first, that I have been very much pleased by your analysis of the situation, Mr. Babbitt. As you surmise, it's necessary in My Position to be conservative, and perhaps endeavor to maintain a certain standard of dignity. Yet I think you'll find me somewhat progressive. In our bank, for example, I hope I may say that we have as modern a method of publicity and advertising as any in the city. Yes, I fancy you'll find us oldsters quite cognizant of the shifting spiritual values of the age. Yes, oh yes. And so, in fact, it pleases me to be able to say that though personally I might prefer the sterner Presbyterianism of an earlier era—"

19 Babbitt finally gathered that Eathorne was willing.

20 Chum Frink suggested as part-time press-agent one Kenneth Escott, reporter on the *Advocate-Times.*

21 They parted on a high plane of amity and Christian helpfulness.

22 Babbitt did not drive home, but toward the center of the city. He wished to be by himself and exult over the beauty of intimacy with William Washington Eathorne. □

The physical description of the house characterizes Eathorne, his background, his position, and his attitudes. Did you notice the carefully selected details and the focus of description as your attention was directed from the bulk of the house to the towers and back to the ground in the fern imagery? How effective are words like *dyspeptic* and *anemic* or *immensity* and *cascades?* How do they establish tone while describing the house and characterizing its owner? *Castles* and *testy* reinforce the mood as the allusions to other quality areas nestle among such adjectives as *virtuous, aloof, prim,* and *superior.* The concrete details of scrubbing and polishing add to the description. How?

Babbitt and Chum Frink are revealed as they are placed against the background of the house. What do such words as *catacombs, solid, Standard Sets, traditional,* and *correct* indicate about the house and Babbitt's reaction to it? What does his reaction establish about him?

Narrative flow introduces scraps of dialog which are more revealing than extended dialog would be at this point. Why are Eathorne's early speeches withheld, being presented in exposition? Babbitt's breezy slang seems improper and lacking in correctness. Why? How does Chum Frink's brief dialog contribute to the impression?

When Eathorne's "comfortable little belly" and the "aged pussy" simile introduce his dialog, how do the devices prepare you for the sharp contrast in speech?

Is the statement that "Babbitt finally gathered that Eathorne was willing" irony or understatement or both? Does the tone extend to the end of the passage? What do you observe about pace and proportion in the selection?

What is the point of view from which the incident is told? From whose point of view is it narrated? How do the transitions serve to move the reader from one geographic spot to another? How do the short, choppy, transitionless paragraphs at the end of the account contribute to the total effect?

Analyze every sentence of dialog. How does the dialog reveal each character, his background, his uncertainties, his satisfactions? How effective are clichés and trite phrases, jargon, and slang as they are used in the dialog? How are diction and idiom employed by Lewis?

Stream-of-consciousness, geographic environment, reactions of other characters, and narrative—all combine in the next story, Katherine Mansfield's "Miss Brill," to create a pathetic picture. As you read it, isolate the poetic devices, paying particular attention to the skillful way they are woven into the narrative flow to create reader response. The mood of the story changes from section to section as Miss Brill's attitude changes, but the tone throughout is one of gentle pathos until the final sentence. There, understatement suggests heartbreak, recalling the scene in Anton Chekhov's *The Cherry Orchard* when the heartstring breaks. One central character (Miss Brill) and many minor ones with foil purpose create a character sketch and extend it into a short story. Trace the changes in Miss Brill from the beginning to the end, noticing how subtle the changes are. No one great incident causes her to realize anything. Instead, a steadily mounting body of evidence finally becomes so weighty that she realizes something that has been insidiously suggesting itself from the beginning of the story. Decide, as you read, why Miss Brill's first name is never revealed.

Read the story first in its entirety.

Miss Brill

by Katherine Mansfield

1 Although it was so brilliantly fine—the blue sky powdered with gold and great spots of light like white wine splashed over the Jardins Publiques—Miss Brill

was glad that she had decided on her fur. The air was motionless, but when you opened your mouth there was just a faint chill, like a chill from a glass of iced water before you sip, and now and again a leaf came drifting—from nowhere, from the sky. [. . .]

A strong appeal to the reader's senses opens this story. His eyes are assaulted by light, the brilliant gold and white creating a memory of looking at bright, eye-hurting skies. A crisp, dry-moist appeal to the sense of touch pervades the white wine image. It is doubly effective as the reader remembers the cooling evaporation of alcohol on the skin and simultaneously equates it with the delightful chill of sunny, cool days. The tensions of the language also cause the reader to smell the clean taste of wine and extend the fermented odor into the heady smell of invigorating days. Examine the effect achieved by the contrast of the participles *powdered* and *splashed* in the first sentence. A clean luxury, as of talcum and cologne after a bath, is also implicit. Taste also receives attention in the sipped iced water image, and the reader is cleverly involved by the use of the second person pronoun. The leaf image employs gentle samvegha as *nowhere* is extended to *sky* and nature becomes an absolute backdrop. However, midpoint in the reader involvement (and in the paragraph), Miss Brill is introduced.

[. . .] Miss Brill put up her hand and touched her fur. Dear little thing! It was nice to feel it again. She had taken it out of its box that afternoon, shaken out the moth-powder, given it a good brush, and rubbed the life back into the dim little eyes. "What has been happening to me?" said the sad little eyes. Oh, how sweet it was to see them snap at her again from the red eiderdown! . . . But the nose, which was of some black composition, wasn't at all firm. It must have had a knock, somehow. Never mind—a little dab of black sealing-wax when the time came—when it was absolutely necessary. . . . Little rogue! Yes, she really felt like that about it. Little rogue biting its tail just by her left ear. She could have taken it off and laid it on her lap and stroked it. She felt a tingling in her hands and arms, but that came from walking, she supposed. And when she breathed, something light and sad—no, not sad, exactly—something gentle seemed to move in her bosom.

The shift of focus from the general setting to Miss Brill seems natural and easy. Her antiseptic, faded person was established in the pastels of the preceding sentences. Possession becomes almost palpable as a Brill characteristic as the word *her* is repeated in the line introducing the fur. *Moth-powder* is extended into the personal experience, and the invigorating atmosphere is localized in her hands and arms, which tingle. The point of view is hers; the third person omniscient point of view is limited to her as her thoughts are selected and arranged to create a total picture. Should the reader pause to reflect, he would realize the thinking process is not this ordered, but he has been trapped into identification, so he remembers only the singular *feeling* of such thought processes. He can, then, accept the pattern. In so doing, he accepts Miss Brill as being as self-centered and organized in petty detail as a teacher of English might be. When Miss Brill's profession is casually introduced later, the reader will be rewarded by his astuteness. The words *sad* and *gentle* summarize the tone for the reader. The phrase "move in her bosom" serves as transition.

2 There were a number of people out this afternoon, far more than last Sunday. And the band sounded louder and gayer. That was because the Season had begun. For although the band played all the year round on Sundays, out of season it was never the same. It was like some one playing with only the family to listen; it didn't care how it played if there weren't any strangers present. Wasn't the conductor wearing a new coat, too? She was sure it was new. He scraped with his foot and flapped his arms like a rooster about to crow, and the bandsmen sitting in the green rotunda blew out their cheeks and glared at the music. Now there came a little "flutey" bit—very pretty!—a little chain of bright drops. She was sure it would be repeated. It was; she lifted her head and smiled.

The sense of movement grows from the word *move* in the earlier sentence, while immediacy is established in "*this* afternoon." Miss Brill's solitary state is revealed in her pathetic assessment of the vigor with which the band plays "in season." Her unsophisticated background is indicated by the "rooster about to crow" simile; and her acquired knowledge, pretentious and old-maidish, is revealed in her idiomatic word *flutey.* The "little chain of bright drops" might be a necklace she would choose. And, of course, since the beads would be unobtrusive, she would add a second strand, so she expects a repetition of the sound.

3 Only two people shared her "special" seat: a fine old man in a velvet coat, his hands clasped over a huge carved walking-stick, and a big old woman, sitting upright, with a roll of knitting on her embroidered apron. They did not speak. This was disappointing, for Miss Brill always looked forward to the conversation. She had become really quite expert, she thought, at listening as though she didn't listen, at sitting in other people's lives just for a minute while they talked round her.

4 She glanced, sideways, at the old couple. Perhaps they would go soon. Last Sunday, too, hadn't been as interesting as usual. An Englishman and his wife, he

wearing a dreadful Panama hat and she button boots. And she'd gone on the whole time about how she ought to wear spectacles; she knew she needed them; but that it was no good getting any; they'd be sure to break and they'd never keep on. And he'd been so patient. He'd suggested everything—gold rims, the kind that curved round your ears, little pads inside the bridge. No, nothing would please her. "They'll always be sliding down my nose!" Miss Brill had wanted to shake her.

[5]The old people sat on the bench, still as statues. Never mind, there was always the crowd to watch. To and fro, in front of the flower-beds and the band rotunda, the couples and groups paraded, stopped to talk, to greet, to buy a handful of flowers from the old beggar who had his tray fixed to the railings. Little children ran among them, swooping and laughing; little boys with big white silk bows under their chins, little girls, little French dolls, dressed up in velvet and lace. And sometimes a tiny staggerer came suddenly rocking into the open from under the trees, stopped, stared, as suddenly sat down "flop," until its small high-stepping mother, like a young hen, rushed scolding to its rescue. Other people sat on the benches and green chairs, but they were nearly always the same, Sunday after Sunday, and—Miss Brill had often noticed—there was something funny about nearly all of them. They were odd, silent, nearly all old, and from the way they stared they looked as though they'd just come from dark little rooms or even—even cupboards!

Her isolation from life becomes clearer as she "shares" a seat with the colorful old couple—he so elegant, she so homey with her embroidered apron and knitting. Miss Brill's exclusion is painful, but her reflection about "sitting in other people's lives" makes it more painful. The flashback, contrasting the English couple, intensifies the pain—Miss Brill's memory suggests her agonized need of someone to allow her petulance, to be concerned enough to tolerate selfishness in her. Did you notice how skillfully the flashback was inserted, how the return to the present was accomplished in the reference to the elegant old couple? The statues simile assures the reader the couple has not intruded on the flashback. Their continued immobility projects her conscious thoughts into the color and movement of the crowd, so young, so colorful, so alive! The contrast of moving people and seated observers is also painful as Miss Brill thinks the old people may have come from "even cupboards!"—and the end of the story is foreshadowed.

[6]Behind the rotunda the slender trees with yellow leaves down drooping, and through them just a line of sea, and beyond the blue sky with gold-veined clouds.

[7]Tum-tum-tum tiddle-um! tiddle-um! tum tiddley-um tum ta! blew the band.

[8]Two young girls in red came by and two young soldiers in blue met them, and they laughed and paired and went off arm-in-arm. Two peasant women with funny

straw hats passed, gravely, leading beautiful smoke-colored donkeys. A cold, pale nun hurried by. A beautiful woman came along and dropped her bunch of violets, and a little boy ran after to hand them to her, and she took them and threw them away as if they'd been poisoned. Dear me! Miss Brill didn't know whether to admire that or not! And now an ermine toque and a gentleman in gray met just in front of her. He was tall, stiff, dignified, and she was wearing the ermine toque she'd bought when her hair was yellow. Now everything, her hair, her face, even her eyes, was the same color as the shabby ermine, and her hand, in its cleaned glove, lifted to dab her lips, was a tiny yellowish paw. Oh, she was so pleased to see him—delighted! She rather thought they were going to meet that afternoon. She described where she'd been—everywhere, here, there, along by the sea. The day was so charming—didn't he agree? And wouldn't he, perhaps? . . . But he shook his head, lighted a cigarette, slowly breathed a great deep puff into her face, and, even while she was still talking and laughing, flicked the match away and walked on. The ermine toque was alone; she smiled more brightly than ever. But even the band seemed to know what she was feeling and played more softly, played tenderly, and the drum beat, "The Brute! The Brute!" over and over. What would she do? What was going to happen now? But as Miss Brill wondered, the ermine toque turned, raised her hand as though she'd seen some one else, much nicer, just over there, and pattered away. And the band changed again and played more quickly, more gayly than ever, and the old couple on Miss Brill's seat got up and marched away, and such a funny old man with long whiskers hobbled along in time to the music and was nearly knocked over by four girls walking abreast.

The open sky is contrasted with the cupboard image. Color, repeated from the opening of the story, serves as a unifying element and as a transition between old, dark images and bright ones. But reds and blues mute to smoky gray and into cold paleness as Miss Brill's selection reveals her drooping spirits. Youth and age meet over the violets (flowers of spring or the color of elderly ladies) and foreshadowing again is inserted in the story. Pathos becomes almost unbearable as Miss Brill identifies her own needs with the needs of the woman in the ermine toque. Miss Brill's response to the music indicates her response to the scene as it grows sad, then becomes determinedly gay.

9 Oh, how fascinating it was! How she enjoyed it! How she loved sitting here, watching it all! It was like a play. It was exactly like a play. Who could believe the sky at the back wasn't painted? But it wasn't till a little brown dog trotted on solemn and then slowly trotted off, like a little "theatre" dog, a little dog that had been drugged, that Miss Brill discovered what it was that made it so exciting. They were all on the stage. They weren't only the audience, not only looking on; they were acting. Even she had a part and came every Sunday. No doubt somebody would

have noticed if she hadn't been there; she was part of the performance after all. How strange she'd never thought of it like that before! And yet it explained why she made such a point of starting from home at just the same time each week—so as not to be late for the performance—and it also explained why she had quite a queer, shy feeling at telling her English pupils how she spent her Sunday afternoons. No wonder! Miss Brill nearly laughed out loud. She was on the stage. She thought of the old invalid gentleman to whom she read the newspaper four afternoons a week while he slept in the garden. She had got quite used to the frail head on the cotton pillow, the hollowed eyes, the open mouth and the high pinched nose. If he'd been dead she mightn't have noticed for weeks; she wouldn't have minded. But suddenly he knew he was having the paper read to him by an actress! "An actress!" The old head lifted; two points of light quivered in the old eyes. "An actress—are ye?" And Miss Brill smoothed the newspaper as though it were the manuscript of her part and said gently: "Yes, I have been an actress for a long time."

Miss Brill's need to be included in life (which has rejected her) grows out of the ermine toque incident. It is made manifest in her revealing statement about her profession. Her rationalization as she endows her dull existence with the glamour of the stage may be delusionary, but it lifts her spirits.

10 The band had been having a rest. Now they started again. And what they played was warm, sunny, yet there was just a faint chill—a something, what was it?—not sadness—no, not sadness—a something that made you want to sing. The tune lifted, lifted, the light shone; and it seemed to Miss Brill that in another moment all of them, all the whole company, would begin singing. The young ones, the laughing ones who were moving together, they would begin, and the men's voices, very resolute and brave, would join them. And then she too, she too, and the others on the benches—they would come in with a kind of accompaniment—something low, that scarcely rose or fell, something so beautiful—moving. . . . And Miss Brill's eyes filled with tears and she looked smiling at all the other members of the company. Yes, we understand, we understand, she thought—though what they understood she didn't know.

11 Just at that moment a boy and a girl came and sat down where the old couple had been. They were beautifully dressed; they were in love. The hero and heroine, of course, just arrived from his father's yacht. And still soundlessly singing, still with that trembling smile, Miss Brill prepared to listen.

Her mood is reflected in her reaction to the music, but sadness lurks just out of her conscious range. So intense is her need for inclusion that she fancies a *group* singing as youth replaces age and she prepares to sit in other people's lives unobtrusively.

12 "No, not now," said the girl. "Not here, I can't."

13 "But why? Because of that stupid old thing at the end there?" asked the boy. "Why does she come here at all—who wants her? Why doesn't she keep her silly old mug at home?"

14 "It's her fu-fur which is so funny," giggled the girl. "It's exactly like a fried whiting."

15 "Ah, be off with you!" said the boy in an angry whisper. Then: "Tell me, ma petite chère—"

16 "No, not here," said the girl. "Not *yet*."

. . . .

17 On her way home she usually bought a slice of honeycake at the baker's. It was her Sunday treat. Sometimes there was an almond in her slice, sometimes not. It made a great difference. If there was an almond it was like carrying home a tiny present—a surprise—something that might very well not have been there. She hurried on the almond Sundays and struck the match for the kettle in quite a dashing way.

18 But to-day she passed the baker's by, climbed the stairs, went into the little dark room—her room like a cupboard—and sat down on the red eiderdown. She sat there for a long time. The box that the fur came out of was on the bed. She unclasped the necklet quickly; quickly, without looking, laid it inside. But when she put the lid on she thought she heard something crying. □

However, youth denies her intrusion, finding her weakest point—the fur symbol—and dashing her into harsh reality. While the dialog is limited, it seems intensely real. Can you see why?

The row of dots between paragraphs 16 and 17 suggests that occasionally a scene should not be written. If it is left to the reader's imagination, he will do a better job than the author could. This is such a scene. The reader, remembering absolute humiliation at some point in his life, creates Miss Brill's collapse for himself. Had the author written this scene, it might have been at odds with the reader's ability to participate through personal experience. Such unwritten scenes are understatement at its ultimate level.

In the last two paragraphs, the little things of Miss Brill's life—things she has endowed with meaning—are no longer possessed of magic. The fur, like the violets earlier in the story, has been "poisoned." The foil use of the woman in the ermine toque becomes obvious at this point. To intensify the effect here, the author inserts the honeycake information. Understatement in the final sentence brings the story to a shattering close. Had it ended in dramatic hyperbole, what different effect would have resulted? Would that conclusion be as effective?

Frame narrative is frequently employed in fiction to give verisimilitude to a situation. You have already encountered it in "The Run on the Cherokee Strip," pp. 52–56. It is a story within a story, allowing the author to narrate at the conversational level. Dialog or remembered monolog as in the earlier work then supplies the narrative flow. "Boless" by Maxim Gorky, which follows, utilizes the technique effectively. The first person limited point of view is especially effective as it removes the author from the story, yet allows him to pervade it. The reader assumes the account has been refined in the author's retelling; therefore, the inept treatment of an amateur is overcome.

As you read this story, be aware, from the beginning, that it is *not* Teresa's story. It is Pan (Polish for "Mr.") Student's. He changes; Teresa does not. His reaction to her reveals his character. She may or may not, in actuality, resemble his depiction. She is Teresa from his point of view. That point of view may be colored by many things. See if you can spot them as you read.

Boless

by Maxim Gorky

1 An acquaintance of mine once told me the following story:

"While still a student at Moscow I happened to be living alongside one of those—well, she was a Polish woman, Teresa by name. A tall, powerfully built brunet with heavy, bushy eyebrows, and a large coarse, vulgar face, as if carved out with an ax—the animal gleam of her eyes, the deep bass voice, the gait and manners of a cabman, and her immense strength like that of a market-woman, inspired me with an inexpressible horror. I lived in the garret of the house, and her room was opposite mine. I never opened my door when I knew that she was in. But this, of course, happened very rarely. Sometimes I chanced to meet her on the landing, staircase, or in the yard, and she would look at me with a smile which seemed to me cynical and rapacious. Occasionally I saw her in her cups, with bleary eyes, her hair and clothes in disorder and with a particularly loathsome smile. On such occasions she would meet my eye with an impudent stare and say:

2 " 'How are you, Pan Student?'

3 "And her stupid laugh would increase my dislike for her still more. I would have liked nothing better than to change my quarters in order to get rid of her proximity, but my room was so nice, and the view from my window was so fine, the street below so quiet and peaceful, that I concluded to endure it.

4 "One morning after I had dressed and was sprawling on the cot, trying to invent some sort of an excuse for not attending my classes, the door of my room suddenly opened, and the disgusting bass voice of the Polish woman sounded from the threshold:

5 " 'Good morning, Pan Student!'

6 " 'What is it you wish?' I asked her. I saw she looked confused and had in her face a kind of pleading expression, something unusual with her.

7 " 'You see, Pan Student, I came to beg you to do me a great favor. Don't refuse me, please!'

8 "Lying there on my cot I thought that it was just some pretext or other to make my further acquaintance. Take care, my boy!

9 " 'You see, I have to send a letter to my native country,' she continued in a supplicating, low, tremulous voice.

10 " 'Well,' I thought, 'the devil take you. If you wish I will write it for you.' And springing to my feet I sat down to the table, took some paper and said: 'Well, come nearer; sit down and dictate.'

11 "She came over; sat down cautiously on the edge of the chair and looked at me in rather a guilty way.

12 " 'To whom shall I write?'

13 " 'To Boleslav Kapshat, in the town Sventsiani, on the Warsaw railroad.'

14 " 'Well, what shall I write? Speak.'

15 " 'My dearest Boless, my heart's delight, my beloved. May the Mother of God protect you! My golden heart, why have you not written for so long a time to your sorrowing dove, Teresa—'

16 "I could hardly keep from laughing. A sorrowing dove, indeed! Almost six feet tall, with the fists of a prize-fighter, and a face so black that it seemed as if the 'dove' had been sweeping chimneys all her life and had never thoroughly washed herself. But I somehow kept my face straight and asked:

17 " 'Who is this Bolesst?'

18 " 'Boless, Pan Student,' she replied, seemingly offended because of my mispronouncing the name. 'He is my affianced.'

19 " 'Affianced!'

20 " 'And why are you so astonished? Can not I, a girl, have an affianced?'

21 "She—a girl! well, this beats everything I ever heard. Oh, well, who can tell about such matters! Everything is possible in this world.

22 " 'And have you been long engaged?'

23 " 'The sixth year.'

24 " 'Oh, oh!' I thought and then said aloud: 'Well, go ahead with your letter.'

25 "And I must confess—so tender and loving was this message—that I would have willingly exchanged places with this Boless had the fair correspondent been any one else but Teresa.

26 " 'I thank you from my inmost soul for your favor, Pan Student,' Teresa said, bowing low. 'Can I in any way be of service to you?'

27 "'No, thank you.'

28 " 'But maybe the Pan's shirts or trousers need mending?'

29 "This made me quite angry. I felt that this mastodon in petticoats was making the blood mount to my cheeks, and I told her quite sharply that her services were not required; and she departed.

30 "Two weeks or so passed. One evening I was sitting at my window, softly whistling and thinking hard how to get away from myself. I felt very bored. The weather was as nasty as it could be. To go out that evening was out of the question, and having nothing better to do I began from sheer ennui a course of self-analysis. This proved dull enough work, but there was nothing else to do. Suddenly the door opened, thank God! Some one was coming to see me.

31 " 'Are you very busy just now, Pan Student?'

32 " 'Teresa! H'm—' I thought I would have preferred any one at all to her. Then I said aloud:

33 " 'No, what is it you want now?'

34 " 'I wish to ask the Pan Student to write me another letter.'

35 " 'Very well. Is it again to Boless you wish me to write?'

36 " 'No, this time I want you to write a letter from Boless to me.'

37 " 'Wha-at?'

38 " 'I beg your pardon, Pan Student. How stupid of me! It is not for me, this letter, but for a friend of mine, a man acquaintance; he has a fiancée. Her name is like mine, Teresa. He does not know how to write, so I want the Pan Student to write for him a letter to that Teresa—'

39 "I looked at her. She seemed very confused and frightened, and her fingers trembled. And tho I failed at first to understand what was the matter with her I at last understood.

40 " 'Look here, my lady,' I said to her. 'You have been telling me a pack of lies. There are no Bolesses nor Teresas among your acquaintances. It is only a pretext for coming in here. I tell you outright that there is no use of coming sneaking around me, as I do not wish to have anything to do with you. Do you understand?'

41 "She grew very red in the face and I saw that she was strangely frightened and confused, and moved her lips so oddly, wishing to say something, without being able to say it. And somehow I began to think that I had misjudged her a little. There was something behind all this. But what?

42 “‘Pan Student,’ she suddenly began, but broke off, and turning toward the door, walked out of the room.

43 “I remained with a very unpleasant feeling in my heart. I heard her shut her own door with a bang; evidently the poor girl was very angry—I thought the matter over and decided to go in to her and induce her to return; I would write her the letter she wished.

44 “I entered her room. She was sitting at the table with her head pressed in her hands.

45 “‘Teresa,’ I said, ‘will you listen to me a moment?’

46 “Whenever I come to this turn of the story I always feel very awkward and embarrassed. But let us return to my narrative. Seeing that she did not reply I repeated:

47 “‘Listen to me, my girl—’

48 “She sprang to her feet, came close up to me, with eyes flashing, and placing her two hands on my shoulders she began to whisper, or rather to hum in her deep bass voice:

49 “Look you here, Pan Student. What of it, what of it if there is no Boless? And what if there is no Teresa? What difference does it make to you? Is it so hard for you to draw a few lines on the paper! Oh, you! And I thought you such a good fellow, such a nice fair-haired little boy. Yes, it is true—there is no Boless, and there is no Teresa, there is only me! Well, what of it?’

50 “‘Allow me,’ I said, greatly disconcerted by this reception. ‘What is it you are saying? Is there no Boless?’

51 “‘Yes, there is none. But what of it?’

52 “‘And no Teresa either?’

53 “‘No, no Teresa either; that is, yes, I am her.’

54 “I could not understand a word. I stared straight into her eyes, trying to determine which of us two had lost our reason. And she returned once more to the table, rummaged for some time in the drawer, and coming back to me said in an offended tone:

55 “‘Here is the letter you wrote for me, take it back. You do not wish to write me a second one anyway. Others will probably be kinder than you and would do so.’

56 “I recognized the letter she held out to me as the one I wrote for her to Boless. Humph!

57 “‘Look here, Teresa,’ I said to her. ‘Will you please explain to me what it all means? Why do you ask people to write letters for you when you do not find it necessary even to post them?’

58 “‘Post them? Where to?’

59 “‘Why, to this Boless, of course.’

60 “‘But he does not exist!’

61 "I really could not understand a word. There was nothing left for me to do but to spit and walk out of the room. But she explained herself.

62 " 'Well, what of it?' she began in an offended voice. 'He does not exist. He does not, so,' and she extended her hands as if she could not herself clearly understand why he did not exist in reality. 'But I want him to. Am I not as much of a human being as the others? Of course I—I know— But it does no harm to any one, that I am writing to him—'

63 " 'Allow me—to whom?'

64 " 'To Boless, of course.'

65 " 'But he does not exist.'

66 " 'Oh, Mother of God! What if he does not exist? He does not; still to me he does. And Teresa—this is myself, and he replies to my letters, and I write to him again.'

67 "I understood. I felt so sick at heart, so ashamed of myself to know that alongside of me, only three paces removed, lived a human being who had no one in the whole world to love and sympathize with her, and that this being had to invent a friend for herself.

68 " 'Here you have written a letter from me to Boless, and I gave it to another to read, and when I hear it read it really begins to seem to me as if there is a Boless. And then I ask that a letter be written from Boless to Teresa—that is to me. And when such a letter is written and is read to me then I am almost entirely convinced that there is a Boless, and that makes my life easier.'

69 "Yes, the devil take it all," continued my acquaintance. "To make a long story short I began from that time on to write with the greatest punctuality twice a week letters to Boless and vice versa. I wrote splendid replies to her. She used to listen to my reading of those epistles and to weep in her bass voice. In return for this she used to mend my clothes and darn my socks.

70 "Three months later she was thrown into prison for some reason or other and by now she must surely be dead."

71 My acquaintance blew the ashes from his cigaret, looked thoughtfully at the sky, and concluded:

72 "Y-e-s, the more a human being has drunk of the cup of bitterness the more ardently he longs for sweetness. And we, enveloped in our worn-out virtues and gazing at each other through the haze of self-sufficiency and convinced of our righteousness, fail to understand it.

73 "And the whole affair turns out very stupid, and very cruel. Fallen people we say—but who and what are those fallen ones? First of all they are human beings of the very same bone and blood, of the very

same flesh and nerves as ourselves. We have been told the very same thing for whole ages, day in and day out. And we listen and—and the devil alone knows how stupid it all is! In reality we, too, are but fallen people and more deeply fallen too, probably—into the abyss of self-sufficiency, convinced of our own sinlessness and superiority, the superiority of our own nerves and brains over the nerves and brains of those who are only less crafty than we are, and who can not, as we can, feign a goodness they do not possess—but enough of this. It is all so old and stale—so old and stale indeed that one is ashamed to speak of it—" □

What is the first indication that Pan Student disliked Teresa from the beginning? (Hyperbole gives way to simple statement at this point.) What do the adjectives he applies to Teresa suggest about *him?* What does his statement about his room and view reveal? (Do not read his words at their surface meaning only; they indicate a great deal about his character which he does not know—or prefers to conceal, even from himself.) How serious are his academic intentions? What do his thoughts reveal? (Notice: "Take care, my boy!") Why was he angry at Teresa's offer to mend his clothing? From what did her offer spring? What do his boredom, ennui, and self-analysis reveal about him? What does his use of "lady" and "pack of lies" reveal about his personality as he upbraids Teresa? Explain his use of "H'm" and "Humph!" What does the statement beginning "Y-e-s, the more a human being . . ." indicate about his character? Be alert! Why is "Y-e-s" used instead of "Yes"? Why does his tale dwindle away without resolution? How realistic is his conversational flow as he narrates the tale? Does he realize he is revealing so much about himself?

The creation of believable dialog of extended length requires careful and determined attention to real conversations. No two people—if they are individuals—use the same vocabulary, idioms, or inflections. If two people are twins in speech, they lack fictional interest. Even Babbitt and Chum Frink differed!

In the following selection from Compton Mackenzie's *Vestal Fire,* Mrs. Ambrogio is an amazing character. She is revealed almost exclusively through dialog. Read the passage, then, aware of it as speech, reread it aloud, using the inflections you feel necessary. Listen to your reading. Decide how the author achieved such verisimilitude:

[1]Mrs. Ambrogio was a handsome woman of about forty, ample in the style of feminine beauty that was so much admired when King Edward VII was Prince of Wales. She was the type that used to look so queenly in silver and plush photograph-frames on the occasional tables of houses untainted by aestheticism. Indeed,

there were people to assure you that as a young woman she was a rival of the Jersey Lily herself. There was an element of mystery about her which Mrs. Ambrogio, had she wanted to, was incapable of dispelling, because she was incapable of stringing together a sufficiently intelligible long sentence. She had certainly been married before, but whether she divorced her husband or he divorced her, whether she had been a widow when she married Pietro Ambrogio, a Neapolitan lawyer practising in Sirene, or whether she had eloped from England with him nobody on the island had ever discovered. There were twenty legends in Sirene of her origin, which varied from the unrepeatable to the faintly suggestive.

Humor dominates the selection from the first sentence. Account for "beauty that was so much admired when King Edward VII was Prince of Wales" or "houses untainted by aestheticism." What does the allusion to the "Jersey Lily" add? Is "unrepeatable to the faintly suggestive" hyperbole or litotes? Justify your answer. How much background is given in the opening paragraphs?

[2]"Talk to me. Talk to me," she spluttered to Follett, her bottlegreen dress of moiré silk swishing an accompaniment to her bubbling ejaculations which issued as from a syphon that from time to time jams and fizzes impotently. "Can't stand Americans. Hate Americans. Not the dear Miss Nortons of course. Bless their hearts, the darling old pets!" This was delivered at the top of her voice, and turning round she blew three or four resonant kisses across the room to where Miss Virginia was fluttering and hovering over each little tea-table like a big pearly moth, and where Miss Maimie with eager watchful eyes was piloting fat Rosina with a tray of crême de menthe. "Hate Americans," she continued, swishing round again to Follett. "Always hunted when I was young. Go over anything. Show you my picture if you like in a riding-habit when I was a girl. Considered jolly good-looking as a girl. Ugly as sin now. Can't help it. Must grow older. Married an Italian. Peter. Where is he? Want to introduce you to him. Gone out to look over the garden. Mad on gardens. Can't grow anything. Flowers never come up. Loves them just as much. Looks after them like a mother. Only honest lawyer in Italy. Don't know why. Stupid fool, I always tell him. But Peter can't help it. Never make any money. God knows what we shall do."

Dialog and narrative are artfully interwoven. How easy it would be to present this scene on a stage, the narrative sections serving as stage directions! Observe the use of definite descriptions, such as "bottlegreen dress of moiré silk." Notice how speech and narrative complement each other as she "spluttered" or emitted "bubbling ejaculations." How effective is the syphon simile? How does narrative serve as a binder for the dialog? How does coherence result in unity?

3Macadam, who was not too drunk not to understand that his chance of discussing the problem of the monkey and the pole was gone, had risen rather unsteadily and crossed the room in search of another victim.

4"Dear old Macadam! Bless his heart," exclaimed Mrs. Ambrogio, blowing a kiss after him. "Drinks like a fish. Love him just the same. Love all the English. English myself. Always a gentleman, poor old boy. Lives next door to Peter and me. Found him lying on his back in our front garden the other night. Too drunk to get up. Put on his hat and took it off again. Perfect manners. Said 'Good evening, Mrs. Ambrogio, I'm sorry I find myself unable to move out of your way. Would you mind stepping over me?' Always a gentleman. Drinks like a fish and never forgets his manners. Four bottles of brandy a day, but always a gentleman. Hate Americans. Can't stand Americans. Love the dear English. English myself."

5"I fear that I have the misfortune to be an American, Mrs. Ambrogio," said Follett.

6"Can't help it. Not your fault. Always speak my mind. Always offending people. No brains. Take it or leave it. Can't help it if they don't like me. Love the darling old Nortons."

7"I certainly agree that the Miss Pepworth-Nortons must inspire a very great affection in all who have the good fortune to make their acquaintance."

8"Love the old pets. *Love* them! Came here over forty years ago before I was born. Miss Virginia fell in love with a coachman. Stole all her money and ran away. Tell you lots of stories about the foreigners here, but never talk. Peter's sake. Mustn't talk if you marry a lawyer. Used to talk a lot before I married dear old Peter. Never talk now. Bad for his business. Weren't you chatting to Mrs. Neave just now? *Dear* woman! Had an affair with Duncan Maxwell last year. Only repeat what other people tell me. Hate scandal. You walked down with Nigel Dawson. Such a dear boy! One of those. But what does it matter? Why shouldn't he be? Don't care what anybody is. Love everybody."

9"I had the good fortune to meet Mr. Maxwell in Bavaria recently," said Follett.

10"Isn't he a dear? I like him so much. If you hear that he steals people's geraniums, don't believe it. Don't believe anything you hear in Sirene."

11"But why should people accuse a highly intellectual man like Mr. Maxwell of stealing their geraniums?" Follett asked in amazement.

12"People here accuse you of anything. I was accused of keeping a disorderly house in Naples. Don't care what they say. Married the only honest lawyer in Italy, so don't care a dam what they say now."

13"But geraniums?" Follett persisted.

14"Building a house. Making a garden. Must get geraniums somewhere. Engaged three boys with spades and large baskets. Worked all night. Next morning all the geraniums in Sirene growing in Mr. Maxwell's garden. Other people's gardens nothing but feetmarks, footmarks, feetmarks. Don't know which you say. No grammar. No brains. Footmarks everywhere. Major Natt was so angry. That's Major

Natt over there. Like him so much. Mean as he can be. Such an old darling. Weighs out the sugar for the kitchen himself every morning. Has hundreds of naughty books. Wish I could read them. Can't read. Love reading, but can't read. No brains. Let his villa this year—Major Natt, I mean—and the tenants kept chickens in the bathroom."

15 "Chickens?" Follett gasped. "Why, I could understand keeping ducks in a bathroom, but chickens . . ."

16 "No water. Driest place in the house. Major Natt cut off the water from the bathroom before he went away. Sells it to the *contadini* at ten centesimi a bottle. Goes to Switzerland every Summer to save money. Say he milks Swiss peasants' cows himself to save paying for his lunch. Don't believe a word of it. Don't you believe it. Such lies. Plenty of cherry brandy when you go there to tea. Love him. There's Peter!" She waved excitably, her face crimsoning, to a neatly dressed little Italian who came in from the garden at that moment. "Peter! Peter! Vous venn, Peter!" She turned back to Follett. "Always speak French to Peter. Peter can't speak English and I can't speak Italian. Servants understand me perfectly and I understand them. Peter made love to my dear Assunta. Turned her out at once. Wouldn't stand it. Caught him kissing her and he said he was spongeing the statue of Venus. Such lies. Hate lies! Most truthful woman in Sirene. Peter! Vous venn! Vous venn!"

How does the narrative transition work to advantage as she changes the subject? How does the author manipulate the conversation to include material he has selected? Does it seem logical and natural? Does Mrs. Ambrogio's gossip seem malicious? Is it? How does she steer the conversation and reveal her own character?

17 The little lawyer approached and was presented by his wife to the American.

18 "Peter, this is Mr.—didn't hear your name. Never hear names. Doesn't matter. Forget them if I did. No brains."

19 "Follett."

20 "This is Peter. That's bang, Peter. Vous va. Parling to Mr. Folly—Fuller—Filly. Vous va. Vous va."

21 The little lawyer, who somehow understood from this that his wife was engaged in conversation and that he was to go away, again bowed courteously and retired.

22 "I love my Peter, bless his heart," she cried warmly. "Loves me too, but can't resist fat girls. Can't help it. Too excitable. Pants. Always know. 'Peter,' I say, and I give him such a look. Went to Mrs. Neave's last week. Thought he was pinching her Carmela. Pinched me instead. How I laughed! Serve him right. All Napolitans the same. Come back to Sirene black and blue after a day's shopping in Naples. There's dear old Mrs. Pape. Kindest woman in Sirene. Brought six blind old women from America to see the island this Summer. Heart of gold."

[23]"Oh, I understood from Mr. Dawson that they were three deaf and dumb girls."

[24]"Perhaps they were. So kind. Rolling in money. Frightfully delicate. Five months child. Brought up in a kind of aquarium and fed with a squirt."

[25]Follett gazed at old Mrs. Pape whose high-domed benevolent head was nodding in amicable conversation with the nebulous and deferential Mr. Cartright, an English painter from Anasirene.

[26]"That's poor old Cartright. Don't care for him much. Painted his wife naked and sent her to the Academy, but don't believe he beat her to death as everybody says. Can't get naked girls in Sirene now. Priests won't let them. Quite right. Can't trust painters. Any excuse. Love my Church. Not a Protestant, thank God. Love my Church. Kept me from going wrong. Sit there in the hot weather. Lovely and cool. Wonder when this French count's coming. Don't believe he's a count at all."

Why is Peter introduced?

[27]At this moment Miss Virginia called for silence, because Mr. Burlingham had so very kindly consented to play for them.

[28]The monumental man who had passed Follett and Nigel Dawson in a carriage earlier that afternoon rose and proceeded toward the piano.

[29]"So like a policeman," Mrs. Ambrogio whispered. "Used to be in the dragoons. Masses of money. Spent it all on . . ." She stopped. "Don't know you well enough yet to say what he spent it on. Hardly any money left, but still spends it on the same thing."

[30]"I'll play the Polonaise in A," Burlingham announced stolidly, unfastening his big cuffs and turning them back over his sleeves.

[31]"Oh, my dear, how too utterly divine," breathed Nigel Dawson.

[32]Burlingham paid no heed to this ecstasy, but after brushing back his white moustache and fixing the ceiling with his light blue globular eyes immediately began.

[33]"Love music," said Mrs. Ambrogio. "Can't play, but love it. Listen to it for hours. Mr. Burlingham plays so beautifully. Always perspires. Watch his forehead. He'll begin in a minute. Love music. Wish I had a pianola. Can't afford it. Could have once. Always hunted every Winter in . . ."

[34]And then Miss Maimie hushed her severely.

[35]"Dear old soul," Mrs. Ambrogio exploded, blowing a kiss that came out like a champagne-cork.

[36]But now Miss Maimie herself began to fidget, because the sound of carriage wheels was audible, and they must be the wheels of dear Count Bob's carriage. The Polonaise was working up every moment. Mr. Burlingham's globular eyes stared into vacancy. Would he ever forgive her rudeness if she rose and went down to meet the Count? Perhaps the music would stop in time. It surely must stop soon.

[37] "Know he'll burst one hot afternoon," Mrs. Ambrogio declared to Follett. "Wish I could play like that. Get so melancholy sometimes when I think of dear old England."

[38] Everybody had heard the carriage wheels, and everybody was hoping that the Polonaise would stop. Everybody felt that Chopin was a mistake when a rich French count was on the verge of entering Sirene society. □

Narrative and dialog become more entwined as Count Bob's entry becomes the focal point. How is anticipation built from "At this moment Miss Virginia called for silence"?

The main purposes of this excerpt as it is found in the novel are multifold. A great deal of information is given to the reader, but he is so charmed by Mrs. Ambrogio as a character that he is unaware of the device. What does her account add to the mood of the party? Would the party seem the same if the focus had been on another character? Point of view becomes apparent as a vital ingredient in such scenes as this.

Alexander Pope is only one of many who have translated Homer's *Iliad* into English. His translation does have the distinction of being dull enough in its monotonous repetition of heroic couplets to remove the virility from that great work. However, he prefaced his translation with an assessment of the importance of character and dialog in a work of fiction, and there are few, if any, better critical evaluations of those two elements:

We come now to the characters of his persons; and here we shall find no author has ever drawn so many, with so visible and surprising a variety, or given us such lively and affecting impressions of them. Every one has something so singularly his own, that no painter could have distinguished them more by their features, than the poet has by their manners. Nothing can be more exact than the distinctions he has observed in the different degrees of virtues and vices. The single quality of courage is wonderfully diversified in the several characters of the Iliad. That of Achilles is furious and intractable; that of Diomede forward, yet listening to advice, and subject to command; that of Ajax is heavy and self-confiding; of Hector, active and vigilant: the courage of Agamemnon is inspirited by love of empire and ambition; that of Menelaüs mixed with softness and tenderness for his people: we find in Idomeneus a plain direct soldier; in Sarpedon a gallant and generous one. Nor is this judicious and astonishing diversity to be found only in the principal quality which constitutes the main of each character, but even in the under parts of it, to which he takes care to give a tincture of that principal one. For example: the main characters of Ulysses and Nestor consist in wisdom; and they are distinct in this, that the wisdom of one is artificial and various, of the other natural, open, and regular. But they have, besides, characters of courage; and this quality also takes a different turn in each from the difference of his prudence; for one in the war depends still upon caution, the other upon experience. It would be endless to produce instances of these kinds. . . .

The speeches are to be considered as they flow from the characters; being perfect or defective as they agree or disagree with the manners of those who utter them. As there is more variety of characters in the Iliad, so there is of speeches, than in any other poem. 'Everything in it has manner' (as Aristotle expresses it); that is, everything is acted or spoken. It is hardly credible, in a work of such length, how small a number of lines are employed in narration. In Virgil the dramatic part is less in proportion to the narrative; and the speeches often consist of general reflections or thoughts, which might be equally just in any person's mouth upon the same occasion. As many of his persons have no apparent characters, so many of his speeches escape being applied and judged by the rule of propriety. We oftener think of the author himself when we read Virgil, than when we are engaged in Homer; all which are the effects of a colder invention, that interests us less in the action described: Homer makes us hearers, and Virgil leaves us readers.*

Suggested Activities. 1. Write a character sketch that is general enough to apply to a *group* of people. The stock concept of an English teacher, a young hoodlum, or a self-centered girl—these may serve as examples. You will have to isolate the character traits through careful analysis, select the ones you wish to use, and arrange them in the best order. Then you might find specific illustrations for one or two of them. Sharpen them with well-used poetic devices (avoiding purple patchwork). Revise and refine your sketch until you are ready for it to be criticized. Remember: there are *five* senses!

2. Choose a person from life. Analyze his character before you begin to list the character traits you will include and the illustrative points that make them concrete. As you arrange the material into an outline, be sure you have one dominant impression toward which everything builds. Look at the final sentence of "The Squatter" again (p. 133). Concentrate on action verbs and verbals. Use adjectives and adverbs sparingly. Write a character sketch.

Suggested Assignments. 1. Robert Frost's "The Death of the Hired Man" (pp. 157–162) is a short story written in blank verse. The characters and dialog create the plot and reveal the changes that occur in the characters. What little description is employed can be summed up as: merely excellent. Eudora Welty's "Death of a Travelling Salesman"

* *The Iliad of Homer,* tr. Alexander Pope (London, 1715), pp. ix–xi.

(pp. 162–173) was her first published short story. In a distinguished career, she has never written a better story. Few, if any, better ones exist in the language. Compare the two works in a brief paper, concerning yourself with the development of character as it is revealed in dialog (remembering that interior monolog is a part of dialog).

2. Stanley Ellin's "The Question My Son Asked" (pp. 174–181) and Björnstjerne Björnson's "The Father" (pp. 181–184) are both concerned with the father-son relationship, duty, and death. Compare the characters of the fathers as they are revealed through the devices chosen by the authors.

3. Flannery O'Connor's "A Good Man Is Hard to Find" (pp. 184–198) is as violent a story as you will ever read. Attempt to isolate point of view in the story and write a defense of your decisions about it. Account for your dislike of the mother in the first half of the story and your like or dislike of her in the second half. You might prefer to compare Bailey and The Misfit as they are both sons shaped and molded by their mothers. How does O'Connor create two characters that are so different and yet so similar?

The Death of the Hired Man

Mary sat musing on the lamp-flame at the table
Waiting for Warren. When she heard his step,
She ran on tip-toe down the darkened passage
To meet him in the doorway with the news
And put him on his guard. 'Silas is back.'
She pushed him outward with her through the door
And shut it after her. 'Be kind,' she said.
She took the market things from Warren's arms
And set them on the porch, then drew him down
To sit beside her on the wooden steps.

'When was I ever anything but kind to him?
But I'll not have the fellow back,' he said.
'I told him so last haying, didn't I?
"If he left then," I said, "that ended it."
What good is he? Who else will harbour him
At his age for the little he can do?
What help he is there's no depending on.
Off he goes always when I need him most.
"He thinks he ought to earn a little pay,
Enough at least to buy tobacco with,

So he won't have to beg and be beholden."
"All right," I say, "I can't afford to pay
Any fixed wages, though I wish I could."
"Someone else can." "Then someone else will have to."
I shouldn't mind his bettering himself
If that was what it was. You can be certain,
When he begins like that, there's someone at him
Trying to coax him off with pocket-money,—
In haying time, when any help is scarce.
In winter he comes back to us. I'm done.'

'Sh! not so loud: he'll hear you,' Mary said.

'I want him to: he'll have to soon or late.'

'He's worn out. He's asleep beside the stove.
When I came up from Rowe's I found him here,
Huddled against the barn-door fast asleep,
A miserable sight, and frightening, too—
You needn't smile—I didn't recognise him—
I wasn't looking for him—and he's changed.
Wait till you see.'

'Where did you say he'd been?'

'He didn't say. I dragged him to the house,
And gave him tea and tried to make him smoke.
I tried to make him talk about his travels.
Nothing would do: he just kept nodding off.'

'What did he say? Did he say anything?'

'But little.'

'Anything? Mary, confess
He said he'd come to ditch the meadow for me.'

'Warren!'

'But did he? I just want to know.'

'Of course he did. What would you have him say?
Surely you wouldn't grudge the poor old man

Some humble way to save his self-respect.
He added, if you really care to know,
He meant to clear the upper pasture, too.
That sounds like something you have heard before?
Warren, I wish you could have heard the way
He jumbled everything. I stopped to look
Two or three times—he made me feel so queer—
To see if he was talking in his sleep.
He ran on Harold Wilson—you remember—
The boy you had in haying four years since.
He's finished school, and teaching in his college.
Silas declares you'll have to get him back.
He says they two will make a team for work:
Between them they will lay this farm as smooth!
The way he mixed that in with other things.
He thinks young Wilson a likely lad, though daft
On education—you know how they fought
All through July under the blazing sun,
Silas up on the cart to build the load,
Harold along beside to pitch it on.'

'Yes, I took care to keep well out of earshot.'

'Well, those days trouble Silas like a dream.
You wouldn't think they would. How some things linger!
Harold's young college boy's assurance piqued him.
After so many years he still keeps finding
Good arguments he sees he might have used.
I sympathise. I know just how it feels
To think of the right thing to say too late.
Harold's associated in his mind with Latin.
He asked me what I thought of Harold's saying
He studied Latin like the violin
Because he liked it—that an argument!
He said he couldn't make the boy believe
He could find water with a hazel prong—
Which showed how much good school had ever done him.
He wanted to go over that. But most of all
He thinks if he could have another chance
To teach him how to build a load of hay—'

'I know, that's Silas' one accomplishment.
He bundles every forkful in its place,

And tags and numbers it for future reference,
So he can find and easily dislodge it
In the unloading. Silas does that well.
He takes it out in bunches like big birds' nests.
You never see him standing on the hay
He's trying to lift, straining to lift himself.'

'He thinks if he could teach him that, he'd be
Some good perhaps to someone in the world.
He hates to see a boy the fool of books.
Poor Silas, so concerned for other folk,
And nothing to look backward to with pride,
And nothing to look forward to with hope,
So now and never any different.'

Part of a moon was falling down the west,
Dragging the whole sky with it to the hills.
Its light poured softly in her lap. She saw it
And spread her apron to it. She put out her hand
Among the harp-like morning-glory strings,
Taut with the dew from garden bed to eaves,
As if she played unheard some tenderness
That wrought on him beside her in the night.
'Warren,' she said, 'he has come home to die:
You needn't be afraid he'll leave you this time.'

'Home,' he mocked gently.

'Yes, what else but home?
It all depends on what you mean by home.
Of course he's nothing to us, any more
Than was the hound that came a stranger to us
Out of the woods, worn out upon the trail.'

'Home is the place where, when you have to go there,
They have to take you in.'

'I should have called it
Something you somehow haven't to deserve.'

Warren leaned out and took a step or two,
Picked up a little stick, and brought it back

And broke it in his hand and tossed it by.
'Silas has better claim on us you think
Than on his brother? Thirteen little miles
As the road winds would bring him to his door.
Silas has walked that far no doubt to-day.
Why didn't he go there? His brother's rich,
A somebody—director in the bank.'

'He never told us that.'

'We know it though.'

'I think his brother ought to help, of course.
I'll see to that if there is need. He ought of right
To take him in, and might be willing to—
He may be better than appearances.
But have some pity on Silas. Do you think
If he had any pride in claiming kin
Or anything he looked for from his brother,
He'd keep so still about him all this time?'

'I wonder what's between them.'

'I can tell you.
Silas is what he is—we wouldn't mind him—
But just the kind that kinsfolk can't abide.
He never did a thing so very bad.
He don't know why he isn't quite as good
As anybody. Worthless though he is,
He won't be made ashamed to please his brother.'

'*I* can't think Si ever hurt anyone.'

'No, but he hurt my heart the way he lay
And rolled his old head on that sharp-edged chairback.
He wouldn't let me put him on the lounge.
You must go in and see what you can do.
I made the bed up for him there to-night.
You'll be surprised at him—how much he's broken.
His working days are done; I'm sure of it.'

'I'd not be in a hurry to say that.'

'I haven't been. Go, look, see for yourself.
But, Warren, please remember how it is:
He's come to help you ditch the meadow.
He has a plan. You mustn't laugh at him.
He may not speak of it, and then he may.
I'll sit and see if that small sailing cloud
Will hit or miss the moon.'

It hit the moon.
Then there were three there, making a dim row,
The moon, the little silver cloud, and she.

Warren returned—too soon, it seemed to her,
Slipped to her side, caught up her hand and waited.

'Warren?' she questioned.

'Dead,' was all he answered.

Robert Frost

Death of a Travelling Salesman

by Eudora Welty

1 R. J. Bowman, who for fourteen years had travelled for a shoe company through Mississippi, drove his Ford along a rutted dirt path. It was a long day! The time did not seem to clear the noon hurdle and settle into soft afternoon. The sun, keeping its strength here even in winter, stayed at the top of the sky, and every time Bowman stuck his head out of the dusty car to stare up the road, it seemed to reach a long arm down and push against the top of his head, right through his hat—like the practical joke of an old drummer, long on the road. It made him feel all the more angry and helpless. He was feverish, and he was not quite sure of the way.

2 This was his first day back on the road after a long siege of influenza. He had had very high fever, and dreams, and had become weakened and pale, enough to tell the difference in the mirror, and he could not think clearly. . . . All afternoon, in the midst of his anger, and for no reason, he had thought of his dead grandmother. She had been a comfortable soul. Once more Bowman wished he could fall into the big feather bed that had been in her room. . . . Then he forgot her again.

[3] This desolate hill country! And he seemed to be going the wrong way—it was as if he were going back, far back. There was not a house in sight. . . . There was no use wishing he were back in bed, though. By paying the hotel doctor his bill he had proved his recovery. He had not even been sorry when the pretty trained nurse said good-bye. He did not like illness, he distrusted it, as he distrusted the road without signposts. It angered him. He had given the nurse a really expensive bracelet, just because she was packing up her bag and leaving.

[4] But now—what if in fourteen years on the road he had never been ill before and never had an accident? His record was broken, and he had even begun almost to question it. . . . He had gradually put up at better hotels, in the bigger towns, but weren't they all, eternally, stuffy in summer and draughty in winter? Women? He could only remember little rooms within little rooms, like a nest of Chinese paper boxes, and if he thought of one woman he saw the worn loneliness that the furniture of that room seemed built of. And he himself—he was a man who always wore rather wide-brimmed black hats, and in the wavy hotel mirrors had looked something like a bull-fighter, as he paused for that inevitable instant on the landing, walking downstairs to supper. . . . He leaned out of the car again, and once more the sun pushed at his head.

[5] Bowman had wanted to reach Beulah by dark, to go to bed and sleep off his fatigue. As he remembered, Beulah was fifty miles away from the last town, on a gravelled road. This was only a cow trail. How had he ever come to such a place? One hand wiped the sweat from his face, and he drove on.

[6] He had made the Beulah trip before. But he had never seen this hill or this petering-out path before—or that cloud, he thought shyly, looking up and then down quickly—any more than he had seen this day before. Why did he not admit he was simply lost and had been for miles? . . . He was not in the habit of asking the way of strangers, and these people never knew where the very roads they lived on went to; but then he had not even been close enough to anyone to call out. People standing in the fields now and then, or on top of the haystacks, had been too far away, looking like leaning sticks or weeds, turning a little at the solitary rattle of his car across their countryside, watching the pale sobered winter dust where it chunked out behind like big squashes down the road. The stares of these distant people had followed him solidly like a wall, impenetrable, behind which they turned back after he had passed.

[7] The cloud floated there to one side like the bolster on his grandmother's bed. It went over a cabin on the edge of a hill, where two

bare chinaberry trees clutched at the sky. He drove through a heap of dead oak leaves, his wheels stirring their weightless sides to make a silvery melancholy whistle as the car passed through their bed. No car had been along this way ahead of him. Then he saw that he was on the edge of a ravine that fell away, a red erosion, and that this was indeed the road's end.

[8] He pulled the brake. But it did not hold, though he put all his strength into it. The car, tipped toward the edge, rolled a little. Without doubt, it was going over the bank.

[9] He got out quietly, as though some mischief had been done him and he had his dignity to remember. He lifted his bag and sample case out, set them down, and stood back and watched the car roll over the edge. He heard something—not the crash he was listening for, but a slow un-uproarious crackle. Rather distastefully he went to look over, and he saw that his car had fallen into a tangle of immense grape vines as thick as his arm, which caught it and held it, rocked it like a grotesque child in a dark cradle, and then, as he watched, concerned somehow that he was not still inside it, released it gently to the ground.

[10] He sighed.

[11] Where am I? he wondered with a shock. Why didn't I do something? All his anger seemed to have drifted away from him. There was the house, back on the hill. He took a bag in each hand and with almost childlike willingness went toward it. But his breathing came with difficulty, and he had to stop to rest.

[12] It was a shotgun house, two rooms and an open passage between, perched on the hill. The whole cabin slanted a little under the heavy heaped-up vine that covered the roof, light and green, as though forgotten from summer. A woman stood in the passage.

[13] He stopped still. Then all of a sudden his heart began to behave strangely. Like a rocket set off, it began to leap and expand into uneven patterns of beats which showered into his brain, and he could not think. But in scattering and falling it made no noise. It shot up with great power, almost elation, and fell gently, like acrobats into nets. It began to pound profoundly, then waited irresponsibly, hitting in some sort of inward mockery first at his ribs, then against his eyes, then under his shoulder blades, and against the roof of his mouth when he tried to say, "Good afternoon, madam." But he could not hear his heart—it was as quiet as ashes falling. This was rather comforting; still, it was shocking to Bowman to feel his heart beating at all.

[14] Stockstill in his confusion, he dropped his bags, which seemed

to drift in slow bulks gracefully through the air and to cushion themselves on the grey prostrate grass near the doorstep.

15 As for the woman standing there, he saw at once that she was old. Since she could not possibly hear his heart, he ignored the pounding and now looked at her carefully, and yet in his distraction dreamily, with his mouth open.

16 She had been cleaning the lamp, and held it, half blackened, half clear, in front of her. He saw her with the dark passage behind her. She was a big woman with a weather-beaten but unwrinkled face; her lips were held tightly together, and her eyes looked with a curious dulled brightness into his. He looked at her shoes, which were like bundles. If it were summer she would be barefoot. . . . Bowman, who automatically judged a woman's age on sight, set her age at fifty. She wore a formless garment of some grey coarse material, rough-dried from a washing, from which her arms appeared pink and unexpectedly round. When she never said a word, and sustained her quiet pose of holding the lamp, he was convinced of the strength in her body.

17 "Good afternoon, madam," he said.

18 She stared on, whether at him or at the air around him he could not tell, but after a moment she lowered her eyes to show that she would listen to whatever he had to say.

19 "I wonder if you would be interested—" He tried once more. "An accident—my car . . ."

20 Her voice emerged low and remote, like a sound across a lake. "Sonny he ain't here."

21 "Sonny?"

22 "Sonny ain't here now."

23 Her son—a fellow able to bring my car up, he decided in blurred relief. He pointed down the hill. "My car's in the bottom of the ditch. I'll need help."

24 "Sonny ain't here, but he'll be here."

25 She was becoming clearer to him and her voice stronger, and Bowman saw that she was stupid.

26 He was hardly surprised at the deepening postponement and tedium of his journey. He took a breath, and heard his voice speaking over the silent blows of his heart. "I was sick. I am not strong yet. . . . May I come in?"

27 He stooped and laid his big black hat over the handle on his bag. It was a humble motion, almost a bow, that instantly struck him as absurd and betraying of all his weakness. He looked up at the woman, the wind blowing his hair. He might have continued for a long time in this unfamiliar attitude; he had never been a patient man, but

when he was sick he had learned to sink submissively into the pillows, to wait for his medicine. He waited on the woman.

28 Then she, looking at him with blue eyes, turned and held open the door, and after a moment Bowman, as if convinced in his action, stood erect and followed her in.

29 Inside, the darkness of the house touched him like a professional hand, the doctor's. The woman set the half-cleaned lamp on a table in the centre of the room and pointed, also like a professional person, a guide, to a chair with a yellow cowhide seat. She herself crouched on the hearth, drawing her knees up under the shapeless dress.

30 At first he felt hopefully secure. His heart was quieter. The room was enclosed in the gloom of yellow pine boards. He could see the other room, with the foot of an iron bed showing, across the passage. The bed had been made up with a red-and-yellow pieced quilt that looked like a map or a picture, a little like his grandmother's girlhood painting of Rome burning.

31 He had ached for coolness, but in this room it was cold. He stared at the hearth with dead coals lying on it and iron pots in the corners. The hearth and smoked chimney were of the stone he had seen ribbing the hills, mostly slate. Why is there no fire? he wondered.

32 And it was so still. The silence of the fields seemed to enter and move familiarly through the house. The wind used the open hall. He felt that he was in a mysterious, quiet, cool danger. It was necessary to do what? . . . To talk.

33 "I have a nice line of women's low-priced shoes . . ." he said.

34 But the woman answered, "Sonny'll be here. He's strong. Sonny'll move your car."

35 "Where is he now?"

36 "Farms for Mr. Redmond."

37 Mr. Redmond. Mr. Redmond. That was someone he would never have to encounter, and he was glad. Somehow the name did not appeal to him. . . . In a flare of touchiness and anxiety, Bowman wished to avoid even mention of unknown men and their unknown farms.

38 "Do you two live here alone?" He was surprised to hear his old voice, chatty, confidential, inflected for selling shoes, asking a question like that—a thing he did not even want to know.

39 "Yes. We are alone."

40 He was surprised at the way she answered. She had taken a long time to say that. She had nodded her head in a deep way too. Had she wished to affect him with some sort of premonition? he wondered unhappily. Or was it only that she would not help him, after all, by talk-

ing with him? For he was not strong enough to receive the impact of unfamiliar things without a little talk to break their fall. He had lived a month in which nothing had happened except in his head and his body—an almost inaudible life of heartbeats and dreams that came back, a life of fever and privacy, a delicate life which had left him weak to the point of—what? Of begging. The pulse in his palm leapt like a trout in a brook.

41 He wondered over and over why the woman did not go ahead with cleaning the lamp. What prompted her to stay there across the room, silently bestowing her presence upon him? He saw that with her it was not a time for doing little tasks. Her face was grave; she was feeling how right she was. Perhaps it was only politeness. In docility he held his eyes stiffly wide; they fixed themselves on the woman's clasped hands as though she held the cord they were strung on.

42 Then, "Sonny's coming," she said.

43 He himself had not heard anything, but there came a man passing the window and then plunging in at the door, with two hounds beside him. Sonny was a big enough man, with his belt slung low about his hips. He looked at least thirty. He had a hot, red face that was yet full of silence. He wore muddy blue pants and an old military coat stained and patched. World War? Bowman wondered. Great God, it was a Confederate coat. On the back of his light hair he had a wide filthy black hat which seemed to insult Bowman's own. He pushed down the dogs from his chest. He was strong with dignity and heaviness in his way of moving. . . . There was the resemblance to his mother.

44 They stood side by side. . . . He must account again for his presence here.

45 "Sonny, this man, he had his car to run off over the prec'pice an' wants to know if you will git it out for him," the woman said after a few minutes.

46 Bowman could not even state his case.

47 Sonny's eyes lay upon him.

48 He knew he should offer explanations and show money—at least appear either penitent or authoritative. But all he could do was to shrug slightly.

49 Sonny brushed by him going to the window, followed by the eager dogs, and looked out. There was effort even in the way he was looking, as if he could throw his sight out like a rope. Without turning Bowman felt that his own eyes could have seen nothing: it was too far.

50 "Got me a mule out there an' got me a block an' tackle," said

Sonny meaningfully. "I *could* catch me my mule an' git me my ropes, an' before long I'd git your car out the ravine."

51 He looked completely round the room, as if in meditation, his eyes roving in their own distance. Then he pressed his lips firmly and yet shyly together, and with the dogs ahead of him this time, he lowered his head and strode out. The hard earth sounded, cupping to his powerful way of walking—almost a stagger.

52 Mischievously, at the suggestion of those sounds, Bowman's heart leapt again. It seemed to walk about inside him.

53 "Sonny's goin' to do it," the woman said. She said it again, singing it almost, like a song. She was sitting in her place by the hearth.

54 Without looking out, he heard some shouts and the dogs barking and the pounding of hoofs in short runs on the hill. In a few minutes Sonny passed under the window with a rope, and there was a brown mule with quivering, shining, purple-looking ears. The mule actually looked in the window. Under its eyelashes it turned target-like eyes into his. Bowman averted his head and saw the woman looking serenely back at the mule, with only satisfaction in her face.

55 She sang a little more, under her breath. It occurred to him, and it seemed quite marvellous, that she was not really talking to him, but rather following the thing that came about with words that were unconscious and part of her looking.

56 So he said nothing, and this time when he did not reply he felt a curious and strong emotion, not fear, rise up in him.

57 This time, when his heart leapt, something—his soul—seemed to leap too, like a little colt invited out of a pen. He stared at the woman while the frantic nimbleness of his feeling made his head sway. He could not move; there was nothing he could do, unless perhaps he might embrace this woman who sat there growing old and shapeless before him.

58 But he wanted to leap up, to say to her, I have been sick and I found out then, only then, how lonely I am. Is it too late? My heart puts up a struggle inside me, and you may have heard it, protesting against emptiness. . . . It should be full, he would rush on to tell her, thinking of his heart now as a deep lake, it should be holding love like other hearts. It should be flooded with love. There would be a warm spring day . . . Come and stand in my heart, whoever you are, and a whole river would cover your feet and rise higher and take your knees in whirlpools, and draw you down to itself, your whole body, your heart too.

59 But he moved a trembling hand across his eyes, and looked at the placid crouching woman across the room. She was still as a statue.

He felt ashamed and exhausted by the thought that he might, in one more moment, have tried by simple words and embraces to communicate some strange thing—something which seemed always to have just escaped him . . .

60 Sunlight touched the farthest pot on the hearth. It was late afternoon. This time to-morrow he would be somewhere on a good gravelled road, driving his car past things that happened to people, quicker than their happening. Seeing ahead to the next day, he was glad, and knew that this was no time to embrace an old woman. He could feel in his pounding temples the readying of his blood for motion and for hurrying away.

61 "Sonny's hitched up your car by now," said the woman. "He'll git it out the ravine right shortly."

62 "Fine!" he cried with his customary enthusiasm.

63 Yet it seemed a long time that they waited. It began to get dark. Bowman was cramped in his chair. Any man should know enough to get up and walk around while he waited. There was something like guilt in such stillness and silence.

64 But instead of getting up, he listened. . . . His breathing restrained, his eyes powerless in the growing dark, he listened uneasily for a warning sound, forgetting in wariness what it would be. Before long he heard something—soft, continuous, insinuating.

65 "What's the noise?" he asked, his voice jumping into the dark. Then wildly he was afraid it would be his heart beating so plainly in the quiet room, and she would tell him so.

66 "You might hear the stream," she said grudgingly.

67 Her voice was closer. She was standing by the table. He wondered why she did not light the lamp. She stood there in the dark and did not light it.

68 Bowman would never speak to her now, for the time was past. I'll sleep in the dark, he thought, in his bewilderment pitying himself.

69 Heavily she moved on to the window. Her arm, vaguely white, rose straight from her full side and she pointed out into the darkness.

70 "That white speck's Sonny," she said, talking to herself.

71 He turned unwillingly and peered over her shoulder; he hesitated to rise and stand beside her. His eyes searched the dusky air. The white speck floated smoothly toward her finger, like a leaf on a river, growing whiter in the dark. It was as if she had shown him something secret, part of her life, but had offered no explanation. He looked away. He was moved almost to tears, feeling for no reason that she had made

a silent declaration equivalent to his own. His hand waited upon his chest.

72 Then a step shook the house, and Sonny was in the room. Bowman felt how the woman left him there and went to the other man's side.

73 "I done got your car out, mister," said Sonny's voice in the dark. "She's settin' a-waitin' in the road, turned to go back where she come from."

74 "Fine!" said Bowman, projecting his own voice to loudness. "I'm surely much obliged—I could never have done it myself—I was sick. . . ."

75 "I could do it easy," said Sonny.

76 Bowman could feel them both waiting in the dark, and he could hear the dogs panting out in the yard, waiting to bark when he should go. He felt strangely helpless and resentful. Now that he could go, he longed to stay. From what was he being deprived? His chest was rudely shaken by the violence of his heart. These people cherished something here that he could not see, they withheld some ancient promise of food and warmth and light. Between them they had a conspiracy. He thought of the way she had moved away from him and gone to Sonny, she had flowed toward him. He was shaking with cold, he was tired, and it was not fair. Humbly and yet angrily he stuck his hand into his pocket.

77 "Of course I'm going to pay you for everything—"

78 "We don't take money for such," said Sonny's voice belligerently.

79 "I want to pay. But do something more . . . Let me stay—tonight. . . ." He took another step toward them. If only they could see him, they would know his sincerity, his real need! His voice went on, "I'm not very strong yet, I'm not able to walk far, even back to my car, maybe, I don't know—I don't know exactly where I am—"

80 He stopped. He felt as if he might burst into tears. What would they think of him!

81 Sonny came over and put his hands on him. Bowman felt them pass (they were professional too) across his chest, over his hips. He could feel Sonny's eyes upon him in the dark.

82 "You ain't no revenuer come sneakin' here, mister, ain't got no gun?"

83 To this end of nowhere! And yet *he* had come. He made a grave answer. "No."

84 "You can stay."

85 "Sonny," said the woman, "you'll have to borry some fire."

86 "I'll go git it from Redmond's," said Sonny.

87 "What?" Bowman strained to hear their words to each other.

88 "Our fire, it's out, and Sonny's got to borry some, because it's dark an' cold," she said.

89 "But matches—I have matches—"

90 "We don't have no need for 'em," she said proudly. "Sonny's goin' after his own fire."

91 "I'm goin' to Redmond's," said Sonny with an air of importance, and he went out.

92 After they had waited a while, Bowman looked out the window and saw a light moving over the hill. It spread itself out like a little fan. It zigzagged along the field, darting and swift, not like Sonny at all. . . . Soon enough, Sonny staggered in, holding a burning stick behind him in tongs, fire flowing in his wake, blazing light into the corners of the room.

93 "We'll make a fire now," the woman said, taking the brand.

94 When that was done she lit the lamp. It showed its dark and light. The whole room turned golden-yellow like some sort of flower, and the walls smelled of it and seemed to tremble with the quiet rushing of the fire and the waving of the burning lampwick in its funnel of light.

95 The woman moved among the iron pots. With the tongs she dropped hot coals on top of the iron lids. They made a set of soft vibrations, like the sound of a bell far away.

96 She looked up and over at Bowman, but he could not answer. He was trembling. . . .

97 "Have a drink, mister?" Sonny asked. He had brought in a chair from the other room and sat astride it with his folded arms across the back. Now we are all visible, to one another, Bowman thought, and cried, "Yes sir, you bet, thanks!"

98 "Come after me and do just what I do," said Sonny.

99 It was another excursion into the dark. They went through the hall, out to the back of the house, past a shed and a hooded well. They came to a wilderness of thicket.

100 "Down on your knees," said Sonny.

101 "What?" Sweat broke out on his forehead.

102 He understood when Sonny began to crawl through a sort of tunnel that the bushes made over the ground. He followed, startled in spite of himself when a twig or a thorn touched him gently without making a sound, clinging to him and finally letting him go.

103 Sonny stopped crawling and, crouched on his knees, began to dig with both his hands into the dirt. Bowman shyly struck matches and

made a light. In a few minutes Sonny pulled up a jug. He poured out some of the whisky into a bottle from his coat pocket, and buried the jug again. "You never know who's liable to knock at your door," he said, and laughed. "Start back," he said, almost formally. "Ain't no need for us to drink outdoors, like hogs."

104 At the table by the fire, sitting opposite each other in their chairs, Sonny and Bowman took drinks out of the bottle, passing it across. The dogs slept; one of them was having a dream.

105 "This is good," said Bowman. "That is what I needed." It was just as though he were drinking the fire off the hearth.

106 "He makes it," said the woman with quiet pride.

107 She was pushing the coals off the pots, and the smells of corn bread and coffee circled the room. She set everything on the table before the men, with a bone-handled knife stuck into one of the potatoes, splitting out its golden fibre. Then she stood for a minute looking at them, tall and full above them where they sat. She leaned a little toward them.

108 "You-all can eat now," she said, and suddenly smiled.

109 Bowman had just happened to be looking at her. He set his cup back on the table in unbelieving protest. A pain pressed at his eyes. He saw that she was not an old woman. She was young, still young. He could think of no number of years for her. She was the same age as Sonny, and she belonged to him. She stood with the deep dark corner of the room behind her, the shifting yellow light scattering over her head and her grey formless dress, trembling over her tall body when it bent over them in its sudden communication. She was young. Her teeth were shining and her eyes glowed. She turned and walked slowly and heavily out of the room, and he heard her sit down on the cot and then lie down. The pattern on the quilt moved.

110 "She goin' to have a baby," said Sonny, popping a bite into his mouth.

111 Bowman could not speak. He was shocked with knowing what was really in this house. A marriage, a fruitful marriage. That simple thing. Anyone could have had that.

112 Somehow he felt unable to be indignant or protest, although some sort of joke had certainly been played upon him. There was nothing remote or mysterious here—only something private. The only secret was the ancient communication between two people. But the memory of the woman's waiting silently by the cold hearth, of the man's stubborn journey a mile away to get fire, and how they finally brought out their food and drink and filled the room proudly with all they had to show, was suddenly too clear and too enormous within him for response. . . .

113 "You ain't as hungry as you look," said Sonny.

114 The woman came out of the bedroom as soon as the men had finished, and ate her supper while her husband stared peacefully into the fire.

115 Then they put the dogs out, with the food that was left.

116 "I think I'd better sleep here by the fire, on the floor," said Bowman.

117 He felt that he had been cheated, and that he could afford now to be generous. Ill though he was, he was not going to ask them for their bed. He was through with asking favours in this house, now that he understood what was there.

118 "Sure, mister."

119 But he had not known yet how slowly he understood. They had not meant to give him their bed. After a little interval they both rose and looking at him gravely went into the other room.

120 He lay stretched by the fire until it grew low and dying. He watched every tongue of blaze lick out and vanish. "There will be special reduced prices on all footwear during the month of January," he found himself repeating quietly, and then he lay with his lips tight shut.

121 How many noises the night had! He heard the stream running, the fire dying, and he was sure now that he heard his heart beating, too, the sound it made under his ribs. He heard breathing, round and deep, of the man and his wife in the room across the passage. And that was all. But emotion swelled patiently within him, and he wished that the child were his.

122 He must get back to where he had been before. He stood weakly before the red coals, and put on his overcoat. It felt too heavy on his shoulders. As he started out he looked and saw that the woman had never got through with cleaning the lamp. On some impulse he put all the money from his billfold under its fluted glass base, almost ostentatiously.

123 Ashamed, shrugging a little, and then shivering, he took his bags and went out. The cold of the air seemed to lift him bodily. The moon was in the sky.

124 On the slope he began to run, he could not help it. Just as he reached the road, where his car seemed to sit in the moonlight like a boat, his heart began to give off tremendous explosions like a rifle, bang bang bang.

125 He sank in fright onto the road, his bags falling about him. He felt as if all this had happened before. He covered his heart with both hands to keep anyone from hearing the noise it made.

126 But nobody heard it. □

The Question My Son Asked

by Stanley Ellin

1 I am an electrocutioner . . . I prefer this word to executioner; I think words make a difference. When I was a boy, people who buried the dead were undertakers, and then somewhere along the way they became morticians and are better off for it.

2 Take the one who used to be the undertaker in my town. He was a decent, respectable man; very friendly if you'd let him be, but hardly anybody would let him be. Today, his son—who now runs the business—is not an undertaker but a mortician, and is welcome everywhere. As a matter of fact, he's an officer in my Lodge and is one of the most popular members we have. And all it took to do that was changing one word to another. The job's the same but the word is different, and people somehow will always go by words rather than meanings.

3 So, as I said, I am an electrocutioner—which is the proper professional word for it in my state where the electric chair is the means of execution.

4 Not that this is my profession. Actually, it's a sideline, as it is for most of us who perform executions. My real business is running an electrical supply and repair shop just as my father did before me. When he died I inherited not only the business from him, but also the position of state's electrocutioner.

5 We established a tradition, my father and I. He was running the shop profitably even before the turn of the century when electricity was a comparatively new thing, and he was the first man to perform a successful electrocution for the state. It was not the state's first electrocution, however. That one was an experiment and was badly bungled by the engineer who installed the chair in the state prison. My father, who had helped install the chair, was the assistant at the electrocution, and he told me that everything that could go wrong that day did go wrong. The current was eccentric, his boss froze on the switch, and the man in the chair was alive and kicking at the same time he was being burned to a crisp. The next time, my father offered to do the job himself, rewired the chair, and handled the switch so well that he was offered the job of official electrocutioner.

6 I followed in his footsteps, which is how a tradition is made, but I am afraid this one ends with me. I have a son, and what I said to him and what he said to me is the crux of the matter. He asked me a question—well, in my opinion, it was the kind of question that's at

the bottom of most of the world's troubles today. There are some sleeping dogs that should be left to lie; there are some questions that should not be asked.

7 To understand all this, I think you have to understand me, and nothing could be easier. I'm sixty, just beginning to look my age, a little overweight, suffer sometimes from arthritis when the weather is damp. I'm a good citizen, complain about my taxes but pay them on schedule, vote for the right party, and run my business well enough to make a comfortable living from it.

8 I've been married thirty-five years and never looked at another woman in all that time. Well, looked maybe, but no more than that. I have a married daughter and a granddaughter almost a year old, and the prettiest, smilingest baby in town. I spoil her and don't apologize for it, because in my opinion that is what grandfathers were made for—to spoil their grandchildren. Let mama and papa attend to the business; grandpa is there for the fun.

9 And beyond all that I have a son who asks questions. The kind that shouldn't be asked.

10 Put the picture together, and what you get is someone like yourself. I might be your next-door neighbor, I might be your old friend, I might be the uncle you meet whenever the family gets together at a wedding or a funeral. I'm like you.

11 Naturally, we all look different on the outside but we can still recognize each other on sight as the same kind of people. Deep down inside where it matters we have the same feelings, and we know that without any questions being asked about them.

12 "But," you might say, "there is a difference between us. You're the one who performs the executions, and I'm the one who reads about them in the papers, and that's a big difference, no matter how you look at it."

13 Is it? Well, look at it without prejudice, look at it with absolute honesty, and you'll have to admit that you're being unfair.

14 Let's face the facts, we're all in this together. If an old friend of yours happens to serve on a jury that finds a murderer guilty, you don't lock the door against him, do you? More than that: if you could get an introduction to the judge who sentences that murderer to the electric chair, you'd be proud of it, wouldn't you? You'd be honored to have him sit at your table, and you'd be quick enough to let the world know about it.

15 And since you're so willing to be friendly with the jury that convicts and the judge that sentences, what about the man who has to

pull the switch? He's finished the job you wanted done, he's made the world a better place for it. Why must he go hide away in a dark corner until the next time he's needed?

16 There's no use denying that nearly everybody feels he should, and there's less use denying that it's a cruel thing for anyone in my position to face. If you don't mind some strong language, it's a damned outrage to hire a man for an unpleasant job, and then despise him for it. Sometimes it's hard to abide such righteousness.

17 How do I get along in the face of it? The only way possible—by keeping my secret locked up tight and never being tempted to give it away. I don't like it that way, but I'm no fool about it.

18 The trouble is that I'm naturally easygoing and friendly. I'm the sociable kind. I like people, and I want them to like me. At Lodge meetings or in the clubhouse down at the golf course I'm always the center of the crowd. And I know what would happen if at any such time I ever opened my mouth and let that secret out. A five minute sensation, and after that the slow chill setting in. It would mean the end of my whole life then and there, the kind of life I want to live, and no man in his right mind throws away sixty years of his life for a five minute sensation.

19 You can see I've given the matter a lot of thought. More than that, it hasn't been idle thought. I don't pretend to be an educated man, but I'm willing to read books on any subject that interests me, and execution has been one of my main interests ever since I got into the line. I have the books sent to the shop where nobody takes notice of another piece of mail, and I keep them locked in a bin in my office so that I can read them in private.

20 There's a nasty smell about having to do it this way—at my age you hate to feel like a kid hiding himself away to read a dirty magazine—but I have no choice. There isn't a soul on earth outside of the warden at state's prison and a couple of picked guards there who knows I'm the one pulling the switch at an execution, and I intend it to remain that way.

21 Oh, yes, my son knows now. Well, he's difficult in some ways, but he's no fool. If I wasn't sure he would keep his mouth shut about what I told him, I wouldn't have told it to him in the first place.

22 Have I learned anything from those books? At least enough to take a pride in what I'm doing for the state and the way I do it. As far back in history as you want to go there have always been executioners. The day that men first made laws to help keep peace among themselves was the day the first executioner was born. There have always been lawbreakers; there must always be a way of punishing them. It's as simple as that.

[23]The trouble is that nowadays there are too many people who don't want it to be as simple as that. I'm no hypocrite, I'm not one of those narrow-minded fools who thinks that every time a man comes up with a generous impulse he's some kind of crackpot. But he can be mistaken. I'd put most of the people who are against capital punishment in that class. They are fine, high-minded citizens who've never in their lives been close enough to a murderer or rapist to smell the evil in him. In fact, they're so fine and high-minded that they can't imagine anyone in the world not being like themselves. In that case, they say anybody who commits murder or rape is just a plain, ordinary human being who's had a bad spell. He's no criminal, they say, he's just sick. He doesn't need the electric chair; all he needs is a kindly old doctor to examine his head and straighten out the kinks in his brain.

[24]In fact, they say there is no such thing as a criminal at all. There are only well people and sick people, and the ones who deserve all your worry and consideration are the sick ones. If they happen to murder or rape a few of the well ones now and then, why, just run for the doctor.

[25]This is the argument from beginning to end, and I'd be the last one to deny that it's built on honest charity and good intentions. But it's a mistaken argument. It omits the one fact that matters. When anyone commits murder or rape he is no longer in the human race. A man has a human brain and a God-given soul to control his animal nature. When the animal in him takes control he's not a human being any more. Then he has to be exterminated the way any animal must be if it goes wild in the middle of helpless people. And my duty is to be the exterminator.

[26]It could be that people just don't understand the meaning of the word *duty* any more. I don't want to sound old-fashioned, God forbid, but when I was a boy things were more straightforward and clear-cut. You learned to tell right from wrong, you learned to do what had to be done, and you didn't ask questions every step of the way. Or if you had to ask any questions, the ones that mattered were *how* and *when.*

[27]Then along came psychology, along came the professors, and the main question was always *why.* Ask yourself *why, why, why* about everything you do, and you'll end up doing nothing. Let a couple of generations go along that way, and you'll finally have a breed of people who sit around in trees like monkeys, scratching their heads.

[28]Does this sound far-fetched? Well, it isn't. Life is a complicated thing to live. All his life a man finds himself facing one situation after another, and the way to handle them is to live by the rules. Ask yourself *why* once too often, and you can find yourself so tangled up that you go under. The show must go on. Why? Women and children first.

Why? My country, right or wrong. Why? Never mind your duty. Just keep asking *why* until it's too late to do anything about it.

29 Around the time I first started going to school my father gave me a dog, a collie pup named Rex. A few years after Rex suddenly became unfriendly, the way a dog will sometimes, and then vicious, and then one day he bit my mother when she reached down to pat him.

30 The day after that I saw my father leaving the house with his hunting rifle under his arm and with Rex on a leash. It wasn't the hunting season, so I knew what was going to happen to Rex and I knew why. But it's forgivable in a boy to ask things that a man should be smart enough not to ask.

31 "Where are you taking Rex?" I asked my father. "What are you going to do with him?"

32 "I'm taking him out back of town," my father said. "I'm going to shoot him."

33 "But why?" I said, and that was when my father let me see that there is only one answer to such a question.

34 "Because it has to be done," he said.

35 I never forgot that lesson. It came hard; for a while I hated my father for it, but as I grew up I came to see how right he was. We both knew why the dog had to be killed. Beyond that, all questions would lead nowhere. Why the dog had become vicious, why God had put a dog on earth to be killed this way—these are the questions that you can talk out to the end of time, and while you're talking about them you still have a vicious dog on your hands.

36 It is strange to look back and realize now that when the business of the dog happened, and long before it and long after it, my father was an electrocutioner, and I never knew it. Nobody knew it, not even my mother. A few times a year my father would pack his bag and a few tools and go away for a couple of days, but that was all any of us knew. If you asked him where he was going he would simply say he had a job to do out of town. He was not a man you'd ever suspect of philandering or going off on a solitary drunk, so nobody gave it a second thought.

37 It worked the same way in my case. I found out how well it worked when I finally told my son what I had been doing on those jobs out of town, and that I had gotten the warden's permission to take him on as an assistant and train him to handle the chair himself when I retired. I could tell from the way he took it that he was as thunderstruck at this as I had been thirty years before when my father had taken me into his confidence.

38 "Electrocutioner?" said my son. "An *electrocutioner?*"

39 "Well, there's no disgrace to it," I said. "And since it's got to be done, and somebody has to do it, why not keep it in the family? If you knew anything about it, you'd know it's a profession that's often passed down in a family from generation to generation. What's wrong with a good, sound tradition? If more people believed in tradition you wouldn't have so many troubles in the world today."

40 It was the kind of argument that would have been more than enough to convince me when I was his age. What I hadn't taken into account was that my son wasn't like me, much as I wanted him to be. He was a grown man in his own right, but a grown man who had never settled down to his responsibilities. I had always kept closing my eyes to that, I had always seen him the way I wanted to and not the way he was.

41 When he left college after a year, I said, all right, there are some people who aren't made for college, I never went there, so what difference does it make. When he went out with one girl after another and could never make up his mind to marrying any of them, I said, well, he's young, he's sowing his wild oats, the time will come soon enough when he's ready to take care of a home and family. When he sat day-dreaming in the shop instead of tending to business I never made a fuss about it. I knew when he put his mind to it he was as good an electrician as you could ask for, and in these soft times people are allowed to do a lot more dreaming and a lot less working than they used to.

42 The truth was that the only thing that mattered to me was being his friend. For all his faults he was a fine-looking boy with a good mind. He wasn't much for mixing with people, but if he wanted to he could win anyone over. And in the back of my mind all the while he was growing up was the thought that he was the only one who would learn my secret some day, and would share it with me, and make it easier to bear. I'm not secretive by nature. A man like me needs a thought like that to sustain him.

43 So when the time came to tell him he shook his head and said no. I felt that my legs had been kicked out from under me. I argued with him and he still said no, and I lost my temper.

44 "Are you against capital punishment?" I asked him. "You don't have to apologize if you are. I'd think all the more of you, if that's your only reason."

45 "I don't know if it is," he said.

46 "Well, you ought to make up your mind one way or the other," I told him. "I'd hate to think you were like every other hypocrite

around who says it's all right to condemn a man to the electric chair and all wrong to pull the switch."

47 "Do I have to be the one to pull it?" he said. "Do you?"

48 "Somebody has to do it. Somebody always has to do the dirty work for the rest of us. It's not like the Old Testament days when everybody did it for himself. Do you know how they executed a man in those days? They laid him on the ground tied hand and foot, and everybody around had to heave rocks on him until he was crushed to death. They didn't invite anybody to stand around and watch. You wouldn't have had much choice then, would you?"

49 "I don't know," he said. And then because he was as smart as they come and knew how to turn your words against you, he said, "After all, I'm not without sin."

50 "Don't talk like a child," I said. "You're without the sin of murder on you or any kind of sin that calls for execution. And if you're so sure the Bible has all the answers, you might remember that you're supposed to render unto Caesar the things that are Caesar's."

51 "Well," he said, "in this case I'll let you do the rendering."

52 I knew then and there from the way he said it and the way he looked at me that it was no use trying to argue with him. The worst of it was knowing that we had somehow moved far apart from each other and would never really be close again. I should have had sense enough to let it go at that. I should have just told him to forget the whole thing and keep his mouth shut about it.

53 Maybe if I had ever considered the possibility of his saying no, I would have done it. But because I hadn't considered any such possibility I was caught off balance, I was too much upset to think straight. I will admit it now. It was my own fault that I made an issue of things and led him to ask the one question he should never have asked.

54 "I see," I told him. "It's the same old story, isn't it? Let somebody else do it. But if they pull your number out of a hat and you have to serve on a jury and send a man to the chair, that's all right with you. At least, it's all right as long as there's somebody else to do the job that you and the judge and every decent citizen wants done. Let's face the facts, boy, you don't have the guts. I'd hate to think of you even walking by the death house. The shop is where you belong. You can be nice and cozy there, wiring up fixtures and ringing the cash register. I can handle my duties without your help."

55 It hurt me to say it. I had never talked like that to him before, and it hurt. The strange thing was that he didn't seem angry about it; he only looked at me puzzled.

56 "Is that all it is to you?" he said. "A duty?"

57 "Yes."

58 "But you get paid for it, don't you?"

59 "I get paid little enough for it."

60 He kept looking at me that way. "Only a duty?" he said, and never took his eyes off me. "But you enjoy it, don't you?"

61 That was the question he asked.

62 *You enjoy it, don't you?* You stand there looking through a peephole in the wall at the chair. In thirty years I have stood there more than a hundred times looking at that chair. The guards bring somebody in. Usually he is in a daze; sometimes he screams, throws himself around and fights. Sometimes it is a woman, and a woman can be as hard to handle as a man when she is led to the chair. Sooner or later, whoever it is is strapped down and the black hood is dropped over his head. Now your hand is on the switch.

63 The warden signals, and you pull the switch. The current hits the body like a tremendous rush of air suddenly filling it. The body leaps out of the chair with only the straps holding it back. The head jerks, and a curl of smoke comes from it. You release the switch and the body falls back again.

64 You do it once more, do it a third time to make sure. And whenever your hand presses the switch you can see in your mind what the current is doing to that body and what the face under the hood must look like.

65 Enjoy it?

66 That was the question my son asked me. That was what he said to me, as if I didn't have the same feeling deep down in me that we all have.

67 Enjoy it?

68 But, my God, how could anyone *not* enjoy it! □

The Father

by Björnstjerne Björnson

1 The man whose story is here to be told was the wealthiest and most influential person in his parish; his name was Thord Overaas. He appeared in the priest's study one day, tall and earnest.

2 "I have gotten a son," said he, "and I wish to present him for baptism."

3 "What shall his name be?"

4 "Finn—after my father."

5 "And the sponsors?"

6 They were mentioned, and proved to be the best men and women of Thord's relations in the parish.

7 "Is there anything else?" inquired the priest, and looked up.

8 The peasant hesitated a little.

9 "I should like very much to have him baptized by himself," said he, finally.

10 "That is to say on a week-day?"

11 "Next Saturday, at twelve o'clock noon."

12 "Is there anything else?" inquired the priest.

13 "There is nothing else"; and the peasant twirled his cap, as though he were about to go.

14 Then the priest rose. "There is yet this, however," said he, and walking toward Thord, he took him by the hand and looked gravely into his eyes: "God grant that the child may become a blessing to you!"

15 One day sixteen years later, Thord stood once more in the priest's study.

16 "Really, you carry your age astonishingly well, Thord," said the priest; for he saw no change whatever in the man.

17 "That is because I have no troubles," replied Thord.

18 To this the priest said nothing, but after a while he asked: "What is your pleasure this evening?"

19 "I have come this evening about that son of mine who is going to be confirmed to-morrow."

20 "He is a bright boy."

21 "I did not wish to pay the priest until I heard what number the boy would have when he takes his place in church tomorrow."

22 "He will stand number one."

23 "So I have heard; and here are ten dollars for the priest."

24 "Is there anything else I can do for you?" inquired the priest, fixing his eyes on Thord.

25 "There is nothing else."

26 Thord went out.

27 Eight years more rolled by, and then one day a noise was heard outside of the priest's study, for many men were approaching, and at their head was Thord, who entered first.

28 The priest looked up and recognized him.

29 "You come well attended this evening, Thord," said he.

30 "I am here to request that the banns may be published for my son; he is about to marry Karen Storliden, daughter of Gudmund, who stands here beside me."

31 "Why, that is the richest girl in the parish."

32 "So they say," replied the peasant, stroking back his hair with one hand.

33 The priest sat a while as if in deep thought, then entered the names in his book, without making any comments, and the men wrote their signatures underneath. Thord laid three dollars on the table.

34 "One is all I am to have," said the priest.

35 "I know that very well; but he is my only child, I want to do it handsomely."

36 The priest took the money.

37 "This is now the third time, Thord, that you have come here on your son's account."

38 "But now I am through with him," said Thord, and folding up his pocket-book he said farewell and walked away.

39 The men slowly followed him.

40 A fortnight later, the father and son were rowing across the lake, one calm, still day, to Storliden to make arrangements for the wedding.

41 "This thwart is not secure," said the son, and stood up to straighten the seat on which he was sitting.

42 At the same moment the board he was standing on slipped from under him; he threw out his arms, uttered a shriek, and fell overboard.

43 "Take hold of the oar!" shouted the father, springing to his feet and holding out the oar.

44 But when the son had made a couple of efforts he grew stiff.

45 "Wait a moment!" cried the father, and began to row toward his son. Then the son rolled over on his back, gave his father one long look, and sank.

46 Thord could scarcely believe it; he held the boat still, and stared at the spot where his son had gone down, as though he must surely come to the surface once again. There rose some bubbles, then some more, and finally one large one that burst; and the lake lay there as smooth and bright as a mirror again.

47 For three days and three nights people saw the father rowing round and round the spot, without taking either food or sleep; he was dragging the lake for the body of his son. And toward morning of the third day he found it, and carried it in his arms up over the hills to his gard.

48 It might have been about a year from that day, when the priest, late one autumn evening, heard someone in the passage outside of the door, carefully trying to find the latch. The priest opened the door, and in walked a tall, thin man, with bowed form and white hair. The priest looked long at him before he recognized him. It was Thord.

49 "Are you out walking so late?" said the priest, and stood still in front of him.

50 "Ah, yes! it is late," said Thord, and took a seat.

51 The priest sat down also, as though waiting. A long, long silence followed. At last Thord said:

52 "I have something with me that I should like to give to the poor; I want it to be invested as a legacy in my son's name."

53 He rose, laid some money on the table, and sat down again. The priest counted it.

54 "It is a great deal of money," said he.

55 "It is half the price of my gard. I sold it today."

56 The priest sat long in silence. At last he asked, but gently:

57 "What do you propose to do now, Thord?"

58 "Something better."

59 They sat there for a while, Thord with downcast eyes, the priest with his eyes fixed on Thord. Presently the priest said, slowly and softly:

60 "I think your son has at last brought you a true blessing."

61 "Yes, I think so myself," said Thord, looking up, while two big tears coursed slowly down his cheeks. □

A Good Man Is Hard to Find

by Flannery O'Connor

1 The grandmother didn't want to go to Florida. She wanted to visit some of her connections in east Tennessee and she was seizing at every chance to change Bailey's mind. Bailey was the son she lived with, her only boy. He was sitting on the edge of his chair at the table, bent over the orange sports section of the *Journal*. "Now look here, Bailey," she said, "see here, read this," and she stood with one hand on her thin hip and the other rattling the newspaper at his bald head. "Here this fellow that calls himself The Misfit is aloose from the Federal Pen and headed toward Florida and you read here what it says he did to these people. Just you read it. I wouldn't take my children in any direction with a criminal like that aloose in it. I couldn't answer to my conscience if I did."

2 Bailey didn't look up from his reading so she wheeled around then and faced the children's mother; a young woman in slacks, whose face was as broad and innocent as a cabbage and was tied around with a green head-kerchief that had two points on the top like rabbit's ears.

She was sitting on the sofa, feeding the baby his apricots out of a jar. "The children have been to Florida before," the old lady said. "You all ought to take them somewhere else for a change so they would see different parts of the world and be broad. They never have been to east Tennessee."

3 The children's mother didn't seem to hear her, but the eight-year-old boy, John Wesley, a stocky child with glasses, said, "If you don't want to go to Florida, why dontcha stay at home?" He and the little girl, June Star, were reading the funny papers on the floor.

4 "She wouldn't stay at home to be queen for a day," June Star said without raising her yellow head.

5 "Yes, and what would you do if this fellow, The Misfit, caught you?" the grandmother asked.

6 "I'd smack his face," John Wesley said.

7 "She wouldn't stay at home for a million bucks," June Star said. "Afraid she'd miss something. She has to go everywhere we go."

8 "All right, Miss," the grandmother said. "Just remember that the next time you want me to curl your hair."

9 June Star said her hair was naturally curly.

10 The next morning the grandmother was the first one in the car, ready to go. She had her big black valise that looked like the head of a hippopotamus in one corner, and underneath it she was hiding a basket with Pitty Sing, the cat, in it. She didn't intend for the cat to be left alone in the house for three days because he would miss her too much and she was afraid he might brush against one of the gas burners and accidentally asphyxiate himself. Her son, Bailey, didn't like to arrive at a motel with a cat.

11 She sat in the middle of the back seat with John Wesley and June Star on either side of her. Bailey and the children's mother and the baby sat in the front and they left Atlanta at eight forty-five with the mileage on the car at 55890. The grandmother wrote this down because she thought it would be interesting to say how many miles they had been when they got back. It took them twenty minutes to reach the outskirts of the city.

12 The old lady settled herself comfortably, removing her white cotton gloves and putting them up with her purse on the shelf in front of the back window. The children's mother still had on slacks and still had her head tied up in a green kerchief, but the grandmother had on a navy blue straw sailor hat with a bunch of white violets on the brim and a navy blue dress with a small white dot in the print. Her collar and cuffs were white organdy trimmed with lace and at her neckline she had pinned a purple spray of cloth violets containing a sachet. In

case of an accident, anyone seeing her dead on the highway would know at once that she was a lady.

13 She said she thought it was going to be a good day for driving, neither too hot nor too cold, and she cautioned Bailey that the speed limit was fifty-five miles an hour and that the patrolmen hid themselves behind billboards and small clumps of trees and sped out after you before you had a chance to slow down. She pointed out interesting details of the scenery: Stone Mountain; the blue granite that in some places came up to both sides of the highway; the brilliant red clay banks slightly streaked with purple; and the various crops that made rows of green lace-work on the ground. The trees were full of silver-white sunlights and the meanest of them sparkled. The children were reading comic magazines and their mother had gone back to sleep.

14 "Let's go through Georgia fast so we won't have to look at it much," John Wesley said.

15 "If I were a little boy," said the grandmother, "I wouldn't talk about my native state that way. Tennessee has the mountains and Georgia has the hills."

16 "Tennessee is just a hillbilly dumping ground," John Wesley said, "and Georgia is a lousy state too."

17 "You said it," June Star said.

18 "In my time," said the grandmother, folding her thin veined fingers, "children were more respectful of their native states and their parents and everything else. People did right then. Oh look at the cute little pickaninny!" she said and pointed to a Negro child standing in the door of a shack. "Wouldn't that make a picture, now?" she asked and they all turned and looked at the little Negro out of the back window. He waved.

19 "He didn't have any britches on," June Star said.

20 "He probably didn't have any," the grandmother explained. "Little niggers in the country don't have things like we do. If I could paint, I'd paint that picture," she said.

21 The children exchanged comic books.

22 The grandmother offered to hold the baby and the children's mother passed him over the front seat to her. She set him on her knee and bounced him and told him about the things they were passing. She rolled her eyes and screwed up her mouth and stuck her leathery thin face into his smooth bland one. Occasionally he gave her a faraway smile. They passed a large cotton field with five or six graves fenced in the middle of it, like a small island. "Look at the graveyard!" the grandmother said, pointing it out. "That was the old family burying ground. That belonged to the plantation."

23 "Where's the plantation?" John Wesley asked.

24 "Gone With the Wind," said the grandmother. "Ha. Ha."

25 When the children finished all the comic books they had brought, they opened the lunch and ate it. The grandmother ate a peanut butter sandwich and an olive and would not let the children throw the box and the paper napkins out the window. When there was nothing else to do they played a game by choosing a cloud and making the other two guess what shape it suggested. John Wesley took one the shape of a cow and June Star guessed a cow and John Wesley said, no, an automobile, and June Star said he didn't play fair, and they began to slap each other over the grandmother.

26 The grandmother said she would tell them a story if they would keep quiet. When she told a story, she rolled her eyes and waved her head and was very dramatic. She said once when she was a maiden lady she had been courted by a Mr. Edgar Atkins Teagarden from Jasper, Georgia. She said he was a very good-looking man and a gentleman and that he brought her a watermelon every Saturday afternoon with his initials cut in it, E. A. T. Well, one Saturday, she said, Mr. Teagarden brought the watermelon and there was nobody at home and he left it on the front porch and returned in his buggy to Jasper, but she never got the watermelon, she said, because a nigger boy ate it when he saw the initials, E. A. T.! This story tickled John Wesley's funny bone and he giggled and giggled but June Star didn't think it was any good. She said she wouldn't marry a man that just brought her a watermelon on Saturday. The grandmother said she would have done well to marry Mr. Teagarden because he was a gentleman and had bought Coca-Cola stock when it first came out and that he had died only a few years ago, a very wealthy man.

27 They stopped at The Tower for barbecued sandwiches. The Tower was a part-stucco and part-wood filling station and dance hall set in a clearing outside of Timothy. A fat man named Red Sammy Butts ran it and there were signs stuck here and there on the building and for miles up and down the highway saying, TRY RED SAMMY'S FAMOUS BARBECUE. NONE LIKE FAMOUS RED SAMMY'S! RED SAM! THE FAT BOY WITH THE HAPPY LAUGH. A VETERAN! RED SAMMY'S YOUR MAN!

28 Red Sammy was lying on the bare ground outside The Tower with his head under a truck while a gray monkey about a foot high, chained to a small chinaberry tree, chattered nearby. The monkey sprang back into the tree and got on the highest limb as soon as he saw the children jump out of the car and run toward him.

29 Inside, The Tower was a long dark room with a counter at one end and tables at the other and dancing space in the middle. They all sat down at a broad table next to the nickelodeon and Red Sam's wife, a tall burnt-brown woman with hair and eyes lighter than her skin,

came and took their order. The children's mother put a dime in the machine and played "The Tennessee Waltz," and the grandmother said that tune always made her want to dance. She asked Bailey if he would like to dance but he only glared at her. He didn't have a naturally sunny disposition like she did and trips made him nervous. The grandmother's brown eyes were very bright. She swayed her head from side to side and pretended she was dancing in her chair. June Star said play something she could tap to so the children's mother put in another dime and played a fast number and June Star stepped out onto the dance floor and did her tap routine.

30 "Ain't she cute?" Red Sam's wife said, leaning over the counter. "Would you like to come be my little girl?"

31 "No, I certainly wouldn't," June Star said. "I wouldn't live in a broken-down place like this for a million bucks!" and she ran back to the table.

32 "Ain't she cute?" the woman repeated, stretching her mouth politely.

33 "Aren't you ashamed?" hissed the grandmother.

34 Red Sam came in and told his wife to quit lounging on the counter and hurry up with these people's order. His khaki trousers reached just to his hip bones and his stomach hung over them like a sack of meal swaying under his shirt. He came over and sat down at a table nearby and let out a combination sigh and yodel. "You can't win," he said. "You can't win," and he wiped his sweating red face off with a gray handkerchief. "These days you don't know who to trust," he said. "Ain't that the truth?"

35 "People are certainly not nice like they used to be," said the grandmother.

36 "Two fellers come in here last week," Red Sammy said, "driving a Chrysler. It was a old beat-up car but it was a good one and these boys looked all right to me. Said they worked at the mill and you know I let them fellers charge the gas they bought? Now why did I do that?"

37 "Because you're a good man!" the grandmother said at once.

38 "Yes'm, I suppose so," Red Sam said as if he were struck with this answer.

39 His wife brought the orders, carrying the five plates all at once without a tray, two in each hand and one balanced on her arm. "It isn't a soul in this green world of God's that you can trust," she said. "And I don't count nobody out of that, not nobody," she repeated, looking at Red Sammy.

40 "Did you read about that criminal, The Misfit, that's escaped?" asked the grandmother.

41 "I wouldn't be a bit surprised if he didn't attact this place right here," said the woman. "If he hears about it being here, I wouldn't be none surprised to see him. If he hears it's two cent in the cash register, I wouldn't be a tall surprised if he. . . ."

42 "That'll do," Red Sam said. "Go bring these people their Co'Colas," and the woman went off to get the rest of the order.

43 "A good man is hard to find," Red Sammy said. "Everything is getting terrible. I remember the day you could go off and leave your screen door unlatched. Not no more."

44 He and the grandmother discussed better times. The old lady said that in her opinion Europe was entirely to blame for the way things were now. She said the way Europe acted you would think we were made of money and Red Sam said it was no use talking about it, she was exactly right. The children ran outside into the white sunlight and looked at the monkey in the lacy chinaberry tree. He was busy catching fleas on himself and biting each one carefully between his teeth as if it were a delicacy.

45 They drove off again into the hot afternoon. The grandmother took cat naps and woke up every few minutes with her own snoring. Outside of Toombsboro she woke up and recalled an old plantation that she had visited in this neighborhood once when she was a young lady. She said the house had six white columns across the front and that there was an avenue of oaks leading up to it and two little wooden trellis arbors on either side in front where you sat down with your suitor after a stroll in the garden. She recalled exactly which road to turn off to get to it. She knew that Bailey would not be willing to lose any time looking at an old house, but the more she talked about it, the more she wanted to see it once again and find out if the little twin arbors were still standing. "There was a secret panel in this house," she said craftily, not telling the truth but wishing that she were, "and the story went that all the family silver was hidden in it when Sherman came through but it was never found. . . ."

46 "Hey!" John Wesley said. "Let's go see it! We'll find it! We'll poke all the woodwork and find it! Who lives there? Where do you turn off at? Hey Pop, can't we turn off there?"

47 "We never have seen a house with a secret panel!" June Star shrieked. "Let's go to the house with the secret panel! Hey, Pop, can't we go see the house with the secret panel!"

48 "It's not far from here, I know," the grandmother said. "It wouldn't take over twenty minutes."

49 Bailey was looking straight ahead. His jaw was as rigid as a horseshoe. "No," he said.

50 The children began to yell and scream that they wanted to see the

house with the secret panel. John Wesley kicked the back of the front seat and June Star hung over her mother's shoulder and whined desperately into her ear that they never had any fun even on their vacation, that they could never do what THEY wanted to do. The baby began to scream and John Wesley kicked the back of the seat so hard that his father could feel the blows in his kidney.

51 "All right!" he shouted and drew the car to a stop at the side of the road. "Will you all shut up? Will you all just shut up for one second? If you don't shut up, we won't go anywhere."

52 "It would be very educational for them," the grandmother murmured.

53 "All right," Bailey said, "but get this. This is the only time we're going to stop for anything like this. This is the one and only time."

54 "The dirt road that you have to turn down is about a mile back," the grandmother directed. "I marked it when we passed."

55 "A dirt road," Bailey groaned.

56 After they had turned around and were headed toward the dirt road, the grandmother recalled other points about the house, the beautiful glass over the front doorway and the candle lamp in the hall. John Wesley said that the secret panel was probably in the fireplace.

57 "You can't go inside this house," Bailey said. "You don't know who lives there."

58 "While you all talk to the people in front, I'll run around behind and get in a window," John Wesley suggested.

59 "We'll all stay in the car," his mother said.

60 They turned onto the dirt road and the car raced roughly along in a swirl of pink dust. The grandmother recalled the times when there were no paved roads and thirty miles was a day's journey. The dirt road was hilly and there were sudden washes in it and sharp curves on dangerous embankments. All at once they would be on a hill, looking down over the blue tops of trees for miles around, then the next minute, they would be in a red depression with the dust-coated trees looking down on them.

61 "This place had better turn up in a minute," Bailey said, "or I'm going to turn around."

62 The road looked as if no one had traveled on it in months.

63 "It's not much farther," the grandmother said and just as she said it, a horrible thought came to her. The thought was so embarrassing that she turned red in the face and her eyes dilated and her feet jumped up, upsetting her valise in the corner. The instant the valise moved, the newspaper top she had over the basket under it rose with a snarl and Pitty Sing, the cat, sprang onto Bailey's shoulder.

64 The children were thrown to the floor and their mother, clutching the baby, was thrown out the door onto the ground; the old lady was thrown into the front seat. The car turned over once and landed right-side-up in a gulch on the side of the road. Bailey remained in the driver's seat with the cat—gray-striped with a broad white face and an orange nose—clinging to his neck like a caterpillar.

65 As soon as the children saw they could move their arms and legs, they scrambled out of the car, shouting, "We've had an ACCIDENT!" The grandmother was curled up under the dashboard, hoping she was injured so that Bailey's wrath would not come down on her all at once. The horrible thought she had had before the accident was that the house she had remembered so vividly was not in Georgia but in Tennessee.

66 Bailey removed the cat from his neck with both hands and flung it out the window against the side of a pine tree. Then he got out of the car and started looking for the children's mother. She was sitting against the side of the red gutted ditch, holding the screaming baby, but she only had a cut down her face and a broken shoulder. "We've had an ACCIDENT!" the children screamed in a frenzy of delight.

67 "But nobody's killed," June Star said with disappointment as the grandmother limped out of the car, her hat still pinned to her head but the broken front brim standing up at a jaunty angle and the violet spray hanging off the side. They all sat down in the ditch, except the children, to recover from the shock. They were all shaking.

68 "Maybe a car will come along," said the children's mother hoarsely.

69 "I believe I have injured an organ," said the grandmother, pressing her side, but no one answered her. Bailey's teeth were clattering. He had on a yellow sport shirt with bright blue parrots designed in it and his face was as yellow as the shirt. The grandmother decided that she would not mention that the house was in Tennessee.

70 The road was about ten feet above and they could see only the tops of the trees on the other side of it. Behind the ditch they were sitting in there were more woods, tall and dark and deep. In a few minutes they saw a car some distance away on top of a hill, coming slowly as if the occupants were watching them. The grandmother stood up and waved both arms dramatically to attract their attention. The car continued to come on slowly, disappeared around a bend and appeared again, moving even slower, on top of the hill they had gone over. It was a big black battered hearselike automobile. There were three men in it.

71 It came to a stop just over them and for some minutes, the driver looked down with a steady expressionless gaze to where they were

sitting, and didn't speak. Then he turned his head and muttered something to the other two and they got out. One was a fat boy in black trousers and a red sweat shirt with a silver stallion embossed on the front of it. He moved around on the right side of them and stood staring, his mouth partly open in a kind of loose grin. The other had on khaki pants and a blue striped coat and a gray hat pulled down very low, hiding most of his face. He came around slowly on the left side. Neither spoke.

72 The driver got out of the car and stood by the side of it, looking down at them. He was an older man than the other two. His hair was just beginning to gray and he wore silver-rimmed spectacles that gave him a scholarly look. He had a long creased face and didn't have on any shirt or undershirt. He had on blue jeans that were too tight for him and was holding a black hat and a gun. The two boys also had guns.

73 "We've had an ACCIDENT!" the children screamed.

74 The grandmother had the peculiar feeling that the bespectacled man was someone she knew. His face was as familiar to her as if she had known him all her life but she could not recall who he was. He moved away from the car and began to come down the embankment, placing his feet carefully so that he wouldn't slip. He had on tan and white shoes and no socks, and his ankles were red and thin. "Good afternoon," he said. "I see you all had you a little spill."

75 "We turned over twice!" said the grandmother.

76 "Oncet," he corrected. "We seen it happen. Try their car and see will it run, Hiram," he said quietly to the boy with the gray hat.

77 "What you got that gun for?" John Wesley asked. "Whatcha gonna do with that gun?"

78 "Lady," the man said to the children's mother, "would you mind calling them children to sit down by you? Children make me nervous. I want all you all to sit down right together there where you're at."

79 "What are you telling US what to do for?" June Star asked.

80 Behind them the line of woods gaped like a dark open mouth. "Come here," said their mother.

81 "Look here now," Bailey began suddenly, "we're in a predicament! We're in. . . ."

82 The grandmother shrieked. She scrambled to her feet and stood staring.

83 "You're The Misfit!" she said. "I recognized you at once!"

84 "Yes'm," the man said, smiling slightly as if he were pleased in spite of himself to be known, "but it would have been better for all of you, lady, if you hadn't of reckernized me."

85 Bailey turned his head sharply and said something to his mother that shocked even the children. The old lady began to cry and The Misfit reddened.

86 "Lady," he said, "don't you get upset. Sometimes a man says things he don't mean. I don't reckon he meant to talk to you thataway.

87 "You wouldn't shoot a lady, would you?" the grandmother said and removed a clean handkerchief from her cuff and began to slap at her eyes with it.

88 The Misfit pointed the toe of his shoe into the ground and made a little hole and then covered it up again. "I would hate to have to," he said.

89 "Listen," the grandmother almost screamed, "I know you're a good man. You don't look a bit like you have common blood. I know you must come from nice people!"

90 "Yes mam," he said, "finest people in the world." When he smiled he showed a row of strong white teeth. "God never made a finer woman than my mother and my daddy's heart was pure gold," he said. The boy with the red sweat shirt had come around behind them and was standing with his gun at his hip. The Misfit squatted down on the ground. "Watch them children, Bobby Lee," he said. "You know they make me nervous." He looked at the six of them huddled together in front of him and he seemed to be embarrassed as if he couldn't think of anything to say. "Ain't a cloud in the sky," he remarked, looking up at it. "Don't see no sun but don't see no cloud neither."

91 "Yes, it's a beautiful day," said the grandmother. "Listen," she said, "you shouldn't call yourself The Misfit because I know you're a good man at heart. I can just look at you and tell."

92 "Hush!" Bailey yelled. "Hush! Everybody shut up and let me handle this!" He was squatting in the position of a runner about to sprint forward but he didn't move.

93 "I pre-chate that, lady," The Misfit said and drew a little circle in the ground with the butt of his gun.

94 "It'll take a half a hour to fix this here car," Hiram called, looking over the raised hood of it.

95 "Well, first you and Bobby Lee get him and that little boy to step over yonder with you," The Misfit said, pointing to Bailey and John Wesley. "The boys want to ast you something," he said to Bailey. "Would you mind stepping back in them woods there with them?"

96 "Listen," Bailey began, "we're in a terrible predicament! Nobody realizes what this is," and his voice cracked. His eyes were as blue and intense as the parrots in his shirt and he remained perfectly still.

97 The grandmother reached up to adjust her hat brim as if she were going to the woods with him but it came off in her hand. She stood staring at it and after a second she let it fall on the ground. Hiram pulled Bailey up by the arm as if he were assisting an old man. John Wesley caught hold of his father's hand and Bobby Lee followed. They went off toward the woods and just as they reached the dark edge, Bailey turned and supporting himself against a gray naked pine trunk, he shouted, "I'll be back in a minute, Mamma, wait on me!"

98 "Come back this instant!" his mother shrilled but they all disappeared into the woods.

99 "Bailey Boy!" the grandmother called in a tragic voice but she found she was looking at The Misfit squatting on the ground in front of her. "I just know you're a good man," she said desperately. "You're not a bit common!"

100 "Nome, I ain't a good man," The Misfit said after a second as if he had considered her statement carefully, "but I ain't the worst in the world neither. My daddy said I was different breed of dog from my brothers and sisters. 'You know,' Daddy said, 'it's some that can live their whole life out without asking about it and it's others has to know why it is, and this boy is one of the latters. He's going to be into everything!' " He put on his black hat and looked up suddenly and then away deep into the woods as if he were embarrassed again. "I'm sorry I don't have on a shirt before you ladies," he said, hunching his shoulders slightly. "We buried our clothes that we had on when we escaped and we're just making do until we can get better. We borrowed these from some folks we met," he explained.

101 "That's perfectly all right," the grandmother said. "Maybe Bailey has an extra shirt in his suitcase."

102 "I'll look and see terrectly," The Misfit said.

103 "Where are they taking him?" the children's mother screamed.

104 "Daddy was a card himself," The Misfit said. "You couldn't put anything over on him. He never got in trouble with the Authorities though. Just had the knack of handling them."

105 "You could be honest too if you'd only try," said the grandmother. "Think how wonderful it would be to settle down and live a comfortable life and not have to think about somebody chasing you all the time."

106 The Misfit kept scratching in the ground with the butt of his gun as if he were thinking about it. "Yes'm, somebody is always after you," he murmured.

107 The grandmother noticed how thin his shoulder blades were just

behind his hat because she was standing up looking down on him. "Do you ever pray?" she asked.

108 He shook his head. All she saw was the black hat wiggle between his shoulder blades. "Nome," he said.

109 There was a pistol shot from the woods, followed closely by another. Then silence. The old lady's head jerked around. She could hear the wind move through the tree tops like a long satisfied insuck of breath. "Bailey Boy!" she called.

110 "I was a gospel singer for a while," The Misfit said. "I been most everything. Been in the arm service, both land and sea, at home and abroad, been twict married, been an undertaker, been with the railroads, plowed Mother Earth, been in a tornado, seen a man burnt alive oncet," and he looked up at the children's mother and the little girl who were sitting close together, their faces white and their eyes glassy; "I even seen a woman flogged," he said.

111 "Pray, pray," the grandmother began, "pray, pray. . . ."

112 "I never was a bad boy that I remember of," The Misfit said in an almost dreamy voice, "but somewheres along the line I done something wrong and got sent to the penitentiary. I was buried alive," and he looked up and held her attention to him by a steady stare.

113 "That's when you should have started to pray," she said. "What did you do to get sent to the penitentiary that first time?"

114 "Turn to the right, it was a wall," The Misfit said, looking up again at the cloudless sky. "Turn to the left, it was a wall. Look up it was a ceiling, look down it was a floor. I forget what I done, lady. I set there and set there, trying to remember what it was I done and I ain't recalled it to this day. Oncet in a while, I would think it was coming to me, but it never come."

115 "Maybe they put you in by mistake," the old lady said vaguely.

116 "Nome," he said. "It wasn't no mistake. They had the papers on me."

117 "You must have stolen something," she said.

118 The Misfit sneered slightly. "Nobody had nothing I wanted," he said. "It was a head-doctor at the penitentiary said what I had done was kill my daddy but I known that for a lie. My daddy died in nineteen ought nineteen of the epidemic flu and I never had a thing to do with it. He was buried in the Mount Hopewell Baptist churchyard and you can go there and see for yourself."

119 "If you would pray," the old lady said, "Jesus would help you."

120 "That's right," The Misfit said.

121 "Well then, why don't you pray?" she asked trembling with delight suddenly.

122 "I don't want no hep," he said. "I'm doing all right by myself."

123 Bobby Lee and Hiram came ambling back from the woods. Bobby Lee was dragging a yellow shirt with bright blue parrots in it.

124 "Throw me that shirt, Bobby Lee," The Misfit said. The shirt came flying at him and landed on his shoulder and he put it on. The grandmother couldn't name what the shirt reminded her of. "No, lady," The Misfit said while he was buttoning it up, "I found out the crime don't matter. You can do one thing or you can do another, kill a man or take a tire off his car, because sooner or later you're going to forget what it was you done and just be punished for it."

125 The children's mother had begun to make heaving noises as if she couldn't get her breath. "Lady," he asked, "would you and that little girl like to step off yonder with Bobby Lee and Hiram and join your husband?"

126 "Yes, thank you," the mother said faintly. Her left arm dangled helplessly and she was holding the baby, who had gone to sleep, in the other. "Hep that lady up, Hiram," The Misfit said as she struggled to climb out of the ditch, "and Bobby Lee, you hold onto that little girl's hand."

127 "I don't want to hold hands with him," June Star said. "He reminds me of a pig."

128 The fat boy blushed and laughed and caught her by the arm and pulled her off into the woods after Hiram and her mother.

129 Alone with The Misfit, the grandmother found that she had lost her voice. There was not a cloud in the sky nor any sun. There was nothing around her but woods. She wanted to tell him that he must pray. She opened and closed her mouth several times before anything came out. Finally she found herself saying, "Jesus. Jesus," meaning, Jesus will help you, but the way she was saying it, it sounded as if she might be cursing.

130 "Yes'm," The Misfit said as if he agreed. "Jesus thown everything off balance. It was the same case with Him as with me except He hadn't committed any crime and they could prove I had committed one because they had the papers on me. Of course," he said, "they never shown me my papers. That's why I sign myself now. I said long ago, you get you a signature and sign everything you do and keep a copy of it. Then you'll know what you done and you can hold up the crime to the punishment and see do they match and in the end you'll have something to prove you ain't been treated right. I call myself The Misfit," he said, "because I can't make what all I done wrong fit what all I gone through in punishment."

131 There was a piercing scream from the woods, followed closely

by a pistol report. "Does it seem right to you, lady, that one is punished a heap and another ain't punished at all?"

132 "Jesus!" the old lady cried. "You've got good blood! I know you wouldn't shoot a lady! I know you come from nice people! Pray! Jesus, you ought not to shoot a lady. I'll give you all the money I've got!"

133 "Lady," The Misfit said, looking beyond her far into the woods, "there never was a body that give the undertaker a tip."

134 There were two more pistol reports and the grandmother raised her head like a parched old turkey hen crying for water and called, "Bailey Boy, Bailey Boy!" as if her heart would break.

135 "Jesus was the only One that ever raised the dead," The Misfit continued, "and He shouldn't have done it. He thown everything off balance. If He did what He said, then it's nothing for you to do but thow away everything and follow Him, and if He didn't then it's nothing for you to do but enjoy the few minutes you got left the best way you can—by killing somebody or burning down his house or doing some other meanness to him. No pleasure but meanness," he said and his voice had become almost a snarl.

136 "Maybe He didn't raise the dead," the old lady mumbled, not knowing what she was saying and feeling so dizzy that she sank down in the ditch with her legs twisted under her.

137 "I wasn't there so I can't say He didn't," The Misfit said. "I wisht I had of been there," he said, hitting the ground with his fist. "It ain't right I wasn't there because if I had of been there I would of known. Listen lady," he said in a high voice, "if I had of been there I would of known and I wouldn't be like I am now." His voice seemed about to crack and the grandmother's head cleared for an instant. She saw the man's face twisted close to her own as if he were going to cry and she murmured, "Why, you're one of my babies. You're one of my own children!" She reached out and touched him on the shoulder. The Misfit sprang back as if a snake had bitten him and shot her three times through the chest. Then he put his gun down on the ground and took off his glasses and began to clean them.

138 Hiram and Bobby Lee returned from the woods and stood over the ditch, looking down at the grandmother who half sat and half lay in a puddle of blood with her legs crossed under her like a child's and her face smiling up at the cloudless sky.

139 Without his glasses, The Misfit's eyes were red-rimmed and pale and defenseless-looking. "Take her off and thow her where you thown the others," he said, picking up the cat that was rubbing itself against his leg.

140 "She was a talker, wasn't she?" Bobby Lee said, sliding down the ditch with a yodel.

141 "She would of been a good woman," The Misfit said, "if it had been somebody there to shoot her every minute of her life."

142 "Some fun!" Bobby Lee said.

143 "Shut up, Bobby Lee," The Misfit said. "It's no real pleasure in life." □

CHAPTER V

Point of View: Mortar of Narrative Structure

You have now worked with the major ingredients of the short story: narrative, description, characters, and dialog. You know that plot is the skeleton outline of the action of the story, and that narrative flow is the combined result of pace and proportion as they blend to present a unified, coherent account with enough movement to sustain the reader's interest. Incidents happen against some sort of geographical, physical, and emotional background to establish mood, tone, and a sense of scene. And these incidents happen to people as a result of other people. The characters are involved in some sort of conflict with nature, a thing in nature, another person, or themselves. In speaking to themselves or to others, they reveal themselves and their changing attitudes. If the basic ingredients of fiction are logically developed and coherent as a result of unifying factors, change will occur in the main character and the change will reveal a basic truth or generalization that becomes specific in the application. The arrival at that truth or generalization made specific will serve as an amusing journey or as a distinct revelation to you, the reader. You will be satisfied because you will have had a worthwhile literary experience.

You have already seen (in the discussion of "The Book of Ruth," p. 20) how an author's choice of point of view enlarges or restricts the possibilities of a given story. To be specific, the use of a particular point of view may determine the sequence of events (when the author first plots his story), establish the meaning of symbols (different characters will see symbols differently), and allow theme to emerge as a result of your understanding of a character. Thus, a closer and more extensive look at the subject of point of view may be helpful.

Visualize a story with its action as a unit, in this case, a circle:

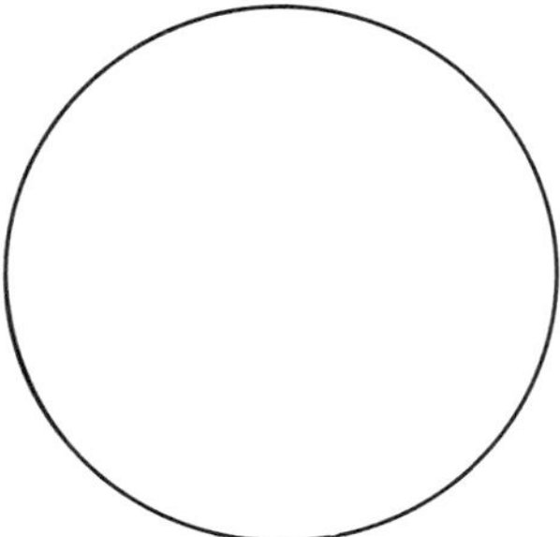

The line making the circle delineates the plot of the story. The group of scenes which make up the story is herein removed in time and space to create a unique, small world wherein characters live their lives. Oliver LaFarge (whose novel *Laughing Boy* won the Pulitzer Prize for fiction in 1929) has said of such a fictional world:

> Fiction, narrative non-fiction, history, biography, all have characters, plot, beginning, ending, and a climax of some sort. They have a background or setting. There is the development not only of the principal characters but of the minor ones, who usually are, or should be, far more completely worked out in the writer's mind than appears in the finished book. . . .
>
> So here is a whole imaginary world. It may be a familiar world, derived from observed, present reality and close to it, but it is broken off from the real world. Inside this a writer must move, observe, respond.*

Visualize those characters as letters encased in their individual small worlds of personality:

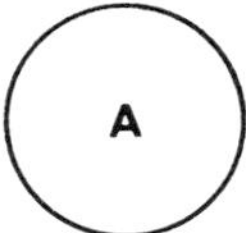

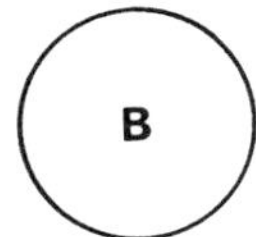

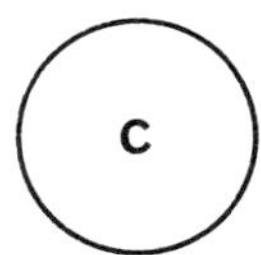

Someone tells the story. He may be simply the author, or he may be a character within the story—either major or minor. Visualize this narrator:

* *The Man with the Calabash Pipe,* ed. Winfield Townley Scott (New York, 1966), p. 88.

N

The narrator (N) may be allowed limited or unlimited access to the thoughts of the characters. If he is allowed to enter the mind of a character, such access will be marked with an arrow, indicating his penetrative power:

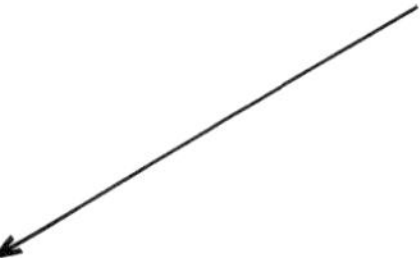

If he is allowed only external knowledge of actions and overheard conversation but is blocked from entering the mind of a character, the line will be blunted:

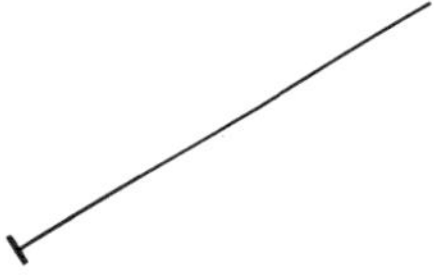

Four points of view are most common in prose fiction, as you saw earlier (p. 20): the *omniscient, limited omniscient, first person,* and *objective.* The most elaborate and inclusive is the *omniscient* point of view. When this point of view is used, the narrator—almost always the author—recounts the story in the third person as if he has the powers of God and can enter any mind at will:

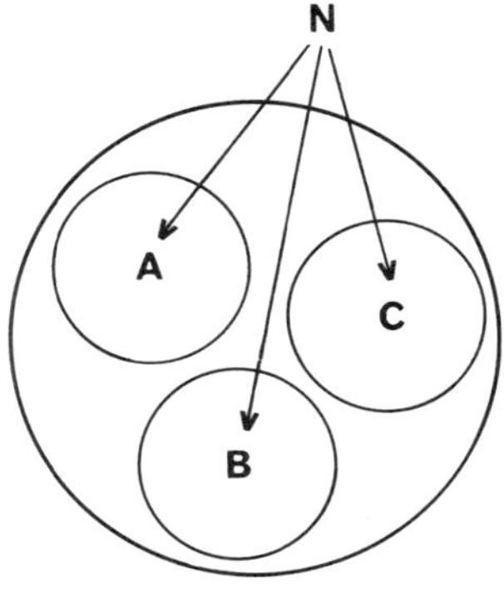

He may comment on or explain thoughts and actions. He is confined only by his choice of what he prefers to divulge (this is, of course, *selection,* the author's choice of incident to suit his fictional purpose). Skillfully used, the omniscient point of view adds scope and depth to a story. Certain dangers are present in its use, however: the author as artist rather than as narrator may become obtrusive, destroying verisimilitude. Dramatic impact may be spoiled as suspense is destroyed. Uncertainty creates suspense for the reader, and, if he knows all, suspense fails to build. Few contemporary stories are written completely from the omniscient point of view, but it is frequently employed in a section or sections of a story told from a more limited point of view. Carefully controlled, it can add excellence to the overall effect. If, however, the use of omnisciency is an apparent violation (literally, a breaking of the imposed rule) of point of view, it will seem artificial and may destroy verisimilitude by jarring the reader out of his acceptance of the fictional world.

Closely allied to the omniscient is the *limited omniscient* point of view, wherein the author is seldom the narrator. Instead, a major character or a minor one (the latter called *peripheral* because he is observing the action from its edge) tells the story, usually in the third person. As the omniscience is limited, the narrator is allowed access to only one mind. Anything may be revealed about or through that character, but information about other characters is limited to what he participates in, sees, or has reported to him. Actually, this point of view is similar to real life existence. It may be visualized thusly:

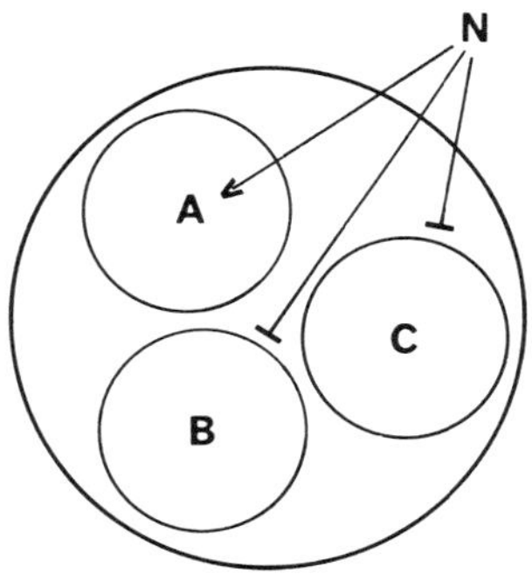

The *first person* point of view, which uses the personal pronoun *I,* combines the narrator and a character who can reveal himself *as he understands himself:*

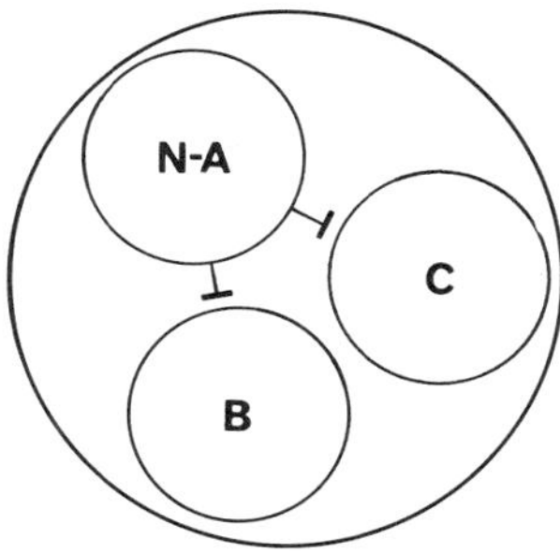

Again, the narrator-character may be major or peripheral, and he suffers the same limitations of movement and reportage that the limited omniscient narrator does. However, the candor, naivete, and limitations of the "I" allow dramatic irony to occur, for the reader may become aware (by interpreting the narrator's statements) of the significance of facts the narrator does not understand or cannot evaluate as he reports them. The limitations of dramatic irony in such a point of view are noted by Wayne C. Booth in *The Rhetoric of Fiction:*

> There can be no dramatic irony, by definition, unless the author and audience can somehow share knowledge which the characters do not hold. Though reliable narration is by no means the only way of conveying to the audience the facts on which dramatic irony is based, it is a useful way, and in some works, works in which no one but the author can conceivably know what needs to be known, it may be indispensable.*

In the twentieth century, the *objective* or *dramatic* point of view has gained wide favor, perhaps as a result of our eagerness to remain uninvolved. In either first or third person, this point of view allows only observable actions to be chronicled, only spoken words to be recorded. *Interior monolog* (thoughts of characters—the soliloquy of Shakespeare) is not permitted, nor is authorial examination of characters' motives. Because this point of view creates a fast-paced, interesting story of action, it is most suited to revelations of violence. Ernest Hemingway's "The Killers" is a classic example. When a story is successful as a result of the author's control of objective point of view, it is subtle and rewarding in ways stories told from other points of view may not be.

*Chicago, 1961, p. 175.

The peripheral narrator is often employed in such stories, frequently so far removed from the center of action that he lacks identity and is therefore said to be *effaced*—without distinguishing characteristics of any kind. William Faulkner's remarkable "A Rose for Emily" is an example of this type:

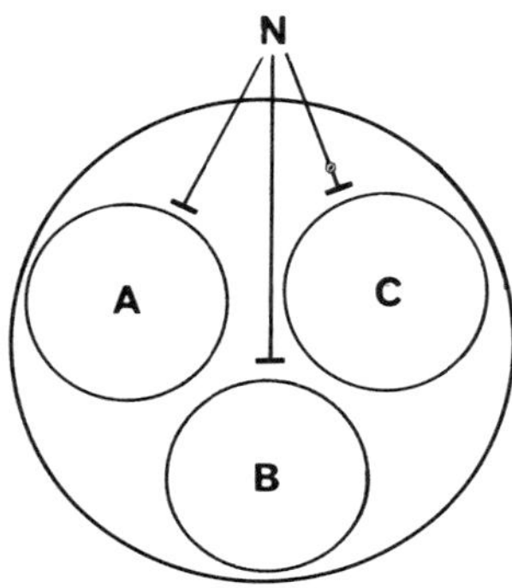

Once again, why is it important for *you* to be aware of point of view? Consider a routine conversational exchange from the four different point of view possibilities:

Objective

Joan and Peggy almost collided on the street that morning. Peggy was the first to speak. "You're so preoccupied, you almost ran over me," she said.

Laughing as she spoke, Joan said, "How wonderful you look this morning."

You have a definite attitude at this point. You may like both women, dislike both, like only one, or be indifferent. But you have an attitude. It springs from your recollections of similar meetings, your reaction to names, your response to the different cadences of speech of the two women, preconceived notions about speaking first, employing meaningless phrases, and so on. Further, as the author does not suggest voice inflections with such indications as "she said angrily" or "she accused" or "she responded happily," you must supply them from your own assessment of the conversation. And you do.

First Person

I did not see Peggy that morning on the street. When she spoke, her voice indicted me, and I was guilty.

"You're so preoccupied, you almost ran over me," she accused.

I couldn't let her know I'd have detoured for blocks to avoid such a collision; so I laughed and lied, "How wonderful you look this morning."

The shift in point of view changes the meaning of the encounter. It reveals different characters because you identify with the one you know the most about. Is Peggy really a person to be avoided? Did she really speak accusingly? In the mind of the first person narrator she did, and you accept the assessment. But should you? What motivates Joan's beliefs? Is she honest with you? Is she honest with herself?

Limited Omniscient

Peggy saw Joan halfway down the block. They must pass and speak or pass in silence. Unlike J. Alfred Prufrock, she would have no time to consider. Intuitively, she hurried her step. "Soonest begun, soonest done," Maman had always said.

As they came abreast, Peggy's dread turned to irritation. Joan wasn't ignoring her; she was unaware of her! Peggy scarcely recognized her own voice as she heard herself saying the unconsidered words, "You're so preoccupied, you almost ran over me."

Joan seemed startled, recalled to a world she had escaped—Peggy's world! "How wonderful you look this morning," she said, and she laughed happily.

"She's glad to see me," Peggy thought. "Do I really look wonderful?"

Again the meaning is changed. Again you have a distinct impression. But again you must challenge it. Would you have the same impression had the omiscience been limited to Joan rather than to Peggy?

Omniscient

Joan was unaware of Peggy until she spoke that morning on the street.

"You're so preoccupied you almost ran over me," she said, and she hated Joan and her ability to isolate herself intellectually from an ugly world.

"Why, Peggy!" Joan laughed the words as she had learned to do to disguise her distaste for interlopers. "How wonderful you look this morning!"

With the omniscient point of view, you seem to know everything—but do you? Actually, you know what the narrator has chosen to reveal *plus* whatever interpretation you place on phrases and revealed actions. You know Joan was unaware of Peggy, but why? Was she merely preoccupied? Did she have so little regard for Peggy she did not take cognizance of what her eyes revealed to her brain? Did she deliberately block sight of Peggy? Is Peggy the sort of person anyone would wish to avoid seeing? How consistent are "preoccupied" and "ran over me" as indicators of character? Is the world "ugly" through Peggy's or Joan's eyes? Is it actually ugly through the eyes of both—or neither?

An author chooses the point of view that will most contribute to the mood, tone, theme, plot, and characterizations he wishes to employ. The reader is then involved as he assesses the material presented to him from that particular point of view, and he must assess the truth or accuracy of the reportage as it is presented to him. Subtlety and innuendo are frequently employed by the author to establish the tone and mood of the story.

"Some of the Time, All of the Time" by S. Dorman appeared in *The Saturday Evening Post.* It is an excellent story for study purposes as the structure is clear and logical; the characters and descriptions, excellent; dialog, exact and revealing; symbol and theme, apparent but not oversimplified. As you read it, isolate the basic ingredients. Notice how they are skillfully blended yet individually identifiable. Pay particular attention as narrative flow speeds on exposition, slows in panorama, and focuses narrowly to create scene. Observe the pace and proportion of the beginning, the middle, and the end of the story. Unity and tone are apparent throughout the story, and atmosphere is almost palpable. In the descriptive passages, notice the effect on character. Stock and foil characters are used in this story. Observe the way Miss Dorman utilizes them to make the main characters round and full. As mention is made of each person or thing in the story, consider Chekhov's claim that a short story must contain no superfluous matter. In fact, he argued, if a gun hangs on a wall early in a work, it must *without fail* be discharged later in the story. Pay particular attention to the point of view as it reveals Marie's unconscious attitudes. Constantly ask yourself, does she believe what she thinks she does? Is she deceiving herself? How accurate are her evaluations? Also, as you read the story, you will notice no mention is made of children after the first paragraph. Does Marie want children? Does Ernie? Does either *not* want children?

Read the story first in its entirety.

Some of the Time, All of the Time

by S. Dorman

1 Marie knew that Ernie was the kind of guy who liked to smell supper cooking when he came home to the apartment, even though Marie got home from work only a little time before he did. Sometimes she wondered how women with children even managed to get a meal on the table; at other times she wished she had a chance to find out, but in six years it hadn't happened.

2 "Hi?" Ernie said this evening, as always, when he came into the foyer and clanged his lunch box down by the telephone. Marie heard it where she sat in one of the fat armchairs in front of the red living-room drapes. There was a magazine in her lap, which she closed when Ernie came in.

[3]"Baby?" Ernie said. "Don't you feel good?" There was no smell of supper cooking.

[4]Marie raised her head. She had a thin, sweet face and her brow was surrounded by brown curls. "Hi," she said softly. "I was reading." She held out to him the magazine with a blue cover. Across the top it said: *Descant: A Magazine of Poetry.*

[5]"What's that?" Ernie asked. "What the hell is that?"

[6]"It was on the subway this morning when I went to work. It was just lying there, so I picked it up for something to read." She added, "I've been sort of reading it all day."

[7]"Poetry?" Ernie said, in that voice which she could recognize. It was the same voice in which he had said, "Your father?" when he first met Mr. Walters, who wore vests and twinkled at the ladies and got drunk at the wedding.

[8]Marie smiled tentatively at her husband. "I didn't have anything else to read. Do you want supper?"

[9]"Of course I want supper," Ernie said, but he sat down in the other fat armchair under the velvet drapery of the valance. His motion stirred nothing in the small, warm living room. "I knew you always read funny stuff, like essays, like that, but are you sure you feel OK? I mean, who reads poetry?"

[10]Marie threw the magazine down to the white-velvet footstool on which no one ever put his feet. She said in a quiet voice, "I feel fine," and stood up. She went toward the kitchen, saying, "Down, down into the brine. Sleep of sharks."

[11]"Zot!" Ernie muttered, pretending to shoot himself in the head. [. . .]

The main characters are introduced and conflict is suggested in the first paragraph as Marie resents having to work and meet the demands of a supper schedule. Her use of the word *supper* rather than *dinner* provides information about both her and Ernie. So do their names. So does her use of *guy* instead of *husband, man, person,* or *fellow.* Exposition in paragraph 1 so effectively removes focus from Marie's stated desire for children that you may have missed it completely. If so, reread the second sentence. The author does not withhold information; she merely focuses your attention away from it.

Ernie's entrance reveals his character. He comes in and says "Hi?"—and it is "as always." He "clangs" his lunch box down. The lunch box indicates manual labor and associates him a second time with oral gratifications. His greeting and action suggest insensitivity. The armchairs are "fat," the drapes (not "draperies") are red (a violent color suggesting Marie's hidden resentments but which also suggests richness to her; the drapes are, therefore, pretentious, masking more than windows). A magazine did not lie in her lap; it "was" (existed) there where the result of the creative impulse (a child) would be—if there were children. Subtle semantic ambiguity results as the reader realizes Marie "closed" the book, but, grammatically, she "closed" her lap against Ernie's arrival.

The third person limited omniscient point of view is Marie's. What she emphasizes has meaning. *She* thinks Ernie noticed the absence of supper smells. She was *prepared* to think so in the opening sentence. Her resentments in the second sentence explain both her refusal to greet him with supper smells and her feelings of guilt as a result of such refusal. Because Ernie associates food with his needs, Marie usually attempts to greet him with food smells. But, since "in six years it hadn't happened," resentment forces her to withhold his satisfactions just as hers have been withheld. Ironically, he calls her "Baby" and he uses *good* in asking about her health. However, were you aware of the following subtlety: he knew immediately that something was wrong? Is he utterly insensitive? Is she aware of her own observation? She could have failed to notice, but her point of view includes the information.

Marie's immaturity is indicated as she is described (a little girl's face) and her action reported (she extends the magazine as a child would). Ernie's reaction to the magazine is resentful ("What the hell is that?"). She identifies his resentment with another suppressed resentment of her own. Are you convinced he used any particular tone of voice in saying, "Your father?" It is she who describes her father as one who "twinkled at the ladies and got drunk at the wedding." Is Ernie the type who would find either action strange in any way? Such information reveals far more about Marie than it does about Ernie.

Her explanation of the poetry and her question reveal her uneasiness, and her guilty feeling. His concern and his inability to understand her reading preferences indicate his character—the reader realizes Ernie is married to a woman he can't understand and must, as a result, cherish as a lovely, fragile thing. Description is employed to reveal a second "fat" armchair and the "velvet drapery of the valance." The "small, warm living room" seems overcrowded. How much choice has Ernie had in the furnishings? The footstool of white velvet is pretentiously opulent and unfunctional. Isn't Ernie the sort who would use a footstool, even if it were so covered, if he dared? He has lived with frustrations too—frustrations the reader recognizes from point of view, not from exposition or Marie's *conscious* revelations.

Marie's poetic quotation and Ernie's comic strip *Zot!* sharpen the contrasts built to this point. The fertile sea image of *brine* (wherein life begins and grows) is shattered by *shark;* but the sharks are no danger to life—they sleep. Nothing stirs in that brine yet to awaken them.

[. . .]He got up and went after her to the kitchen where the organdy frills of the curtains blew in and out in the breeze from the air shaft. There was a comforting hum of radios, voices, and dinnerware from the other apartments. Ernie sometimes stuck his head out that window into the air shaft, and cocked one ear to listen. "Listen," he would say, "isn't that something? All those people living? All those guys come home to supper and their wives, just like me?"

12 "I'm sorry," Marie said, flustering around. "There's just salad." She put two plates of salmon salad and some warm, hard-boiled eggs on the table. Ernie sat down, and picked up a sports magazine from the windowsill, but instead of reading, he eyed his wife. Once or twice he reached up and rubbed the bald area on the top of his head.

13 Marie said, "You aren't eating. I'm sorry about the salad."

14 "It's OK, long as you don't do it too often. You know you cook like an angel, when you try."

15 "I don't do anything like an angel," Marie said resentfully.

16 "That magazine must have shook you up," Ernie said. "I was going bowling tonight, but you want me to stay home? You feel like you're coming down with something?"

17 Marie answered, "You go bowling. I don't know if I'm getting something or not."

18 "You want to go to a movie? What's wrong with you?" He pushed the remains of a hard-boiled egg under a piece of lettuce.

19 "I'm all right. I'm going to read, anyway."

20 "That magazine?"

21 "Probably."

The "organdy frills" are indicative of Marie's femininity. The reportage of Ernie's air shaft comment serves two purposes. Marie is aware of the value he places on their home life. He is naively pleased with a sense of belonging and a sense of delighted possession. Why does Marie "fluster" around? Contrast and conflict are intensified as he picks up "a sports magazine." While Marie is not depicted as consciously resentful of the subject matter, why does she classify the periodical? Why doesn't she call it simply "a magazine"? Why is *eyed* his wife more effective than *watched?* Is this diction or idiom at work? Is it Ernie's or Marie's word? Ernie has not been described in any physical way to this point. Did you have a picture of him? How does his rubbing "the bald area on the top of his head" change your picture? This physical detail and the character trait of rubbing will be repeated later. They characterize Ernie and reveal something about him. He is puzzled, unsure; so he touches the bald spot because it too is something he can't accept or rationalize. It is a weakness he can't control. Perhaps Marie has a "bald spot" too. If you experience difficulty in separating point of view from author intrusion at this point, check back. Is Miss Dorman *explaining* anything to you, or is the information biased from Marie's assessment? Does that assessment not allow you to understand Marie also, however? The author could step in and explain it all very quickly, but one function of the short story is to *show* rather than *tell* how character change comes about.

Unknowingly, Ernie finds one of Marie's weak areas when he uses the "angel" simile. Is it ironic that, unknowingly, Ernie has at least some poetic instinct? Is it ironic that "like an angel" is applied to the domestic role of cooking? Quite deliberately ironic, for, later, he is to tell Marie he first loved her purity on their first date, and angels are sexless beings whose role is to serve man. At this point, Marie is rebellious of the image she has created of herself: an angelic doll in a doll house. This moment foreshadows the scene in the bedroom when she suggests they go to bed naked.

Ernie again reveals his "commonness" in the phrase "shook you up." He also indicates his concern, for he is willing to forego his bowling night. Bowling is important to Ernie; he offers to make a sacrifice. What does he reveal as he pushes the remains of the egg under the lettuce? What does Marie reveal as she reports it? While the warm egg reveals haste and a seeming lack of conscious forethought in her supper preparations, an egg is also the beginning of life if it is kept warm. How aware of the veiled symbol is she? Is there more than a conscious reason for Ernie's hiding the egg? Did you notice it follows his movie offer? Is he not suggesting she submerge her intellect and emotions with the opiate of motion pictures? Mention of the poetry magazine re-creates the heavy silence.

22 They were silent again while they ate their melon. Occasionally Marie looked up with guilty reserve and saw him watching her. She was uncertain about what had happened, but whenever she met Ernie's eyes something sharp touched her; some awkwardness she had never felt before; some deepness she had refused to recognize. Was it hers? Was it anything they could share?

Point of view has been established so well before this time that the reader is not disturbed at the reflective insert. Midway in the paragraph, Miss Dorman explains Marie's uncertainty—this exposition would be beyond Marie's understanding. The questions are Marie's, however, as she attempts to evaluate events. The author must intrude in this paragraph to make the reader aware of Marie's inability to analyze herself. The return to Marie's point of view assures the reader Marie is making an honest attempt.

[23]"Well, don't go getting eyestrain," Ernie said. "I'll be back early."

[24]Marie went to the door with him, and when he had gone down the hall to the elevator she went back to her chair in the living room and picked up the magazine. There was a smudge of office carbon on one page, and she blurred it with her fingers. After a while she took up a pencil and began writing along the margin of a page:

I am sinking in a deep
Where dreams swim green
Where I can't find sleep
And the doors are gone

[25]Marie put the pencil down. For years she seemed to have been sinking into something deep, which she pretended not to know about, and now she went on pretending and couldn't finish writing the poem. She had missed a good movie on television. Marie threw the magazine away. It fluttered, and landed under the couch with one wing bent back. It isn't going to fly anymore, Marie thought.

Character is revealed in Ernie's reliance on a cliché as he leaves, but listen to the word *eyestrain*—it is pronounced "I-strain." Is this conscious or unconscious ambiguity? How does Marie hear it? The smudge of office carbon is symbolic of the resentment Marie felt in the opening paragraph of the story. It foreshadows her stated desire to stop working. Examine Marie's poem. It reveals more than she consciously admits. Why does she continually return to birth imagery (the sea, which is the source of life, where her *dreams* swim green, the color of life, where she can't suspend conscious thought in sleep because the doors of knowledge and awareness can no longer be closed—they "are gone")? Is their six-year failure to have children Ernie's fault entirely? Her confusion is made apparent as she regrets missing a television film which, like a movie, would have supplied a suspension of conscious thought. But could she have escaped disturbing near-realizations that way? The allusion to Pegasus (a winged horse, symbol of creativity in poetry) is apparent in the broken "wing" of the magazine.

[26]It was very hot in the living room, and terribly full of furniture, each and every piece dear to her heart and polished to a high shine on Saturday mornings while she ran in and out of the rooms with her hair in curlers, planning the evening out.

The warm living room where Ernie's motion stirred nothing in the opening scene now becomes hot (uncomfortable because of the mental strains?). Her attitude about the furniture becomes increasingly apparent as it seems to crowd the room. She has relied on other creative activities in the past. Poetry merely offers a more exact substitute. She had pretended in the past; she pretends now; but pretense is harder to accept. She is very warm.

27 For over six years she had been polishing, putting up new drapes and heavier valances; she had made room for just one more bench, table, chair, knickknack shelf, lining the nest for herself and Ernie. Things, things, Marie said to herself, and the doors are gone. Marie went into the bedroom and looked at herself in the blued mirror. Thin, large-nosed, her face appeared to her like a donkey's, or a rabbit's. She glared at it. She took her brush and swept all her curls back, but it was still her own face.

As she had "lined the nest" with furniture, she had shut out awareness with the doors of possessiveness. What sort of imagery is "lined the nest"? Do birds line a nest for themselves or for eggs? Now "the doors are gone." Did you observe symbol and transition working together? The transitional element is subtle as she goes into the bedroom: she went through another "door" to stand before a "blued" mirror that would be less truthful than a clear one. Why does she use the donkey-rabbit simile? Is this merely description? Has she big ears or protruding teeth? Is she seeing mental similarities? What do *donkey* and *rabbit* achieve connotatively? How are they effective in symbolic contrast?

28 While she was posturing there, hoping to turn into someone new, Ernie's key sounded in the door. "Baby?" Ernie called.

29 "Here," she said, listening to him come heavily toward the room.

30 "I came home early, I figured you didn't want to be alone," he said.

31 Marie was touched that he had thought of it, and angry, because she did need to be alone, and ashamed, because she had never needed to be alone before. The deep pang struck her again.

32 "You ought to go to bed and get a good night's sleep," Ernie said. "Maybe if you rest up, you'll be all right tomorrow."

33 "Maybe," she said sadly.

34 "I'll hit the sack, too. Snore you to sleep, OK?" he asked. He was trying to be gentle, Marie saw, but she was too busy hugging her strange new needs to herself to let him reach her. Yet in another moment she felt she needed him terribly. He was sitting on the edge of the bed, and he threw his shoes off, one-two, letting them thump.

35 ". . . the apartment below . . ." Marie said, using their usual domestic shorthand.

36 Ernie didn't answer. He began to unbutton his shirt with one hand, and

switched off the lamp with the other. "Don't put your pajamas on," Marie said, before she could think what she was asking.

37 "What?" he demanded.

38 She whispered, "Don't put your pajamas on."

39 "What's the matter with you? You want me to catch cold?"

40 Marie said, "No."

41 "But you want me to sleep raw?"

42 "Yes," Marie said, and sat down in the farthest corner of the room on a green-satin stool, with her hands in her lap and her cheek resting against the cool plaster of the wall. She was going to cry.

43 After what seemed an infinite silence, Ernie asked, "Are you planning to sleep raw, too?"

44 "If you want." No, she wasn't going to cry. If there was no way he could reach her, to understand what was happening to her, then he would just have to hold her until she understood it herself.

45 She could see his square outline in the half dark. He asked, "Why are you suddenly acting like this?"

46 "I thought it would be a change."

47 Ernie shot out of bed and landed thump, one-two, like his shoes. "You got an urge for change? You want me to find a change, too?"

48 "Oh, don't get angry," Marie begged.

49 "I'm not angry," he said. "I'm just upset. You say you want a change, what am I to think?"

50 "I meant a change for us. You know I don't want anybody else."

51 He sat down on the bed. After a while he slowly unbuttoned the top of his pajamas, and dropped it on the floor. After another while, he shucked off the pajama pants. He sat scrunched up on the edge of the bed, and Marie didn't move. Ernie said, "All right. I took them off. I suppose you want me to put the light on?"

52 Marie said quickly, "Oh, no."

53 "Ha," Ernie said. "I'm ahead of you for once, anyway. Go on, then. Take off your nightie."

54 Marie slid it over her head and sat down again on the stool.

55 "Is that where you're going to spend the night?" Ernie asked.

56 Marie got up. She was halfway across the room when Ernie snapped the lamp on, totally blinding her. The light felt icy on her skin; she had never felt such nakedness, and the tears swelled in her eyes. She put her hands over her face.

57 "So there," Ernie said, and shut the lamp off. "You women. You thought all of a sudden you were going to act wild. But that's not for you, you're not that kind. I wouldn't have married you if you'd been like that."

58 While his voice went on, Marie stood, still stripped and blind, with her hands over her face. Each word of Ernie's entered her heart and nailed her more securely to her failure.

59 "The reason I married you," Ernie was saying, "is the way you trembled and shook that first night we went out. I never forgot it. I tried to kiss you on our first date and you shook and shivered, and I said to myself, boy, that's for me, I know she's never been touched by anybody. What are you doing standing there?"

60 Marie crossed the floor as though she were wading, and he moved over in the bed to give her room. They lay not touching their bare bodies, Marie curled up with her cold hands clasped around her knees.

61 "Marie?" he asked, troubled. "What was the idea?"

62 "I don't know," she said miserably. "I wanted us to be different, I wanted us to be closer, maybe. I don't know why. I wanted to change me, anyhow."

63 "Now don't you change," Ernie said, rolling over and holding her. "I like you fine. You're sweet and you're nice and that's how I like you. You want me to put the pajama top back on?"

64 "I don't care," Marie said.

How *completely* honest is her concern? What does the word *posturing* suggest? Ernie's premature return (why does he come "heavily"?) forces her to see her own selfishness. She recognizes it utterly as "she felt she needed him terribly." Do you see the constancy of Marie's character here? She had been ambivalent as she threw the magazine and regretted missing the television movie; she has old needs and new needs at odds with each other, needs that have grown to this point in contrasting symbols.

The dialog is particularly effective as Marie and Ernie discuss their night attire. She wants nothing between them so he "could hold her until she understood it herself." Physical description of Ernie: "his square outline in the half dark." Is he tall and thin, short and stocky? The shoes, introduced earlier, now serve to make description vivid as he "landed thump, one-two, like his shoes." Why are poetic devices (onomatopoeia, alliteration, simile, and rhyme) so very effective in these seven words?

The word *change* becomes weighted in its denotative and connotative meanings in this exchange. Examine the various implications carefully. *Exactly* what does she mean by "You know I don't want anybody else"? Is the statement ambiguous? Notice the use of idiom in *shucked* and *scrunched up.* Why is it effective? What does its use reveal about Ernie's character? How does his question about the light become more meaningful because of his "scrunched up" position?

Is Ernie's action of turning on the light one of calculated cruelty, revenge, or kindness in showing Marie a stark truth? Is it a combination of these? Does he know why he did it? Marie has an opinion: she has been crucified ("Each word of Ernie's entered her heart and nailed her more securely to her failure"). The religious allusion is doubly effective as it reveals her attitude and serves as transition into the "angel" revelation he makes.

Marie's immaturity is subtly symbolized in the womb posture she assumes in bed. What does she reveal in her statement about "closeness" and "change"? Remember that change may be both mental and physical. Her "I don't care" is effective understatement, revealing an attitude toward many things besides the pajamas. Assumed indifference often nails us to our failures very securely, and she has failed once again to be honest with herself, thereby allowing Ernie to understand her need.

65 Sunday afternoon Marie's father came in for a visit. He was a slim man, with a creased face and deeply set small gray eyes. Ernie was watching a ball game. Mr. Walters didn't care for sports, so he went to the kitchen with his daughter for a cup of coffee and a chat. "Everything okey-dokey with my baby?" Mr. Walters asked her.

66 "Everything's fine," Marie said.

67 There were two new books on the kitchen windowsill, and now Marie casually draped the Sunday comics over them.

68 Mr. Walters was sharp enough to catch her at it. "What's that?" he asked, lifting the comics aside. "Books?" he asked, the creases of his face folding tighter as he spoke.

69 Ernie came in for another can of beer. "Yeah," he said to his father-in-law. "She's reading again. Guess what?"

70 Mr. Walters examined one of the books. "Poetry!"

71 Marie drank her coffee and said nothing.

72 "Why, what are you doing with a book like that?" Mr. Walters asked. He put the book down with a flip that made it land hard on the table.

73 "She's beating her brains out," Ernie said, puncturing the beer can twice, one-two, and taking it back to the living room.

74 "Well, I'll be," Mr. Walters said, and twinkled at her with all his surfaces. "You weren't a romantic child, that I remember. You didn't even like nursery rhymes."

75 "I still don't," Marie said sharply, pained by the false cover of her father's twinkle and grin.

76 "Now that's no way to speak, Marie. I don't come over often enough to be in your way, just once in a blue moon, that's all. That's the world, though, isn't it?" he asked, giving her a sad smile. "When you're young, the world's your oyster, and when you're old, nobody wants you anymore. I hope you never find out how it is, to be old and lonesome."

77 "Papa, you know you're welcome here anytime. There's no reason for you to be so lonesome."

78Her father stood up and looked down with an expression that was absorbed and private. "Well, Marie, I suppose it's nice that you don't understand. But I wish you did. It's a shame for you not to understand what I'm talking about."

79Oh, you damned old fool, Marie said to herself, and put her hand over her mouth, although she hadn't spoken aloud. Perhaps she would never be able to speak aloud, and would have to spend the rest of her life hiding behind shaky hands. "I'm sorry," she said. "I have a headache from the movies last night. I woke up with a headache and it made me cross. You know I don't want to hurt you."

80Marie's mother used to say that, "Paul, I don't want to hurt you." Marie couldn't remember her mother's face anymore, but could hear her voice. Her mother used to dream of strange and wonderful landscapes, and tell her dreams to Marie at breakfast after her father had left for work.

81Marie's father adjusted his pearly felt hat and said, "It's all right. You have a good time while you're young, baby. Nothing lasts forever." He was moving out through the foyer toward the door as he spoke, and she tagged behind him. "Good-bye, Ernie," Mr. Walters called over the shouts of a final inning. "Take good care of my little Marie."

82"Yessir," Ernie said, switching the television to another channel where a game had not yet ended. "Good-bye, come for dinner soon, oh brother! look at that jerk, he can't catch a thing."

A narrative gap is bridged with chronological transition. Marie's father is more carefully described physically than either main character. His "okey-dokey" and "baby" are immediately apparent, however, as being the same popular, non-communicative idiom Ernie uses. His reaction to the books (facial creases folding tighter) is essentially the same as Ernie's to the magazine; and he pronounces "poetry" with an exclamation point. Notice Ernie's puncturing the beer can "one-two." The description is picked up from the dropped shoes and his shooting out of bed—each act an irritant to Marie. Mr. Walters' behavior is becoming more irritating too as he "twinkled at her with all his surfaces" and she is pained by "the false cover." Her "false cover" is apparent as she reacts "sharply" to "nursery rhymes," which are veiled symbolism. He makes her feel guilty, however, as she realizes how lonely he is; but she cannot communicate with him any more than she can with Ernie—and she knows she is partly at fault because she is "hiding behind shaky hands." Marie parrots her mother's "I don't want to hurt you" and remembers the woman who "used to dream of strange and wonderful landscapes." As Mr. Walters leaves, Marie seems suspended between two people, equally unaware of her as a woman. To her father, she is "baby" and "my little Marie." To Ernie, she is a baby requiring attention at certain times. This is not one of those times, and his preoccupation with the televised ball game is focused in his ironic comment. Applied to the game, the words are merely commonplace triteness; applied to Mr. Walters and Ernie, they are psychologically revealing. Are not the men "brothers" in their reactions to their wives? To Marie, are they not both "jerks" who "can't catch a thing"?

83 Marie closed the door softly, softly, on her father, and went back to the kitchen. She picked up the memo pad and chewed pencil, and began to write.

84 *First they cut off my wings*
then wanted to remove the webs
but afraid of further surgery
tied my feet into shoes.

85 *Baby darling baby say the words*
mama daddy I prove my love.

86 *They told me where I come from*
but not where I am going
they put my brain under
to hide its busy head.

87 *Baby darling baby sing the song*
mama daddy now I belong.

88 *They left me then for safe*
in a corner where my breath
is forming shapely shadows
and I'm naming wings and webs.

89 *Baby darling baby dirty paper*
mama daddy hide your eyes in water.

90 After this, she stared at what she had written. She was beginning to understand, and it frightened her. All the words she had been taught not to say, the thoughts she mustn't think, were being put down on paper.

Some doors *are* gone, if Marie's poetry is to be believed. Others are growing harder to close. She is, apparently, finding the door between her father and herself such a door. She closes the physical one "softly, softly." Marie's poem is less poetry than therapy. (John Ciardi once delivered an address to a group of business men; its title, "An Ulcer, Gentlemen, Is An Unwritten Poem," suggests the use of poetic therapy such as this.) Blaming her parents for early refusals to allow her poetic flight, she observes they forced her to use the traditional language that communicates nothing but parrottings. Such words are meaningless and do not "prove my love." By teaching her the "song" of acceptance, they accepted her. The corner of marriage was "safe" and she is again trying poetic flight, but new parents (Ernie and Mr. Walters) would slap her hands and say "dirty paper," training her again, keeping her from discovering where she is going as an adult woman.

The effectiveness of the poetic therapy frightens her because she is "beginning to understand."

91 Ernie leaned over her shoulder and began reading aloud, his voice gradually rising into a querulous upper pitch:

"Baby darling baby . . ."

he chanted at the top of his vocal range.

". . . hide your eyes in water."

His eyebrows strained upward with his voice. "Now what does that mean?" he asked, out of breath.

92 "It means cry. It also means go soak your head."

93 "I'll smack you if you talk to me like that," he said in outrage. "I don't know what's wrong with you, but for three days you haven't been fit to live with."

94 Marie turned and put her arms around him. "I didn't say it to you, Ernie. I said it to all the other people."

95 "Come on," Ernie said, patting her head. "What's the matter?"

96 He backed off from her. "I don't believe it's all on account of reading some poetry. How could that change you?"

97 "I guess whatever it is was here all the time, only I didn't know it."

98 Ernie said, "Can't you stop writing this stuff? It's making us both miserable."

99 Marie looked at him without expecting any help, and he looked past her to the poem she had written. He looks scared too, Marie thought. Then who's going to help me?

100 "What can I do?" Ernie asked.

101 "Maybe if you leave me alone, it'll go away," Marie said, but that wasn't what she wanted anymore. If it went away, before she even got a good grip on it, she would never rest again. She'd go running up and down looking for it. Whatever it was, and no matter how it hurt, she must know it better.

102 "What a character," he tried to kid her. "Some character you turned out to be. Writing poems."

103 "Would it be so awful if I did?" she asked.

104 "You aren't the type. How would you explain it to friends like Irene and Bill?"

105 Marie said, "You could tell them it's a hobby."

106 "Like collecting matchbooks or bottle caps, maybe?"

107 "Why not?"

108 Ernie backed off another step. He reached up and patted his bald spot gently, as though subduing it. He practiced: "Marie writes poetry for a hobby. It just doesn't sound right. They'll think you're cracked."

109 "I don't care, let them think it. You tell them it's a hobby and after a while they'll get used to it, won't they?"

110 "I guess so, but it sounds funny to me. What's for supper?"

111 Marie looked at the books, at the anthology of modern poems, and the textbook that held the secrets. "I dunno, but I'll fix us something."

112 "What's all that paper? It's not income-tax time," Irene said, putting her hand out toward the stack of lined paper. A magazine had been placed over the papers so no one could see what they were.

113 "Just stuff," Marie said, pushing the pile out of reach. Ernie was trying to catch her eye over the card table, but Marie wouldn't look at him.

114 "Stuff!" Bill said, smiling, showing his wonderful white teeth. "Cripes, Ernie, don't you know women always have piles of stuff around?"

115 "Not paper," Irene said. She had recently decided to let her pale hair grow longer, and she kept reaching up to pull it out of the collar of her dress. She was not easily distracted, so after she'd adjusted her hair, she asked, "What is all that paper, Marie?"

116 Ernie put down the cards he'd been shuffling, and said, "Marie's got a hobby."

117 "Good for her," Bill said, smiling all around.

118 "She's got kind of a different hobby," Ernie went on. "Something new. She writes poems."

119 Irene took the cards from Ernie, pulled her hair up from her collar, and began shuffling. Marie pushed the papers and magazine even farther away. Irene said, "I guess it's nice to have a hobby, if you have the time. Personally, when I get home, I don't have time for anything but cleaning and cooking. Did you say she writes poems?" Irene looked angry and cynical.

120 "Hey, are we having a game, or aren't we?" Bill asked.

121 "What kind of poems?" Irene continued.

122 "Just poems," Marie said. "How about dealing?"

123 "Yeah, how about it?" Bill said.

124 Irene said, "Wait," and her body elongated and slithered across the card table until she could get her hands on the papers. She drew a fistful back across the table with her. Selecting a thickly covered page, she began to read aloud.

> 125 *"It's no more useful to marry than to burn.*
> *Since when did ashes put out a fire?*
> *Banked on a domestic hearth the coals*
> *Wait for any breeze to heat them higher."*

126 Ernie reached over and snatched the page from Irene before she could go on. "It's a private hobby," he said.

127 Marie was sitting with her hands limp in her lap, thinking that if she could live through this, she could live through anything. Maybe Ernie would leave her, and she really would be alone. Maybe she deserved that; because if she didn't have the guts to speak up, she didn't have the right to put her thoughts on paper.

128 Irene flicked through the rest of the pages, saying, "If it's a hobby, it can't be private."

129 Marie murmured, "That's one of my worst poems, anyway."

130 "Then read us a good one," Bill said.

131 Irene looked up, and waited. Ernie was folding and folding the one poem between his fingers. Marie tried to guess what the expression on his face meant. She said, "I haven't written any good poems yet."

132 "Come on, let's get on the ball," Bill said, picking up the cards and beginning to deal. Ernie put the tightly folded page in his shirt pocket, over his heart, and Marie wondered if she could make him some explanation.

133 "You haven't got a chance," Bill said, frightening her with his insight, but he was only speaking of the cards.

134 "You going to publish those poems?" Irene asked.

135 "I haven't thought about it. How would I publish them?"

136 "Send them to the paper, why don't you? You might as well get paid for it. What a ball! Scribble a few lines a day and make pocket money," Irene said.

137 It isn't like that, Marie thought. "I don't think those newspaper poems are very good," Marie said.

138 "Don't be a snob," Irene said sincerely. "If they want to pay you for a poem, what do you care what they publish?"

139 They can't pay me for this hurt, Marie thought; and she rebelled completely: I don't want to write them, I don't want to know the truth about any of us, I want to go back and be myself again.

Ernie has no defense at all. He is frightened and shows it. Her reaction is utterly selfish: "Then who's going to help me?" Because she has been protected so long by Ernie and her father, she has become reliant. Now she must help herself admit needs before Ernie can help. And the reality frightens her. Defensively, they both reduce their fears to bantering platitudes, but Ernie reveals his insecurity by patting his bald spot and suggesting food. Does Marie know he has a psychological association with food? If she knows it, does she realize food serves the function for him that poetry does for her at this time? Or does she stop trying her wings again and return to the shoes they tied her feet into?

Foil characters are introduced after a whitespace transition. How is it effective? Bill is characterized by "wonderful white teeth" and he says only kind words. Irene is persistent, not easily distracted, self-important. She is unaware of the rights of others. She is preoccupied with her hair which she keeps adjusting. What insecurity is suggested? Are her needs completely different from Marie's? Notice her statement about having no time for hobbies. Compare it with the second sentence of paragraph 1 of the story. Why did she look "angry and cynical"? Her unpleasantness is intensified as, snake-like, "her body elongated and slithered across the card table." The poem she reads is revealing—even to someone as insensitive as she. Marie's creative needs burn more intensely because, married, she could have a baby, but she is thwarted by Ernie—the one who could fan the banked coals into flame. Ernie's protective impulse sends the folded poem "over his heart." Irene's sincere moment is an accusing one; her insensitivity is a sobering one; Marie is thoroughly frightened.

140 The evening seemed to continue indefinitely. Bill slid lower and lower in his chair, the ashtrays began to overflow, and the smell of cigarette smoke would hang for days in the red-velvet drapes which Marie now hated with all her heart. Irene and Bill stayed so late that Ernie had to mix more highballs.

141 While they were drinking, and eating peanuts, Irene pulled her hair away from her neck and asked, "You really serious about poems? It's going to be a serious hobby?"

142 Marie thought it was time, at last, to speak up, or she would never be able to, so she answered Irene with, "It isn't really a hobby. I take it too seriously for that."

143 "You're not the type, kid."

144 Ernie broke in bitterly. "That's what I told her. Only like she pointed out to me, I never met any poetesses, so how would I know what the type is?"

145 "Everybody knows," Irene said.

146 Bill said, "Aw, come on, live and let live I always say. If she wants to write them, so what? It's better than running up bills, or hitting the bottle, or getting some nervous disease like Andy's wife."

147 "But not much better, huh?" Marie asked. "You listen. I like writing poems. I don't like having you describe it as some kind of sickness, so lay off me."

148 "You never could take it," Irene said, getting up. "I can see it's time to go home. Ernie, when she comes to her senses, let us know, and maybe we can take in a movie like old times."

149 At the door Irene said, "Good night now. Marie, don't carry it too far."

"Nice guy" that he is, Bill slides down in his chair. He is, unfortunately, controlled by Irene. (Why, then, does Irene want Ernie to retain control of Marie? Remember her look of anger and cynicism. Why does Bill encourage Marie's freedom?) Marie now hates the red drapes. While Irene is a foil character about whom little is revealed, what can the reader assume about her fear of change in the relationships of the two *couples?*

150 Marie closed the door and went back to the living room where Ernie was still sitting at the card table. Ridged with folds, the poem was lying in front of him, and he was reading it in a whisper.

151 "It's pretty bad, isn't it?" Marie asked, gathering up the empty glasses.

152 "I don't know," Ernie replied without looking up. His fists lay on the table with the poem between them. "I don't know anything about poems, or about the people who write them, either. I don't know why you suddenly had to come out with this. If you aren't happy with me, you ought to tell me so to my face, and not when there's people here, either."

153 "It wasn't my fault Irene read it."

154 Ernie continued sitting there, and Marie found she was trembling so much that she put the glasses back on the table for fear of breaking them. It wasn't worth it. No poem was worth seeing Ernie sit there like that.

155 "Ernie," she said hopefully.

156 No answer.

157 "Ernie, please. Let me explain it to you."

158 "Explain what? Explain you aren't happy with me? Explain why you spring it on me in public?"

159 "You won't even listen to me."

160 "No, I won't," he said angrily. "And you're done with writing poems. You got something to say, you say it right to my face, and don't be sneaky putting it down in rhyme like it wasn't meant for anything." He lifted both fists and banged them on the table, which collapsed and sent the cards flying in the air.

161 The glasses cracked together, splinters drove into the carpet, and ice cubes lay about like diamonds. Ernie picked the poem out of the air and began tearing it to small shreds.

162 "That's what I think of your poem," he said.

163 "It was a bad poem. I would have torn it up myself," Marie said. "And it's true I have to learn to say what I mean, and speak up. Maybe if I learn to do that, I can learn to write a good poem."

164 "I wish I knew what you meant by a bad poem," Ernie said. He leaned down, tried to pick bits of glass from the rug.

165 "Don't. I'll get the vacuum cleaner," Marie said.

166 "At this hour? They'll bang on the wall. What did you mean by a bad poem?"

[167]"It doesn't say what I mean. It was just words, and I'm sorry Irene picked that one. It doesn't matter, does it?"

[168]"I can't understand why you'd write it if you didn't mean it."

[169]He's more truthful than I am, Marie thought, pressing both hands against her heart where the poem hurt. He knows me, he knows I write what I can't say, he's gone and switched the light on when I'm undressed, again, and now he's going to hate me for being naked.

[170]Ernie said, "How about that last line? You want to burn up in a fire for that blond salesman in your office?"

[171]"It hasn't got anything to do with anybody I know, or with us. It was on account of getting the rhyme. I'm not very good at rhyme, yet,"

[172]"I don't think much of a poem if it hasn't got anything to do with anybody."

[173]"You're right," Marie said, humbly. You're so right, and I can't take it. She began to cry, hoping Ernie would come and comfort her. He would tell her it was all right, it didn't matter, they could finish eating the peanuts and laugh together. But it did matter, and Ernie turned around and went to the bedroom, and went to bed.

[174]While Marie undressed in the dark, Ernie lay silent. She couldn't hear him breathing, so that meant he wasn't asleep. She wanted him to speak, even if it was only to be angry with her. "Don't you believe me about the poem?" she asked.

[175]"I don't know what to believe anymore. You never lied to me, that I know of. You always were honest and nice."

[176]"I'd like to know what you mean by nice," Marie challenged him. "I think you're like Papa. You mean I never did anything that didn't please you. I never showed a mind of my own before."

[177]"Why should you have a mind of your own like that?" Ernie demanded. "Don't I do for both of us? You act like you're through with me, you don't need me anymore."

[178]"I'm sorry you're hurt, Ernie. But I'm hurt, too."

[179]Ernie said, "I been a good husband. I never asked questions when you spent money, I never been with another woman. I come home to dinner almost every night. And now you act like you could throw me away."

[180]"I need you very much, but I need you for something different, something more, I guess. And you have to need me for something more, too." She sat on the edge of the bed and slid her slippers off.

[181]After a long time, Ernie touched her back with his fingers. "I don't know what kind of more you want."

[182]"I don't either. Only we never did really talk to each other, and now it doesn't seem real. It seems we've been pretending for six years, and we can't even talk to each other."

[183]Ernie said, "If I could just understand. I been trying to understand."

[184]Marie got under the covers and felt her muscles ache, as though she'd worked

hard all evening to hold herself together. "Well," she said, "I can't help you and you can't help me."

185 "That leaves us exactly nowhere."

186 Marie sighed. "That's right. Nowhere. It's an awful place to be."

Marie recognizes her love for Ernie when she knows "No poem was worth seeing Ernie sit there like that." Suddenly she can explain, but now he can't let her. Notice the poetic devices in the paragraph beginning "The glasses cracked together." The description is remarkable in establishing a cold, cutting, destructive tone. Why?

Marie is learning something about herself as she says she may learn to write a good poem when she learns to say what she means. Ernie's contrition is apparent in words and actions. The "domestic shorthand" from the shoes scene is recalled here. Marie recognizes "He's more truthful than I am." And she resents the realization because "he's gone and switched the light on when I'm undressed again, and now he's going to hate me for being naked." Platitudes do not save this scene for Marie. She is forced to say, "you're like Papa." The truth is out. And he compounds the agony of truth with "Don't I do for both of us?" She finds words to suggest she wants a mature marriage with a husband rather than with a father who protects his sweet little girl, but Ernie and she both miss the import of her longing words.

187 In the morning when they got up, Ernie didn't seem to notice that she walked hunched up, as if she had a cramp in her stomach. He slammed out to work with hardly a word, and Marie sat cramped, uncombed, and grieving at the kitchen table. The two books she had bought lay on the windowsill uselessly. They couldn't help her, and there were no secrets in them.

188 She walked from bedroom to living room to kitchen, and back again. The fat, hot furniture gave her no room to move. All this time she'd spent collecting it, filling the cabinets with dishes, the closets with clothes, and she hated them all.

Marie's illness is one of the soul as well as of the menstrual cycle. She somehow knows a basic truth which isn't completely manifest as yet; therefore there are no secrets in the poetry books. She hates the stage effects of the lie she too has helped build and live for six years.

189 Ernie came home at the end of the day and found her lying on the bed in her bathrobe. "You're sick," he accused.

190 "Am I?"

191 "You didn't go to work."

192 "I wish I never had to go to work again."

193 "Going to stay home and write poems?"

194 "I'd like to," she said. "I'll send some to a magazine."

195 "You mean they might pay you money for them?" he exclaimed.

196 "Who knows?" Marie sat up and pulled the robe tight around her for protection. "What difference does it make? I've got what you think is a sickness, and I don't even think I want to be cured."

197 "Oh, don't talk like that. I didn't mean you were sick like that."

198 "You damn well did mean it."

199 "Don't talk like that, it doesn't sound nice. You're a nice girl."

200 "I don't want to be nice," she screamed. "I'm tired of being sweet and domestic. I'm so tired of hearing about how nice I am, as long as I keep quiet and do what you tell me."

201 Ernie grunted. Then he said, "Look, if you want to quit work for a while, that's OK. I don't mind."

202 Marie took his hands and pulled at him until he sat down on the bed. She touched his hair, and held onto his arms, trying to get the feel of him, to see who he was, and hoping he would reflect her strongly enough so that she could tell what she was, too.

203 Ernie bore her investigation quietly, and then asked, "Do you want to get divorced? Is that what you want?"

204 "Where would I go!"

205 Appalled, he drew back from her. "Is that all I am? Somebody to keep you in an apartment?"

206 This was so close to the truth of what they had lived on for six years that she was silent with shame.

207 Ernie asked, "You know what that makes you?"

208 "Yes," Marie answered. "I know what it makes us both. Maybe that's why I'm sick."

209 "That doesn't explain the poems, does it? How come you picked up a magazine one morning, and discovered all this?"

210 Marie said, "I started to think. I mean, I began thinking before I could stop myself, like I usually do. And then," she went on, in a rush, "I thought that if something like one poem could speak to me like that, I wanted to speak, too."

211 "I wish to God you'd never thought," he said, getting up. "You want me to get a divorce? Because if that's all I am, somebody to keep you in food and clothes, I don't like it very much."

212 "But you're the one who said it. You said you were a good husband, because of just that. Because you let me buy clothes, and came home to dinner."

213 "But! I mean, it isn't just that, for God's sake, Marie, no guy marries a woman just to keep her in clothes."

214 "You married me like I was a new chair, because nobody else had had me."

Ernie is less solicitous of her illness now. He "accused." She will not be naked again; she pulls her robe tight "for protection" and says "damn." When he chides her as a father might, she lashes out that she doesn't want to be nice. Their conversation slides them to the edge of shared truth. But only to the edge.

215 Ernie walked out of the room, and Marie sat bent over, wondering where she would go. She heard the doorbell ring, and then her father's voice. Don't let him in, she silently asked, please, I can't stand his sad old smiles and silly talk like I was still in pigtails.

216 She heard Ernie say to her father, "She wants a divorce," and her father's voice, incredulous and angry.

217 "Marie! Baby!" he said, coming in to the bedroom.

218 "I'm not a baby. I'm a grown woman," Marie said. She was so hardened at last by all that had happened that she could look him right in the eye and say anything she felt. She did look at him so, and saw his loneliness and fear, his rage at being tricked by life into the loneliness, his despair at not being able to make anyone understand. Marie saw in his eyes everything that she had been feeling.

219 "I suppose you're grown up," her father said, coming across the room to her. "I hope you are. But you're still my baby. What's this nonsense about a divorce? What's the trouble with you two? You can't get a divorce just because you've quarreled."

220 "We haven't quarreled. We just don't want to be married anymore."

221 He bent over, looking into her face, and she drew back from him. "Is that all your marriage means to you?" he asked.

222 "Evidently."

223 "Now that's not my Marie talking—"

224 "Oh yes it is," she said, rising up to her knees on the bed. "Oh yes, it's your Marie talking. It's your Marie who's going to get out of the trap before it's too late, before she turns into the owner of a red-velvet museum full of walking corpses."

225 Mr. Walters reached out and gave her a shove which made her sit down hard on the bed. "You don't know what you're talking about," he shouted at her. "You wait until you live alone in a furnished room. You wait until you spend Sundays reading in the park before you talk about walking corpses. You wait until you sleep alone every night, and eat your breakfast in a drugstore every morning, before you talk about being in a trap. I'm an old fool, but at least I know it. You ask your father about being alone in solitude and he can tell you. Ernie?"

The arrival of Mr. Walters frees her from childhood self-love. She *sees* her father for the first time. And being seen forces Mr. Walters to be honest—possibly also for the first time. He stops being a stock character (a role assigned him by Marie) and becomes a round one here. Point of view becomes quite interesting and cleverly manipulated at this point.

226 Ernie came in, and Marie wondered if he had seen that her father wasn't being phony anymore. I should have known him better, she thought. I guess I never dared to find him out, before.

227 Mr. Walters asked, "Ernie, what's the complaint? I mean, what brought this on?"

228 "She started writing poems, and got her head full of ideas, and then she told me all I was, was somebody to keep her."

229 "I never—" Marie started, but her father said, "Be quiet. You let him finish."

230 "That's all. That's enough, isn't it?" Ernie asked.

231 "No," Mr. Walters said. "You are supposed to keep her, aren't you? Just like she's supposed to keep you, too? Cook for you? Wash your socks? You want something more than that?"

232 "Sure I do," Ernie said angrily.

233 "What about you, Marie? You want something more, too?"

234 She said, "I did. Now I just want to be left alone."

235 Her father said quietly, "That's the rottenest thing that can happen to anybody, to be left alone."

236 Marie shook her head at both the men, and said, "The reason he married me is because I was a virgin. He said so. That's ridiculous. It's like wanting to own a brand-new car, or something. How can you make a marriage out of that?"

237 "You're both ridiculous," Mr. Walters said. "You aren't either of you grown up. I don't know what you expect out of marriage, but you've both got the most glorified damned ideas I ever heard. Ernie wants his sweet little woman to stay that way forever, and Marie wants her big strong husband to talk to her by moonlight, and you better fight it out your own way, because I haven't got another thing to say to either of you kids."

238 "I won't stop writing poetry," Marie said.

239 "You don't have to, do you?" her father asked. "Personally, I think it's silly, but I don't care."

240 "Why shouldn't she stay sweet and nice?" Ernie asked.

241 "She isn't a doll, Ernie, she's a woman. Only a doll smiles all the time."

242 Marie asked, "Why should we stay married, just because neither of us wants to live alone?"

243 Mr. Walters crushed his hat down on his head and went to the door. "You both seem to want more than that." He looked at his daughter. "I was wrong to always treat you like a baby. But you're old enough by now to know that I was wrong." He went out through the living room, and they heard him close the apartment door.

Marie hopes Ernie can see what she sees. She no longer imposes her evaluations on him, however. She is maturing rapidly now. Mr. Walters assesses their desires objectively, and he makes his own admissions: "I was wrong to always treat you like a baby. But you're old enough by now to know that I was wrong." He has forced Ernie to admit he wants more than food and creature comforts, but he can't tell them they both want a baby; that they must discover together.

244 Marie went to the dresser, where she began to brush her hair with hard strokes. In the mirror she saw Ernie watching her, and she spoke to his reflection. "Are we going to try, some more?"

245 "I don't want a divorce. You did. Only I don't want it."

246 "What do you want, then?"

247 They looked at each other in the mirror. Ernie shook his head. "If I'm just somebody to keep you, and you're the same, is that enough?"

248 "I guess it depends on how well we keep each other, doesn't it? Or would you rather live alone?"

249 "Not me," Ernie said.

250 "Me neither," Marie said. "It's awfully late. If you open a can of soup, I'll make some sandwiches."

251 Ernie went to the kitchen, and Marie put on some lipstick and went out there, too. They sat down and ate without conversation. When Marie had cleared the table, and they were drinking coffee, Ernie asked, "Honest, is that all? I've never been any better than that to you?"

252 "Yes," Marie said, lowering her eyes. "Much more, sometimes. Some of the time it's been fine."

253 He half rose from his chair and leaned until his face was close to hers. "I don't want anybody else, only you," he said. After a moment of balancing there, his face sad and disappointed, he went into the living room and Marie heard him sit down heavily. She pushed her cup away and picked up pencil and paper. She wrote, and crossed out words, and wrote some more, all the time listening to the blood circulating in her veins, keeping her painfully alive. The pencil rolled from her fingers, and she put her head down on her arms. I want to be alive, she cried to herself. I want to love, I want to try.

Marie's insecurity manifests itself in attention to her hair, recalling Irene's action. Is this significant? She suggests, "If you open a can of soup, I'll make some sandwiches." Symbolically, she will share his psychological needs—even if he won't share hers. And in that decision, Marie becomes mature enough to be a mother, to share of Self while realizing the satisfactions given to another person work always to remove the child's need of the parent. That was Mr. Walters' realization. And it was how he knew Marie was mature enough to become a mother. Ernie leaves her to her poetry.

254 She was still crumpled there when Ernie came back to the kitchen, and said, "Hey. You want to look at this?"

255 A piece of paper drifted down by her arm. Sitting up, she rubbed her face with her hands. Ernie had already gone back to the other room, and turned the television on. She picked up the sheet of lined paper on which Ernie had written:

I am married to a girl
who writes poems in the kitchen
and keeps me thin on egg salad
but she used to cook steaks.

256 "Oh, Ernie," Marie said, edging through the living room to approach him. "Ernie, what a poem! But I love you."

257 Ernie was nestled in the arms of one of the fat red chairs. When Marie spoke, he drew his chin in. "I couldn't find any rhyme for kitchen," he said. "I didn't know it was so hard to write one."

258 "It doesn't have to rhyme, anyway," Marie said. She closed her eyes and began wading toward him through the darkness. When she bumped into the chair, Ernie took her hand. Finally she opened her eyes, and leaning down, she put her lips against his cheek.

259 Ernie said, "If it's been right with us some of the time, maybe we can make it all of the time." He twisted away to look at her. "If you can write a poem, you can try something real hard, like being married to me, can't you?"

260 "Yes," Marie said, "I'm not a baby, you know. I wanted to marry you."

261 "I know you did," Ernie said.

262 "That's why I shook, that first date of ours. I wanted you to kiss me."

263 "That's why I kissed you," Ernie said. □

But he had not left her. He had shared her psychological longing too. His effort is no better than her menu, but the desire to understand is love. The climax brings full realization of that love.

As she goes into the living room, "Ernie was nestled in the arms of one of the fat red chairs." Notice the "nest" allusion? Their problems are not solved, but the reader feels they will be one day. If Ernie is mature enough to share her psychological needs, he knows what love demands, and that makes him capable of the creative act of parenthood also.

A brief beginning of one paragraph, a carefully-wrought middle, and a quick ending seem the proper proportion for this story. The pace is as brisk as the character changes will allow. Had the story been hurried, someone would have "come to realize" and the plot would have been lost. The slow unfolding, step by step, with realization beginning, growing, and blooming is far better pacing. The fat chairs, food, poetry—such symbols give unity to the story as the subtlety of the psychology challenges the reader and a theme emerges. It will not necessarily be the same theme for every reader, for his experience and understanding will influence that theme. But each reader should now be able to state what he feels the theme of this story to be—and he should be able to explain why he thinks as he does.

Suggested Activity. With awareness of how carefully such plots are constructed, attempt a short story. Try the following plan. Later, as you become proficient, you will find your own best way. Use this plan until you discover your own:

1. Interest yourself in a character or situation. If a situation interests you first, establish characters for it.
2. Write a working sketch of the characters. It need not be a finished work as only you will see it. In the sketch, establish physical details, distinguishing characteristics, and habits. Construct the characters' backgrounds and beliefs. In short, get to know your characters so well you are aware of things about them that will not appear in the finished story. This will aid in establishing verisimilitude. Establish speech patterns as a part of character.
3. Write working sketches of a brief nature for stock, foil, and minor characters. If a speech or behavioral characteristic is helpful, become so accustomed to it that, when you think of the character, you will hear or see the trait. Know what purpose the character will have in the story.
4. Isolate the précis. Write it out. As you plot, keep it in mind. As it represents the general theme, you must know what you wish to suggest to the reader.
5. Write a running narrative of your story without attention to scene or description or dialog. Make sure there is a problem, complications, conflict, and a climax.
6. Outline the summary:

   I. Beginning
   II. Middle
   III. End

7. Supply scene details of characterization and description; for example:

A. Sam worries spider with a stick.
   1. Spider and setting described.
      a. Golden garden spider.
   2. Sam's basic sadism suggested.
      a. Spider struggles under stick and loses leg.
      b. Sam smiles and grinds leg into ground.
      c. Returns to spider.
   3. Sun in spider's eyes and Sam's reveals wary quality in both creatures.

B. Mary Jane calls from house.

8. Make sure the major characters and crucial situations are introduced in the opening scenes.

9. Indicate theme development points.

10. Be sure the narrative progression is logical and orderly.

11. Complications should be paced well and be of pertinence to the plot. If they do not reveal conflict in the basic story line, they should be eliminated.

12. Pace the story outline so that the suspense mounts steadily to a climax.

13. Keep concluding scenes relatively brief, making sure any decisions or results of characters' decisions are defensible.

14. Write your first draft, not worrying about excellence of prose. Concentrate on the flow of narrative and character development. You can improve description and dialog in revision.

15. Read the draft. Does the story begin at a point which will interest the reader immediately? Should a scene be used where narrative panorama now bridges scenes? Do not let impatience ruin your story. Is the order of scenes logical? If flashbacks are necessary, are the transitions into and out of them logical, smooth, and effective?

16. Check your point of view. Is it maintained? Do you violate it at all? If so, why?

17. Revise your draft, paying attention to the narrative. Is it smooth? Check transitions. In scenes, did you employ diction and idiom advantageously? Poetic devices? Does all description serve a definite, stateable purpose? Are all five senses appealed to? Do characters behave believably? Is dialog "right"? Can the reader tell who is speaking without identifying statements?

18. Revise as many times as you feel necessary, remembering that there is no such thing as good writing—there is only good rewriting.

Suggested Assignments. 1. Examine one of the stories in the next chapter just as you have examined "Some of the Time, All of the Time." Write a three-paragraph statement of theme as you see it, enforcing your opinion with arguments based on character, point of view, and symbol.

2. Read the stories in Chapter VI carefully, noting the authors' use of character, symbol, theme, and point of view. The first story relies on plot much more than the second does; the second relies on plot more than the third does; yet all three are concerned with character revelation as it is influenced by a third "absent yet present" character. In a brief paper, decide which is the more realistic story, remembering that reality is not a simple thing to assess. Use caution.

CHAPTER VI

Beginning to Discriminate: Types of Fiction

If, through the years, you had recorded the titles of all the literary works you had read, you would probably have an amazingly long list of surprisingly diversified titles. Prose and poetry, fiction and non-fiction, the important and the trivial—all would be represented. You would, however, probably find the number of short narratives larger than all the other forms combined.

The earliest stories on your list would be simple tales from childhood: myths, fables, fairy tales, and biblical accounts employing limited vocabulary. These would give way to stories of greater length and complexity as well as more elaborate vocabulary. However, stories including lengthy descriptive passages, authorial interpretations, and background commentary would be far less numerous than those with fast-paced, easily followed plots. Those "action-packed" stories would probably make up the bulk of your freely chosen reading experiences, becoming sprinkled with more ambitious works as teachers assigned material designed to make you aware of the complexities of your world and the subtleties of interpersonal human relations.

In one sense, all stories are *didactic*—that is, designed to instruct or teach moral concepts. In the less sophisticated stories, a *moral,* or ethical lesson, is almost painfully obvious. The good guys wear the white hats while justice triumphs . . . and triumphs . . . and triumphs. As stories become more complex, the good guys' hats may grow a little dingy, but they're still white, and justice still triumphs, although now she may have to rely on questionable legal technicalities. In stories of greatest depth, all the hats are gray—only shades of the one color exist—and justice is happy to settle out of court if, in the first place, she can find a lawyer.

The reader's preference for one of the three types

is, in many ways, indicative of his maturity, ability to recognize reality, and desire to find fictional analogies to his life. All readers demand one thing of a story, however. It must be interesting enough, well written enough, imaginative enough to constitute a literary experience. If it fails to create an illusion of some form of reality, it does not become an experience. Failing to identify with the characters, the reader merely stands outside the story and observes without emotional involvement. And reading is not a spectator sport; it demands conscious participation if a literary experience is to occur. That participation is called reader *identification.*

If identification allows you to forget your personal problems as you read, to suspend your own existence and vicariously assume the life and adventures of a character in the story, to become an adventurous, swashbuckling, exciting human beyond the confines of personal, trivial existence, you are probably reading a story that can be classified as *escape literature.* It will be characterized by a plot that is "action-packed," in which suspense is generated steadily as incident leads into incident quickly and without great concern for character development. The characters will, in fact, be basically stock in their appearance, behavior, and response. One of them (a hero or heroine of sorts, at least) will lend himself to easy identification in your mind. If he is a detective, he will be either handsome, clever, successful with women, and indestructible, or homely, clever, successful with women, and indestructible. If he is a sportsman, he will, after overcoming seemingly insurmountable obstacles, win the game, catch the big fish, or shoot the wily bear. If he is a cowboy, he will retrieve the rustled cattle, save the ranch, and overcome the villain. In all cases, good (here broadly defined as "right" rather than "moral") will overcome evil ("wrong" by any number of yardsticks) and the reader will happily realize that the theme confirms any opinions he held before he began reading. He can return to the world of reality without the necessity of examining his beliefs in light of the literary experience. If anything, his optimism about life will be reinforced and, somehow, God will be in His heaven and all will be right with the world even more than before.

Such escape stories will ordinarily appear in anthologies devoted to the type (detective, sports, love, western, science fiction, fantasy) or in *pulp magazines*—those which are printed on inexpensive paper (high in wood pulp rather than rag content) for quick sale at lower cost than other magazines. Like their anthology counterparts, these magazines are devoted to one general type of story: *Teen Story Love, Western Tales, Super Science Fiction, Exciting Sports,* and so on. Nor do the authors of such stories expect them to be read and reread by future generations as a result of their literary merit. They are usually written to be read quickly —and as quickly forgotten. This candid appraisal is, under no circumstances, to be considered a snide criticism of such stories. Escape literature needs no defense, numbering among its titles much that *is* lasting and valuable. *Treasure Island, Robinson Crusoe, Peter Pan,* the Sherlock Holmes stories—all are escape literature of high caliber.

The most sophisticated reader will, quite frequently, turn to escape reading—especially detective or spy stories—deliberately and delightedly. Leaders of nations (America in particular) have made no effort to conceal their taste for escape reading, citing its therapeutic value. The grand dame of escape literature writers is Agatha Christie, the best selling single author of all time. Only the Bible has sold more copies than her total works.

However, any but the most immature reader will eventually turn to more serious fiction (that which reveals something about our world, ourselves, and others), which is called *revelatory* or *interpretative* because it offers us insights which might otherwise escape us. At its simplest level, the interpretative short story falls into the category of *slick fiction* (that which is published in mass market magazines on a better grade of glazed—slick—paper, more expensive because the circulation is larger, the audience more demanding). Much that characterizes escape literature is also observable in slick fiction. The plots are predictably *formula structures* (created according to certain prescribed recipes such as boy meets girl, boy loses girl, boy wins girl), but the formula possibilities are more numerous than they are in escape literature. While the major portion of slick fiction deals with young love of one kind or another, it also includes marital-problem plots (but they *must* end satisfactorily), the innocent wisdom of the very young (from a sentimental point of view), or the experienced wisdom of the aged (from an equally sentimental point of view). Occasionally an animal story appears, but the ubiquitous wisely-young or clear-thinking-old inevitably become paramount in the plot. With the advent of the magazines designed for sophisticated males, fantasy and science fiction have received new respectability since they lend themselves to the anxious libido searching for its particular concept of truth.

Finally, the most complex, demanding stories are called *quality fiction.* Their artistic intent is considerably greater than that of pulp or slick stories. At times, they may seem deliberately obscure, thoroughly disorganized, and appallingly incomprehensible. Their authors do not deliberately create difficulties for the reader, however; the nature of the communication (in terms of theme, symbol, allegory, and unity) is so subtle, so evasive, so important that the simplicity and easy answers of pulp and slick fiction reveal themselves as obviously shallow—if not false—when given quality story treatment. In the pulp story, good always triumphs over evil, the boy always wins the girl. Slick fiction perpetrates the pattern but intensifies the difficulties by examining motives more honestly, approaching reality a little closer. Quality story authors and readers accept the inevitability of certain circumstances: evil frequently defeats good in real life; children are often unspeakably cruel in their conduct; the elderly are frequently senile, drooling nuisances whose deaths are eagerly anticipated by those on whom responsibility falls. In short, the quality story attempts to re-create the truth of life rather than to encourage rationalization. Readers who cannot accept such examinations of truth will, naturally, find the stories incomprehensible—but so is life for such people.

Nona Balakian, a contemporary commentator on the literary scene, has observed of recent quality fiction:

> More consciously and to a greater degree than ever before, the writer is striving to make the language, the tone, the very cadence of his prose, as well as the story's essential form, contain and control his meaning.
>
> The aesthetic distance thus achieved has both its dangers and its rewards. If it complicates communication by placing a greater load on the reader's power of interpretation, it also makes communication more creatively challenging.*

Distinguishing between pulp or slick, between slick or quality, is not always easy. The pulp story may contain quality ingredients, the slick may contain ingredients of both. Restraint and subtlety may be manifest in all stories, but attention to plot devices will be more evident in the pulp than in the quality, action will be more important, suspense will be more apparent. Slick stories usually balance the importance of theme and symbol against the necessities of plot, creating, in many ways, stories of greatest transparency and least interest because they seem superficial and pretentious to the reader who knows that "Life just isn't like that."

Theme and symbol are employed in almost all stories. Pulp fiction always contains at least one readily apparent theme which, because it is the broadest generalization in the story, is not explicitly stated by the author but is implicit throughout the work, revealing itself fully in the climax. In slick stories, the theme is often less easily isolated, but it will manifest itself as the story is examined logically. It becomes much less apparent in quality fiction because broad generalizations are unsubtle and lead to oversimplification if not outright error in logic and reality.

* *The Creative Present,* ed. Nona Balakian and Charles Simmons (New York, 1963), p. xi.

Symbols often indicate theme in fiction of all classifications, sometimes obviously, sometimes subtly. The *direct symbol* is most easily identified: the flag represents patriotism and love of country; the cross represents sacrifice, spiritual love, or salvation. As the direct symbol is so easily understood (being an outright cliché as it is in these examples), it is most often employed in pulp fiction. It does appear in slick and quality stories, however, when the author finds it desirable. The *context symbol* may be encountered in pulp fiction, but its greatest use is in slick and quality stories. Any object may be developed into a context symbol since the author employs it in conjunction with specific activities, creating contextual associations within the framework of plot. If you have ever read Tennyson's "The Lady of Shalott," you will recall the loom whereon the Lady wove her unreal tapestry. The object and the activity became a vivid part of her existence, revealing a great deal about her character. When she eventually decided to leave the tower, to go to Camelot, to join the world of reality, the tapestry ripped apart. Contextually, it creates an awareness in the reader of the Lady's withdrawal from life and her inability to rejoin those living in reality. Symbol becomes apparent at this point and theme emerges.

The *cumulative symbol* builds a pattern of associations, either in setting or character or both. In Hawthorne's novel *The Scarlet Letter,* for instance, the primeval forest and darkness (including night) become indicative of superstition and evil, beginning with the early passage describing the prison as the "black rose of society." Sunlight and bright color suggest knowledge and good and are repeatedly placed in tension against the opposing symbols. As the novel progresses, the pattern grows from the direct symbol (the scarlet letter *A* for "adultress") with its cumulative features (gold design wrought by Hester) through such passages as the forest scene wherein sunlight pierces the gloom and Pearl's dark anger forces Hester to replace the discarded ornament. The beclouding presence of Chillingworth, the dark night of Dimsdale's confession, and the dark-light dichotomy of Pearl's personality build the cumulative symbolism to its eventual revelation of the theme of the novel. At that point, allegory becomes apparent through symbol and theme as the reader realizes what his identity is in relation to the characters of the book. Such subtle revelation marks a quality work, for plot action is merely the thread on which revelatory episodes, like bright beads, are strung.

The scarlet letter itself functions in the story as a *multiple perspective symbol*—one which may seem to symbolize different things to various beholders. Some of the townspeople see it as the symbol of an adultress, others as a symbol for an angel. In another great novel, *Moby-Dick,*

Melville represents the great white whale as a symbol of evil to Ahab, the co-existence of good and evil to Ishmael, and any number of possibilities to the reader. It is, therefore, a symbol of multiple perspective. Obviously, such symbols will be almost totally absent in pulp fiction, seldom included in slick fiction, but frequent in quality works. Identification and evaluation of such symbols are more demanding than the reader of the first two classifications has inclination for; therefore, authors seldom employ them in less sophisticated works.

The symbol most difficult for the reader is the *author's personal symbol,* one which has meaning for him but which may lack personal meaning for the reader. The poet William Butler Yeats had a special fondness for the swan, a bird that could symbolize anything from desire for lost youth to political abuse. When he began to write one of his most admired poems, "Leda and the Swan," his stated intention was to create a political statement. However, as his material (the allusion to the myth) assumed shape, it worked away from the political to become larger in scope, more abstract in conception until Yeats alone knew the exact meaning of the swan (in "Leda and the Swan," probably both the god Zeus and the symbolic sexual protagonist—if an *exact* meaning exists). In prose forms, Ernest Hemingway employed bullfight imagery in any number of his works, but the symbolic possibilities are so multiple and, in many ways, so abstract that it becomes apparent personal symbolism at work. A precise, all-inclusive statement becomes impossible, and the reader must construct, from internal evidence, what he believes the symbol to mean. At any rate, that personal symbol becomes a part of the thematic development of the work. Carson McCullers, in "A Personal Preface" to *The Square Root of Wonderful,* summed it up as follows:

> . . . Why does anyone write at all? I suppose a writer writes out of some inward compulsion to transform his own experience (much of it is unconscious) into the universal and symbolical. The themes the artist chooses are always deeply personal. I suppose my central theme is the theme of spiritual isolation. Certainly I have always felt alone.*

At the heart of a work, a theme of some sort exists and is intricately bound up with the plot. A series of events (often called *narrative flow* and misunderstood by many to be a synonym for plot) leads logically one into another to reveal character and character change until the reader finally understands the significance of the events, of the change in character. That significance is the theme. It may be reduced to a cliché:

* Boston, 1958, p. viii.

"Man is his own worst enemy" or "Love conquers all." The cliché itself, however, is *not* the theme; it is a *reduction of theme* to a stateable level. An understanding and experiencing of the truth of the cliché by the reader is the theme in essence. In Mansfield's "Miss Brill" (pp. 138–144), the fur piece symbolizes Miss Brill's dreams by allowing her to communicate with something. When the dream is shattered and the fur is placed back in its box, her cupboard closes in on her. She too is shelved, and the theme becomes poignant as allegorical realization overtakes the reader and he experiences the *truth* of the theme which he can reduce to a cliché—if he can overcome his natural disinclination to inflict such abuse on the story.

Each of the three stories that make up the remainder of this chapter is well written, interesting, and imaginative enough to constitute a literary experience. As you read each story, you should be aware of its plot, the expository matter, description, dialog, and character development as they combine to form the total structure of the story.

"Joy Cometh in the Morning" by Dorothy Thomas rests on a readily apparent plot structure. You would have no difficulty outlining the story. The characters are interesting but superficial, lacking complexity. Theme unfolds without artifice and fairly demands to be understood. To reduce it to a stateable cliché requires no agonizing effort; yet it is an important statement. Unfortunately, such easy oversimplifications invite sentimentality rather than understanding for the reader, and the importance of the statement is lost. A pulp story, it appeared in a Christmas issue of *Redbook,* an issue designed to appeal to the emotion of the season, create a lump in the throat of the reader, and give her a warm glow that might be mistaken for a new depth of understanding of old problems. As you read the story, isolate the techniques employed by the author to capture your emotions and make you suspend your critical judgments.

Joy Cometh in the Morning

by Dorothy Thomas

1 Augusta sang and rocked her baby to sleep in the little rocking chair, the only piece of furniture not homemade in the little sod-fronted house dug out of the side of a creek bank. Then she put the baby in his cradle, brought out tablet and brown ink, sat down at the table and wrote in her careful hand:

"Norton, Kansas
December 18, 1889

Dear Ma,
We are all three in good health and baby is growing wondrously. I know you are counting on Mr. Thomas fetching us home for Christmas, as he told you in my hearing he would do when we were home last Easter. I am counting on it too and living toward it and have done much sewing to get us ready. While he has said nothing further about it since summer, I remind myself and baby that he is a man of few words, but as good as they, and am not anxious."

2 Here Augusta raised her quill and reread the little she had written. Then, being an honest girl, she drew a line through "am not anxious," only to see that the retracted words set the letter itself at naught. She tore the page from the tablet and put it in the stove. Then she brought two potatoes and a small head of cabbage from the vegetable cave at the back of the dugout, took the bag of corn meal from the box cupboard and started to prepare supper, softly but determinedly whistling as she worked.

3 To his very young wife Mr. Thomas was indeed a man of few words—and those few often puzzling. Long before little Ozro was born, Augusta had discerned, not without dismay and some indignation, that her husband, once he had printed matter within sight, heard not a word she said unless she stamped her foot on the earthen floor of their soddy and cried aloud, "Mr. Thomas!" Then he would look up from his reading to ask pleasantly, "Were you speaking to me, my dear?" If she had just said something it had taken her days, weeks, to gather the courage to say, it was all she could do to keep from crying. She did not cry only because she remembered the first time she had wept because of his all-unintended remoteness. Then he had said repentantly yet teasingly, "I should not have married you when I did, should not have let you talk me into it. I should have waited for you to grow up!"

4 Righteous wrath had stopped her tears on the instant. "Talked him into it" indeed! Had he not told her mother that he had decided when she was only eleven to wait for her to grow up, and to choose no other wife? Had he not soon begun to write her delightful letters, which she answered painstakingly, copybook and Webster's blueback speller at hand? Had he not, when she was fourteen, begun his courting, taking her horseback riding, telling her when they rested their horses that when she was old enough he hoped to marry her and wanted her to begin to get used to the idea? And as for waiting for her to grow up, had she

not been almost seventeen when they married? Had she not gone willingly, eagerly, to live with him in his dugout soddy on his claim forty miles away, with never a word against the fear of floods, prairie fires, rattlers, tramps and loneliness? Never a protest against the hard work—the washing and ironing, the carrying in of water from the well and cobs for the little cookstove and the keeping of the little unfloored, one-windowed house—while he rode off over the Kansas prairie swells to teach in his country school or visit the sick of his congregation? Hardly ever any more a cry against his long silences and his almost constant reading in the evenings? Never a complaint against his sometimes answering her smilingly, when she did get his attention, with riddles, quotations from unfamiliar verses, saws, jingles—some of the latter really rather shocking? But no matter what he said or forgot to say, she must remind herself that he was never intentionally unkind to her, that he loved her—as indeed he told her almost daily. She must not let him see her cry if she could help it. And always there was the baby, strong and beautiful, her treasure and boon companion, ever glad to hear her talk to him.

5 Augusta could not yet bring herself to call her husband by his given name, Willard. (It was only later, after the baby began to call him "Mr. Stomps" in his effort to say "Mr. Thomas," that she was to let herself call him "Papa.") Yet always when he came back to her from the world of his thoughts and reading he was tender, loving, appreciative. Never did he go from her, on even a short errand, without coming to lay his hands on her shoulders and kiss her brow or the part in her dark hair. If only he could have found it in his heart to talk with her more, or even simply to read aloud to her more often, instead of saying so positively, "This would not interest you, my dear"!

6 That evening, while supper was on the stove and Mr. Thomas, home from his school, was reading the weekly newspaper, Augusta sat down by the cradle, and while the baby chewed on a harness ring, she told him a story of what she thought was to be. As she talked she knitted and kept the cradle rocking with her foot.

7 "Yes, darling boy, this is your blanket I am knitting," she told him. "In just a few days now, when school is out and your father's Christmas program has been given, Mr. Thomas will bring the fillies and the buggy around to the door, early in the morning, and I shall wrap you in this blanket, you all handsomely dressed in the new hood and new chamois booties I have made you. I'll carry you out, hand you up to your father, spring up myself, and with you snug in my arms but sitting so you can watch the horses, see the land and the sky and every

bird that flies, the lap robe tucked snugly about us, away we'll go across the prairie to Grandpa Dodge's for Christmas. It will be night, dark, when we get there. Pa and Ma and your little aunt Bird and uncle Knowles will come hurrying out to meet us, Pa with the lantern held high. Ma will take you, hug you, and little Bird will be hopping up and down, her braids dancing too, saying, 'Oh, let me see him, hold him!' How she will love you, want to play with you, the whole time we are home! We'll all go into the warm kitchen, and there will be Grandma Rall by the chimney, waiting for me to set you on her knees. You'll look up at her, your brown eyes so wide, not crying, and she'll say, '*This* child is a Rall! *Bless* the boy!'

8 "Pa will come in, after helping Mr. Thomas put the team away, warm his hands over the stove and say, 'Now, let's have a look at this boy!' At first you may be a little afraid of his dark beard, but not for long. How he will love you! How they all will love you and make over you! After supper some of the cousins will come in, and you'll fly from one pair of arms to another, until time for me to rock you to sleep. Yes, we are going home for Christmas, little son!"

9 Little Ozro threw the harness ring and crowed. And Mr. Thomas looked up from his paper and asked, "What? What are you saying, my dear?"

10 Mrs. Thomas threw her knitting aside, jumped up, blushed and went to stir the corn-meal mush bubbling in the iron kettle on the stove. She lifted the stove lid and put in more cobs, and the light played on her childishly rounded cheeks and her dark hair. "I had no idea you were listening," she said. "I was simply telling Ozro how, in three or four days, we'll be going home for Christmas."

11 Mr. Thomas folded the paper, creased it on his knee with his palm and looked troubled indeed. "What have I said to give you the idea I was taking you home for Christmas?" he asked.

12 Mrs. Thomas paled. "You said . . . you said a day last summer, just before school took up, when we had planned to go home, and then someone died and you had to preach his funeral sermon, 'Never mind. There will be Christmas. I can take you home then.' " She set her teeth on her underlip to keep it from trembling and turned her head away.

13 "I did?" he asked, his voice as sad as it was astonished. "If you say I did, I did. I'm sorry to have completely forgotten saying it."

14 "We're not going?" she whispered.

15 "We can't. Christmas Day I am driving fifteen miles in the other direction to marry a young couple. And by the bye—I'm sorry it slipped my mind—I'm supposed to bring you and the baby to the wedding. Thank you for reminding me." He looked up at her very seriously. "I

am sorry indeed. But you have said nothing at all of this counting on going home for Christmas. How was I to know?"

[16] How was he to *know?* Had he utterly forgotten his promise to her mother? Had he not seen her sewing the little gifts she had made for her family? How could he be unaware of the work she had done, making the new clothes for the baby, the new red dress for herself and even a tuck-bosom shirt for him? Had she not, night after night, talked with the baby while her husband read, told him how she and his father would take him to church in all their new finery so that all her cousins and old schoolmates would marvel at his beauty and intelligence, be awed by his father's dignity in his black broadcloth and new white shirt and see her own womanliness and motherhood?

[17] She bowed her head, answering nothing, and after a moment found the presence of mind to spoon the mush into bowls and sprinkle it with brown sugar, to pour the coffee and to say in a voice that trembled only a little, "Will you come to supper now, Mr. Thomas?"

[18] While they ate he talked to her, said, "I wish your parents were here, with their tuning forks and their fine voices, to perfect the singing for the Christmas program. One of the older girls has been to singing school, can read music. But I fear her voice, her pitch and rhythm, leave something to be desired. Only in my mind can I read the notes. It is eternally too bad I cannot carry a tune."

[19] Augusta wanted to say, "I could have taught the children their songs, had you asked me. I can read music, and Pa says my voice is true." But she could not trust herself to say anything.

[20] When the supper dishes were on the shelf she rocked the baby to sleep, and again brought out paper and pen, sat down at the table and wrote her mother that they would not be home for Christmas after all. Not a word of complaint was in the letter. Her family must see that she was a woman grown and could take life as it came. She did not seal the letter but left it for Mr. Thomas to add to it, as he liked to do, for he loved her parents.

[21] She had saved the potato water, and set the bread sponge before she went to bed. Mr. Thomas was asleep before she blew out the light. Well to her side of the bunk bed, with a hill of her feather bed between them, she wept as silently as she could, her wrist tight pressed to her mouth to try to still the sobs that shook her. The wedding to which she was so belatedly invited, and which under other circumstances would have filled her with happy anticipation, she did not want to think about.

[22] Augusta overslept, and wakened to see the baby sitting astride

his father's knee, listening raptly to a poem chanted in Greek. Then her husband trotted the baby merrily, singing in his monotone, "Old Grimes, he had a yeller dog."

23 When he saw she was awake he said, "Don't get up, darling, until the house is warmer. I'm getting breakfast." He brought the baby to her to nurse and, smiling down on them, said, "Why don't you come to school with me today? The big girls would be glad to mind the baby while you hear the little ones say their Christmas pieces. And after recess, in the afternoon, we could have a spelldown in your honor."

24 Augusta's heart leaped at his "come to school," but sank again at the thought of possibly missing a word and being spelled down by one of the children. She shook her head on the pillow, told him she had best stay home for she had bread to bake.

25 "Your letter will go directly to your mother, and today," he said. "Neighbors near the school are taking calves to Smith Center and will stay the night at your folks' place on the way. I added a few lines to your letter before Ozro woke up, made a clean breast of forgetting I was to take you home for Christmas and explained why I cannot bring you."

26 Augusta scarcely heard what he said beyond the news that a wagon was leaving for her parents' home today. "Oh," she cried, "do you suppose I could go with them—take the baby and go, and stay until you can come for us after Christmas?"

27 "On first thought, a good idea," he said. "On second, a poor one. There's no seat on their wagon. You could not stand up all the way, among the calves. A raw wind is blowing this morning. It would be too hard on you both."

28 Augusta nodded agreement, acceptance. She was too busy fighting tears to protest that she could wrap the baby well and sit on a box in a corner of the wagon bed. To be denied the trip, promised, long planned, seemed all but unbearable.

29 Most mornings, the weather fit, Augusta caught up the baby and, the two of them wrapped in her shawl, went out to the buggy with her husband, to be kissed once again and then to stand by the well, watching him out of sight. This morning she stayed where she was, by the cradle. He kissed them both, said he would see the letter on its way and went. He did not mention again the broken promise.

30 When Mr. Thomas had been gone long enough for her to be sure he would not be back, she gave way to tears and cried with abandon. The baby watched, puzzled. He threw the harness ring away, and when she did not retrieve it for him added his crying to hers. She put him on the bunk bed and swung to the gate before it that made

it a safe place for him to creep. She had not the heart for sewing or work of any kind. When the bread had risen she kneaded it, and in spite of all she could do to stop them, wiping her eyes with her wrist, her tears fell on the dough. Not even the smell of the bread baking, which usually made her feel so housewifely and proud, could cheer her. She moped the day away, ate only because she knew she must, to feed the baby. And only when it was nearly time for her husband to come home did she make up the bed and sweep the earthen floor, with an indifference that would have shocked her grandmother. Then she washed some potatoes, put them in the oven to bake and lay down with a cold, damp cloth over her smarting eyes. The baby would not let the cloth be, but kept yanking it away and crying, "Peek!" in his own remarkable language.

31 Then, as though he could understand her sorrow and the cause of it, she began to explain his father to him. "You see, Son, your father sees Christmas purely as the day sacred to the Savior's birth. Just that! His ma died, went to heaven, when he was only five, and his stepmother was cruel, unkind, unfair. His father is a stern man who does not hold with there being anything jolly about Christmas, and they never gave gifts, had secrets, surprises. . . ." She began to cry again at the thought of his mother's dying before Mr. Thomas should have learned the full meaning of Christmas, and hugged the baby to her and held him close to protect him from a Christmasless boyhood and a wicked stepmother.

32 The baby struggled to be free, and to keep him she sang, sobbingly, "My only, my treasure, my precious, wondrous son! I mind most for Ma and my sister Bird not to have seen you in all these months of your growing. Now you'll be walking, talking, it may be, before they see you again." Then she looked at the clock, saw how late it was, got up and went to bathe her eyes again, recoiled her hair and, looking into Mr. Thomas' shaving mirror, tried to smile.

33 In the following days, with never a word of rebuke or any really sullen looks, Augusta punished her husband with long silences and remoteness for forgetting his promise and disappointing her. She saw to it that his clean shirt was ready each morning, made good lunches for him to take to school and had good suppers ready when he came in from doing the chores. When he tried to talk with her, she answered as briefly and politely as she could. But she smiled only at the baby. To her surprise and chagrin, he did not take her in his arms and say, "Come, let's make an end of this and be good to one another."

34 Friday came, the last day of school, and neighbors stopped by to give them a ride to the schoolhouse. Everyone said the Christmas pro-

gram went very well. Everyone admired the baby. But even that prideful pleasure could not lift Augusta's gloom.

35 When they were home again and the baby was in his cradle, Mr. Thomas said, "If the weather holds, we'll drive into town in the morning and you may spend a fortune."

36 "A fortune?" Augusta asked, with a literalness he sometimes found amusing, sometimes dismaying.

37 "Yes, a fortune," he said, and took a ten-dollar gold piece from his vest pocket and laid it in her palm. "This was given me by a neighbor in appreciation for my talking a lad out of running away from home and into staying in school another year—advice I doubt I should have taken, in his place."

38 Augusta looked down at the little gold coin and thought, For less than half of this, Ozro and I could have gone home on the train. Without looking up at him, she asked, "What are we to buy?"

39 "Something for you and Cosmos here," he said, nodding toward the cradle. "Something you want for the house. Some folly, if you like." There was tenderness in his voice.

40 She looked away toward the window, where the lamp flame was reflected, and said, "It likely will snow."

41 In the night the baby fretted and she got up to make sure that he was well covered, and when she had quieted him, she went to the window. It was too dark to see whether it was snowing, but she was ashamed of saying only that it likely would snow, of not responding to her husband's wish to be good to her. When she got back into bed her cold foot touched his, and without waking he drew away. His unconscious rejection set her crying again, although only briefly. Not since the early weeks of their marriage, when she was beginning to be aware of there being worlds for him he would not or could not share with her, had she cried so much.

42 When she awoke to hear the wind and see sugary snow under the door, her lips set on the "I told you so" she did not dare speak aloud. It frightened her to think how many days had gone without her being loving and warm and merry. She got up, washed, dressed, nursed her baby, and when Mr. Thomas came in with the milk, went out into the gray morning and saw that the snow, while not deep, would keep them from going anywhere in the buggy. When she came in and hung her shawl on its peg, Mr. Thomas had strained the milk into the milk pan and was grinding the coffee and singing to the baby.

43 "Have you your list ready?" he asked. "I'll have to go to town on horseback. Anything I cannot get into the saddlebag I'll have sent out by mail next week. Tell me what you'd have me bring home."

44 "The list is long made," she said, "and the things will easily fit in the saddlebag. I have a package ready I want you to mail for me." The only luxuries she had added after he showed her the coin were a sliver of citron rind and a half pound of raisins for the making of a Christmas cake.

45 When Mr. Thomas was ready to go she longed to relent, to throw herself into his arms, make her peace with him and be comforted. Never before had she let him go from her farther than to the schoolhouse with a difference between them unrighted. Yet there had been no real falling out, no words, no quarrel. It might be that she only imagined he knew how deeply he had hurt her; perhaps he had forgotten all about it.

46 He took the baby up and kissed him, then kissed her and said, "This is no blizzard. It will be dark when I get home, but there is nothing to worry about. I have got you in fuel and water. Good-by, my love."

47 She whispered, "Good-by," and he went out, got on his waiting horse and rode away. This time she did not stand at the window, holding the baby, to wave his hand with hers until the rise of the bank hid him from sight, but stood by the cradle, suddenly unsure in her righteous resentment, and lonely.

48 Then, as it always did eventually, responsible housewifery came mightily upon her. A change was worked in her, not through thought or resolutions but through the passing of time and the fact that her busy, creative tasks demanded good spirits uppermost. She heated water, scoured the unpainted tabletop and chairs, the washbench and shelves, with homemade soap and ashes. She polished the stove, washed the little window and put up the other pair of white curtains, refilled the lamp and polished its chimney and the spares. With a dampened broom she swept the earthen floor with such vigor she loosed a tuft of grass roots that had fretted the broom from the first day of her housekeeping in the dugout. She knelt and repacked the earth into the hole. Then she went over the floor with a damp cloth wrung from warm water with a little coal oil in it to make the floor shine. When it was dry she brought a roll of rag carpet her mother had given her—the carpet strip she had saved, new, against a day company might be coming—and spread it between the bed and doorway. Then she lifted the baby from his haven in the bunk bed and said, "Come—creep! Crawl on the pretty, warm new carpet!" She tossed him up, then held him to her and said, "Now our house is all clean, let us have our baths, wash our hair and be *happy!*" On the word "happy," a last sob came up from

within her. She whirled the baby about. Her hair came down, uncoiled, as she danced. At last, breathless, she sat down in the little rocking chair that had been her father's gift to her home and rocked her boy, kissed him, spanked him lovingly while he crowed and laughed, and when she got her breath she sang:

"Weeping may endure, may endure
for a night,
But joy cometh in the morning!"

49 Would it always be thus? she wondered. Would she know hurt, indignation, resentful loneliness, her life with Mr. Thomas darkened for hours or for days through some slight or seeming indifference on his part, only to find after a spasm of housework great happiness and even delight in life itself welling up in her, past any need for forgiving?

50 Augusta wrapped the baby in her shawl, put on Mr. Thomas' chore coat and her mittens and went out, set the baby in the snow and went back for the copper washboiler to fill it with snow. The baby promptly struggled from his shawl cocoon, got himself upright, took two steps and fell, and strove to get up again. She ran to him, caught him up and cried, "Your first steps you take not where it is easy, on the warm rug in the house, but where it is hard, out in the cold and the snow! Oh, if only Ma or Bird were here to see you take them!"

51 When they had had their baths Augusta sat with her damp hair about her shoulders, and with the baby wrapped in a blanket, nursed him and recalled how Mr. Thomas had once called her, as she sat rocking the baby while her hair dried, "The Madonna of the rocking chair."

52 Mr. Thomas rode slowly along the wagon trail in the spitting snow, the reins loose on the horse's neck, and remembered, as he seldom let himself remember at any length, his early childhood. There was no Christmastime to recall. His mother had been a small woman, sturdy and fair, come of gentle Dutch people, some of them Quakers. His memories of her were few, but he recalled them as a man recalls blossoms and birdsong in a long winter. Of those times he had but one memory of his father that was in anywise tender. He remembered his mother's voice saying, "Poor Willie has played himself out and has fallen asleep on the stairs." His father had come to take him up, to carry him to bed, and the hand that pressed his head to his shoulder was kind, almost loving.

53 His mother had died when he was five, and he had been amazed to see his father kneel by her bed and sob, as amazed as he was to touch his mother's hand and find it cold and uncaring.

54 The stepmother his father brought home had been a schoolteacher. She was tall, straight-backed, unsmiling. She had lost a hand in a feed-chopper as a child, but could do as much work with her one hand as most women did with two, and was a passionate housekeeper. He would stand mesmerized to watch her knit, the sock on the stump of her wrist, the needles twinkling under the fiercely purposed, flying fingers of her hand. At table she sat with a switch across her lap for the stinging of the children's legs should dangling heels reach for chair rungs. Unmindful of his cries, she held her stepson's chapped feet under the very hot water in the little wooden foot tub, her arm stump pressed hard across his knees, and scrubbed his feet and shins with a stiff-bristled brush and homemade lye soap, the while she said, through her teeth, "You must be clean, clean, clean!"

55 When his father came home from his pastoral journeyings she would go out to meet him, stand by his horse, and while he was still in the saddle tell every wrong and dreadful thing his sons had done and every fine and good thing their sons had done, and his father, never asking to hear his sons' side of any story, took them to the stable and strapped them before he would sit down to the good meal prepared for him.

56 At nine, after an undeserved thrashing that had stiffened and all but lamed him, Willard had run away from home and begun to make his own way in the world, chopping wood and herding cows for a place to sleep and food handed from kitchen doors. Finally, wanting to see his younger sister and brother and wanting his father to be at least a little proud of him, that he had survived, he returned home. But at fifteen he left once more, never again to live under his father's roof, but always to keep in touch with him, to write him when he had made some advancement in his life, longing ever for recognition and a first "Well done."

57 Unbidden, a memory came to his mind, of his near drowning when he was seven. As he was going down for the third time he saw two turtledoves running along the muddy riverbank and thought, "The last thing I see is two pretty birds." Someone saved him, and when he opened his eyes on the bank, he saw his father bending over him, yearning love in his face.

58 Riding in the sparsely falling snow toward town, to do what he could to make up for disappointing his young wife, Mr. Thomas felt a wave of homesickness for the early childhood he could barely remember, for his only sister and younger brother and for the father approval he had never known, and said aloud in the middle of the white, wide Kansas prairie, "I should not have failed her, forgotten. She is so little,

so tender, and such a *maid* still. I am failing her most in letting her make of the child a supernatural being, a prince royal, a confidant, a doll—her very life. I fear for the boy, and hope there will be other children."

59 Augusta marveled at the baby's having taken his first steps, and longed for Mr. Thomas to come home and be told about them. Kneeling on the carpet strip, she coaxed him to try again, but he chose only to creep—away from the carpet and onto the cold floor. She put him on the bed, but he climbed the gate and would have fallen from it. She tied him in his cradle, where he roared and struggled in a rage that frightened her. Kneeling on the carpet beside him, her arm about him, she got him to nurse and talked to him soothingly until he was appeased and fell asleep.

60 Then, sitting in her rocker, her finger tapping her lips, Augusta planned Christmas decorations for her house. From newspapers she cut camels and kings three and tried to paste them to the window panes, but the flour paste she had made in the bowl of a teaspoon would not stick to the steam-wet glass. From her trunk she brought out a piece of buckram she had been saving for the making of her new bustle. Using the paper pattern, she cut the camels and kings from the buckram, with a bit of desert for them to walk upon, then carefully folded the desert base and stood the cutout before the window. Then she stood off to admire her work and softly clapped her hands. Next she pulled her hatbox from under the bed, took out her bonnet and carefully ripped from it the red berries and tacked them to the window frame. She replenished the fire and washed three potatoes and put them in the oven to bake. Mr. Thomas would slice the salt pork when he came. "Never touch the butcher knife, the hatchet or ax when I am away," he had cautioned her.

61 While she made biscuit-dough cinnamon rolls Augusta thought and thought as to what she might use for the guiding star, and when the rolls were in the oven she searched in her scrap bag for a piece of gold slipper satin her Aunt Matt had given her, and after drawing many patterns, cut out a five-pointed star from it and pinned it to the lintel above the window. This time her hand-clapping woke the baby.

62 "You be good, now," she told him, "while I get into my new dress. Just before Mr. Thomas comes, I'll array you in your new dress and petticoat, for you to wear only for his welcome. Then I'll take it off you and put it away for this wedding we are to attend on Christmas Day, providing the weather is fit for you and me to make the trip. When he opens the door, how astonished Mr. Thomas will be!"

63 The new dress, when she got herself into it and fastened its twenty-odd buttons, was even prettier than she had thought in its last trying-on. And her pleated newspaper bustle made the back peplum stand out most satisfyingly. She must remember to sit on the edge of the buggy seat and of her chair at the wedding and not crush it. Going to the wedding would not be like going home, but it would be going somewhere—it would be a trip.

64 While she was dressing the baby she said, "Now that you can walk—you *will* walk, won't you, for Mr. Thomas when he comes, bear me out when I tell him that you did walk, can walk, took two steps? —I'll make you short dresses from some of the long ones you have outgrown. You will be falling many times, learning. May you never hurt yourself! I could not bear it for you to hurt yourself, nor for anything or anyone to hurt you." Her eyes darkened, remembering the time Mr. Thomas had spoken sharply to the child and had threatened with his hand, as though he would slap the baby's hand when he had torn a book left on a chair. She had snatched the boy up and away before the hand descended on him, and cried out, *"Mr. Thomas!"* in incredulous reproach.

65 About her very slender waist Augusta tied the white Sunday apron with the three-inch crocheted border that her grandmother had made for her. She set the table with great precision, using the wedding-silver knives and forks instead of the everyday pewter ones. She set the lighted lamp in the window, to be moved later to the supper table. "Now let's go out and see the Wise Men and the star," she said to the baby. She swirled her shawl, nestled it about the two of them and went out into the cold.

66 In the dusk, the lamplight threw angled, grotesque shadow kings and camels on the snow. The buckram Biblical beings in the window were pricked with light that shone through the weaving, and were beautiful. "Look!" she said to the baby, who seemed determined to look everywhere else.

67 Then the boy cried out, and in his excitement almost threw himself from her arms. Coming suddenly through the dark were a horse and rider. Mr. Thomas had come home. And peeking from behind him, her dark eyes catching the light and sparkling, was Augusta's little sister, Bird.

68 "Oh, Bird, Bird!" Augusta cried as Mr. Thomas swung the child down and freed her to run staggeringly on cold, stiffened legs to embrace Augusta and the baby.

69 "Ma couldn't come as Mr. Thomas asked in his letter," Bird explained, "so she sent me on the train."

70 "Alone?" Augusta gasped.

71 "No, in the care of the stationmaster's wife. She made the trip both ways especially to look after me. I had a ticket, a half-fare ticket. A one-way one that Mr. Thomas sent the money for."

72 "One way?" Augusta echoed, and moved toward the horse and looked up into her husband's face. "Has anything happened at home that Bird should be sent to me?"

73 "No, no, Gussie," the little girl cried, nimble now and beginning to jump up and down in the snow while she clung to her sister's arm. "Everything's fine at home. Don't you see? I am Mr. Thomas' Christmas gift to you, sent on the train with a one-way, half-fare ticket. I can stay until Mr. Thomas finds time to take us all home, maybe before New Year's."

74 The baby was struggling, wanting to be lifted up, to ride with his father to the stable, to be set in the hay while his father fed the horses. This time his mother made no protest, did not fret that he might catch cold or fall from the horse. She whipped the shawl from around them, wrapped him in it and thrust him into his father's arms. Then, standing by his stirrup, smiling on her little sister, she laid her head against her husband's thigh and smoothed her cheek against the snow-dampened, pungent wool of his breeches and felt the warmth and strength of his muscles beneath, and said, "It is wonderful. *Thank* you, and Merry Christmas, dear Mr. Thomas!"

75 He looked down and saw the lamplight glint in the tear that slid on the round of her cheek. He vowed in his heart ever to do what he could to give her and her children the kind of Christmas she wanted for them—the kind she had known in her own childhood, filled with joy. □

Omniscient point of view allows the author of "Joy Cometh in the Morning" a great deal of latitude. Expository matter is freely employed throughout, enabling the author to make any number of unsupported evaluations of the characters. Early in the story, for example, Augusta is characterized as being "an honest girl." That honesty becomes questionable as she punishes her husband "with long silences and remoteness," but the story is designed to elicit reader sympathy for her, so the author justifies Augusta's silence with implications of physical youth and emotional immaturity, the loneliness of the Kansas prairie, inconveniences in the sod house, and actual culpability in Mr. Thomas. The story is written for the female reader, and her biases, prejudices, and personal resentments are manipulated with skill and precision.

However, if Augusta is to continue living with such an insensitive man, he must have redeeming features, and the inclusion of those features prescribes the omniscient point of view. The reader must be allowed access to the man's thoughts as he rides through the falling snow which has conveniently confined Augusta to the soddy. The easy, pat recollections of abuse in childhood (even to a "cruel, unkind, unfair" stepmother) satisfy the casual reader—the one looking for easy answers and acceptable rationalizations. So satisfactory are these distractions, in fact, that the reader accepts the author's dishonesty in failing to foreshadow Bird's arrival.

With her arrival, the reader is relieved to realize Mr. Thomas had not only "made a clean breast of forgetting I was to take you home for Christmas and explained why I cannot bring you," he had also asked Bird and Augusta's mother to come to the soddy. This information has been withheld, not even suggested, but the reader is so pleased that all ends well, she does not question the author's failure to be honest with her.

Nor does Augusta change or grow. In actuality, she regresses. Like a child pleased with getting its own way, she is temporarily happy. And she "rewards" Mr. Thomas by laying her head against his thigh and thanking him. He has been a successful father to Augusta even as he has failed at being a husband. With his infant child, however, he has failed as a father because Augusta will not allow him to discipline Ozro. For his part, he accepts the father-to-Augusta role, vowing to keep her happy as she was in childhood. The woman who reads the story will fail to realize the unfortunate implications. After all, Augusta is happy *now*. And Mr. Thomas has proved that making his wife happy now is man's mission in life. The thoughtful reader will, naturally, find all of this pretty gamy fare, but, then, the thoughtful reader doesn't ordinarily seek his literary insights in *Redbook* magazine.

On the other hand, even the thoughtful reader has his moments of doubt, loneliness, and fear—moments when he wants to believe happiness is, if not a warm puppy, no more complicated than the act of getting one's Christmas wish fulfilled. And he will prefer to escape into the roseate world of such fiction, knowing the real world will still be as uncompromising after the literary escape as it was before. During those moments of respite from it, he may at least rest enough to return to his battles refreshed by the euphoria of the pulp story, for little intellectual effort has been demanded of him. Panoramic treatment dominates this story, even in those passages which seem to be narrowly focused scene. Setting and atmosphere are employed, dialog abounds, but an incisive analysis of the meaning of such scenes is beyond even the good reader. Augusta lacks depth as a fictional character and as a human being. She is as emotionally appealing as a child is, but she is intellectually tiresome. How dreary an afternoon in her company would be! No wonder Mr. Thomas withdraws into his reading matter and closes his mind to her inconsequential monologs. His story (unwritten and suggested only in the stock situation flashback to his childhood) would be interesting indeed. Why, in all honesty, did he marry this young flibbertigibbet? What hidden needs does he pander to as he spins out his days on the loom of her ill-defined landscape? Ah, there's another story, and it wouldn't be escape literature either!

And therein, paradoxically, lies another argument for reading such stories. While they may offer little surface challenge, they offer much reflective material for analysis. The reader can speculate at length on the unwritten material, even become belligerent in discussions about it. At such times, he becomes something of a writer too. His intellectual involvement, his emotional responses indicate he too possesses that vein of expression that runs through seemingly unpromising sites. He can, with the pick and shovel of simple involvement, begin to mine in that fashion suggested by Henry David Thoreau in *Walden:*

> The intellect is a cleaver; it discerns and rifts its way into the secret of things. I do not wish to be any more busy with my hands than is necessary. My head is hands and feet. I feel all my best faculties concentrated in it. My instinct tells me that my head is an organ for burrowing, as some creatures use their snout and fore paws, and with it I would mine and burrow my way through these hills. I think that the richest vein is somewhere hereabouts; so by the divining-rod and thin rising vapors I judge; and here I will begin to mine.
>
> *"Where I Lived, and What I Lived For"*

Such mining has long been the delight of the intellectually curious. In the next story, Susan Glaspell offers the reader such an exploratory site. "A Jury of Her Peers" is slick fiction of a caliber so professionally excellent it almost becomes a quality story. In the best tradition of escape literature (and, remember, there is quite a bit of the pulp in the slick story), it offers suspense, sharply defined conflict, and action that is as engrossing as the final minutes of a close football game. The quality story elements include penetrating analyses of human motivations and examination of a world removed from romantic concepts.

As you read "A Jury of Her Peers," you should notice that the setting is markedly more realistic than that of "Joy Cometh in the Morning," where nostalgic charm overlays the soddy of Augusta and Mr. Thomas. Such details as carrying in "cobs for the little cookstove and the keeping of the little unfloored, one-windowed house" were sugared with diminutives and made snugly agreeable from the opening of the story where "Augusta sang and rocked her baby to sleep in the little rocking chair, the only piece of furniture not homemade in the little sod-fronted house dug out of the side of a creek bank." No such diminutives or picture-book suggestions creep into "A Jury of Her Peers." In Glaspell's story, houses are not impeccably clean; farm women of earlier days worked long hours at hard tasks and devoted their "resting" time to housework. Chores have roughened the hands of Susan Glaspell's characters while Augusta Thomas doubtless has hands as untouched by the harshness of lye soap as they are by time.

Even the references to food reveal differing story levels. Augusta made mouth-watering potato water bread sponge and biscuit-dough cinnamon rolls; Martha Hale makes just plain old sifted flour bread.

Nature itself is harsher in the Glaspell story: "When Martha Hale opened the storm door and got a cut of the north wind she ran back for her big woolen scarf." When Augusta's trip to town was cancelled by weather, "she awoke to hear the wind and see sugary snow under the door."

Still, Susan Glaspell does not remove all traces of romance from her story. Mrs. Hale fears her son "wasn't dressed warm enough" and she remembers "the afternoon I put my cherries up last summer." Sentimentality invades the story as Minnie Foster, ex-choir girl, wrapped her dead songbird in a piece of silk so reminiscent of the beautiful clothes she had worn those long ago days. Symbolism can become as sticky as burst fruit—and it is such weaknesses in the story that bar it from the realm of quality. As you read it, look for other evidence linking it with escape literature on the one hand, quality on the other.

A Jury of Her Peers

by Susan Glaspell

1 When Martha Hale opened the storm door and got a cut of the north wind she ran back for her big woolen scarf. As she hurriedly wound that round her head her eye made a scandalized sweep of her kitchen. It was no ordinary thing that called her away; it was probably further from ordinary than anything that had ever happened in Dickson County. But what her eye took in was that her kitchen was in no shape for leaving: her bread all ready for mixing, half the flour sifted and half unsifted.

2 She hated to see things half done, but she had been at that when

the team from town stopped to get Mr. Hale, and then the sheriff came running in to say his wife wished Mrs. Hale would come too, adding, with a grin, that he guessed she was getting scary and wanted another woman along. So she had dropped everything right where it was.

3 "Martha!" now came her husband's impatient voice. "Don't keep folks waiting out here in the cold."

4 She again opened the storm door, and this time joined the three men and the one woman waiting for her in the big two-seated buggy.

5 After she had the robes tucked around her she took another look at the woman who sat beside her on the back seat. She had met Mrs. Peters the year before at the county fair, and the thing she remembered about her was that she didn't seem like a sheriff's wife. She was small and thin and didn't have a strong voice. Mrs. Gorman, sheriff's wife before Gorman went out and Peters came in, had a voice that somehow seemed to be backing up the law with every word. But if Mrs. Peters didn't look like a sheriff's wife, Peters made it up in looking like a sheriff. He was to a dot the kind of man who could get himself elected sheriff, a heavy man with a big voice, who was particularly genial with the law-abiding, as if to make it plain that he knew the difference between criminals and noncriminals. And right there it came into Mrs. Hale's mind, with a stab, that this man who was so pleasant and lively with all of them was going to the Wrights' now as a sheriff.

6 "The country's not very pleasant this time of year," Mrs. Peters at last ventured, as if she felt they ought to be talking as well as the men.

7 Mrs. Hale scarcely finished her reply, for they had gone up a little hill and could see the Wright place now, and seeing it did not make her feel like talking. It looked very lonesome this cold March morning. It had always been a lonesome-looking place. It was down in a hollow, and the poplar trees around it were lonesome-looking trees. The men were looking at it and talking about what had happened. The county attorney was bending to one side of the buggy and kept looking steadily at the place as they drew up to it.

8 "I'm glad you came with me," Mrs. Peters said nervously, as the two women were about to follow the men in through the kitchen door.

9 Even after she had her foot on the door-step, her hand on the knob, Martha Hale had a moment of feeling she could not cross that threshold. And the reason it seemed she couldn't cross it now was simply because she hadn't crossed it before. Time and time again it had been in her mind, *I ought to go over and see Minnie Foster*—she still thought of her as Minnie Foster, though for twenty years she had

been Mrs. Wright. And then there was always something to do and Minnie Foster would go from her mind. But now she could come.

10 The men went over to the stove. The women stood close together by the door. Young Henderson, the county attorney, turned around and said, "Come up to the fire, ladies."

11 Mrs. Peters took a step forward, then stopped. "I'm not—cold," she said.

12 And so the two women stood by the door, at first not even so much as looking around the kitchen.

13 The men talked for a minute about what a good thing it was the sheriff had sent his deputy out that morning to make a fire for them, and then Sheriff Peters stepped back from the stove, unbuttoned his outer coat, and leaned on the kitchen table in a way that seemed to mark the beginning of official business. "Now, Mr. Hale," he said in a sort of semi-official voice, "before we move things about, you tell Mr. Henderson just what it was you saw when you came here yesterday morning."

14 The county attorney was looking around the kitchen.

15 "By the way," he said, "has anything been moved?" He turned to the sheriff. "Are things just as you left them yesterday?"

16 Peters looked from cupboard to sink; from that to a small worn rocker a little to one side of the kitchen table.

17 "It's just the same."

18 "Somebody should have been left here yesterday," said the county attorney.

19 "Oh—yesterday," returned the sheriff, with a little gesture as of yesterday having been more than he could bear to think of. "When I had to send Frank to Morris Center for that man who went crazy; let me tell you, I had my hands full yesterday. I knew you could get back from Omaha by today, George, and as long as I went over everything here myself—"

20 "Well, Mr. Hale," said the county attorney, in a way of letting what was past and gone go, "tell just what happened when you came here yesterday morning."

21 Mrs. Hale, still leaning against the door, had that sinking feeling of the mother whose child is about to speak a piece. Lewis often wandered along and got things mixed up in a story. She hoped he would tell this straight and plain, and not say unnecessary things that would just make things harder for Minnie Foster. He didn't begin at once and she noticed that he looked queer, as if standing in that kitchen and having to tell what he had seen there yesterday morning made him almost sick.

22 "Yes, Mr. Hale?" the county attorney reminded.

23 "Harry and I had started to town with a load of potatoes," Mrs. Hale's husband began.

24 Harry was Mrs. Hale's oldest boy. He wasn't with them now, for the very good reason that those potatoes never got to town yesterday and he was taking them this morning, so he hadn't been home when the sheriff stopped to say he wanted Mr. Hale to come over to the Wright place and tell the county attorney his story there, where he could point it all out. With all Mrs. Hale's other emotions came the fear now that maybe Harry wasn't dressed warm enough; they hadn't any of them realized how that north wind did bite.

25 "We came along this road," Hale was going on, with a motion of his hand to the road over which they had just come, "and as we got in sight of the house I says to Harry, 'I'm goin' to see if I can't get John Wright to take a telephone.' You see," he explained to Henderson, "unless I can get somebody to go in with me they won't come out this branch road except for a price I can't pay. I'd spoke to Wright about it once before; but he put me off, saying folks talked too much anyway, and all he asked was peace and quiet—guess you know about how much he talked himself. But I thought maybe if I went to the house and talked about it before his wife, and said all the women-folks liked the telephones, and that in this lonesome stretch of road it would be a good thing—well, I said to Harry that that was what I was going to say—though I said at the same time that I didn't know what his wife wanted made much difference to John—"

26 Now there he was, saying things he didn't need to say! Mrs. Hale tried to catch her husband's eye, but fortunately the county attorney interrupted with:

27 "Let's talk about that a little later, Mr. Hale. I do want to talk about that, but I'm anxious now to get along to what happened when you got here."

28 When he began this time, it was very deliberately and carefully:

29 "I didn't see or hear anything. I knocked at the door. And still it was all quiet inside. I knew they must be up—it was past eight o'clock. So I knocked again, louder, and I thought I heard somebody say, 'Come in.' I wasn't sure, I'm not sure yet. But I opened the door, this door—" jerking a hand toward the door by which the two women stood—"and there, in that rocker—" pointing to it—"sat Mrs. Wright."

30 Everyone in the kitchen looked at the rocker. It came into Mrs. Hale's mind that that rocker didn't look in the least like Minnie Foster, the Minnie Foster of twenty years before. It was a dingy red, with wooden rungs up the back, and the middle rung was gone, and the chair sagged to one side.

31 "How did she—look?" the county attorney was inquiring.

32 "She looked queer," said Hale.

33 "How do you mean, queer?"

34 As he asked it he took out a notebook and pencil. Mrs. Hale did not like the sight of that pencil. She kept her eyes fixed on her husband, as if to keep him from saying unnecessary things that would go into that notebook and make trouble.

35 Hale did speak guardedly, as if the pencil had affected him too.

36 "Well, as if she didn't know what she was going to do next. And kind of—done up."

37 "How did she seem to feel about your coming?"

38 "Why, I don't think she minded one way or other. She didn't pay much attention. I said, 'Ho' do, Mrs. Wright? It's cold, ain't it?' and she said, 'Is it?' and went on pleatin' at her apron.

39 "Well, I was surprised. She didn't ask me to come up to the stove or to sit down, but just set there, not even lookin' at me. And so I said: 'I want to see John.'

40 "And then she laughed. I guess you would call it a laugh.

41 "I thought of Harry and the team outside, so I said, a little sharp, 'Can I see John?' 'No,' says she kind of dull like. 'Ain't he home?' says I. Then she looked at me. 'Yes,' says she, 'he's home.' 'Then why can't I see him?' I asked her, out of patience with her now. ' 'Cause he's dead,' says she, just as quiet and dull, and fell to pleatin' her apron. 'Dead?' says I, like you do when you can't take in what you've heard.

42 "She just nodded her head, not getting a bit excited, but rocking back and forth.

43 " 'Why—where is he?' says I, not knowing what to say.

44 "She just pointed upstairs—like this," pointing to the room above.

45 "I got up, with the idea of going up there myself. By this time I didn't know what to do. I walked from there to here; then I says: 'Why, what did he die of?'

46 " 'He died of a rope round his neck,' says she; and just went on pleatin' at her apron."

47 Hale stopped speaking and stood staring at the rocker, as if he were still seeing the woman who had sat there the morning before. Nobody spoke; it was as if everyone were seeing the woman who had sat there the morning before.

48 "And what did you do then?" the county attorney broke the silence.

49 "I went out and called Harry. I thought I might need help. I got Harry in and we went upstairs." His voice fell almost to a whisper. "There he was—lying over the—"

50 "I think I'd rather have you go into that upstairs," the county

attorney interrupted, "where you can point it all out. Just go on now with the rest of the story."

51 "Well, my first thought was to get that rope off. It looked—"

52 He stopped, his face twitching. "But Harry, he went up to him, and he said, 'No, he's dead all right and we'd better not touch anything.' So we went downstairs.

53 "She was still sitting that same way. 'Has anybody been notified?' I asked. 'No,' says she, unconcerned.

54 " 'Who did this, Mrs. Wright?' said Harry. He said it businesslike, and she stopped pleatin' her apron. 'I don't know,' she says. 'You don't know?' says Harry. 'Weren't you sleepin' in the bed with him?' 'Yes,' says she, 'but I was on the inside.' 'Somebody slipped a rope round his neck and strangled him and you didn't wake up?' says Harry. 'I didn't wake up,' she said after him.

55 "We may have looked as if we didn't see how that could be, for after a minute she said, 'I sleep sound.'

56 "Harry was going to ask her more questions, but I said maybe that weren't our business; maybe we ought to let her tell her story first to the coroner or the sheriff. So Harry went fast as he could over to High Road, the Rivers' place, where there's a phone."

57 "And what did she do when she knew you had gone for the coroner?" The attorney got his pencil in his hand all ready for writing.

58 "She moved from that chair to this one over here," Hale pointed to a small chair in the corner, "and just sat there with her hands held together and looking down. I got a feeling that I ought to make some conversation, so I said I had come in to see if John wanted to put in a telephone; and at that she started to laugh, and then she stopped and looked at me, scared."

59 At the sound of a moving pencil the man who was telling the story looked up.

60 "I dunno, maybe it wasn't scared," he hastened; "I wouldn't like to say it was. Soon Harry got back, and then Dr. Lloyd came, and you, Mr. Peters, and so I guess that's all I know that you don't."

61 He said that last with relief and moved a little, as if relaxing. Everyone moved a little. The county attorney walked toward the stair door.

62 "I guess we'll go upstairs first, then out to the barn and around there."

63 He paused and looked around the kitchen.

64 "You're convinced there was nothing important here?" he asked the sheriff. "Nothing that would—point to any motive?"

65 The sheriff too looked all around, as if to reconvince himself.

66 "Nothing here but kitchen things," he said, with a little laugh for the insignificance of kitchen things.

67 The county attorney was looking at the cupboard, a peculiar, ungainly structure, half closet and half cupboard, the upper part of it being built in the wall, and the lower part just the old-fashioned kitchen cupboard. As if its queerness attracted him, he got a chair and opened the upper part and looked in. After a moment he drew his hand away sticky.

68 "Here's a nice mess," he said resentfully.

69 The two women had drawn nearer and now the sheriff's wife spoke.

70 "Oh, her fruit," she said, looking to Mrs. Hale for sympathetic understanding. She turned back to the county attorney and explained: "She worried about that when it turned so cold last night. She said the fire would go out and her jars might burst."

71 Mrs. Peters' husband broke into a laugh.

72 "Well, can you beat the women! Held for murder and worrying about her preserves!"

73 The young attorney set his lips.

74 "I guess before we're through with her she may have something more serious than preserves to worry about."

75 "Oh, well," said Mrs. Hale's husband, with good natured superiority, "women are used to worrying over trifles."

76 The two women moved a little closer together. Neither of them spoke. The county attorney seemed suddenly to remember his manners and think of his future.

77 "And yet," said he, with the gallantry of a young politician, "for all their worries, what would we do without the ladies?"

78 The women did not speak, did not unbend. He went to the sink and began washing his hands. He turned to wipe them on the roller towel; whirled it for a cleaner place.

79 "Dirty towels! Not much of a housekeeper, would you say, ladies?"

80 He kicked his foot against some dirty pans under the sink.

81 "There's a great deal of work to be done on a farm," said Mrs. Hale stiffly.

82 "To be sure. And yet," with a little bow to her, "I know there are some Dickson County farmhouses that do not have such roller towels." He gave it a pull to expose its full length again.

83 "Those towels get dirty awful quick. Men's hands aren't always as clean as they might be."

84 "Ah, loyal to your sex, I see," he laughed. He stopped and gave her a keen look. "But you and Mrs. Wright were neighbors. I suppose you were friends too."

85 Martha Hale shook her head.

86 "I've seen little enough of her of late years. I've not been in this house—it's more than a year."

87 "Why was that? You didn't like her?"

88 "I liked her well enough," she replied with spirit. "Farmers' wives have their hands full, Mr. Henderson. And then—" She looked around the kitchen.

89 "Yes?" he encouraged.

90 "It never seemed a cheerful place," said she, more to herself than to him.

91 "No," he agreed, "I don't think anyone would call it cheerful. I shouldn't say she had the homemaking instinct."

92 "Well, I don't know as Wright had, either," she muttered.

93 "You mean they didn't get on very well?" he was quick to ask.

94 "No, I don't mean anything," she answered with decision. As she turned a little away from him, she added, "But I don't think a place would be any the cheerfuller for John Wright bein' in it."

95 "I'd like to talk to you about that a little later, Mrs. Hale," he said. "I'm anxious to get the lay of things upstairs now."

96 He moved toward the stair door, followed by the two men.

97 "I suppose anything Mrs. Peters does'll be all right?" the sheriff inquired. "She was to take in some clothes for her, you know, and a few little things. We left in such a hurry yesterday."

98 The county attorney looked at the two women they were leaving alone there among the kitchen things.

99 "Yes—Mrs. Peters," he said, his glance resting on the woman who was not Mrs. Peters, the big farmer woman who stood behind the sheriff's wife. "Of course Mrs. Peters is one of us," he said, in a manner of entrusting responsibility. "And keep your eye out, Mrs. Peters, for anything that might be of use. No telling; you women might come upon a clue to the motive and that's the thing we need."

100 Mr. Hale rubbed his face after the fashion of a showman getting ready for a pleasantry.

101 "But would the women know a clue if they did come upon it?" he said; and, having delivered himself of this, he followed the others through the stair door.

102 The women stood motionless and silent, listening to the footsteps, first upon the stairs, then in the room above.

103 Then, as if releasing herself from something strange, Mrs. Hale

began to arrange the dirty pans under the sink, which the county attorney's disdainful push of the foot had deranged.

104 "I'd hate to have men comin' into my kitchen," she said testily, "snoopin' round and criticizin'."

105 "Of course it's no more than their duty," said the sheriff's wife, in her manner of timid acquiescence.

106 "Duty's all right," replied Mrs. Hale bluffly, "but I guess that deputy sheriff that come out to make the fire might have got a little of this on." She gave the roller towel a pull. "Wish I'd thought of that sooner! Seems mean to talk about her for not having things slicked up when she had to come away in such a hurry."

107 She looked around the kitchen. Certainly it was not "slicked up." Her eye was held by a bucket of sugar on a low shelf. The cover was off the bucket and beside it was a paper bag, half full.

108 Mrs. Hale moved toward it.

109 "She was putting this in there," she said to herself slowly.

110 She thought of the flour in her kitchen at home, half sifted, half not sifted. She had been interrupted, and had left things half done. What had interrupted Minnie Foster? Why had that work been left half done? She made a move as if to finish it; unfinished things always bothered her; and she didn't want Mrs. Peters to get that feeling she had got of work begun and then for some reason not finished.

111 "It's a shame about her fruit," she said and walked toward the cupboard that the county attorney had opened, and got on the chair, murmuring: "I wonder if it's all gone."

112 It was a sorry enough looking sight, but, "Here's one that's all right," she said at last. She held it toward the light. "This is cherries, too." She looked again. "I declare, I believe that's the only one."

113 With a sigh, she got down from the chair, went to the sink and wiped off the bottle.

114 "She'll feel awful bad, after all her hard work in the hot weather. I remember the afternoon I put up my cherries last summer."

115 She set the bottle on the table and, with another sigh, started to sit down in the rocker. But she did not sit down. Something kept her from sitting down in that chair. She straightened, stepped back and, half turned away, stood looking at it, seeing the woman who had sat there "pleatin' at her apron."

116 The thin voice of the sheriff's wife broke in upon her: "I must be getting those things from the front-room closet." She opened the door into the other room, started in, stepped back. "You coming with me, Mrs. Hale?" she asked nervously. "You—you could help me get them."

117 They were soon back; the stark coldness of that shut-up room was not a thing to linger in.

118 "My!" said Mrs. Peters, dropping the things on the table and hurrying to the stove.

119 Mrs. Hale stood examining the clothes the woman who was being detained in town had said she wanted.

120 "Wright was close!" she exclaimed, holding up a shabby black skirt that bore the marks of much making over. "I think maybe that's why she kept so much to herself. I s'pose she felt she couldn't do her part; and then, you don't enjoy things when you feel shabby. She used to wear pretty clothes and be lively when she was Minnie Foster, one of the town's girls, singing in the choir. But that—oh, that was twenty years ago."

121 With a carefulness in which there was something tender, she folded the shabby clothes and piled them at one corner of the table. She looked up at Mrs. Peters, and there was something in the other woman's look that irritated her.

122 "She don't care," she said to herself. "Much difference it makes to her whether Minnie Foster had pretty clothes when she was a girl."

123 Then she looked again and she wasn't so sure; in fact, she hadn't at any time been perfectly sure about Mrs. Peters. She had that shrinking manner, and yet her eyes looked as if they could see a long way into things.

124 "This all you was to take in?" asked Mrs. Hale.

125 "No," said the sheriff's wife, "she said she wanted an apron. Funny thing to want," she ventured in her nervous way, "for there's not much to get you dirty in jail, goodness knows. But I suppose just to make her feel more natural. If you're used to wearing an apron—She said they were in the bottom drawer of this cupboard. Yes, here they are. And then her little shawl that always hung on the stair door."

126 She took the small gray shawl from behind the door leading upstairs and stood a minute looking at it.

127 Suddenly Mrs. Hale took a quick step toward the other woman.

128 "Mrs. Peters!"

129 "Yes, Mrs. Hale?"

130 "Do you think she—did it?"

131 A frightened look blurred the other thing in Mrs. Peters' eyes.

132 "Oh, I don't know," she said in a voice that seemed to shrink away from the subject.

133 "Well, I don't think she did," affirmed Mrs. Hale stoutly. "Asking for an apron and her little shawl. Worryin' about her fruit."

134 "Mr. Peters says—" Footsteps were heard in the room above; she

stopped, looked up, then went on in a lowered voice, "Mr. Peters says—it looks bad for her. Mr. Henderson is awful sarcastic in a speech and he's going to make fun of her saying she didn't—wake up."

135 For a moment Mrs. Hale had no answer. Then, "Well, I guess John Wright didn't wake up when they was slippin' that rope under his neck," she muttered.

136 "No, it's *strange,*" breathed Mrs. Peters. "They think it was such a funny way to kill a man."

137 She began to laugh; at the sound of the laugh, abruptly stopped.

138 "That's just what Mr. Hale said," said Mrs. Hale, in a resolutely natural voice. "There was a gun in the house. He says that's what he can't understand."

139 "Mr. Henderson said, coming out, that what was needed for the case was a motive. Something to show anger—or sudden feeling."

140 "Well, I don't see any signs of anger around here," said Mrs. Hale. "I don't—"

141 She stopped. It was as if her mind tripped on something. Her eye was caught by a dishtowel in the middle of the kitchen table. Slowly she moved toward the table. One half of it was wiped clean, the other half messy. Her eyes made a slow, almost unwilling turn to the bucket of sugar and the half empty bag beside it. Things begun and not finished.

142 After a moment she stepped back and said, in that manner of releasing herself:

143 "Wonder how they're finding things upstairs? I hope she had a little more red up up there. You know," she paused, and feeling gathered, "it seems kind of sneaking: locking her up in town and coming out here to get her own house to turn against her!"

144 "But, Mrs. Hale," said the sheriff's wife, "the law is the law."

145 "I s'pose 'tis," answered Mrs. Hale shortly.

146 She turned to the stove, saying something about that fire not being much to brag of. She worked with it a minute and when she straightened up she said aggressively:

147 "The law is the law and a bad stove is a bad stove. How'd you like to cook on this?"—pointing with the poker to the broken lining. She opened the oven door and started to express her opinion of the oven; but she was swept into her own thoughts, thinking of what it could mean, year after year, to have that stove to wrestle with. The thought of Minnie Foster trying to bake in that oven and the thought of her never going over to see Minnie Foster—

148 She was startled by hearing Mrs. Peters say: "A person gets discouraged and loses heart."

149 The sheriff's wife had looked from the stove to the sink, to the pail of water which had been carried in from outside. The two women stood there silent, above them the footsteps of the men who were looking for evidence against the woman who had worked in that kitchen. That look of seeing into things, of seeing through a thing to something else, was in the eyes of the sheriff's wife now. When Mrs. Hale next spoke to her, it was gently.

150 "Better loosen up your things, Mrs. Peters. We'll not feel them when we go out."

151 Mrs. Peters went to the back of the room to hang up the fur tippet she was wearing. A moment later she exclaimed, "Why, she was piecing a quilt," and held up a large sewing basket piled high with quilt pieces.

152 Mrs. Hale spread some of the blocks on the table.

153 "It's a log-cabin pattern," she said, putting several of them together. "Pretty, isn't it?"

154 They were so engaged with the quilt that they did not hear the footsteps on the stairs. Just as the stair door opened Mrs. Hale was saying:

155 "Do you suppose she was going to quilt it or just knot it?"

156 The sheriff threw up his hands.

157 "They wonder whether she was going to quilt it or just knot it!"

158 There was a laugh for the ways of women, a warming of hands over the stove, and then the county attorney said briskly:

159 "Well, let's go right out to the barn and get that cleared up."

160 "I don't see as there's anything so strange," Mrs. Hale said resentfully, after the outside door had closed on the three men, "our taking up our time with little things while we're waiting for them to get the evidence. I don't see as it's anything to laugh about."

161 "Of course they've got awful important things on their minds," said the sheriff's wife apologetically.

162 They returned to an inspection of the block for the quilt. Mrs. Hale was looking at the fine, even sewing, and preoccupied with thoughts of the woman who had done that sewing, when she heard the sheriff's wife say in a queer tone:

163 "Why, look at this one."

164 She turned to take the block held out to her.

165 "The sewing," said Mrs. Peters, in a troubled way. "All the rest of them have been so nice and even—but—this one. Why, it looks as if she didn't know what she was about!"

166 Their eyes met, something flashed to life, passed between them; then, as if with an effort, they seemed to pull away from each other. A moment Mrs. Hale sat there, her hands folded over that sewing which

was so unlike all the rest of the sewing. Then she had pulled a knot and drawn the threads.

167 "Oh, what are you doing, Mrs. Hale?" asked the sheriff's wife, startled.

168 "Just pulling out a stitch or two that's not sewed very good," said Mrs. Hale mildly.

169 "I don't think we ought to touch things," Mrs. Peters said a little helplessly.

170 "I'll just finish up this end," answered Mrs. Hale, still in that mild, matter-of-fact fashion.

171 She threaded a needle and started to replace bad sewing with good. For a little while she sewed in silence. Then, in that thin, timid voice she heard:

172 "Mrs. Hale!"

173 "Yes, Mrs. Peters?"

174 "What do you suppose she was so—nervous about?"

175 "Oh, I don't know," said Mrs. Hale, as if dismissing a thing not important enough to spend much time on. "I don't know as she was—nervous. I sew awful queer sometimes when I'm just tired."

176 She cut a thread and out of the corner of her eye looked up at Mrs. Peters. The small, lean face of the sheriff's wife seemed to have tightened up. Her eyes had that look of peering into something. But next moment she moved and said in her thin, indecisive way:

177 "Well, I must get those clothes wrapped. They may be through sooner than we think. I wonder where I could find a piece of paper and string."

178 "In that cupboard, maybe," suggested Mrs. Hale, after a glance around.

179 One piece of the crazy sewing remained unripped. Mrs. Peters' back turned, Martha Hale now scrutinized that piece, compared it with the dainty, accurate sewing of the other blocks.

180 The difference was startling. Holding this block made her feel queer, as if the distracted thoughts of the woman who had perhaps turned to it to try and quiet herself were communicating themselves to her.

181 Mrs. Peters' voice roused her.

182 "Here's a bird cage," she said. "Did she have a bird, Mrs. Hale?"

183 "Why, I don't know whether she did or not." She turned to look at the cage Mrs. Peters was holding up. "I've not been here in so long." She sighed. "There was a man round last year selling canaries cheap but I don't know as she took one. Maybe she did. She used to sing real pretty herself."

184 Mrs. Peters looked around the kitchen.

185 "Seems kind of funny to think of a bird here." She half laughed, an attempt to put up a barrier. "But she must have had one or why would she have a cage? I wonder what happened to it."

186 "I suppose maybe the cat got it," suggested Mrs. Hale, resuming her sewing.

187 "No; she didn't have a cat. She's got that feeling some people have about cats, being afraid of them. When they brought her to our house yesterday, my cat got in the room and she was real upset and asked me to take it out."

188 "My sister Bessie was like that," laughed Mrs. Hale.

189 The sheriff's wife did not reply. The silence made Mrs. Hale turn around. Mrs. Peters was examining the bird cage.

190 "Look at this door," she said slowly. "It's broke. One hinge has been pulled apart."

191 Mrs. Hale came nearer.

192 "Looks as if someone must have been rough with it."

193 Again their eyes met, startled, questioning, apprehensive. For a moment neither spoke nor stirred. Then Mrs. Hale, turning away, said brusquely:

194 "If they're going to find any evidence, I wish they'd be about it. I don't like this place."

195 "But I'm awful glad you came with me, Mrs. Hale." Mrs. Peters put the bird cage on the table and sat down. "It would be lonesome for me sitting here alone."

196 "Yes—it would, wouldn't it?" agreed Mrs. Hale, a certain determined naturalness in her voice. She had picked up the sewing, but now it dropped in her lap and she murmured in a different voice: "But I tell you what I do wish, Mrs. Peters. I wish I had come over sometimes when she was here. I wish I had."

197 "But of course you were awful busy, Mrs. Hale. Your house and your children."

198 "I could've come," retorted Mrs. Hale shortly. "I stayed away because it weren't cheerful and that's why I ought to have come. I—" she looked around—"I've never liked this place. Maybe because it's down in a hollow and you don't see the road. I don't know what it is, but it's a lonesome place and always was. I wish I had come over to see Minnie Foster sometimes. I can see now—" She did not put it into words.

199 "Well, you mustn't reproach yourself," counseled Mrs. Peters. "Somehow, we just don't see how it is with other folks till something comes up."

200 "Not having children makes less work," mused Mrs. Hale, after a

silence, "but it makes a quiet house, and Wright out to work all day, and no company when he did come in. Did you know John Wright, Mrs. Peters?"

201 "Not to know him. I've seen him in town. They say he was a good man."

202 "Yes—good," conceded John Wright's neighbor grimly. "He didn't drink and kept his word as well as most, I guess, and paid his debts. But he was a hard man, Mrs. Peters. Just to pass the time of day with him—" She stopped, shivered a little. "Like a raw wind that gets to the bone." Her eye fell upon the cage on the table before her, and she added, almost bitterly: "I should think she would've wanted a bird!"

203 Suddenly she leaned forward, looking intently at the cage. "But what do you s'pose went wrong with it?"

204 "I don't know," returned Mrs. Peters, "unless it got sick and died."

205 But after she said it she reached over and swung the broken door. Both women watched it as if somehow held by it.

206 "You didn't know her?" Mrs. Hale asked, a gentler note in her voice.

207 "Not till they brought her yesterday," said the sheriff's wife.

208 "She—come to think of it, she was kind of like a bird herself. Real sweet and pretty, but kind of timid and—fluttery. How she did change."

209 That held her for a long time. Finally, as if struck with a happy thought and relieved to get back to everyday things, she exclaimed:

210 "Tell you what, Mrs. Peters, why don't you take the quilt in with you? It might take up her mind."

211 "Why, I think that's a real nice idea, Mrs. Hale," agreed the sheriff's wife, as if she too were glad to come into the atmosphere of a simple kindness. "There couldn't possibly be any objection to that, could there? Now, just what will I take? I wonder if her patches are in here and her things."

212 They turned to the sewing basket.

213 "Here's some red," said Mrs. Hale, bringing out a roll of cloth. Underneath that was a box. "Here, maybe her scissors are in here and her things." She held it up. "What a pretty box! I'll warrant that was something she had when she was a girl."

214 She held it in her hand a moment; then, with a little sigh, opened it.

215 Instantly her hand went to her nose.

216 "Why—"

217 Mrs. Peters drew nearer, then turned away.

218 "There's something wrapped up in this piece of silk," faltered Mrs. Hale.

219 "This isn't her scissors," said Mrs. Peters in a shrinking voice.

220 Her hand not steady, Mrs. Hale raised the piece of silk. "Oh, Mrs. Peters!" she cried. "It's—"

221 Mrs. Peters bent closer.

222 "It's the bird," she whispered.

223 "But, Mrs. Peters!" cried Mrs. Hale. "Look at it! Its neck—look at its neck! It's all—other side to."

224 She held the box away from her.

225 The sheriff's wife again bent closer.

226 "Somebody wrung its neck," said she in a voice that was slow and deep.

227 And then again the eyes of the two women met, this time clung together in a look of dawning comprehension, of growing horror. Mrs. Peters looked from the dead bird to the broken door of the cage. Again their eyes met. And just then there was a sound at the outside door.

228 Mrs. Hale slipped the box under the quilt pieces in the basket and sank into the chair before it. Mrs. Peters stood holding to the table. The county attorney and the sheriff came in from outside.

229 "Well, ladies," said the county attorney, as one turning from serious things to little pleasantries, "have you decided whether she was going to quilt it or knot it?"

230 "We think," began the sheriff's wife in a flurried voice, "that she was going to—knot it."

231 He was too preoccupied to notice the change in her voice.

232 "Well, that's very interesting, I'm sure," he said tolerantly. He caught sight of the bird cage. "Has the bird flown?"

233 "We think the cat got it," said Mrs. Hale in a voice curiously even.

234 He was walking up and down, as if thinking something out.

235 "Is there a cat?" he asked absently.

236 Mrs. Hale shot a look up at the sheriff's wife.

237 "Well, not now," said Mrs. Peters. "They're superstitious, you know; they leave."

238 She sank into her chair.

239 The county attorney did not heed her. "No sign at all of anyone having come in from the outside," he said to Peters in the manner of continuing an interrupted conversation. "Their own rope. Now let's go upstairs again and go over it, piece by piece. It would have to have been someone who knew the—"

240 The stair door closed behind them.

241 The two women sat motionless, not looking at each other, but as if peering into something and at the same time holding back. When they spoke now it was as if they were afraid of what they were saying, but as if they could not help saying it.

242 "She liked the bird," said Martha Hale, low and slowly. "She was going to bury it in that pretty box."

243 "When I was a girl," said Mrs. Peters, under her breath, "my kitten—there was a boy took a hatchet, and before my eyes—before I could get there—" She covered her face an instant. "If they hadn't held me back I would have—" she caught herself, looked upstairs where footsteps were heard, and finished weakly—"hurt him."

244 "I wonder how it would seem," Mrs. Hale at last began, as if feeling her way over strange ground, "never to have had any children around?" Her eyes made a slow sweep of the kitchen, as if seeing what that kitchen had meant through all the years. "No, Wright wouldn't like the bird," she said after that, "a thing that sang. She used to sing. He killed that too."

245 Mrs. Peters moved uneasily.

246 "Of course we don't know who killed the bird."

247 "I knew John Wright," was Mrs. Hale's answer.

248 "It was an awful thing was done in this house that night, Mrs. Hale," said the sheriff's wife. "Killing a man while he slept, slipping a thing round his neck that choked the life out of him."

249 Mrs. Hale's hand went out to the bird cage.

250 "His neck. Choked the life out of him."

251 "We don't know who killed him," whispered Mrs. Peters wildly.

252 Mrs. Hale had not moved. "If there had been years and years of—nothing, then a bird to sing to you, it would be awful—still—after the bird was still."

253 It was as if something within her not herself had spoken and it found in Mrs. Peters something she did not know as herself.

254 "I know what stillness is," she said, in a queer, monotonous voice. "When we homesteaded in Dakota and my first baby died and me with no other—"

255 Mrs. Hale stirred.

256 "How soon do you suppose they'll be through looking for evidence?"

257 "I know what stillness is," repeated Mrs. Peters in just the same way. Then she too pulled back. "The law has got to punish crime, Mrs. Hale," she said in her tight little way.

258 "I wish you'd seen Minnie Foster," was the answer, "when she

wore a white dress with blue ribbons and stood up there in the choir and sang."

259 The picture of that girl, the fact that she had lived neighbor to that girl for twenty years and had let her die for lack of life, was suddenly more than she could bear.

260 "Oh, I wish I'd come over here once in awhile!" she cried. "That was a crime! Who's going to punish that?"

261 "We mustn't take on," said Mrs. Peters with a frightened look.

262 "I might 'a' known she needed help! I tell you, it's queer, Mrs. Peters. We live close together and we lived far apart. We all go through the same things, it's all just a different kind of the same thing! If it weren't—why do you and I understand? Why do we know what we know this minute?"

263 She dashed her hand across her eyes. Then, seeing the jar of fruit on the table, she reached for it.

264 "If I was you I wouldn't tell her her fruit was gone! Tell her it ain't. Tell her it's all right—all of it. Here, I'd take this in to prove it to her! She—she may never know it was broke."

265 She turned away.

266 Mrs. Peters reached out for the bottle of fruit as if she were glad to take it, as if touching a familiar thing, having something to do, could keep her from something else. She got up, looked about for something to wrap the fruit in, took a petticoat from the pile of clothes she had brought from the front room and nervously started winding that round the bottle.

267 "My!" she began in a high, false voice, "it's a good thing the men couldn't hear us! Getting all stirred up over a little thing like a—dead canary." She hurried over that. "My wouldn't they laugh?"

268 Footsteps were heard on the stairs.

269 "Maybe they would," muttered Mrs. Hale, "maybe they wouldn't."

270 "No, Peters," said the county attorney incisively, "it's all perfectly clear, except the reason for doing it. But you know juries when it comes to women. If there was some definite thing, something to show—"

271 In a covert way Mrs. Hale looked at Mrs. Peters. Mrs. Peters was looking at her. Quickly they looked away from each other. The outer door opened and Mr. Hale came in.

272 "I've got the team round now," he said. "Pretty cold out there."

273 "I'm going to stay here awhile by myself," the county attorney suddenly announced. "You can send Frank out for me, can't you?" he asked the sheriff. "I'm not satisfied we can't do better."

274 Again, for one brief moment, the two women's eyes found one another.

275 The sheriff came up to the table.

276 "Did you want to see what Mrs. Peters was going to take in?"

277 The county attorney picked up the apron. He laughed.

278 "Oh, I guess they're not very dangerous things the ladies have picked out."

279 Mrs. Hale's hand was on the sewing basket in which the box was concealed. She felt that she ought to take her hand off the basket. She did not seem able to. He picked up one of the quilt blocks which she had piled on to cover the box. Her eyes felt like fire. She had a feeling that if he took up the basket she would snatch it from him.

280 But he did not take it up. With another little laugh, he turned away, saying:

281 "No, Mrs. Peters doesn't need supervising. For that matter, a sheriff's wife is married to the law. Ever think of it that way, Mrs. Peters?"

282 Mrs. Peters was standing beside the table. Mrs. Hale shot a look up at her, but she could not see her face. Mrs. Peters had turned away. When she spoke, her voice was muffled.

283 "Not—just that way," she said.

284 "Married to the law!" chuckled Mrs. Peters' husband. He moved toward the door into the front room, and said to the county attorney:

285 "I just want you to come in here a minute, George. We ought to take a look at these windows."

286 "Oh, windows," said the county attorney scoffingly.

287 "We'll be right out, Mr. Hale," said the sheriff to the farmer, who was still waiting by the door.

288 Hale went to look after the horses. The sheriff followed the county attorney into the other room. Again, for one final moment, the two women were alone in that kitchen.

289 Martha Hale sprang up, her hands tight together, looking at that other woman, with whom it rested. At first she could not see her eyes, for the sheriff's wife had not turned back since she turned away at that suggestion of being married to the law. But now Mrs. Hale made her turn back. Her eyes made her turn back. Slowly, unwillingly, Mrs. Peters turned her head until her eyes met the eyes of the other woman. There was a moment when they held each other in a steady, burning look in which there was no evasion nor flinching. Then Martha Hale's eyes pointed the way to the basket in which was hidden the thing that would make certain the conviction of the other woman—that woman who was not there and yet who had been there with them all through that hour.

290 For a moment Mrs. Peters did not move. And then she did it. With a rush forward, she threw back the quilt pieces, got the box,

tried to put it in her handbag. It was too big. Desperately she opened it, started to take the bird out. But there she broke, she could not touch the bird. She stood there helpless, foolish.

291 There was the sound of a knob turning in the inner door. Martha Hale snatched the box from the sheriff's wife and got it in the pocket of her big coat just as the sheriff and the county attorney came back into the kitchen.

292 "Well, Henry," said the county attorney facetiously, "at least we found out that she was not going to quilt it. She was going to—what is it you call it, ladies?"

293 Mrs. Hale's hand was against the pocket of her coat.

294 "We call it—knot it, Mr. Henderson." □

Limited omniscience sets the tone of "A Jury of Her Peers" from the first paragraph which reveals Martha Hale as a woman who hates loose ends and unfinished business. Enveloping action is sketched in rapidly and clearly with panoramic sweep rather than expository detail. Every "explanation" carries a descriptive fragment or a shred of characterization with it as the author remains completely outside the story, admitting only that observation which is accessible to Martha. It would be difficult to state whether a man or a woman wrote this work if it were anonymous. If you are quick to argue that a man would not understand the female mind so well, pause and remember that Shakespeare created Juliet and Lady Macbeth, Flaubert created Emma Bovary, and Tolstoy created Anna Karenina!

The men of the story are completely stock characters, an authorial decision that adds tonal and thematic unity to the work, for are men not unsubtle, unobservant, and almost unconscious in the narrative flow? And, for that matter, who are Minnie Foster Wright's "peers"? Certainly not the men. They may sit in lofty judgment, but it is Mrs. Hale and Mrs. Peters who weigh the evidence and destroy it in an unstated conspiracy. "The Law" is ordered and predictable reality—as are the male, stock, static characters. Justice is more abstract, bending blindly to meet individual needs as they are weighed in her delicately balanced scales. The women tip those scales ever so slightly and become round, developing characters in the process.

Generating circumstances grow out of the forward flow of narrative on rapidly paced dialog, fragmentary flashbacks, and reflective, indirect interior monolog. Rising action begins with paragraph 30 (compare the description here with the expository statement of paragraph 16) and a mosaic begins to form. It will not be completed until the end of the story, but the bits and pieces that mean so little in isolation are beginning to be juxtaposed, creating the expanding picture with each new addition.

While it is not entirely absent from the story, appeal to the emotions is much less evident in this story than it was in "Joy Cometh in the Morning." A grim kind of logic—the logic of interrelationships, shared resentments, and dull guilt—pervades the growing awareness of the two women as the absent Minnie Foster Wright seems to haunt the kitchen in the silent messages of her half-finished tasks and the mute evidences of the slow kindlings which were to flare up in violent flames. As the pattern of her conflicts accrue in the awareness of the women, finally to re-create the climactic moment of death upstairs, their conflicts grow apace. The nebulous bond of sex binds them loosely together until, in paragraph 75, Mr. Hale knots the thread of female loyalties, a thread which will grow tighter with each passing sentence. Compare paragraph 149 of this story with paragraph 4 of "Joy Cometh in the Morning" to see the subtle difference between pulp and slick treatment of identical symbols (well water and stove).

Little shreds of evidence—little tidying actions. Slowly, carefully, methodically, Mrs. Hale begins to destroy those traces which would create a motive in their total pattern, a pattern as logical and as "pieced" as the quilt with its assembled blocks. Symbols again add thematic unity as Mrs. Hale replaces "bad sewing with good" (paragraph 171).

The movement of the men creates complicating action throughout the story, their inopportune comings and goings generating a greater air of tenseness than already exists in the kitchen. In paragraph 228, the moment of illumination occurs to the women. They have reconstructed the entire sequence of events. Irony is corrosive in Mrs. Peters' observation in paragraph 230. Irony grows into paragraph 270, surges ahead to paragraph 281, and explodes in realization of theme in the final paragraph where, by way of climax, the women close ranks against the cruelties and thoughtless words of the men. The reader's moment of illumination comes at this point.

Much more subtle than "Joy Cometh in the Morning," "A Jury of Her Peers" employs many of the same materials, but the answers are not as pat, not as oversimplified. The reader is relatively satisfied that Minnie Foster Wright will be freed by those twelve good men and true because there is nothing definite to show by way of reason for the murder. Mrs. Hale and Mrs. Peters have tidied up the kitchen; of course they wouldn't "know a clue if they did come upon it" (paragraph 101), would they? One wouldn't even consider the kitchen a place for clues, for, as the sheriff says, "Nothing here but kitchen things," and they are insignificant, aren't they?

The significance of the seemingly insignificant completely separates the next story from the first two and establishes it as quality fiction. Almost devoid of action, "Miss Tempy's Watchers" by Sarah Orne Jewett lacks the emotional sentimentality of "Joy Cometh in the Morning" and the dramatic tensions of "A Jury of Her Peers." Yet it is quietly gripping, embodying in its calm narrative a clear depiction of reality that the other stories fail to achieve.

Dorothy Thomas's Kansas of the late nineteenth century is similar to a thirty minute television presentation in color. Self-conscious, attempting to achieve reader identification with obvious tricks of language, picture-postcard imagery, and surface exploration of shallow characters, it encourages the reader to forget the tensions and strains of life, to withdraw to a bucolic past when life was simple and undemanding, its major problems centered in loneliness created by physical distance.

Susan Glaspell's Nebraska of the early twentieth century is a clearer, sharper study. Like an artfully contrived motion picture, it explores the limited setting with a camera of exceptional ability to focus on small details, weave them into a growing body of evidence, and achieve a deliberately understated climax of power and impact. But the self-consciousness of craft is apparent in it also. The characters are more credible, less ingenuous, but they are still actors striving to create the reality of a dramatic self-awareness growing out of the loneliness created by the great gulf between men and women. Oversimplifications exist here too, but they encourage the reader to challenge them, and, when he does, they lead to complexities beyond the story.

Sarah Orne Jewett's late nineteenth-century New Hampshire resembles nothing as technical as television and movies. Rather, it is like a muted painting of a simple incident wherein light comes from many sources to illuminate first one element of the total work, then another, finally to produce a reaction in the viewer that causes him to understand the significance of the canvas if not the component parts. As you read "Miss Tempy's Watchers," you will find you cannot state the plot—it has none beyond roman numeral I. Narrative flow reflects the setting: in the course of a long spring night, death is observed, and it gives way to life forces that strain against enforced imprisonment. No dramatic, full-blooming theme emerges at the climax, but new, tender shoots of reader understanding promise, one day, to bear sudden flowers. That promise is not suggested by Jewett; it *exists* for the individual reader, defying reduction to a cliché. Truths about human nature are at the heart of the promise, but even those truths must be assessed in relation to the reader's nondramatic life. Awareness grows and a simple fact emerges: loneliness is the confining prison we build for ourselves with the materials of our own selfish viewpoints. Jewett's point of view is omniscient, but she is nowhere apparent as author; rather, the inherent truths are so overpoweringly real that some suprahuman intelligence seems to illuminate the dim canvas of this story.

Miss Tempy's Watchers

by Sarah Orne Jewett

1 The time of year was April; the place was a small farming town in New Hampshire, remote from any railroad. One by one the lights had been blown out in the scattered houses near Miss Tempy Dent's; but as her neighbors took a last look out-of-doors, their eyes turned with instinctive curiosity toward the old house, where a lamp burned steadily. They gave a little sigh. "Poor Miss Tempy!" said more than one bereft acquaintance; for the good woman lay dead in her north chamber, and the light was a watcher's light. The funeral was set for the next day, at one o'clock.

2 The watchers were two of the oldest friends, Mrs. Crowe and Sarah Ann Binson. They were sitting in the kitchen, because it seemed less awesome than the unused best room, and they beguiled the long hours by steady conversation. One would think that neither topics nor opinions would hold out, at that rate, all through the long spring night; but there was a certain degree of excitement just then, and the two women had risen to an unusual level of expressiveness and confidence. Each had already told the other more than one fact that she had determined to keep secret; they were again and again tempted into statements that either would have found impossible by daylight. Mrs. Crowe was knitting a blue yarn stocking for her husband; the foot was already so long that it seemed as if she must have forgotten to narrow it at the proper time. Mrs. Crowe knew exactly what she was about, however; she was of a much cooler disposition than Sister Binson, who made futile attempts at some sewing, only to drop her work into her lap whenever the talk was most engaging.

3 Their faces were interesting,—of the dry, shrewd, quick-witted New England type, with thin hair twisted neatly back out of the way. Mrs. Crowe could look vague and benignant, and Miss Binson was, to quote her neighbors, a little too sharp-set; but the world knew that she had need to be, with the load she must carry of supporting an inefficient widowed sister and six unpromising and unwilling nieces and nephews. The eldest boy was at last placed with a good man to learn the mason's

trade. Sarah Ann Binson, for all her sharp, anxious aspect, never defended herself, when her sister whined and fretted. She was told every week of her life that the poor children never would have had to lift a finger if their father had lived, and yet she had kept her steadfast way with the little farm, and patiently taught the young people many useful things, for which, as everybody said, they would live to thank her. However pleasureless her life appeared to outward view, it was brimful of pleasure to herself.

4 Mrs. Crowe, on the contrary, was well to do, her husband being a rich farmer and an easy-going man. She was a stingy woman, but for all that she looked kindly; and when she gave away anything, or lifted a finger to help anybody, it was thought a great piece of beneficence, and a compliment, indeed, which the recipient accepted with twice as much gratitude as double the gift that came from a poorer and more generous acquaintance. Everybody liked to be on good terms with Mrs. Crowe. Socially she stood much higher than Sarah Ann Binson. They were both old schoolmates and friends of Temperance Dent, who had asked them, one day, not long before she died, if they would not come together and look after the house, and manage everything, when she was gone. She may have had some hope that they might become closer friends in this period of intimate partnership, and that the richer woman might better understand the burdens of the poorer. They had not kept the house the night before; they were too weary with the care of their old friend, whom they had not left until all was over.

5 There was a brook which ran down the hillside very near the house, and the sound of it was much louder than usual. When there was silence in the kitchen, the busy stream had a strange insistence in its wild voice, as if it tried to make the watchers understand something that related to the past.

6 "I declare, I can't begin to sorrow for Tempy yet. I am so glad to have her at rest," whispered Mrs. Crowe. "It is strange to set here without her, but I can't make it clear that she has gone. I feel as if she had got easy and dropped off to sleep, and I'm more scared about waking her up than knowing any other feeling."

7 "Yes," said Sarah Ann, "it's just like that, ain't it? But I tell you we are goin' to miss her worse than we expect. She's helped me through with many a trial, has Temperance. I ain't the only one who says the same, neither."

8 These words were spoken as if there were a third person listening; somebody beside Mrs. Crowe. The watchers could not rid their minds of the feeling that they were being watched themselves. The spring wind whistled in the window crack, now and then, and buffeted the little house in a gusty way that had a sort of companionable effect. Yet,

on the whole, it was a very still night, and the watchers spoke in a half-whisper.

9 "She was the freest-handed woman that ever I knew," said Mrs. Crowe, decidedly. "According to her means, she gave away more than anybody. I used to tell her 't wa'n't right. I used really to be afraid that she went without too much, for we have a duty to ourselves."

10 Sister Binson looked up in a half-amused, unconscious way, and then recollected herself.

11 Mrs. Crowe met her look with a serious face. "It ain't so easy for me to give as it is for some," she said simply, but with an effort which was made possible only by the occasion. "I should like to say, while Tempy is laying here yet in her own house, that she has been a constant lesson to me. Folks are too kind, and shame me with thanks for what I do. I ain't such a generous woman as poor Tempy was, for all she had nothin' to do with, as one may say."

12 Sarah Binson was much moved at this confession, and was even pained and touched by the unexpected humility. "You have a good many calls on you"—she began, and then left her kind little compliment half finished.

13 "Yes, yes, but I've got means enough. My disposition's more of a cross to me as I grow older, and I made up my mind this morning that Tempy's example should be my pattern henceforth." She began to knit faster than ever.

14 " 'T ain't no use to get morbid: that's what Tempy used to say herself," said Sarah Ann, after a minute's silence. "Ain't it strange to say 'used to say'?" and her own voice choked a little. "She never did like to hear folks git goin' about themselves."

15 " 'T was only because they're apt to do it so as other folks will say 't wasn't so, an' praise 'em up," humbly replied Mrs. Crowe, "and that ain't my object. There wa'n't a child but what Tempy set herself to work to see what she could do to please it. One time my brother's folks had been stopping here in the summer, from Massachusetts. The children was all little, and they broke up a sight of toys, and left 'em when they were going away. Tempy come right up after they rode by, to see if she couldn't help me set the house to rights, and she caught me just as I was going to fling some of the clutter into the stove. I was kind of tired out, starting 'em off in season. 'Oh, give me them!' says she, real pleading; and she wropped 'em up and took 'em home with her when she went, and she mended 'em up and stuck 'em together, and made some young one or other happy with every blessed one. You'd thought I'd done her the biggest favor. 'No thanks to me. I should ha' burnt 'em, Tempy,' says I."

16 "Some of 'em came to our house, I know," said Miss Binson.

"She'd take a lot o' trouble to please a child, 'stead o' shoving of it out o' the way, like the rest of us when we're drove.

17 "I can tell you the biggest thing she ever done, and I don't know's there's anybody left but me to tell it. I don't want it forgot," Sarah Binson went on, looking up at the clock to see how the night was going. "It was that pretty-looking Trevor girl, who taught the Corners school, and married so well afterwards, out in New York State. You remember her, I dare say?"

18 "Certain," said Mrs. Crowe, with an air of interest.

19 "She was a splendid scholar, folks said, and give the school a great start; but she'd overdone herself getting her education, and working to pay for it, and she all broke down one spring, and Tempy made her come and stop with her a while,—you remember that? Well, she had an uncle, her mother's brother, out in Chicago, who was well off and friendly, and used to write to Lizzie Trevor, and I dare say make her some presents; but he was a lively, driving man, and didn't take time to stop and think about his folks. He hadn't seen her since she was a little girl. Poor Lizzie was so pale and weakly that she just got through the term o' school. She looked as if she was just going straight off in a decline. Tempy, she cosseted her up a while, and then, next thing folks knew, she was tellin' round how Miss Trevor had gone to see her uncle, and meant to visit Niagary Falls on the way, and stop over night. Now I happened to know, in ways I won't dwell on to explain, that the poor girl was in debt for her schoolin' when she come here, and her last quarter's pay had just squared it off at last, and left her without a cent ahead, hardly; but it had fretted her thinking of it, she paid it all; those might have dunned her that she owed it to. An' I taxed Tempy about the girl's goin' off on such a journey till she owned up, rather'n have Lizzie blamed, that she'd given her sixty dollars, same's if she was rolling in riches, and sent her off to have a good rest and vacation."

20 "Sixty dollars!" exclaimed Mrs. Crowe. "Tempy only had ninety dollars a year that came in to her; rest of her livin' she got by helpin' about, with what she raised off this little piece o' ground, sand one side an' clay the other. An' how often I've heard her tell, years ago, that she'd rather see Niagary than any other sight in the world!"

21 The women looked at each other in silence; the magnitude of the generous sacrifice was almost too great for their comprehension.

22 "She was just poor enough to do that!" declared Mrs. Crowe at last, in an abandonment of feeling. "Say what you may, I feel humbled to the dust," and her companion ventured to say nothing. She never had given away sixty dollars at once, but it was simply because she never had it to give. It came to her very lips to say in explanation,

"Tempy was so situated;" but she checked herself in time, for she would not betray her own loyal guarding of a dependent household.

23 "Folks say a great deal of generosity, and this one's being public-sperited, and that one free-handed about giving," said Mrs. Crowe, who was a little nervous in the silence. "I suppose we can't tell the sorrow it would be to some folks not to give, same's 't would be to me not to save. I seem kind of made for that, as if 't was what I'd got to do. I should feel sights better about it if I could make it evident what I was savin' for. If I had a child, now, Sarah Ann," and her voice was a little husky,—"if I had a child, I should think I was heapin' of it up because he was the one trained by the Lord to scatter it again for good. But here's Mr. Crowe and me, we can't do anything with money, and both of us like to keep things same's they've always been. Now Priscilla Dance was talking away like a mill-clapper, week before last. She'd think I would go right off and get one o' them new-fashioned gilt-and-white papers for the best room, and some new furniture, an' a marble-top table. And I looked at her, all struck up. 'Why,' says I, 'Priscilla, that nice old velvet paper ain't hurt a mite. I shouldn't feel 't was my best room without it. Dan'el says 't is the first thing he can remember rubbin' his little baby fingers on to it, and how splendid he thought them red roses was.' I maintain," continued Mrs. Crowe stoutly, "that folks wastes sights o' good money doin' just such foolish things. Tearin' out the insides o' meetin'-houses, and fixin' the pews different; 't was good enough as 't was with mendin'; then times come, an' they want to put it all back same's 't was before."

24 This touched upon an exciting subject to active members of that parish. Miss Binson and Mrs. Crowe belonged to opposite parties, and had at one time come as near hard feelings as they could, and yet escape them. Each hastened to speak of other things and to show her untouched friendliness.

25 "I do agree with you," said Sister Binson, "that few of us know what use to make of money, beyond every-day necessities. You've seen more o' the world than I have, and know what's expected. When it comes to taste and judgment about such things, I ought to defer to others;" and with this modest avowal the critical moment passed when there might have been an improper discussion.

26 In the silence that followed, the fact of their presence in a house of death grew more clear than before. There was something disturbing in the noise of a mouse gnawing at the dry boards of a closet wall near by. Both the watchers looked up anxiously at the clock; it was almost the middle of the night, and the whole world seemed to have left them alone with their solemn duty. Only the brook was awake.

27 "Perhaps we might give a look up-stairs now," whispered Mrs.

Crowe, as if she hoped to hear some reason against their going just then to the chamber of death; but Sister Binson rose, with a serious and yet satisfied countenance, and lifted the small lamp from the table. She was much more used to watching than Mrs. Crowe, and much less affected by it. They opened the door into a small entry with a steep stairway; they climbed the creaking stairs, and entered the cold upper room on tiptoe. Mrs. Crowe's heart began to beat very fast as the lamp was put on a high bureau, and made long, fixed shadows about the walls. She went hesitatingly toward the solemn shape under its white drapery, and felt a sense of remonstrance as Sarah Ann gently, but in a business-like way, turned back the thin sheet.

28 "Seems to me she looks pleasanter and pleasanter," whispered Sarah Ann Binson impulsively, as they gazed at the white face with its wonderful smile. "To-morrow 't will all have faded out. I do believe they kind of wake up a day or two after they die, and it's then they go." She replaced the light covering, and they both turned quickly away; there was a chill in this upper room.

29 " 'T is a great thing for anybody to have got through, ain't it?" said Mrs. Crowe softly, as she began to go down the stairs on tiptoe. The warm air from the kitchen beneath met them with a sense of welcome and shelter.

30 "I don' know why it is, but I feel as near again to Tempy down here as I do up there," replied Sister Binson. "I feel as if the air was full of her, kind of. I can sense things, now and then, that she seems to say. Now I never was one to take up with no nonsense of sperits and such, but I declare I felt as if she told me just now to put some more wood into the stove."

31 Mrs. Crowe preserved a gloomy silence. She had suspected before this that her companion was of a weaker and more credulous disposition than herself. " 'T is a great thing to have got through," she repeated, ignoring definitely all that had last been said. "I suppose you know as well as I that Tempy was one that always feared death. Well, it's all put behind her now; she knows what 't is." Mrs. Crowe gave a little sigh, and Sister Binson's quick sympathies were stirred toward this other old friend, who also dreaded the great change.

32 "I'd never like to forgit almost those last words Tempy spoke plain to me," she said gently, like the comforter she truly was. "She looked up at me once or twice, that last afternoon after I come to set by her, and let Mis' Owen go home; and I says, 'Can I do anything to ease you, Tempy?' and the tears come into my eyes so I couldn't see what kind of a nod she give me. 'No, Sarah Ann, you can't, dear,' says she; and then she got her breath again, and says she, looking at me real

meanin', 'I'm only a-gettin' sleepier and sleepier; that's all there is,' says she, and smiled up at me kind of wishful, and shut her eyes. I knew well enough all she meant. She'd been lookin' out for a chance to tell me, and I don' know's she ever said much afterwards."

33 Mrs. Crowe was not knitting; she had been listening too eagerly. "Yes, 't will be a comfort to think of that sometimes," she said, in acknowledgment.

34 "I know that old Dr. Prince said once, in evenin' meetin', that he'd watched by many a dyin' bed, as we well knew, and enough o' his sick folks had been scared o' dyin' their whole lives through; but when they come to the last, he'd never seen one but was willin', and most were glad, to go. ' 'T is as natural as bein' born or livin' on,' he said. I don't know what had moved him to speak that night. You know he wa'n't in the habit of it, and 't was the monthly concert of prayer for foreign missions anyways," said Sarah Ann; "but 't was a great stay to the mind to listen to his words of experience."

35 "There never was a better man," responded Mrs. Crowe, in a really cheerful tone. She had recovered from her feeling of nervous dread, the kitchen was so comfortable with lamplight and firelight; and just then the old clock began to tell the hour of twelve with leisurely whirring strokes.

36 Sister Binson laid aside her work, and rose quickly and went to the cupboard. "We'd better take a little to eat," she explained. "The night will go fast after this. I want to know if you went and made some o' your nice cupcake, while you was home to-day?" she asked, in a pleased tone; and Mrs. Crowe acknowledged such a gratifying piece of thoughtfulness for this humble friend who denied herself all luxuries. Sarah Ann brewed a generous cup of tea, and the watchers drew their chairs up to the table presently, and quelled their hunger with good country appetites. Sister Binson put a spoon into a small, old-fashioned glass of preserved quince, and passed it to her friend. She was most familiar with the house, and played the part of hostess. "Spread some o' this on your bread and butter," she said to Mrs. Crowe. "Tempy wanted me to use some three or four times, but I never felt to. I know she'd like to have us comfortable now, and would urge us to make a good supper, poor dear."

37 "What excellent preserves she did make!" mourned Mrs. Crowe. "None of us has got her light hand at doin' things tasty. She made the most o' everything, too. Now, she only had that one old quince-tree down in the far corner of the piece, but she'd go out in the spring and tend to it, and look at it so pleasant, and kind of expect the old thorny thing into bloomin'."

38 "She was just the same with folks," said Sarah Ann. "And she'd never git more'n a little apernful o' quinces, but she'd have every mite o' goodness out o' those, and set the glasses up onto her best-room closet shelf, *so* pleased. 'T wa'n't but a week ago tomorrow mornin' I fetched her a little taste o' jelly in a teaspoon; and she says 'Thank ye,' and took it, an' the minute she tasted it she looked up at me as worried as could be. 'Oh, I don't want to eat that,' says she. 'I always keep that in case o' sickness.' 'You're goin' to have the good o' one tumbler yourself,' says I. 'I'd just like to know who's sick now, if you ain't!' An' she couldn't help laughin', I spoke up so smart. Oh, dear me, how I shall miss talkin' over things with her! She always sensed things, and got just the p'int you meant."

39 "She didn't begin to age until two or three years ago, did she?" asked Mrs. Crowe. "I never saw anybody keep her looks as Tempy did. She looked young long after I begun to feel like an old woman. The doctor used to say 't was her young heart, and I don't know but what he was right. How she did do for other folks! There was one spell she wasn't at home a day to a fortnight. She got most of her livin' so, and that made her own potatoes and things last her through. None o' the young folks could get married without her, and all the old ones was disappointed if she wa'n't round when they was down with sickness and had to go. An' cleanin', or tailorin' for boys, or rug-hookin', —there was nothin' but what she could do as handy as most. 'I do love to work,'—ain't you heard her say that twenty times a week?"

40 Sarah Ann Binson nodded, and began to clear away the empty plates. "We may want a taste o' somethin' more towards mornin'," she said. "There's plenty in the closet here; and in case some comes from a distance to the funeral, we'll have a little table spread after we get back to the house."

41 "Yes, I was busy all the mornin'. I've cooked up a sight o' things to bring over," said Mrs. Crowe. "I felt 't was the last I could do for her."

42 They drew their chairs near the stove again, and took up their work. Sister Binson's rocking-chair creaked as she rocked; the brook sounded louder than ever. It was more lonely when nobody spoke, and presently Mrs. Crowe returned to her thoughts of growing old.

43 "Yes, Tempy aged all of a sudden. I remember I asked her if she felt as well as common, one day, and she laughed at me good. There, when Mr. Crowe begun to look old, I couldn't help feeling as if somethin' ailed him, and like as not 't was somethin' he was goin' to git right over, and I dosed him for it stiddy, half of one summer."

44 "How many things we shall be wanting to ask Tempy!" exclaimed

Sarah Ann Binson, after a long pause. "I can't make up my mind to doin' without her. I wish folks could come back just once, and tell us how 't is where they've gone. Seems then we could do without 'em better."

45 The brook hurried on, the wind blew about the house now and then; the house itself was a silent place, and the supper, the warm fire, and an absence of any new topics for conversation made the watchers drowsy. Sister Binson closed her eyes first, to rest them for a minute; and Mrs. Crowe glanced at her compassionately, with a new sympathy for the hard-worked little woman. She made up her mind to let Sarah Ann have a good rest, while she kept watch alone; but in a few minutes her own knitting was dropped, and she, too, fell asleep. Overhead, the pale shape of Tempy Dent, the outworn body of that generous, loving-hearted, simple soul, slept on also in its white raiment. Perhaps Tempy herself stood near, and saw her own life and its surroundings with new understanding. Perhaps she herself was the only watcher.

46 Later, by some hours, Sarah Ann Binson woke with a start. There was a pale light of dawn outside the small windows. Inside the kitchen, the lamp burned dim. Mrs. Crowe awoke, too.

47 "I think Tempy'd be the first to say 't was just as well we both had some rest," she said, not without a guilty feeling.

48 Her companion went to the outer door, and opened it wide. The fresh air was none too cold, and the brook's voice was not nearly so loud as it had been in the midnight darkness. She could see the shapes of the hills, and the great shadows that lay across the lower country. The east was fast growing bright.

49 " 'T will be a beautiful day for the funeral," she said, and turned again, with a sigh, to follow Mrs. Crowe up the stairs. □

In the limited setting of a New England kitchen, two women reveal certain truths about themselves—to each other and to themselves. Human understandings and misunderstandings, selfishness and the greater selfishness of generosity are explored in language as gentle as breath bated in this house of death.

The plot: Two women (acquaintances themselves, but friends of the dead woman upstairs) keep their promise to Miss Tempy by holding the deathwatch and learning some of the things she wanted them to know. Narrative flow assumes the quality of the brook that "ran down the hillside very near the house" with a "strange insistence in its wild voice, as if it tried to make the watchers understand something that related to the past." Dialog and exposition combine to pace the flow, speeding it along to a destination or slowing it in reflective pools where it finds new depths in which the reader can see subtle suggestions, distorted but beckoning him to understanding.

Poetry periodically rises to the surface of the narrative flow, but, like bright blossoms too fragile for the current, it submerges only to reappear again farther downstream. The opening clause is such a fragment. Three iambs trip along through the first syllable of *April,* then droop on an extra syllable. Some years after the line was written, T. S. Eliot was to rediscover the emotion that Jewett here achieves. His line "April is the cruellest month" opens *The Waste Land.* Also in paragraph 1, the clause "and the light was a watcher's light" flickers in the happy tempo of two anapests caught short on a final iamb, the sound reminding the reader again that the spring night is cruel. Again and again such rhythms bob to the surface of the narrative flow, never lingering long enough to become distracting, but relieving the dark flow of words with bright glimpses of brilliant style—an element of good writing you will study more carefully in Chapter VII.

That soft spring night, the flickering light, and the hovering memory of Miss Tempy allow Mrs. Crowe and Sister Binson a candor neither has been capable of prior to this time. If confession is, indeed, good for the soul, these women are to know great good before the night is done.

A penetrating truth rests in the description of the watchers. Mrs. Crowe is selfish and stingy with money, but she looks benign and vague; Sister Binson is generous with her family, and her features are sharp set—appearances are, in reality, often deceiving. The quality story writer does not hesitate to make good people physically ill-favored. Mrs. Crowe dislikes charity for it must be directed to friends and acquaintances since she has no children or other family except her husband. Miss Binson's family is a widowed sister and her six children, and Sarah is pleased to be self-sacrificing for them. She is aware of the pleasure of self-sacrifice, and that too is a kind of selfishness, isn't it?

Dialog crackles in that stern Yankee pattern of using too few words, and the feeling of Miss Tempy's presence refines it even further as the watchers half-whisper their confidences. While Mrs. Crowe confesses her stinginess, the dead woman's plan begins to work, and Sarah Binson's family selfishness grows more obvious with her disclosures about the toys and Lizzie Trevor. The girl's uncle "didn't take time to stop and think about his folks," a harsh judgment from Sister Binson who thinks of no one else. Miss Tempy's "generous sacrifice" was almost too great for either woman to comprehend—but for different reasons. Resentment directs itself against those who do the things we are incapable of doing;

this is a truth of human behavior. Mrs. Crowe and Sarah Binson reveal their humanity in their reactions: "She was just poor enough to do that" and "Tempy was so situated." But before either can be embittered by awareness of the sudden resentment, Temperance Dent's own selfishness is assessed by Mrs. Crowe—not unkindly—not even with personal insight: "I suppose we can't tell the sorrow it would be to some folks not to give."

Small gossip relieves the moment, brings it to new dangers in touching old wounds, and is safely bypassed as new understandings begin to work their magic.

The trip upstairs and the return to the kitchen relieve the moment which could, carried further, become maudlin. And, stirred from shared confidences, the women withdraw briefly from their new understandings, but the spirit of Temperance (and how symbolic the name becomes) makes a new dent (the best authors cannot avoid a good pun) in the defensive armor of the women. As they eat Miss Tempy's preserves, the quince tree serves an allegorical function in the story: Miss Tempy would "go out in the spring and tend to it, and look at it so pleasant, and kind of expect the old thorny thing into bloomin'." On this spring night, the thorny old Crowe and Sarah (like Abraham's wife so long barren) are proof that Tempy got only a "little apernful o' quinces, but she'd have every mite o' goodness out o' those."

Perhaps Tempy did stand watch over her sleeping friends; she would have enjoyed (a little selfishly) the generosity of what the three had shared this night. And as the sun rises in the east, the reader knows the women have been touched with understanding, but it will not outlast the night. After the funeral, life will go on as before: Mrs. Crowe will be stingy; Sarah will still be barren and pour her small largesse on another's children, thereby selfishly filling her empty womb. Somehow, it seems so wrong they should not "come to realize" a great truth at this moment. But life is not like that. Sarah Orne Jewett was a writer of quality fiction, and she recognized reality. Life will continue, no better really and no worse for either Miss Tempy's absence or presence. In the clear light of morning, no great change occurs. An old but comfortable cliché ends the story: " 'T will be a beautiful day for the funeral."

Suggested Assignments. 1. From a current magazine, choose a story you have enjoyed reading. Analyze it and write a defense of your contention that it is pulp, slick, or quality fiction. A word of caution: although the magazine itself may fall into one of the three categories, its stories may range through all three. Editors look first for "good" stories, then for those which will meet the expectations of their readers. Few editors can reject a "good" story, preferring to stretch the minds of their readers just a little. Do not assume too much!

2. Read Katherine Anne Porter's short novel *Noon Wine* (available in paperback or from your library) and compare her concepts of law and justice with Susan Glaspell's concepts in "A Jury of Her Peers." If you wish to do a more elaborate study, add Herman Melville's concepts of law and justice in his short novel *Billy Budd.*

3. Compare the treatment of chairs in the three stories in this chapter. What do these homely pieces of furniture contribute to the total effect of each story?

CHAPTER VII

Style: Why a Reader Discriminates

According to William Faulkner, 'Maybe every novelist wants to write poetry first, finds he can't, and then tries the short story, which is the most demanding form after poetry. And, failing at that, only then does he take up novel writing.' Whether or not this is true, we are generally more conscious of craftsmanship and artistry in the short story than in the novel. The fact that an admiration for skill is usually an acquired taste probably explains why more of the public enjoy novels than short stories, just as more people enjoy symphonies than chamber music. But any really mature literary enjoyment requires an appreciation of the author's artistry, and short stories offer, in addition to their own value as literature, an ideal training ground for this appreciation.°

"Artistry" is inextricably bound up with a nebulous element of all writing—an element called *style.* Style has been described variously and unsatisfactorily by critics as everything from "the man himself" (Buffon) to the author's manner of using language. The latter definition is probably more easily comprehended, the former more accurate. Imagery (compounded of language), symbols (created by language), sentence construction (language patterned in complexity, rhythm, and varying lengths), vocabulary choice (language itself)—all establish the authorship of any identifiably "good" prose or poetry. And style is that elusive quality that allows the sophisticated reader to recognize even an unfamiliar work as the property of a specific author.

Examine the following two excerpts. Each is the opening paragraph of an excellent short story by an exceptional author. The stories share a common setting and theme: a café by night and the negativism of aloneness. Even the plots, numbers of characters, and lengths of the stories are similar. However, you

°Robert Stanton, *An Introduction to Fiction* (New York, 1965), p. 43.

should notice a definite mark of authorship on each as a result of the author's style. Here is the first:

> It was late and every one had left the café except an old man who sat in the shadow the leaves of the tree made against the electric light. In the daytime the street was dusty, but at night the dew settled the dust and the old man liked to sit late because he was deaf and now at night it was quiet and he felt the difference. The two waiters inside the café knew that the old man was a little drunk, and while he was a good client they knew that if he became too drunk he would leave without paying, so they kept watch on him.

The author of this paragraph is noted for the realism of his stories, the naturalism of his style. His sentences have been called "clean, crisp, simple." And so they seem. Are they, however? An insistent rhythm runs through them—a rhythm so insistent that the sentences can be read as poetry. Consider the first clause:

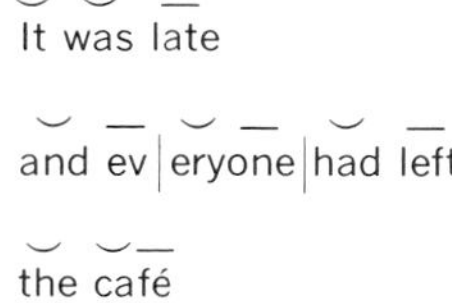

In the first clause, a lilting anapest is placed in tension against connotatively sad words. It is late in time of day, late in the old man's life. Sound and sense are at odds in the three words, creating gentle pathos. However, before it can become oppressive or obvious (thereby destroying the effect) iambs assume control of the next clause. They too are a happy measure but of shorter duration; therefore they minimize the "aloneness" of the line as language intensifies the mood, extending the theme. *The café* comes as subtle saṁvegha, for the mood has not prepared the reader for a locale associated with warmth, security, and happiness. However, the repeated rhythm unifies the two clauses to create a setting the reader must accept in spite of his emotional reservations. Atmosphere is established in the acceptance.

The sentence continues:

except

an old man

who sat|in the shadow

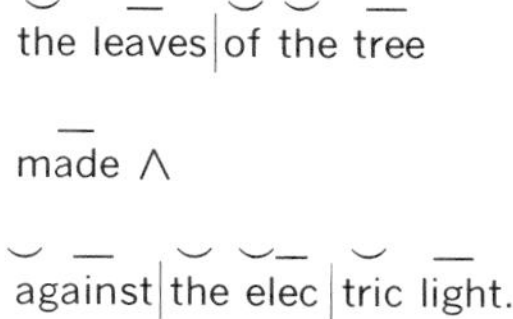

The remainder of the sentence continues to balance iambs against anapests, retaining a crisp, clean flow of sound. However, vocabulary connotations grow more sad, intensifying the reader's emotional ambivalence. *Except* stands alone, set apart in imitation of its denotative effect. The lyrical anapest of *an old man* sharpens the reader's awareness of the sadness of age. The next phrasal grouping contains an extra, unaccented syllable that relieves the monotony of repeated iamb-anapest combinations and recalls the nearly parallel construction of the Twenty-Third Psalm:

Yea, though
I walk|through the valley
of the shadow|of death

Allusion and symbol combine with sound and sense to reveal mood, tone, and theme in the lines. And, as the psalm balances bright hope against dark despair in the next phrasal grouping, a similar rhythm brings light into dark connotations:

I will fear|no evil.
Thy rod|and thy staff,
They com|fort me.

The word *made* stands spondaically isolated, creating sharp, strong imagery in the sentence, tying the natural and the man-made together violently and unnaturally—but coherently—with the logic of symbol. Notice the subtle suggestion created by the rhythm of the final iamb, *-tric(k) light.*

The paragraph continues:

In the | daytime

the street | was dusty,

but at night

the dew | settled | the dust

and the old man

liked to | sit late

because | he was deaf

and now | at night | it was quiet

and he felt

the diff | erence.

A *pyrrhic* (a foot containing two unaccented syllables) places stress on *day-* to create a spondee, emphasizing the harshness of the time and contrasting it with the softness of the anapestic *but at night,* a softness intensified by the conjunctive *but. The street was dusty* grates on harsh consonants and hissing *s*'s to establish unpleasantness. In the fourth line, soft vowels combine with the falling trochee of *settled* to lay the dust and soften age; syntactical ambiguity allows the old man to be "settled" by the dew, a settling that is gentled by three unstressed syllables before *man.* The trochaic *liked to* enforces the "settling down" as rhythm falls into the chair where the old man will *sit late.* His aloneness is further revealed not only *because he was deaf,* but also in the rhythm of the line and its grammatical misplacement. As an adverbial clause, it modifies *felt.* However, placed after *late,* it serves a second adverbial function while contributing to the rhythmical pattern. As the reader has been so steadily exposed to poetic logic rather than to mere prose statement in this paragraph, he can accept the old man's ability to "feel" a difference in sound—a logic prose rhythms could not accomplish. Sound has died away on *it was quiet* as the extra unstressed syllable added to the anapest allows it to die away. The technique is repeated in the last phrase as the iamb falls sharply into silence on the unaccented pyrrhic foot.

In the final sentence of the paragraph, harsh prose rhythms introduce the waiters. No cadencial scanning suggests itself, so the reader is forced, whether he realizes it or not, to certain conclusions: the waiters themselves are prosaic and insensitive. Had the author himself made such an assertion, it would have shattered the mood built thus far. But since style reveals the knowledge, the reader accepts it readily, if unconsciously.

Was the author aware of his technique? Was his poetic style a conscious accomplishment? Certainly he worked hard enough to achieve it—that is a well-documented fact. Was he aware of the alliterative *dew-dust-deaf-difference* in the paragraph? Of slant rhyme in *night-quiet?* Of symbolism? Of allusion? Of the refrain (a word or line regularly repeated to accrue associated meanings) quality of *late?* Perhaps it can be argued he just "felt" everything was "right." Perhaps—until, later in the story, a violent parody of the Lord's Prayer is employed and the reader realizes the symbolism of these earlier lines makes the parody meaningful, allowing theme to emerge.

Incidentally, this is the opening paragraph of "A Clean, Well-Lighted Place,"* one of the most widely admired stories by the father of the tough-guy school of realistic fiction, Ernest Hemingway.

Now consider the opening paragraph of a second story:

> It was raining that morning, and still very dark. When the boy reached the street-car café he had almost finished his route and he went in for a cup of coffee. The place was an all-night café owned by a bitter and stingy man called Leo. After the raw, empty street, the café seemed friendly and bright: along the counter there were a couple of soldiers, three spinners from the cotton mill, and in a corner a man who sat hunched over with his nose and half his face down in a beer mug. The boy wore a helmet such as aviators wear. When he went into the café he unbuckled the chin strap and raised the right flap up over his pink little ear; often as he drank his coffee someone would speak to him in a friendly way. But this morning Leo did not look into his face and none of the men were talking. He paid and was leaving the café when a voice called out to him:
>
> "Son! Hey, son!"

The first sentence and the introductory clause of the second sentence (which can be read syntactically with both sentence 1 and 2) are anapestically structured in much the same fashion as Poe's "Annabel Lee."

* From his first collection of short stories, *Winner Take Nothing* (New York, 1933).

Compare

> ◡ ◡ — ◡ ◡ — ◡ ◡ — ◡◡ —
> It was rain|ing that morn|ing, and still|very dark.
>
> ◡ ◡ — ◡ ◡ — ◡ ◡ —
> When the boy|reached the street|car café

with

> ◡ ◡ — ◡ ◡ — ◡◡ — ◡—
> It was man|y and man|y a year|ago
>
> ◡ ◡ — ◡ ◡ ◡ —
> In a kingdom|by the sea.

The mournful repetition of *-ning* in *raining* and *morning* establishes the same tone of remoteness in time, of detachment from reality that is created by *many and many* in Poe's poem. *Very dark* and *year ago* are both balanced against the mournful sound of falling *n*'s to complete the sense of distance. In both instances, geographical setting grows from the lonesome sound and, even though it is concretely presented, it is imbued with misty distance by the lingering echo and the lilting rhythm as they combine to create the timelessness of fairy tale, thereby creating atmosphere.

From that point, however, the remainder of the paragraph is written in a matter-of-fact prose rhythm. The pace of the prose and the spatial development of the paragraph would be suitable to a theme in any freshman composition class, assuring the student an excellent grade for creating a solid but sensitive scene of studied reality. The ubiquitous *and,* so abused by some writers, is here employed skillfully to establish a sense of everything-happening-at-once. A sense of immediacy and unity of scene results. Adjectives, too often a weakness in unskilled hands, are paired (*bitter and stingy, raw* and *empty, friendly and bright*) to create a progression of attitude which begins in the selfish, proceeds to the impersonal, and culminates in the inclusive. Numbers (*a couple, three spinners, a man*) set the lone figure of the boy apart physically and emotionally as a result of the combined pairings: people and numbers. The boy and the lone man are unpaired; the reader is, therefore, ready for the obvious development. Objective reporting is apparent, but subjective; emotional connotations are cleverly intruded in *paper boy, aviator cap,* and the boy's preparation to be spoken to "in a friendly way." The reader is manipulated into a position where he must be predisposed to sympathy for the boy. *Pink little ear* is emotionally charged language. The baby color, the diminutive *little,* and the unsophisticated and trusting exposure of the ear—all are designed to enlist the reader's sympathy and create a warm reception for a stock character—the orphan. Negativism pervades the scene as "Leo *did not* look into his face" and "*none* of the men were talking." The harsh, journalistic, final line becomes biblical in tone as "a voice" (not a person) calls out and "[My] Son, [My] son" intrudes itself as an allusion.

In "A Tree. A Rock. A Cloud." (which this paragraph begins), Carson McCullers reveals an attitude about love (basically, her philosophy of love) by means of an incident reported from a relatively objective point of view; yet the tone of the story establishes itself as vocabulary choices reveal the attitude she wishes the reader to share.

In examining these two stories in their entirety on the pages that follow, you should be conscious of the construction of each line as well as the structure of the entire story. In both, an incident forms the narrative skeleton, characters become important, and, through them, theme emerges to create an understandable personal allegory for the reader who, by isolating the individual elements, manages to understand them as a whole.

First, however, let's examine the opening paragraph of a third story, equally excellent, by an equally exceptional author. It too deals with the aloneness of people, in this case, a couple seeking to be a part of something removed from love—but not too far removed:

> When the porter's wife, who used to answer the house-bell, announced "A gentleman and a lady, sir," I had, as I often had in those days—the wish being father to the thought—an immediate vision of sitters. Sitters my visitors in this case proved to be; but not in the sense I should have preferred. There was nothing at first however to indicate that they mightn't have come for a portrait. The gentleman, a man of fifty, very high and very straight, with a moustache slightly grizzled and a dark grey walking-coat admirably fitted, both of which I noted professionally—I don't mean as a barber or yet as a tailor—would have struck me as a celebrity if celebrities often were striking. It was a truth of which I had for some time been conscious that a figure with a good deal of frontage was, as one might say, almost never a public institution. A glance at the lady helped to remind me of this paradoxical law: she also looked too distinguished to be a "personality." Moreover one would scarcely come across two variations together.

There is little—if anything—of a distinctly poetic quality in this paragraph; yet a dignified, graceful rhythm forms long cadences of sound that are pleasing to the ear as they immediately establish a tone of something recalled in tranquility. The sentences are long and convoluted, breaking naturally to admit the parenthetical introspection of a contained, urbane raconteur sharing a conversational anecdote with the reader. The parenthetical matter (such as "who used to answer the house-bell" and "the wish being father to the thought") reveals the complexity of the narrator's intellect as well as the ordered correctness of his thought processes. Here is a man of scholarly proportions—a bit obtuse, perhaps, but logically organized.

The second sentence reveals the subtlety of this author's style as, through the intricacies of the controlled, first person point of view, the reader is made to realize that the focus is on the narrator rather than on the couple. Dramatic irony is achieved as the author allows the reader to recognize character traits through the narrator's unconscious revelations. The inverted sentence pattern establishes a focus of interest that is almost completely reversed if the sentence is recast in a traditional order: "My visitors in this case proved to be sitters; but not in the sense I should have preferred." In the recasting, focus is at first narrowed to the visitors rather than to the narrator himself, attention swinging from the couple (clause 1) to the narrator (clause 2). In its grammatically dependent position, clause 2 subordinates the importance of the narrator to the importance of the couple. However, the author chose to place the direct object *sitters* in the inverted, introductory position in the first clause, narrowing focus to the narrator by making his hopes ("the wish being father to the thought") of primary importance and relegating the visitors to a subordinate position.

In the remainder of the paragraph, the couple are described by the narrator, but, in the process, he reveals himself. They are exteriors only; he becomes an entity because his inner self emerges. The final, philosophical pronouncement is delivered with the authority of one unaccustomed to being opposed.

Such complexity of sentence structure, controlled use of "acceptable" and "educated" language, and casual revelation through syntactic deliberation—these mighty achievements stamp this paragraph with the unmistakable style of Henry James. It opens his story entitled "The Real Thing."

Three openings—three styles. The careful reader would, under no circumstances, mistake any two as being the work of the same author. Curiously, the Jamesian prose is so natural in its sound—that is, so fitting to the character of the narrator—that it lacks the self-consciousness of Hemingway's more contrived manipulations of poetic prose. Somewhere between the two styles, Carson McCullers' prose exists.

It might help, at this point, to approach style in a relatively piecemeal fashion, examining, point by point, the following aspects of this elusive feature. While it is not an exhaustive list, it includes the major aspects:

1. *Diction, Idiom, and Syntax:* The critic Cyril Connolly once made a distinction between two distinct styles of prose: what he termed the "Mandarin" and the "Vernacular." The first, he said, is a graceful, cultivated employment of refined, even elegant speech—the kind one seldom hears in daily life. Such authors as Henry James employ the Mandarin style as a result of their close, academic study of the language and very real appreciation of its formal features. Graceful rhythms emerge when language is considered from this intellectual level, and certain social levels are indicated in the rhythms. Diction—that highest, most elegant level of language—becomes the communicative agent, and the reader (if he is unprepared for it) may feel removed from the story, a little ill at ease, for this is not the speech he is accustomed to, therefore comfortable with. But if he recognizes the language for what it is—the natural speech of the author—he will find it a comfortable medium. The author is not "putting on airs" or being consciously pretentious; he is addressing the reader as his social equal, refusing to "speak down" to him, refusing to oversimplify communication out of some misguided notion that his reader is incapable of understanding the elaborate vocabulary and syntax which are the author's natural speech. Once the reader realizes that the author is showing consideration for his intellectual capacity, he can settle down comfortably to listen to that voice, knowing he will not be embarrassed by unreasonable demands.

The second style, the Vernacular, relies primarily on idiom, the ordinary, day-to-day vocabulary, and relaxed, loose, or deliberately blunt cadences that approximate the average man's speech patterns. Paradoxically, far more self-conscious manipulation of language is necessary in this style than in the Mandarin, for the author attempts a closer approximation of life through sound as well as through incident. Because *compression* (reducing words to their fewest number for maximum effect) is such a vital part of the short story (itself a compressed form), the reduction requires elaborate manipulation. Such authors as Ernest Hemingway, then, become the most self-conscious manipulators of language as they try to achieve careless sounding simplicity. Beginning writers, unaware of the countless hours and merciless criticism Hemingway asked of Gertrude Stein as he developed his style, seek to imitate him because his prose sounds so effortless. Of course they fail, for they attempt to shortcut the poetic process he learned as he sought to elicit approval from the rose dragon lady of American letters.

Between the two extremes of the Mandarin and Vernacular styles exist a variety of other styles understandably called "Middle," indicative of the social group responsible for the development of the style as well as, incidentally, of the short story. Poetry and the novel, before the development of the short story as a genre, appealed primarily to the upper classes whose affluence allowed them leisure to pursue the intellectual intricacies of poetry, the time-consuming vagaries of the novel. The lower classes, in the main, lacked both the education and the time to pursue such forms. However, as an emerging middle class separated the two groups, it developed a need of material not available to the lower class, but not as demanding of time and intellectual expenditure as the forms of the upper class. The short story met the need. The Middle style, growing from the middle class and designed to appeal to it, utilized the vibrant rhythms and vocabulary of that group without confining itself utterly to them. Borrowing from the elegant cadences and rich vocabulary of the Mandarin style, it also utilized the slang, argot, and jargon of the streets (from which came much of its subject matter), wedding them to achieve a wide variety of effects, a depth of passion, and an immediacy which the Mandarin and Vernacular styles cannot achieve themselves. Carson McCullers' story utilizes this style at its self-conscious best.

2. *Poetic Devices:* Sensory impressions are most vividly created through controlled metaphors, actual or implied. In Hemingway's paragraph, allusion ("in the shadow of the leaves") creates the metaphor of age and death. In McCullers' paragraph, the "helmet such as aviators wear" makes the boy metaphorically adventurous, symbolizing his need to slip the sullen bonds of earth and find those free reaches of the sky that beckon to all men. On the other hand, the boy's "pink little ear" is, metaphorically, a shell, reminiscent of the sea and its vibrant life force. Allusion is subtly employed here, too, for Venus, the goddess of love, is pictured in art as emerging from the sea, borne on a shell. Love, or the first analysis of it—as abstract as the idea of Venus born from sea foam—is to reach the boy through the shell of that exposed ear. Little need be explained about James' metaphor: "A figure with a good deal of frontage was almost never a public institution." Prose writers vary widely in their reliance on poetic devices, some being more adept than others at employing them. Those most noted for their excellent style, however, are the most frequent and most imaginative users of poetic devices.

3. *Economy:* Compression is a characteristic of poetry and—because it eliminates the obvious, the unnecessary, and the merely decorative—it leads, at times, to obscurity. If transitions, descriptions, and expository material are ruthlessly but intelligently pared in prose, a tightly woven effect of overall unity may be achieved by an author. Needless adjectives and adverbs, scenes and half-scenes of minimal contribution to the story, complications that merely add interest without inten-

sifying the effect—these are sacrificed in the short story as economy becomes important to the author. And the better his judgment in compression, the more artistic his style. When Henry James was writing "The Real Thing," he discussed the story in his notebook. That discussion reveals a great deal about the element of economy as it relates to an author's style. But, let James speak of it himself, for he speaks eloquently:

*On the Genesis of "The Real Thing"**

In pursuance of my plan of writing some very short tales—things of from 7000 to 10,000 words, the easiest length to 'place,' I began yesterday the little story that was suggested to me some time ago by an incident related to me by George du Maurier—the lady and gentleman who called upon him with a word from Frith, an oldish, faded, ruined pair—he an officer in the army—who unable to turn a penny in any other way, were trying to find employment as models. I was struck with the pathos, the oddity and typicalness of the situation—the little tragedy of good-looking gentlefolk, who had been all their life stupid and well-dressed, living, on a fixed income, at country-houses, watering places and clubs, like so many others of their class in England, and were now utterly unable to *do* anything, had no cleverness, no art nor craft to make use of as a *gagne-pain*—could only *show* themselves, clumsily, for the fine, clean, well-groomed animals that they were, only hope to make a little money by—in this manner—just simply *being*. I thought I saw a subject for very brief treatment in this *donnée*—and I think I do still; but to do anything worth while with it I must (as always, great Heavens!) be very clear as to what is in it and what I wish to get out of it. I tried a beginning yesterday, but I instantly became conscious that I must straighten out the little idea. It must be an idea—it can't be a 'story' in the vulgar sense of the word. It must be a picture; it must illustrate something. God knows that's enough—if the thing *does* illustrate. To make little anecdotes of this kind real *morceaux de vie* is a plan quite inspiring enough. *Voyons un peu,* therefore, what one can put into this one—I mean how much of life. One must put a little action—not a stupid, mechanical, arbitrary action, but something that is of the real essence of the subject. I thought of representing the husband as jealous of the wife—that is, jealous of the artist employing her, from the moment that, in point of fact, she begins to sit. But this is vulgar and obvious—worth nothing. What I wish to represent

*Notebook entry for February 22, 1891.

is the baffled, ineffectual, incompetent character of their attempt, and how it illustrates once again the everlasting English amateurishness—the way superficial, untrained, unprofessional effort goes to the wall when confronted with trained, competitive, intelligent, *qualified* art—in whatever line it may be a question of. It is out of *that* element that my little action and movement must come; and now I begin to see just how—as one always *does*—Glory be to the Highest—when one begins to look at a thing hard and straight and seriously—to fix it—as I am so sadly lax and desultory about doing. What subjects I should find—for *everything*—if I could only achieve this more as a habit! Let my contrast and complication here come from the opposition—to my melancholy Major and his wife—of a couple of little vulgar professional people *who know,* with the consequent bewilderment, vagueness, depression of the former—their failure to understand how such people can be better than *they*—their failure, disappointment, disappearance—going forth into the vague again. *Il y a bien quelque chose à tirer de ça.* They have no pictorial sense. They are only clean and stiff and stupid. The others are dirty, even—the melancholy Major and his wife remark on it, wondering. The artist is beginning a big illustrated book, a new edition of a famous novel—say *Tom Jones:* and he is willing to try to work them in—for he takes an interest in their predicament, and feels—sceptically, but, with his flexible artistic sympathy—the appeal of their type. He is willing to give them a trial. Make it out that *he* himself is on trial—he is young and 'rising,' but he has still his golden spurs to win. He can't afford, *en somme,* to make many mistakes. He has regular work in drawing every week for a serial novel in an illustrated paper; but the great project—that of a big house—of issuing an illustrated Fielding promises him a big lift. He has been intrusted with (say) *Joseph Andrews,* experimentally; he will have to do this brilliantly in order to have the engagement for the rest confirmed. He has already 2 models in his service—the 'complication' must come from *them.* One is a common, clever, London girl, of the smallest origin and without conventional beauty, but of aptitude, of perceptions—knowing thoroughly *how.* She says 'lydy' and 'plice' but she has the pictorial sense; and can look like anything he wants her to look like. She poses, in short, in perfection. So does her colleague, a professional Italian, a little fellow—ill dressed, smelling of garlic, but admirably serviceable, quite universal. They must be contrasted, confronted, *juxtaposed* with the others; whom they take for people who *pay,* themselves, till they learn the truth when they are overwhelmed with derisive amazement. The denouncement simply that the melancholy Major and his wife won't do—they're not 'in it.' Their surprise—their helpless, proud assent—without other prospects: yet at the same time *their* degree of more silent amazement at the success of the two inferior people—who are so much less nice-looking than themselves. Frankly, however, is this contrast enough of a *story,* by itself? It seems to me Yes—for it's an IDEA—and how the deuce should I get *more* into 7000 words? It must be simply 50 pp. of my manuscript. The little tale of *The Servant* (*Brooksmith*) which I did the other day for *Black and White* and which I thought of at the same time as this, proved a very tight squeeze into the same tiny number of words, and I probably shall find that there is much more to be done with this than the compass will admit of. Make it tremendously succinct—with a very short pulse or rhythm—and the closest selection of detail—in other words *summarize* intensely and keep down the lateral development. It *should* be a little gem of bright, quick, vivid form. I shall get every grain of 'action' that the space admits of if I make something, for the artist, hang in the balance—depend on the way he does this particular work. It's when he finds that he shall lose his great opportunity if he keeps on with them, that he has to tell the gentlemanly couple, that, frankly, they won't serve his turn—and make them wander forth into the cold world again. I must keep them the age I've made them—50 and 40—because it's more touching; but I must bring up the age of the 2 real models to almost the same thing. That increases the incomprehensibility (to the amateurs) of their usefulness. Picture the immanence, in the latter, of the idle, provided-for, country-house habit—the blankness of their *manière d'être.* But in how tremendously few words I must do it. This is a lesson—a *magnificent* lesson—if I'm to do a good many. Something as admirably compact and *selected* as Maupassant. □

4. *Tone and Aesthetic Distance:* In his notebook entry, James reveals his personal attitude toward his characters and their story. Speaking of space limitations, he reveals his concern for selectivity in words and details. His announced attitude in this story will be one of "pathos" (the second sentence of the notebook entry) and pathos is, indeed, achieved in the tone of the completed story. However, a second tonal element is also apparent. In the story as well as in the notebook entry, the author-artist reveals a superior attitude as if *he* were superior, as a human being, to the "ruined" couple. Thus, an aesthetic pathos emerges—a pathos distinct and separate from the announced tone. In achieving this second type of pathos, James reveals something about *aesthetic distance* (the degree of detachment an author achieves as he views the characters in his work). The extent of that distance is primarily a matter of the reader's personal opinion. *If* James is unaware

of his snobbish attitude in his notebook entry (and he seems to be), that snobbery places him in close proximity to the painter of the story and establishes the author as the narrator in the first person point of view. In such a case, the story ends at the final period, and the writer-painter has learned nothing from the narrative. His aesthetic distance, in such a case, was not great enough; a stunning, pathetic tone results, for the narrator is genuinely to be pitied by the reader who has been made aware of a great truth that the author does not know. On the other hand, if the author-narrator recognizes (and he does) the snobbery of the "ruined" couple as they first view the professional models, and if he draws an understated analogy between their view of the models and his view of them, he understands the "something" about life that he mentions in "It must be a picture; it must illustrate something. God knows that's enough if the thing *does* illustrate." In such a case, the author-narrator assumes the role of a tragic protagonist (no hero he, certainly), for he reveals the strength to struggle against his weakness (in this case, ambition) and the incapacity to be strong enough to win. If such is true, the dramatic irony of the last line of the story is pathos at its shattering best, and James' aesthetic distance is exactly right. The decision rests with the individual reader, however, and no irrefutable pronouncement can be made by anyone, for, as the author stands at his aesthetic distance from his material, the reader reads from his own aesthetic distance. Experience, intellectual attainment, insight, intuition, language awareness, objectivity—these and many other considerations determine how great that distance will be. If author and reader empathize, the distance will probably be about right. If they are sympathetic, certain subjective allowances may be made by the reader and he will stand too close for artistic comfort. If author and reader are antipathetic, the reader's aesthetic distance will be so great he will be utterly unable to "see" the author's attitude, point of view, or philosophy. Nor is it unreasonable to assume the reader will encounter authors with whom he can share no communication. In life, one does not expect to like everyone he meets. The author-reader relationship is, after all, a meeting of two individuals through the medium of print. To cultivate every author one meets would be to abandon discrimination—a possibility no intelligent man could countenance.

5. *Dialog:* It is a rare story that contains no dialog. A few authors, recognizing their inability to hear or re-create patterns of speech realistically, manage to minimize dialog by leaning heavily on narrative and descriptive elements. Other authors, seeming to possess an especially acute ear, create dialog of great verisimilitude. It may be realistic or intensely imaginative yet be thoroughly believable. The reader can

quickly determine whether dialog is artificial or natural, stilted, pretentious, or witty. Most important, he can determine its appropriateness to the characters who speak it. The dialog of Hemingway's characters sounds exceedingly realistic in context; yet, remove it from the story, examine it in isolation, and your reaction will be, "Why, nobody talks like that!" As it is appropriate to the characters and tone of the story, however, it *seems* right. James minimizes dialog, preferring the narrative-descriptive approach, and, if you isolate his dialog, you will quickly see why. It is stilted and unimaginative; stylistically, James is wise to minimize it. Hemingway is famous for his fast-paced stories (realistic dialog is rapid, carrying implication on its flow). James' prose is introspective and slow-paced (absence of realistic dialog demands examination and explanation, both of which are turgid). McCullers, still occupying that middle ground, balances dialog against narrative-descriptive elements, interpreting speech when and if she sees fit. As a result, her prose may speed along, then slow introspectively, or proceed at a leisurely pace as she utilizes dialog, abandons it, or integrates it with narrative-descriptive elements to create a balanced prose blend.

Could you now define style in a clear, concise manner? Of course not. No workable definition exists because the concept of style remains a *concept.* At no point can one isolate some feature of a literary work and say, "This is style." Yet style is probably the one *most* important aspect of an author's work, for it does several things that no isolatable feature such as plot, character, or dialog can do:

First, style sets the tone of a story beyond the author's intention. He may be condescending—as James is in "The Real Thing"—or emphatic —as Hemingway is in "A Clean, Well-Lighted Place"—or deliberately detached yet involved beyond himself—as McCullers is in "A Tree. A Rock. A Cloud." This personal, even unconscious, authorial involvement establishes the author's personal responsibility for the story. An anonymous writer for a true confessions magazine or *Time* adopts its style, submerging his personality, his integrity, and his Self into the magazine's policies. Through this act of submersion, he relieves himself of personal responsibility for belief, attitude, or unique method of statement. James, Hemingway, and McCullers cannot efface themselves from their works because they retain responsibility for their style. Condescending though James may be, the reader realizes James sees the importance of these people, this theme, the implicit and explicit values, for he *chose* to tell the story. With that choice, he accepted responsibility for the tone, regardless of his degree of awareness of the tone. And that acceptance reveals something about his attitude—an attitude that directs the reader's attitudes as he reads the story.

Second, style is the major structural device in a literary work. When plot incidents grow logically one out of another, unity of action results; when characters develop in believable stages and change within the framework of credibility, unity of character results; when language is appropriate and consistent, unity of tone results. None of these unified elements, singly or in combination, creates the totality of impression a story must possess. It is style alone that cements the various components into a cohesive unit. If style is inconsistent, the literary structure will be unsound, for style in literature is comparable to the vision of an architect. He can see beyond the blueprint, building materials, and site, visualizing the completed structure, ensuring it will not consist of a ranch house front, Georgian interior, and Victorian atrium. Each of those features might be unified and sound in isolation, but totality of impression would not result if they were joined together. The architect's vision unifies the separable features into a pleasing whole. The author's style serves a literary work in the same way. Mark Schorer has said of style that it is the "conveyor of vision. Vision is private, but style gives it a public."*

As you read Ernest Hemingway's "A Clean, Well-Lighted Place," observe style at work. You will notice the insignificance of plot, the spare development of characters, the paucity of explicit meaning in the dialog. However, as you finish the story, you should be able to understand the situation, the characters, and the meaning of the dialog, not because, in isolation, they reveal anything, but because Hemingway's style creates the vision you share. Try to see how that vision is communicated.

Read the story first in its entirety.

A Clean, Well-Lighted Place

by Ernest Hemingway

1 It was late and every one had left the café except an old man who sat in the shadow the leaves of the tree made against the electric light. In the daytime the street was dusty, but at night the dew settled the dust and the old man liked to sit late because he was deaf and now at night it was quiet and he felt the difference. The two waiters inside the café knew that the old man was a little drunk, and while he was a good client they knew that if he became too drunk he would leave without paying, so they kept watch on him.

* *The Story: A Critical Anthology* (New York, 1950), p. 338.

The opening paragraph establishes the setting (the geographical location) and the atmosphere (the psychological milieu, the "feel" of the story and the characters) to prepare the reader for the brief conversation between the waiters.

[2]"Last week he tried to commit suicide," one waiter said.

[3]"Why?"

[4]"He was in despair."

[5]"What about?"

[6]"Nothing."

[7]"How do you know it was nothing?"

[8]"He has plenty of money."

[9]They sat together at a table that was close against the wall near the door of the café and looked at the terrace where the tables were all empty except where the old man sat in the shadow of the leaves of the tree that moved slightly in the wind. A girl and a soldier went by in the street. The street light shone on the brass number on his collar. The girl wore no head covering and hurried beside him.

[10]"The guard will pick him up," one waiter said.

[11]"What does it matter if he gets what he's after?"

[12]"He had better get off the street now. The guard will get him. They went by five minutes ago."

The scene is reminiscent of Greek drama, with the old man as the tragic hero and the waiters serving a choric function (one in which onlookers explain or comment on the action, not as individuals or participants but as choral narrators). The late hour is, at first, merely imagistic, but symbolism begins to assume proportion with the seven lines of conversation. The waiters are detached, lacking distinction, of no particular age. A disinterested but emphatic cynicism pervades the brief conversation, and the reader realizes the locale is not America. "He was in despair" is, of course, English, but the quality of the sentence is Spanish. Diction and syntax elevate the denotative possibilities into romance language connotations. Compare an American possibility, "He was despondent," with Hemingway's sentence. Cynicism becomes almost palpable as "Nothing" is given as a reason for lack of despair and "plenty of money" becomes the only "something" of the story. Imagery becomes symbolism illuminating the reader's understanding of many unstated realities. The time is late in the day, in the old man's life, and in a spiritual tradition. This is Catholic Spain, but Christian abstractions have given way to economic realities of little promise. And the death of those abstract hopes has suspended the old man between two worlds. He sits in a modern, artificial world (the café) illuminated by artificial light that casts a "shadow" of Nature on the wall. The Christian tradition is so dim at this late hour in mankind's life that it offers no hope, so suicide (a mortal sin in Catholicism) offers the only exit from the old man's existence in limbo. He "was [existed] in [a state of] despair" from which there was no other escape. So complete is his state of despair that he is deaf—literally and symbolically—to a future promise as abstract as immortality. Sitting alone, isolated in the shadow of Nature that has abandoned all men (and the cynical waiters seem, certainly, to have been abandoned), he drinks himself into unawareness, into forgetting.

"Nothing" becomes, rather than a simple negative, an absolute, a positive statement of the moral emptiness, the meaninglessness that the old man feels in his isolation from other humans, from Nature, and from future promise. Artificial light illuminates the brass number on the soldier's collar, and a second human condition is suggested: war. But even in this nihilistic time when numbers replace names, the biology of immediate desire continues, giving some reason and brief promise to the soldier and the girl. However, she "wore no head covering and hurried beside him." Christianity is not a promise for her either (Catholic women cover their heads for acts of consecration) and she hurries as if to avoid thought as well as guards. The young couple are isolated too within their desire and their need. And they communicate with each other as little as do any others in the story. When one waiter asks, "What does it matter if he gets what he's after?" the condition of "nothingness" becomes acutely obvious. Only the act of the moment is important.

13 The old man sitting in the shadow rapped on his saucer with his glass. The younger waiter went over to him.

14 "What do you want?"

15 The old man looked at him. "Another brandy," he said.

16 "You'll be drunk," the waiter said. The old man looked at him. The waiter went away.

17 "He'll stay all night," he said to his colleague. "I'm sleepy now. I never get into bed before three o'clock. He should have killed himself last week."

18 The waiter took the brandy bottle and another saucer from the counter inside the café and marched out to the old man's table. He put down the saucer and poured the glass full of brandy.

19 "You should have killed yourself last week," he said to the deaf man. The old man motioned with his finger. "A little more," he said. The waiter poured on into the glass so that the brandy slopped over and ran down the stem into the top saucer of the pile. "Thank you," the old man said. The waiter took the bottle back inside the café. He sat down at the table with his colleague again.

Verbal ambiguity serves Hemingway's purpose as the "old" man raps his saucer and the "younger" waiter goes to him. The age relationship of the two waiters is established at this moment. One is younger, one older—the earlier lack of distinction between them begins to disappear, and the insensitivity of the younger waiter manifests itself in his cruel remark to the old man that he should have killed himself last week. Perhaps the old man cannot hear, but he can "feel" differences (paragraph 1). The objective point of view allows no authorial assessment of such statements as "The old man looked at him" (paragraph 15), but the reader realizes the old man thinks *something.* And an impassive look *may* reveal much more than one that can be evaluated. Is the waiter "nothing" to the old man, therefore merely a visual focal point? Is the old man assessing the "feel" of the waiter? Hemingway does not assess the look, but an implication begins here and matures in paragraph 51 as the old man walks away "with dignity." The reader contrasts the old man's awareness of himself with the young waiter's selfishness, and the impossibility of human communication between these two men becomes an overwhelming moral consideration.

20 "He's drunk now," he said.

21 "He's drunk every night."

22 "What did he want to kill himself for?"

23 "How should I know."

24 "How did he do it?"

25 "He hung himself with a rope."

26 "Who cut him down?"

27 "His niece."

28 "Why did they do it?"

29 "Fear for his soul."

30 "How much money has he got?"

31 "He's got plenty."

32 "He must be eighty years old."

33 "Anyway I should say he was eighty."

34 "I wish he would go home. I never get to bed before three o'clock. What kind of hour is that to go to bed?"

35 "He stays up because he likes it."

36 "He's lonely. I'm not lonely. I have a wife waiting in bed for me."

37 "He had a wife once too."

38 "A wife would be no good to him now."

39 "You can't tell. He might be better with a wife."

40 "His niece looks after him."

41 "I know. You said she cut him down."

42 "I wouldn't want to be that old. An old man is a nasty thing."

43 "Not always. This old man is clean. He drinks without spilling. Even now, drunk. Look at him."

44 "I don't want to look at him. I wish he would go home. He has no regard for those who must work."

If the young waiter were merely unaware of the old man as a human being, the episode would lack the compelling power of the conversation in paragraphs 20–44. As the spare, blunt dialog unfolds swiftly, however, the young waiter reveals the intolerance of youth: the knowledge of awareness mixed with a refusal to identify with it. His desires are not intense human needs; they are the pleasures of casual routine. The old man's needs are neither casual nor routine—they are desperate urgencies which will, in time, come to the young waiter. He will become a "nasty thing" himself, but he prefers not to consider that possibility. Now he is young and the sight of the old man disturbs him. As he examines incidents superficially, superficially he decides, "I don't want to look at him." And his refusal to *see* the old man reveals why "nothingness" is a part of his young life. This moment, offering its own possible realizations, is deliberately avoided, and the young waiter's frustrations and fears assume the quality of cliché as, refusing to see himself, he damns the old man: "He has no regard for [me]."

The young waiter reveals his own lack of regard, his spiritual "nastiness" in the observation. He fails to see his selfishness as it is directed against the old man, and he also fails to consider the older waiter. Implicit in his assessment is the unconscious "And you're an old man too; therefore, you are nasty also." But, the reader should note, the vernacular style makes no explicit statement. Carefully selected conversation creates the understatement of everyday speech wherein understatement results from failure to consider the motives, the resentments, the revelations of such words. Hemingway does not state what is meant. He leaves evaluation to the reader.

Reacting with quiet dignity himself (and "dignity" is a key word in this story) the older waiter does not defensively deny the assessment; without sentimentality he observes objectively, "Not always. *This* old man is clean. He drinks without spilling."

45 The old man looked from his glass across the square, then over at the waiters.

46 "Another brandy," he said, pointing to his glass. The waiter who was in a hurry came over.

47 "Finished," he said, speaking with that omission of syntax stupid people employ when talking to drunken people or foreigners. "No more tonight. Close now."

48 "Another," said the old man.

49 "No. Finished." The waiter wiped the edge of the table with a towel and shook his head.

The callowness of the younger waiter contrasted with the emerging identity of the older waiter creates a scene of great stylistic strength. The scene is so strong, in fact, that Hemingway violates his objective point of view (a violation unique in his works) to deliver a moral judgment, a judgment born of human indignation: " 'Finished,' he said, speaking with that omission of syntax *stupid* people employ when talking to drunken people or foreigners."

50 The old man stood up, slowly counted the saucers, took a leather coin purse from his pocket and paid for the drinks, leaving half a peseta tip.

In paragraph 50, over halfway through the story, locale is definitely indicated as the old man counts the saucers (the European equivalent of totaling a bill) and leaves "half a peseta" tip. Hemingway could have offered explicit geography in paragraph 1 of this story, but, by refusing to do so, he creates a general awareness that this is a *human* condition, not a national one. However, the tone of the story and the temperament of the Latin characters create a more intense sense of "nothingness"—the reader sees the action in contrast with the brilliant backdrop of sunny Spain in its dark night of lost hope.

51 The waiter watched him go down the street, a very old man walking unsteadily but with dignity.

52 "Why didn't you let him stay and drink?" the unhurried waiter asked. They were putting up the shutters. "It is not half-past two."

53 "I want to go home to bed."

54 "What is an hour?"

55 "More to me than to him."

56 "An hour is the same."

57 "You talk like an old man yourself. He can buy a bottle and drink at home."

58 "It's not the same."

59 "No, it is not," agreed the waiter with a wife. He did not wish to be unjust. He was only in a hurry.

60 "And you? You have no fear of going home before your usual hour?"

61 "Are you trying to insult me?"

62 "No, hombre, only to make a joke."

63 "No," the waiter who was in a hurry said, rising from pulling down the metal shutters. "I have confidence. I am all confidence."

The young waiter has not dispossessed the old man of everything, for, while he does walk away unsteadily, he walks "with dignity." Nor does the young waiter's insensitive observation ("You talk like an old man yourself") leave the older waiter defenseless, though it does move him to brutality: "You have no fear of going home before your usual hour?" he asks. And the deliberate assault is much kinder than the young waiter's unconscious brutality; yet, self-protectively, the young waiter demands, "Are you trying to insult me?"

Bitter irony pervades "I am all confidence." The younger waiter was not confident enough to look at, to *see* the old man. His fear of the emptiness of life remains veiled, but the reader knows it is thinly veiled.

64 "You have youth, confidence, and a job," the older waiter said. "You have everything."

65 "And what do you lack?"

66 "Everything but work."

67 "You have everything I have."

68 "No. I have never had confidence and I am not young."

69 "Come on. Stop talking nonsense and lock up."

70 "I am of those who like to stay late at the café," the older waiter said. "With all those who do not want to go to bed. With all those who need a light for the night."

71 "I want to go home and into bed."

And now (paragraph 64), Hemingway explicitly states that the kinder waiter is older. And his understanding, his concern, his awareness are explained in paragraph 70 as he admits to his need of human company (his bed is empty) and of light. To be alone in "the night" (how easily the literal becomes symbolic here) is to be in the suicidal state of "nothingness." "Light" (a strong symbol now) will hold back the night, will sustain dignity in public where sheer determination forces man to behave well in front of people. Alone, he knows no such necessity. Again poetry assumes control as iambs and anapests dominate the lines and feet of opposite construction are employed for emphasis:

˘ ¯ ˘ ¯
"I am|of those

˘ ¯ ˘ ¯
who like|to stay

¯ ˘ ˘ ˘ ¯
late at|the café,"

˘ ¯ ˘ ¯ ˘ ¯
the old|er wait|er said.

"With all those

who do | not want

to go | to bed.

With all those

who need | a light

for the night."

The speech breaks easily into ten marvelous lines of iambic dimeter relieved and strengthened by anapests, a trochee, and a spondee dramatically employed. Dialog creates three tercets (three-line stanzas) loosely controlled by imaginative use of rhyme, the one expository line providing a poetic pivot and the rhyme word for the second tercet. This masterful variation directs full attention to line 6 with its reference to the Twenty-Third Psalm's "I shall not want" and recalls the subtle allusion in the opening paragraph of the story. Unity of (1) theme, (2) authorial philosophy, and (3) style results as these lines provide the stylistic transition between parts 1 (paragraphs 1–75) and 2 (paragraphs 76–85) of the narrative. This section is parody of a less violent nature than the Lord's Prayer section which is to follow. However, were this parody omitted, the reader would not be prepared to accept the seeming blasphemy which is to come. This foreshadows the end just as the beginning foreshadowed this.

The four iambs of the first tercet lead musically and happily to the shock of the trochaic *late at,* a pattern that forces the reader to see the significance of *late.* It is very late in life, in tradition. The introductory *I am of those* serves as an incremental refrain introducing each tercet and contributing a balladic effect to the statement. Those "who do not want" are far removed in time and tradition from the protected lambs of God as saṁvegha adds *to go to bed.* The light of the good shepherd has gone out; only the artificial light remains. Short, happy lines; despairing, bitter admissions. The reader shares the helplessness, the hopelessness of the older waiter, for Hemingway has forced participation with the weapon of style. The reader, like the young waiter, might prefer not to share, but he has no choice. Hemingway's poetry has involved the reader, making him stand closer to experience than he really wishes.

But *why* does this passage achieve so much? Rhyme, rhythm, poetic device, structure—all contribute to create just the right aesthetic distance in both writer and reader. Karl Shapiro and Robert Beum explain how aesthetic distance is served by poetic elements:

> Rhyme can help a poet get the aesthetic distance he needs in order to write at all of a subject in which he is intimately involved, and which threatens to overwhelm him with paralyzing emotion as he contemplates it and tries to write of it in the most straightforward way. The necessity of constructing rhyme may in some cases force the poet to move the original experience just far enough to the rear of the immediate feelings involved that he will be able to write about it or some sea-changed aspect of it, without sentimentality or the enervating sense of futility that sometimes results from a realization of the great disparity between the vividness and depth of an original experience and the expression of it or any part of it in verse.
>
> Rhyme, as Wordsworth suggested, creates aesthetic distance for the reader too. Sorrow in verse gives us an experience of something we call beauty, not of the sorrow the poet might have felt at one time, and not the sorrow we would feel in actual life if we were to have the experience the poem deals with. If it were not for the aesthetic distance created by formal elements such as meter and rhyme, and by the general eloquence of expression, we would respond to every poem and play and story in much the same way we would respond to the corresponding situations in real experience. When we are engrossed in a suspenseful novel in which the hero, with whom we have identified ourselves, is about to fall victim to the villain, our pulse may quicken a bit, but we do not turn pale or run out of the room to cry for help. The situation and the language in Alfred Hayes' "The Slaughter-House" [p. 397] are so brutal and repugnant that some slight thread of conscious artifice—the rhyme—seems to be needed, or at least welcomed, to turn into poetry an experience which is unpleasant enough even when vicarious. It seems to be a fact that the more pleasant or dignified, noble or beautiful the subject or experience of a poem, the more easily we can do without such artifices as rhyme and meter (although, paradoxically, such subjects and experiences make the *music* of rhyme and meter most appropriate). Lovely imagery, passionate imagination, and warm or lofty sentiment are their own rewards: it is much more difficult to bring off a poem which presents unpleasant matter in unpleasant language. Only a perverse and amateurish artist, or only an immature one, supposes that sane people will, over a period of years and generations, so violate their human nature as to indulge in ugliness or pain for its own sake. Ugliness must be made attractive and endurable—as Rouault often made his prostitutes and degenerates endurable by the luminosity and delicious coolness of his color. The more a poem deals in guts and gutters, the more we appreciate the aesthetic distance of rhymes and iambs.°

° *A Prosody Handbook* (New York, 1965), pp. 104–5.

And Hemingway is a master of "the aesthetic distance created by formal elements such as meter and rhyme. . . ."

72"We are of two different kinds," the older waiter said. He was now dressed to go home. "It is not only a question of youth and confidence although those things are very beautiful. Each night I am reluctant to close up because there may be some one who needs the café."

73"Hombre, there are bodegas open all night long."

74"You do not understand. This is a clean and pleasant café. It is well lighted. The light is very good and also, now, there are shadows of the leaves."

75"Good night," said the younger waiter.

Paragraph 72 establishes the older waiter as the spokesman and focal character of the story. If someone needs the café which he has made accessible, he is needed. It is clean, therefore has dignity. It is lighted, therefore holds back the dark "nothingness" of the empty bed, the solitary state. And Nature has not rejected it utterly: "there are shadows of the leaves."

76"Good night," the other said. Turning off the electric light he continued the conversation with himself. It is the light of course but it is necessary that the place be clean and pleasant. You do not want music. Certainly you do not want music. Nor can you stand before a bar with dignity although that is all that is provided for these hours. What did he fear? It was not fear or dread. It was a nothing that he knew too well. It was all a nothing and a man was nothing too. It was only that and light was all it needed and a certain cleanness and order. Some lived in it and never felt it but he knew it all was nada y pues nada y nada y pues nada. Our nada who art in nada, nada be thy name thy kingdom nada thy will be nada in nada as it is in nada. Give us this nada our daily nada and nada us our nada as we nada our nadas and nada us not into nada but deliver us from nada; pues nada. Hail nothing full of nothing, nothing is with thee. He smiled and stood before a bar with a shining steam pressure coffee machine.

Interior monolog in paragraph 76 moves the old waiter to a bodega (snack bar) where he will find light and cleanness and order (is not Nature the epitome of order?). He cannot stand at the bar with dignity, but the "nothingness" of the human condition will be tolerable without dignity as long as the other necessities are present. Some (such as the younger waiter) do not realize the human condition is "nothing." But he knows it is "nada y pues nada y nada y pues nada" (nothing and then nothing and nothing and then nothing). The Spanish *nada* is connotatively vaster and more empty than the English *nothing.* In sound, it resembles English *God,* intensifying the nihilistic parody of the Lord's

Prayer and Hail Mary which echo "nada y pues nada," *pues* evoking the English word similar in sound but decaying and festering as it overlays the prayer with unclean, living death until the prayer brings him to the place of little dignity, the bar which serves as an altar for the "shining steam pressure coffee machine." Spiritual God has failed, is "nada"; the mechanical machine is at least clean.

77 "What's yours?" asked the barman.

78 "Nada."

79 "Otro loco mas," said the barman and turned away.

80 "A little cup," said the waiter.

81 The barman poured it for him.

82 "The light is very bright and pleasant but the bar is unpolished," the waiter said.

83 The barman looked at him but did not answer. It was too late at night for conversation.

84 "You want another copita?" the barman asked.

85 "No, thank you," said the waiter and went out. He disliked bars and bodegas. A clean, well-lighted café was a very different thing. Now, without thinking further, he would go home to his room. He would lie in the bed and finally, with daylight, he would go to sleep. After all, he said to himself, it is probably only insomnia. Many must have it. □

Irony reaches its ultimate development as the barman asks, "What's yours?" and the ambiguity of the question makes it, "What's your god?" It is, of course, "Nada"—he has none. And that answer is not understood by the barman, naturally, so the waiter is just "another nut." Now Hemingway suggests the reason dignity cannot stand before the bar (possibly another verbal ambiguity). Unwilling to be dismissed by the barman's turned back, the older waiter participates in the Mass of the coffee machine. As he drinks, he observes that light is present, but cleanness is not. Ironically, the barman looks at him but does not answer—as the old man looked at the younger waiter earlier in the story, without words.

So now, like the old man, the waiter must face the darkness, the empty bed, the "nothingness" of total aloneness, the "nada" of "those who need a light for the night"—all that awaits him at the end of his day's journey. With no thought, he will find insomnia (no sleep) until "daylight" grants him temporary relief from "nothingness" in sleep, a deliberate suspension of consciousness that resembles death and is, therefore, a kind of suicide since it is sought. His suicide will be thwarted as the old man's was, for he will awaken from "nada" to return to the human condition of "nada." And it is the human condition, for "Many must have it."

No single adjective describes Hemingway's style as well as "clean." It is characterized by brevity, by artful selection of narrative elements, and by the clear depth of lucid understatement. Introspective analysis is absent; descriptive features (such as the leaves and the coffee machine) are introduced without preamble, dismissed without explanation. Yet the reader understands the meaning that emerges from the isolated elements. The principle is totality of impression.

Such totality of impression, the "effect" achieved by Hemingway with his Vernacular style, was suggested more than a century ago by Edgar Allan Poe in a review of Hawthorne's *Twice-Told Tales:*

> A skilful literary artist has constructed a tale. If wise, he has not fashioned his thoughts to accommodate his incidents; but having conceived, with deliberate care, a certain unique or single *effect* to be wrought out, he then invents such incidents—he then combines such events as may best aid him in establishing this preconceived effect. If his very initial sentence tend not to the outbringing of this effect, then he has failed in his first step. In the whole composition there should be no word written, of which the tendency, direct or indirect, is not to the one pre-established design. And by such means, with such care and skill, a picture is at length painted which leaves in the mind of him who contemplates it with a kindred art, a sense of the fullest satisfaction. The idea of the tale has been presented unblemished, because undisturbed; and this is an end unattainable by the novel. Undue brevity is just as exceptionable here as in the poem; but undue length is yet more to be avoided.°

Hemingway has indeed constructed a tale around the "effect to be wrought out." Concerned with the human condition of "nothingness," he has created a story about "nothing." To understand the skill in his achievement, attempt to summarize the plot. There is no plot in the traditional sense of incident growing from incident, each a logical outgrowth of earlier ones. The plotlessness is a part of the story, the two incidents being juxtaposed to create an effect rather than to reveal change in characters. The effect is initiated in the opening sentence as poetic lines combine with the sense of lateness, of aloneness, of "nothingness" that is to be developed. Throughout the story, that preconceived design, the creation of "nothingness," is Hemingway's single purpose, and, at the end of the story, one of the shortest in the language, the reader finds a picture painted. Black and utter "nothingness"

° Originally published in *Graham's Magazine,* May 1842.

fill the canvas of the mind, for the reader has seen "nada" created and he recognizes, despairingly, that nothing can be done about it.

Poe added, in the paragraph following the one you have just read: "The true critic will but demand that the design intended be accomplished, to the fullest extent, by the means most advantageously applicable." Hemingway has, with the unifying agent of style, accomplished his design.

No two writers will possess the same style, nor will their critical attitudes necessarily be similar. Eighteen years before Poe published his statement, Washington Irving stated his credo in a letter to Henry Brevoort:

> . . . For my part, I consider a story merely as a frame on which to stretch my materials. It is the play of thought, and sentiment, and language; the weaving in of characters, lightly, yet expressively delineated; the familiar and faithful exhibition of scenes in common life; and the half-concealed vein of humor that is often playing through the whole. . . .°

Carson McCullers' "A Tree. A Rock. A Cloud." might have served as the model from which Irving conceived his idea. As you read it, observe the "frame" (plot) on which McCullers' materials are stretched. Notice how thought, sentiment, and language are combined and characters woven into the fabric of the story. A scene from "common life" does, indeed, emerge—a scene of great importance, for it is focused on love, another vital aspect of the human condition. And through it all runs a "half-concealed vein of humor." You may notice, however, your laughter is never loud, and it is always a little bitter.

Because the story contains only one scene, it cannot be analyzed piecemeal. Therefore, you will have to flip back to noted paragraphs as you read the analysis which follows the story.

A Tree. A Rock. A Cloud.

by Carson McCullers

1 It was raining that morning, and still very dark. When the boy reached the streetcar café he had almost finished his route and he went in for a cup of coffee. The place was an all-night café owned by a bitter and stingy man called Leo. After the raw, empty street the café seemed friendly and bright: along the counter there were a couple of

° December 11, 1824: *The Life and Letters of Washington Irving* (New York, 1869), II, 226.

soldiers, three spinners from the cotton mill, and in a corner a man who sat hunched over with his nose and half his face down in a beer mug. The boy wore a helmet such as aviators wear. When he went into the café he unbuckled the chin strap and raised the right flap up over his pink little ear; often as he drank his coffee someone would speak to him in a friendly way. But this morning Leo did not look into his face and none of the men were talking. He paid and was leaving the café when a voice called out to him:

2 "Son! Hey, son!"

3 He turned back and the man in the corner was crooking his finger and nodding to him. He had brought his face out of the beer mug and he seemed suddenly very happy. The man was long and pale, with a big nose and faded orange hair.

4 "Hey, son!"

5 The boy went toward him. He was an undersized boy of about twelve, with one shoulder drawn higher than the other because of the weight of the paper sack. His face was shallow, freckled, and his eyes were round child eyes.

6 "Yeah, mister?"

7 The man laid one hand on the paper boy's shoulder, then grasped the boy's chin and turned his face slowly from one side to the other. The boy shrank back uneasily.

8 "Say! What's the big idea?"

9 The boy's voice was shrill; inside the café it was suddenly very quiet.

10 The man said slowly: "I love you."

11 All along the counter the men laughed. The boy, who had scowled and sidled away, did not know what to do. He looked over the counter at Leo, and Leo watched him with a weary, brittle jeer. The boy tried to laugh also. But the man was serious and sad.

12 "I did not mean to tease you, son," he said. "Sit down and have a beer with me. There is something I have to explain."

13 Cautiously, out of the corner of his eye, the paper boy questioned the men along the counter to see what he should do. But they had gone back to their beer or their breakfast and did not notice him. Leo put a cup of coffee on the counter and a little jug of cream.

14 "He is a minor," Leo said.

15 The paper boy slid himself up onto the stool. His ear beneath the upturned flap of the helmet was very small and red. The man was nodding at him soberly. "It is important," he said. Then he reached in his hip pocket and brought out something which he held up in the palm of his hand for the boy to see.

16 "Look very carefully," he said.

17 The boy stared, but there was nothing to look at very carefully. The man held in his big, grimy palm a photograph. It was the face of a woman, but blurred, so that only the hat and the dress she was wearing stood out clearly.

18 "See?" the man asked.

19 The boy nodded and the man placed another picture in his palm. The woman was standing on a beach in a bathing suit. The suit made her stomach very big, and that was the main thing you noticed.

20 "Got a good look?" He leaned over closer and finally asked: "You ever seen her before?"

21 The boy sat motionless, staring slantwise at the man. "Not so I know of."

22 "Very well." The man blew on the photographs and put them back into his pocket. "That was my wife."

23 "Dead?" the boy asked.

24 Slowly the man shook his head. He pursed his lips as though about to whistle and answered in a longdrawn way: "Nuuu—" he said, "I will explain."

25 The beer on the counter before the man was in a large brown mug. He did not pick it up to drink. Instead he bent down and, putting his face over the rim, he rested there for a moment. Then with both hands he tilted the mug and sipped.

26 "Some night you'll go to sleep with your big nose in a mug and drown," said Leo. "Prominent transient drowns in beer. That would be a cute death."

27 The paper boy tried to signal to Leo. While the man was not looking he screwed up his face and worked his mouth to question soundlessly: "Drunk?" But Leo only raised his eyebrows and turned away to put some pink strips of bacon on the grill. The man pushed the mug away from him, straightened himself, and folded his loose crooked hands on the counter. His face was sad as he looked at the paper boy. He did not blink, but from time to time the lids closed down with delicate gravity over his pale green eyes. It was nearing dawn and the boy shifted the weight of the paper sack.

28 "I am talking about love," the man said. "With me it is a science."

29 The boy half slid down from the stool. But the man raised his forefinger, and there was something about him that held the boy and would not let him go away.

30 "Twelve years ago I married the woman in the photograph. She was my wife for one year, nine months, three days, and two nights. I loved her. Yes . . ." He tightened his blurred, rambling voice and said

again: "I loved her. I thought also that she loved me. I was a railroad engineer. She had all home comforts and luxuries. It never crept into my brain that she was not satisfied. But do you know what happened?"

31 "Mgneeow!" said Leo.

32 The man did not take his eyes from the boy's face. "She left me. I came in one night and the house was empty and she was gone. She left me."

33 "With a fellow?" the boy asked.

34 Gently the man placed his palm down on the counter. "Why, naturally, son. A woman does not run off like that alone."

35 The café was quiet, the soft rain black and endless in the street outside. Leo pressed down the frying bacon with the prongs of his long fork: "So you have been chasing the floozy for eleven years. You frazzled old rascal!"

36 For the first time the man glanced at Leo. "Please don't be vulgar. Besides, I was not speaking to you." He turned back to the boy and said in a trusting and secretive undertone: "Let's not pay any attention to him. O.K.?"

37 The paper boy nodded doubtfully.

38 "It was like this," the man continued. "I am a person who feels many things. All my life one thing after another has impressed me. Moonlight. The leg of a pretty girl. One thing after another. But the point is that when I had enjoyed anything there was a peculiar sensation as though it was laying around loose in me. Nothing seemed to finish itself up or fit in with the other things. Women? I had my portion of them. The same. Afterwards laying around loose in me. I was a man who had never loved."

39 Very slowly he closed his eyelids, and the gesture was like a curtain drawn at the end of a scene in a play. When he spoke again his voice was excited and the words came fast—the lobes of his large, loose ears seemed to tremble.

40 "Then I met this woman. I was fifty-one years old and she always said she was thirty. I met her at a filling station and we were married within three days. And do you know what it was like? I just can't tell you. All I had ever felt was gathered together around this woman. Nothing lay around loose in me any more but was finished up by her."

41 The man stopped suddenly and stroked his long nose. His voice sank down to a steady and reproachful undertone: "I'm not explaining this right. What happened was this. There were these beautiful feelings and loose little pleasures inside me. And this woman was something like an assembly line for my soul. I run these little pieces of myself through her and I come out complete. Now do you follow me?"

42 "What was her name?" the boy asked.

43 "Oh," he said. "I called her Dodo. But that is immaterial."

44 "Did you try to make her come back?"

45 The man did not seem to hear. "Under the circumstances you can imagine how I felt when she left me."

46 Leo took the bacon from the grill and folded two strips of it between a bun. He had a gray face, with slitted eyes, and a pinched nose saddled by faint blue shadows. One of the mill workers signaled for more coffee and Leo poured it. He did not give refills on coffee free. The spinner ate breakfast there every morning, but the better Leo knew his customers the stingier he treated them. He nibbled his own bun as though he grudged it to himself.

47 "And you never got hold of her again?"

48 The boy did not know what to think of the man, and his child's face was uncertain with mingled curiosity and doubt. He was new on the paper route; it was still strange to him to be out in the town in the black, queer early morning.

49 "Yes," the man said. "I took a number of steps to get her back. I went around trying to locate her. I went to Tulsa where she had folks. And to Mobile. I went to every town she had ever mentioned to me, and I hunted down every man she had formerly been connected with. Tulsa, Atlanta, Chicago, Cheehaw, Memphis . . . For the better part of two years I chased around the country trying to lay hold of her."

50 "But the pair of them had vanished from the face of the earth!" said Leo.

51 "Don't listen to him," the man said confidentially. "And also just forget those two years. They are not important. What matters is that around the third year a curious thing begun to happen to me."

52 "What?" the boy asked.

53 The man leaned down and tilted his mug to take a sip of beer. But as he hovered over the mug his nostrils fluttered slightly; he sniffed the staleness of the beer and did not drink. "Love is a curious thing to begin with. At first I thought only of getting her back. It was a kind of mania. But then as time went on I tried to remember her. But do you know what happened?"

54 "No," the boy said.

55 "When I laid myself down on a bed and tried to think about her my mind became a blank. I couldn't see her. I would take out her pictures and look. No good. Nothing doing. A blank. Can you imagine it?"

56 "Say, Mack!" Leo called down the counter. "Can you imagine this bozo's mind a blank!"

57 Slowly, as though fanning away flies, the man waved his hand. His green eyes were concentrated and fixed on the shallow little face of the paper boy.

58 "But a sudden piece of glass on a sidewalk. Or a nickel tune in a music box. A shadow on a wall at night. And I would remember. It might happen in a street and I would cry or bang my head against a lamppost. You follow me?"

59 "A piece of glass . . ." the boy said.

60 "Anything. I would walk around and I had no power of how and when to remember her. You think you can put up a kind of shield. But remembering don't come to a man face forward—it corners around sideways. I was at the mercy of everything I saw and heard. Suddenly instead of me combing the countryside to find her she begun to chase me around in my very soul. *She* chasing *me,* mind you! And in my soul!"

61 The boy asked finally: "What part of the country were you in then?"

62 "Ooh," the man groaned. "I was a sick mortal. It was like smallpox. I confess, son, that I boozed. I fornicated. I committed any sin that suddenly appealed to me. I am loath to confess it but I will do so. When I recall that period it is all curdled in my mind, it was so terrible."

63 The man leaned his head down and tapped his forehead on the counter. For a few seconds he stayed bowed over in this position, the back of his stringy neck covered with orange furze, his hands with their long warped fingers held palm to palm in an attitude of prayer. Then the man straightened himself; he was smiling and suddenly his face was bright and tremulous and old.

64 "It was in the fifth year that it happened," he said. "And with it I started my science."

65 Leo's mouth jerked with a pale, quick grin. "Well, none of we boys are getting any younger," he said. Then with sudden anger he balled up a dishcloth he was holding and threw it down hard on the floor. "You draggle-tailed old Romeo!"

66 "What happened?" the boy asked.

67 The old man's voice was high and clear: "Peace," he answered.

68 "Huh?"

69 "It is hard to explain scientifically, son," he said. "I guess the logical explanation is that she and I had fled around from each other for so long that finally we just got tangled up together and lay down and quit. Peace. A queer and beautiful blankness. It was spring in Portland and the rain came every afternoon. All evening I just stayed there on my bed in the dark. And that is how the science come to me."

70 The windows in the streetcar were pale blue with light. The two soldiers paid for their beers and opened the door—one of the soldiers combed his hair and wiped off his muddy puttees before they went outside. The three mill workers bent silently over their breakfasts. Leo's clock was ticking on the wall.

71 "It is this. And listen carefully. I meditated on love and reasoned it out. I realized what is wrong with us. Men fall in love for the first time. And what do they fall in love with?"

72 The boy's soft mouth was partly open and he did not answer.

73 "A woman," the old man said. "Without science, with nothing to go by, they undertake the most dangerous and sacred experience in God's earth. They fall in love with a woman. Is that correct, son?"

74 "Yeah," the boy said faintly.

75 "They start at the wrong end of love. They begin at the climax. Can you wonder it is so miserable? Do you know how men should love?"

76 The old man reached over and grasped the boy by the collar of his leather jacket. He gave him a gentle little shake and his green eyes gazed down unblinking and grave.

77 "Son, do you know how love should be begun?"

78 The boy sat small and listening and still. Slowly he shook his head. The old man leaned closer and whispered:

79 "A tree. A rock. A cloud."

80 It was still raining outside in the street: a mild, gray, endless rain. The mill whistle blew for the six-o'clock shift and the three spinners paid and went away. There was no one in the café but Leo, the old man, and the little paper boy.

81 "The weather was like this in Portland," he said. "At the time my science was begun. I meditated and I started very cautious. I would pick up something from the street and take it home with me. I bought a goldfish and I concentrated on the goldfish and I loved it. I graduated from one thing to another. Day by day I was getting this technique. On the road from Portland to San Diego—"

82 "Aw shut up!" screamed Leo suddenly. "Shut up! Shut up!"

83 The old man still held the collar of the boy's jacket; he was trembling and his face was earnest and bright and wild. "For six years now I have gone around by myself and built up my science. And now I am a master, son. I can love anything. No longer do I have to think about it even. I see a street full of people and a beautiful light comes in me. I watch a bird in the sky. Or I meet a traveler on the road. Everything, son. And anybody. All strangers and all loved! Do you realize what a science like mine can mean?"

84 The boy held himself stiffly, his hands curled tight around the counter edge. Finally he asked: "Did you ever really find that lady?"

85 "What? What say, son?"

86 "I mean," the boy asked timidly, "have you fallen in love with a woman again?"

87 The old man loosened his grasp on the boy's collar. He turned away and for the first time his green eyes had a vague and scattered look. He lifted the mug from the counter, drank down the yellow beer. His head was shaking slowly from side to side. Then finally he answered: "No, son, You see, that is the last step in my science. I go cautious. And I am not quite ready yet."

88 "Well!" said Leo. "Well well well!"

89 The old man stood in the open doorway. "Remember," he said. Framed there in the gray damp light of the early morning, he looked shrunken and seedy and frail. But his smile was bright. "Remember I love you," he said with a last nod. And the door closed quietly behind him.

90 The boy did not speak for a long time. He pulled down the bangs on his forehead and slid his grimy little forefinger around the rim of the empty cup. Then without looking at Leo he finally asked:

91 "Was he drunk?"

92 "No," said Leo shortly.

93 The boy raised his clear voice higher. "Then was he a dope fiend?"

94 "No."

95 The boy looked up at Leo, and his flat little face was desperate, his voice urgent and shrill. "Was he crazy? Do you think he was a lunatic?" The paper boy's voice dropped suddenly with doubt. "Leo? Or not?"

96 But Leo would not answer him. Leo had run a night café for fourteen years, and he held himself to be a critic of craziness. There were the town characters and also the transients who roamed in from the night. He knew the manias of all of them. But he did not want to satisfy the questions of the waiting child. He tightened his pale face and was silent.

97 So the boy pulled down the right flap of his helmet and as he turned to leave he made the only comment that seemed safe to him, the only remark that could not be laughed down and despised:

98 "He sure has done a lot of traveling." □

The quality of fairy tale dominates this story from the opening paragraph to the last sentence as declarative sentences assume the narrative pattern of that literary form. Simplicity of syntax and sentence pattern becomes immediately apparent as the reader dimly remembers such beginnings as "Once upon a time in a country beyond the mountains, a boy. . . ." The predawn hour is a time of unreality, a time at the close of things ended, a time before the start of beginnings. Life seems suspended in a café undistinguished by description beyond stools, counter, a door, and windows. It exists in any town in any period: there is always war (the soldiers) and work (spinners from the cotton mill). To complete the isolation of this timeless, placeless setting, rain draws its curtain around the café, shutting out the world. Within this microcosm, this frame, the materials of the story are stretched.

Thought, sentiment, and language create meaning beyond the superficial as the characters are woven in lightly, yet expressively delineated: Leo, the king who rules this tiny kingdom but who is bitter and stingy; the boy who is young and uncomprehending but expectant, hopeful that life will be friendly; the shabby old transient who could be the boy's fairy godfather—or a Cassandra—or a Christ speaking into the winds of incomprehension and cynicism in this kingdom of physical gratifications stingily supplied, in this kingdom cut off by nature (the rain) from the encroachments of war and the machine—cut off at least long enough for this wanderer to offer secrets that could make the boy a prince if he could understand them.

And all of this is a "familiar and faithful exhibition of scenes in common life." What could be more common than this all-night café, this believable assortment of customers, this rainy predawn hour of another day? And how artfully the characters are delineated!

The boy: a stock orphan, small and freckled, innocent and hopeful—the Everyman who searches through life for meaning and reason, the Everyman who can become a prince only if he is touched with the magic of loving unselfishly somewhere in his journey. His "pink little ear" becomes "very small and red" as if the effort of listening has raised its intellectual temperature (paragraph 15) and is covered protectively again in paragraph 97. In paragraph 1, he is hopeful someone will speak to him in a friendly way. In paragraph 9, his shrill voice reveals his distrust. In paragraph 13, he is cautious until Leo makes his decision for him by putting the coffee on the counter. By paragraph 29, he is an unwilling prisoner. By paragraph 37, he is a doubtful ally of the transient. Paragraphs 42, 44, 47, and 52 reveal his involvement in the superficial details, the unassessed narrative. Paragraph 57 reveals his lack of understanding, his inability to hear the message beneath the surface: his face is *shallow.* Paragraphs 59 and 61 indicate his withdrawal as he responds with the most banal conversational gambits in a "familiar and faithful exhibition of scenes in common life." As a result of Leo's outburst in paragraph 65, the boy's interest is revived briefly in paragraph

66 to die again in paragraph 68 as the simplicity of the "science" presents too great an abstraction for the boy to comprehend. Utterly unable to understand, he can only focus his attention on the superficial details, prompting his question in paragraph 84. However, after the transient has gone, the boy meditatively engages in the simple, familiar acts of pulling his bangs and fingering his cup as he seeks words that will phrase his questions (paragraph 90). He needs reassurance that the message was unimportant, merely the chatter of a drunkard, a dope fiend, a lunatic. His need makes his voice shrill, his doubt softens it, for he knows the answers are all negative (paragraph 95). As he leaves the café (paragraph 98), he makes his decision, however unconsciously, and dooms himself to the perpetual paper route of his life which will always be "the town in the black, queer early morning" of paragraph 48. Hypnotized on the stool of youth (paragraph 29), surrounded by the cynicism, fear, and spiritual stinginess of the ruling class (Leo) of this kingdom, the disinterested, uncommunicative workers and warriors of the citizenry (spinners and soldiers), and the lucid prophet who seems drunken, doped, and crazy in comparison, the boy, like Everyman, is exposed to an experience which forces him to decide where to pledge his allegiance. The king cannot command, nor will he supply the answers which might influence the decision. Allegiance is a matter of personal choice. The warrior-workers are unconcerned with the boy's dilemma; they made their choices long ago and are captived in the ruins of choice; they withdraw to their routines. And now, the boy chooses out of fear that he will be laughed at and despised. Preparing to follow the warrior-workers, he closes his ear to truth by pulling down the "right flap of his helmet" and makes the "safe" statement which commits him to nothing while barring him from everything wonderful. He is ready to wander out into the dawn of the loveless world.

But why did he make that decision? Why could he not *hear* what the transient tried to tell him? Because two other characters are as expressively delineated: the transient and Leo. The minor characters (soldiers and spinners) are very lightly delineated: their faceless, non-involved presence distinguishes them more realistically and symbolically than expressive delineation could.

The transient—a comic valentine figure—is, in paragraph 1, partially concealed, his face in a beer mug. As he emerges from it (like Venus from the sea or Lazarus from the tomb) he becomes "long and pale," but the image is made ludicrous as he has "a big nose and faded orange hair." His physical act of examination (paragraph 7) suggests a deviate's action which startles the boy and creates tension in the soldier-spinners.

His unexpected avowal of love amuses them, breaking the tension and relegating him to the level of "just another nut," and they laugh, relieved of the necessity to involve themselves.

The big-nosed, orange-headed disregarder of conventional behavior (notice how details accrue) is "serious and sad" (paragraph 11) as well as gentle, dignified, and unpatronizing. His invitation (paragraph 12) indicates he sees not only a younger person (*son*) but also a human equal beyond the conventional codes of law ("Sit down and have a beer with me") which Leo enforces. The soldier-spinners have abandoned the boy to his decisions by now and offer him no cue. In paragraph 15, the transient nods "soberly," indicating sobriety as well as gravity. Every line of dialog reveals a man of some education as well as of sensitivity and insight. His simple language is elliptical, but it is the economical prose of the instinctively poetic speaker. The photographs he displays may indicate something of a surface view of love: the distinguishing features are clothes (the façade) and the big stomach (the receptacle of life). In its earth-colored mug (paragraph 25), the transient's beer suggests the primitive myths such as Baucis and Philemon, adding a new dimension to the growing spiritual figure.

As he folds his "crooked hands," (paragraph 27) the transient's face is sad, his eyes pale green, and the description evokes the nature god of infinite compassion. The raised forefinger (paragraph 29) recalls Renaissance religious symbolism in art as it serves to transfix the boy. Again one of Irving's criteria becomes obvious: "the half-concealed vein of humor that is often playing through the whole." The Renaissance religious portrait is of a hound-dog-faced old transient with orange hair and green eyes, almost a cartoon or caricature similar to the sketch Irving drew of Ichabod Crane. Even the time elements of the transient's story are humorously rich in symbolism. His chronological exactness reveals itself in threes, the mystical number of so many religions. He was married (paragraph 30) twelve years earlier (4×3); she was his wife one year (4×3), nine months (3×3), three days, and two nights (she left him on the third). When they met, he was fifty-one (17×3) and she said she was thirty (10×3). They were married within three days. That many repetitions of a number can scarcely be coincidental.

The sensitivity claimed by the transient (paragraph 38) is no idle boast. He reveals it as he places "Moonlight. The leg of a pretty girl" in juxtaposition. The spiritual nature of man reacts to the first, the biological to the second—and they are equated in his mind as he reveals the most sensitive element of his nature: an ability to accept truth as well as responsibility. He blames no one but himself for his weakness; it existed because he had not loved. He makes no attempt to "pass the buck." This recital is touching in content and in the gentle poetry of the lines characterized by alliteration, repetition, and a masterful development of ideas from the very general to the very specific, a development that creates a mood of urgency and a tone of verbal power.

Paragraph 39 sketches in the vein of humor as adroitly as if it were comic relief supplied by a twentieth-century Shakespeare. The transition sentence of the expository paragraph invites the reader's attention to the device. To the cartoon countenance, McCullers adds "the lobes of his large, loose ears seemed to tremble," extending the initial image of a sad-faced hound. The poignancy of paragraph 40 is intensified as a result. The sad clown, the eyes of a Pierrot, the Chaplinesque figure—all are evoked and superimposed on the poetic beauty of the statement "Nothing lay around loose in me any more but was finished up by her."

The intensity of the dramatic moment may overpower the reader; so McCullers supplies comic relief again as transition into paragraph 41: the hound-dog's muzzle is stroked. And—unlike the man who asks, "You know what I mean?"—he assumes full responsibility for his communication failure, seeking a more precise analogy. The result is a metaphor of remarkable strength and beauty. Not unlike Dante's purification through love of Beatrice, the transient's concept is couched in machine-age idiom, his seeming grammatical errors creating a recurring process of spiritual rejuvenation: he ran the little pieces of himself through her and came out complete, but the tense errors ambiguously create a historical present statement. The process is constantly recurring; it was not completed in the past as "correct" grammar would indicate. And her name, Dodo, strengthens the ambiguity: she is an alive Dodo (an extinct bird) undergoing the process of extinction as she grows older. While she lives, his spiritual rejuvenation continues.

The "science" of the transient is a statement of natural development. A baby learns to see a floor before he can crawl on it. He crawls until he has the strength and balance and judgment to walk on that floor. Then, when he is adept at walking, he learns to run with control and balance. Each step follows an earlier, easier one, but it can come only after the earlier one has been learned. Man recognizes the need of a patterned learning process in almost everything he attempts—except the ability to love. As the transient realized (paragraphs 71–79), men approach this "dangerous and sacred experience" without preparation, without learning the fundamentals. They attempt to run before they learn to see the floor: "They begin at the climax." And they fail to participate in this sacred experience, a failure that is dangerous, for it leaves them, like the transient before he formulated his science, prey to remembered experience they can neither understand nor escape (paragraph 58). They may bang their heads against lampposts, but the artificial light reveals nothing and they are at the mercy of everything they see and hear. If they manage to close their spiritual eyes and ears, they become the soldier-spinners, accepting violence and routine as the pattern of life because they can learn it, beginning with fundamentals and progressing in understandable stages.

The transient's science? One *learns* to love, not at the climax, but from the beginning. Simple things (a tree, a rock, a cloud) serve as first love objects. He cannot possess, cannot imprison them. But he can experience them since they are animate (a tree), inanimate (a rock), and spiritual (a cloud). Love grows from those three states. Animate it is—alive and growing. Inanimate it must be, existing without reason. Spiritual it becomes when the animate and the inanimate are experienced and understood. And when one learns to love these, he is ready to love a person. But he must first learn the ability to love, for love can exist independently of a human object, and, if it cannot, a man does not love the human—he is merely projecting his needs and calling the projection love. Such projection is not love; it is selfishness.

Paragraph 83 presents the overwhelming question: "Do you realize what a science like mine can mean?" And the old transient becomes a Christ figure at this moment if he has not before. To love according to his science would be to observe Christ's eleventh commandment. That the boy does not understand probably comes as no surprise. This man has known his temptations (paragraph 62) and his Gethsemanes (paragraph 63). But, with bowed "stringy neck covered with orange furze," with his personal "attitude of prayer," he radiates the ecstasy associated with the spiritually elect of history (paragraph 63). He smiles and his face is "bright and tremulous and old" in the same way truth may be: ludicrous in appearance but shining flickeringly—and wise.

Just how the transient passed from the counter to the door (paragraphs 87–89) is not indicated. Leo's "Well! Well well well" serves as the only transition. A mystical ellipsis bridges the paragraphs on Leo's words which the reader is free to interpret as sarcasm, wonder, or symbol—in short, however he prefers. But the exposition revealing the movement is absent. McCullers preferred to leave that passage to the reader. The transient's gentle admonition from the doorway lingers in the reader's consciousness. A quiet dignity attends the words; they have assumed the quality of importance between paragraph 10 where they were first spoken and paragraph 89 where the door closes after them. It may be pathetic to some readers that the old man leaves to go into a loveless world, but the careful reader will sense a victory preceding the transient. The world he touches will contain a little more love because he passes through it.

Even Leo, the cynic, the jaded, world-weary ruler of this small kingdom, is touched by the old man's revelation. His initial cynicism changes into emotional disturbance and becomes, if not self-doubt, the silence of refusal to doubt or to accept an alien view. In a short time after the story ends, Leo will have forgotten the incident—deliberately and self-defensibly forgotten it—and his life will continue as before.

Paragraph 1 introduces him as "bitter and stingy." On this particular morning, he is completely withdrawn, refusing even to share a look with the paper boy. When the transient creates uneasiness in the boy, Leo offers him no support, watching him with a "weary, brittle jeer" (paragraph 11) until the sale of a cup of coffee impels him to remove choice from the boy. He doesn't ask the boy if he wants coffee; he sets it on the counter. That he may be exposing the boy to moral-law transgressions is of no concern to him; he observes the civil law, refusing to serve beer to the child (paragraph 14).

Leo's bitter, stingy nature becomes apparent in sarcasm as he makes his observation in paragraph 26. Lacking humane generosity, he singles out a prominent physical feature ("big nose") and reduces the transient with vicious syllepsis: "prominent transient." The bitter ambiguities in "cute death" reveal a superior, sadistic man. His refusal to answer the boy's soundless "Drunk?" further reveals his stinginess; he refuses to answer, merely raising his eyebrows and beginning to cook his breakfast. He is Leo, the lion, the king of beasts. Carnivorous symbolism begins here and extends to paragraph 31 in Leo's cat call, which suggests his lion quality, makes a crude comment on the sexual needs of the wandering wife, and rips at the soul of the transient. The quiet dignity of the transient confuses Leo. He has become involved in the exchange and he manifests a growing interest now. His observation in paragraph 35 is cutting and sharp, but the vernacular choices of "floozie," "frazzled," and "old rascal" damn the woman and reveal a feeling of camaraderie in Leo. He demonstrates a gentle affection in his comment. Perhaps that inverted kindness prompts the transient to analyze Leo: he is "vulgar" in the sense of being common in his innuendo. If the old man, like an alley cat, has "chased the floozie," a subtle relationship exists between Leo (the lion) and the transient (an old alley cat). The relationship would be "vulgar" to this sincere and kindly man. His suggestion is astute: felines seem to resent being ignored more than any other treatment. It touches their self-esteem.

Leo's long silence then is suggestive of the feline talent for withdrawal. He seems to be engrossed in his own activity, but he is aware of everything in his domain. The physical description in paragraph 46 reveals an aging lion. The stinginess is equally feline. Cats do not willingly share. Guarding that which is theirs, they eat watchfully, grudgingly—as Leo does.

But Leo cannot *be* indifferent to the transient. He is speaking of things alien to Leo—but compelling. The vagabond minstrel, the wandering god, the creature out of the night—whatever he may be—the transient unfolds a tale, a philosophy, a science, a belief—whatever it may be—that threatens Leo's domain, that threatens the stingy, bitter satisfactions Leo finds in his world. Paragraph 50 is more than the sarcasm of a trite phrase delivered scathingly. It is an effort to write "Fini, The End" to the recital before it excludes Leo completely. It is a distractive statement, designed to shatter the hypnotic spell of the old man.

But the old man is on firm ground; he can continue "confidentially," excluding Leo (paragraph 51). And Leo is forced to appeal to the citizenry of his little country. He attempts to enlist their support, but they have learned to remain uninvolved. They do not respond, and the old man brushes Leo off as a pesky irritant (paragraph 57), an act that would be an insufferable affront to the feline sense of dignity. Seething through the next eight paragraphs, Leo attempts the humorous, only to lose self-control and reveal his complete involvement. The transient's recital has cut deeply into Leo's self-containment, and he calls him a "draggle-tailed old Romeo" (paragraph 65), an appelation tantamount to "mangey old alleycat," the epitome of insult from the king of the cats.

But the old man's voice remains "high and clear," indicating his indifference to the hissing, spitting spite directed at him. And Leo's subjects are called to their routines (paragraph 70) as "*Leo's* clock was ticking on the wall." In this world, time is his, but this interloper, this usurper is not bound by Leo's clock. He begins to give the instructions that will free the boy and make him a prince. Leo's throne is in danger and reason deserts him. He wants the boy to hear no more of this science; he wishes to hear no more himself. He "screams" (like a wounded cat) "Shut up!" But the recital runs its course and Leo's "Well!" punctuates it with an inflection that must be supplied by the reader. It might be relief that the recital is done, surprise that the transient has not taken the last step, or the superciliousness of a cliché employed to avoid commitment.

With the closing door, the boy questions Leo, and Leo assures him the man was neither drunk nor a dope fiend. But he will not answer the boy's question, "Was he crazy or a lunatic?" (paragraph 95): "He *did not want* to satisfy the question of the waiting *child.*" The boy has been called by no such diminutive to this point. Ignorance of truth imprisons the young in childhood; Leo imprisons the boy with his silence. But is not Leo a child too? His distress with the recital was not a mature reaction. Does he wish to avoid answering his own questions? He withdraws into the prerogative of rulers: "He tightened his pale face and was silent."

Possessing the quality of a fairy tale, "A Tree. A Rock. A Cloud." does not end with "And they lived happily ever after." Actually, it does not *end* at all. The final period closes the narrative, but the story stretches on into the future as the transient pursues his science in a loveless world, the boy leaves on his endless rounds in the "black, queer early morning," and Leo continues to rule his tiny kingdom, each day making him more bitter and gray of face, more silent and stingy. That stinginess encompasses more than money; it is a stinginess of soul, of spirit, the stinginess of not wanting to answer the child's question.

McCullers stretches her materials on the "frame" of this story. That frame (or plot) is so slight that it summarizes to one incident. Irving, in the letter quoted earlier, said of such writing:

> . . . and there is a constant activity of thought and a nicety of execution required in writings of the kind, more than the world appears to imagine . . . in these shorter writings, every page must have its merit. The author must be continually piquant; woe to him if he makes an awkward sentence or writes a stupid page; the critics are sure to pounce upon it. Yet if he succeed, the very variety and piquancy of his writings—nay, their very brevity, make them frequently recurred to, and when the mere interest of the story is exhausted, he begins to get credit for his touches of pathos or humor; his points of wit or turns of language.

He could have been reviewing McCullers' "A Tree. A Rock. A Cloud." for it rests on that "nicety of execution," is constantly piquant, lacks the awkward sentence, and, when the mere interest of the story is exhausted, the elements of style remain to delight the reader again and again as he returns to the story, somehow certain one more reading will reveal that elusive element that creates the unity of the story, involving him until he finds meaning that changes and grows as he matures intellectually and spiritually. Perhaps therein lies the charm of fairy tales.

Finally, we turn to Henry James' story, "The Real Thing." In the stories of Hemingway and McCullers, brevity creates elliptical difficulties that James avoids in his detailed and analytical tales. His Mandarin style, however, seems complex; the sentences seem difficult to comprehend because the idea, the *donnée,* occupies him so completely. James attempts to chronicle incidents in such minute detail so that the reader will understand the idea exactly as he does. And his understanding grows from a very careful analysis of the subject. As you read in James' notebook entry (p. 299): "I thought I saw a subject for a very brief treatment in this *donnée*— and I think I still do; but to do anything worth while with it I must (as always, great Heavens!) be very clear as to what is in it and what I wish to get out of it." That idea must function, for James, as a "picture; it must illustrate something."

Nathaniel Hawthorne, in the century before James, revealed the same concern with clarity of illustration. In his preface to the 1851 edition of *Twice-Told Tales,* Hawthorne said of his stories:

> . . . The sketches are not, it is hardly necessary to say, profound; but it is rather more remarkable that they so seldom, if ever, show any design on the writer's part to make them so. They have none of the abstruseness of idea, or obscurity of expression, which marks the written communications of a solitary mind with itself. They never need translation. It is, in fact, the style of a man of society. Every sentence, so far as it embodies thought or sensibility, may be understood and felt by anybody who will give himself the trouble to read it, and will take up the book in a proper mood.
>
> This statement of apparently opposite peculiarities leads us to a perception of what the sketches truly are. They are not the talk of a secluded man with his own mind and heart (had it been so, they could hardly have failed to be more deeply and permanently valuable), but his attempts, and very imperfectly successful ones, to open an intercourse with the world.

To create his illustrative "picture" and Hawthorne's "intercourse with the world," James sketches in, in "The Real Thing," all of the descriptive details, the mental processes of his protagonist, narrative action, psychological reaction of characters, and analyses of their changing attitudes. Consequently, little of an interpretative nature is left to the reader. James leads him every step of the narrative way, telling him how to assess every thought and action. Such guidance creates sentences of great grammatical complexity, for dependent and parenthetical ideas cannot stand alone. As slow-paced narrative emerges, suspense cannot build, and the less sophisticated reader becomes bored. Amusement and excitement, the escape elements of so many stories, are absent. Physical action is so unimportant it is scarcely present, while conflict (which generates suspense) never bubbles into violence—it seethes beneath the surface of the story. The reader who prefers not to assess his own subtle reactions, who accepts *obvious* human relations as the guideposts of his life—that reader finds James' prose difficult because, in his own life, he tries to avoid such analyses as James undertakes in fiction. The really great problems of daily life seldom manifest themselves dramatically. They begin casually, grow slowly, reach a climax that is so swaddled in simultaneous complications that they lack drama. As casual complications are pared away by McCullers and Hemingway, the spare, clean, carefully selected narration that remains seems dramatic because background and causative factors are avoided. The immediate actions may be assessed by the reader any way he prefers. James supplies all contributing material, and the reader enters a world that is as complex as his own because of the mass of detail. The resultant story is more "true to life," more realistic than the prose of McCullers and Hemingway, but it is less theatrical, less dramatic, for it forces an understanding of the conscious, subconscious, unconscious processes. Such understanding is so painful and intellectually demanding in personal life that we deliberately refrain from attempting it. James' prose submits us fictionally to what we prefer to avoid in reality. The unsophisticated reader, searching for the narrative thread of the story, skims through such analysis. As the thread is buried in clinical detail, he cannot find it, and he concludes that James and his Mandarin style are "dull." Unfortunately, he thereby pronounces judgment on his own intellectual processes rather than on James' "high style."

As you read "The Real Thing," do not skim. Read carefully and slowly, concentrating on the character development, emerging theme, and Mandarin style. Since you already know the plot from James' notebook entry, do not expect great excitement or elliptical passages. Instead, attempt to understand the attitude, the philosophy, and the point of view of the protagonist—and of James.

Read the story first in its entirety.

The Real Thing

by Henry James

I

[1]When the porter's wife, who used to answer the house-bell, announced "A gentleman and a lady, sir," I had, as I often had in those days—the wish being father to the thought—an immediate vision of sitters. Sitters my visitors in this case proved to be; but not in the sense I should have preferred. There was nothing at first however to indicate that they mightn't have come for a portrait. The gentleman, a man of fifty, very high and very straight, with a moustache slightly grizzled and a dark grey walking-coat admirably fitted, both of which I noted professionally—I

don't mean as a barber or yet as a tailor—would have struck me as a celebrity if celebrities often were striking. It was a truth of which I had for some time been conscious that a figure with a good deal of frontage was, as one might say, almost never a public institution. A glance at the lady helped to remind me of this paradoxical law: she also looked too distinguished to be a "personality." Moreover one would scarcely come across two variations together.

As you saw in the earlier examination of the first paragraph of "The Real Thing," the focus is on the Monarchs, but the point of view is first person, very limited, and the story actually becomes a complete revelation of the artist's attitudes. This revelation begins with the sixth word of the opening sentence. The porter's wife "used" to answer the house-bell. She, obviously, no longer does; the artist is recounting the incidents in retrospect—recounting them from a more comfortable social and economic position in life than he knew when the story happened. And the artist is a snob. The porter's wife sees the genteel quality of the Monarchs, announcing them as "a gentleman and a lady," while the artist equates the words with money rather than with background. Nor has snobbery lessened with affluence: his disclaimer about barbers and tailors establishes his need to feel dissociated from tradesmen. At this point, the casual reader might be hard-pressed to describe the artist in the story, because James supplies no outright statement. However, the careful reader can guess that the artist is utterly undistinguished physically. He would probably pass unnoticed in a crowd of three—and by his own implication. As he is a snob, he is aware his success in art has made him a "personality." As he is also undistinguished, he establishes a syllogism concluding: Celebrities are not distinguished-looking. To achieve so much in one paragraph, James had to bring the full force of his style into play.

[2]Neither of the pair immediately spoke—they only prolonged the preliminary gaze suggesting that each wished to give the other a chance. They were visibly shy; they stood there letting me take them in—which, as I afterwards perceived, was the most practical thing they could have done. In this way their embarrassment served their cause. I had seen people painfully reluctant to mention that they desired anything so gross as to be represented on canvas; but the scruples of my new friends appeared almost insurmountable. Yet the gentleman might have said "I should like a portrait of my wife," and the lady might have said "I should like a portrait of my husband." Perhaps they weren't husband and wife—this naturally would make the matter more delicate. Perhaps they wished to be done together—in which case they ought to have brought a third person to break the news.

Paragraph 2 reveals still more of the self-conscious artist-writer. To be an educated Briton is to be droll naturally—it is traditional and instilled from birth. To be an American transplanted to England with some embarrassment about one's homeland is to be self-consciously droll. James was a transplant of that ilk, and it shows in this paragraph. The actual "quality" of the Monarchs is, ironically, an affront to the artist who is victimized by his own ambivalences. The Monarchs are genteel, but they are not a lady and gentleman because they lack funds. Their natural reticence becomes faintly amusing and he jokes with the reader at the expense of his "new friends" (observe condecension at work). The self-conscious cleverness of his "taking them in" becomes almost painful as he smirkingly suggests the possibility of a "delicate matter" which reduces them further before the artist attains the zenith of his cleverness with the "third person" pronouncement. By now, the sophisticated reader recognizes the artist as a classic example of the inferiority complex at its disguised peak.

[3]"We come from Mr. Rivet," the lady finally said with a dim smile that had the effect of a moist sponge passed over a "sunk" piece of painting, as well as of a vague allusion to vanished beauty. She was as tall and straight, in her degree, as her companion, and with ten years less to carry. She looked as sad as a woman could look whose face was not charged with expression; that is her tinted oval mask showed waste as an exposed surface shows friction. The hand of time had played over her freely, but to an effect of elimination. She was slim and stiff, and so well-dressed, in dark blue cloth, with lappets and pockets and buttons, that it was clear she employed the same tailor as her husband. The couple had an indefinable air of prosperous thrift—they evidently got a good deal of luxury for their money. If I was to be one of their luxuries it would behoove me to consider my terms.

[4]"Ah Claude Rivet recommended me?" I echoed; and I added that it was very kind of him, though I could reflect that, as he only painted landscape, this wasn't a sacrifice.

The ambivalence grows in paragraph 3 as the artist's objective eye analyzes Mrs. Monarch not unkindly, only to associate himself with the tradesmen he dissociated himself from in paragraph 1: "If I was to be one of their luxuries it would behoove me to consider my terms" suggests the practical temperament associated with business rather than with art. The analysis may be astute, but the grammatical "if I was" indicates an unconscious carelessness *or* a deficiency in Latin grammar study, so dear to the English school system. The reflection of paragraph 4 extends the characterization.

5 The lady looked very hard at the gentleman, and the gentleman looked round the room. Then staring at the floor a moment and stroking his moustache, he rested his pleasant eyes on me with the remark: "He said you were the right one."

6 "I try to be, when people want to sit."

7 "Yes, we should like to," said the lady anxiously.

8 "Do you mean together?"

9 My visitors exchanged a glance. "If you could do anything with *me* I suppose it would be double," the gentleman stammered.

10 "Oh yes, there's naturally a higher charge for two figures than for one."

11 "We should like to make it pay," the husband confessed.

12 "That's very good of you," I returned, appreciating so unwonted a sympathy—for I supposed he meant pay the artist.

13 A sense of strangeness seemed to dawn on the lady. "We mean for the illustrations—Mr. Rivet said you might put one in."

14 "Put in—an illustration?" I was equally confused.

15 "Sketch her off, you know," said the gentleman, colouring.

The conversational ambiguity of paragraphs 5–15 is cleverly conceived, but is much too close to real-life speech to be fictionally arresting. Even stylistic artifice cannot raise the ordinary exchange above itself. The reader becomes conscious that James is revealing more than the conversation. The Monarchs are merely reticent; the artist is insensitive (paragraphs 9 and 10) to the point of being dense.

16 It was only then that I understood the service Claude Rivet had rendered me; he had told them how I worked in black-and-white, for magazines, for storybooks, for sketches of contemporary life, and consequently had copious employment for models. These things were true, but it was not less true—I may confess it now; whether because the aspiration was to lead to everything or to nothing I leave the reader to guess—that I couldn't get the honours, to say nothing of the emoluments, of a great painter of portraits out of my head. My "illustrations" were my potboilers; I looked to a different branch of art—far and away the most interesting it had always seemed to me—to perpetuate my fame. There was no shame in looking to it also to make my fortune; but that fortune was by so much further from being made from the moment my visitors wished to be "done" for nothing. I was disappointed; for in the pictorial sense I had immediately *seen* them. I had seized their type—I had already settled what I would do with it. Something that wouldn't absolutely have pleased them, I afterwards reflected.

Naivete seems to color the candid confession of paragraph 16, a confession difficult, at first reading, to understand. The parenthetical suggestion that the reader must "guess" refines the color to black and white, however: the artist, at least, feels the aspiration lead to "everything," and the reader again recognizes a man who can rationalize—indeed, *must* rationalize. He never became the great portrait painter; therefore, what he became is a superior attainment. The reflection of the last sentence indicates the reason he failed as a portrait painter. That he had "*seen* them" and "seized their type" leads logically to the failure; great portrait painters study their subjects to present those features free of a type, the features that make the sitters interesting human beings.

17"Ah you're—you're—a?" I began as soon as I had mastered my surprise. I couldn't bring out the dingy word "models": it seemed so little to fit the case.

18"We haven't had much practice," said the lady.

19"We've got to *do* something, and we've thought that an artist in your line might perhaps make something of us," her husband threw off. He further mentioned that they didn't know many artists and that they had gone first, on the off-chance—he painted views of course, but sometimes put in figures; perhaps I remembered—to Mr. Rivet, whom they had met a few years before at a place in Norfolk where he was sketching.

20"We used to sketch a little ourselves," the lady hinted.

21"It's very awkward, but we absolutely *must* do something," her husband went on.

22"Of course we're not so *very* young," she admitted with a wan smile.

23With the remark that I might as well know something more about them the husband had handed me a card extracted from a neat new pocket-book—their appurtenances were all of the freshest—and inscribed with the words "Major Monarch." Impressive as these words were they didn't carry my knowledge much further; but my visitor presently added: "I've left the army and we've had the misfortune to lose our money. In fact our means are dreadfully small."

24"It's awfully trying—a regular strain," said Mrs. Monarch.

25They evidently wished to be discreet—to take care not to swagger because they were gentlefolk. I felt them willing to recognise this as something of a drawback, at the same time that I guessed at an underlying sense—their consolation in adversity—that they *had* their points. They certainly had; but these advantages struck me as preponderantly social; such for instance as would help to make a drawing-room look well. However, a drawing-room was always, or ought to be, a picture.

26In consequence of his wife's allusion to their age Major Monarch observed: "Naturally it's more for the figure that we thought of going in. We can still hold ourselves up." On the instant I saw that the figure was indeed their strong point. His "naturally" didn't sound vain, but it lighted up the question. "*She* has the best one," he continued, nodding at his wife with a pleasant after-dinner absence of circumlocution. I could only reply, as if we were in fact sitting over our wine, that this didn't prevent his own from being very good; which led him in turn to make answer: "We thought that if you ever have to do people like us we might be something like it. *She* particularly—for a lady in a book, you know."

27 I was so amused by them that, to get more of it, I did my best to take their point of view; and though it was an embarrassment to find myself appraising physically, as if they were animals on hire or useful blacks, a pair whom I should have expected to meet only in one of the relations in which criticism is tacit, I looked at Mrs. Monarch judicially enough to be able to exclaim after a moment with conviction: "Oh yes, a lady in a book!" She was singularly like a bad illustration.

28 "We'll stand up, if you like," said the Major; and he raised himself before me with a really grand air.

29 I could take his measure at a glance—he was six feet two and a perfect gentleman. It would have paid any club in process of formation and in want of a stamp to engage him at a salary to stand in the principal window. What struck me at once was that in coming to me they had rather missed their vocation; they could surely have been turned to better account for advertising purposes. I couldn't of course see the thing in detail, but I could see them make somebody's fortune—I don't mean their own. There was something in them for a waistcoat-maker, an hotel-keeper or a soap-vendor. I could imagine "We always use it" pinned on their bosoms with the greatest effect; I had a vision of the brilliancy with which they would launch a table d'hôte.

30 Mrs. Monarch sat still, not from pride but from shyness, and presently her husband said to her: "Get up, my dear, and show how smart you are." She obeyed, but she had no need to get up to show it. She walked to the end of the studio and then came back blushing, her fluttered eyes on the partner of her appeal. I was reminded of an incident I had accidentally had a glimpse of in Paris—being with a friend there, a dramatist about to produce a play, when an actress came to him to ask to be entrusted with a part. She went through her paces before him, walked up and down as Mrs. Monarch was doing. Mrs. Monarch did it quite as well, but I abstained from applauding. It was very odd to see such people apply for such poor pay. She looked as if she had ten thousand a year. Her husband had used the word that described her: she was in the London current jargon essentially and typically "smart." Her figure was, in the same order of ideas, conspicuously and irreproachably "good." For a woman of her age her waist was surprisingly small, her elbow moreover had the orthodox crook. She held her head at the conventional angle, but why did she come to *me?* She ought to have tried on jackets at a big shop. I feared my visitors were not only destitute but "artistic"—which would be a great complication. When she sat down again I thanked her, observing that what a draughtsman most valued in his model was the faculty of keeping quiet.

Beginning in paragraph 17, the artist's attitude changes. He is more kindly disposed toward the Monarchs, finding the word *model* "dingy" in relation to them. By paragraph 25, he has developed sympathy for their very British stiff-upper-lip attitude. But even that sympathy stamps the portrait James paints of himself as an artist. An American would, of course, find that attitude "correct." Understanding grows from a leveling of social status until, in paragraph 27, he becomes condescendingly superior. The last line brings back the earlier, assumed drollery. His tradesman's eye betrays him again in paragraphs 29–30, and he lapses into frank admiration of the innate quality the Monarchs possess—an admiration at odds with the last line of paragraph 27.

31 "Oh *she* can keep quiet," said Major Monarch. Then he added jocosely: "I've always kept her quiet."

32 "I'm not a nasty fidget, am I?" It was going to wring tears from me, I felt, the way she hid her head, ostrich-like, in the other broad bosom.

33 The owner of this expanse addressed his answer to me. "Perhaps it isn't out of place to mention—because we ought to be quite business-like, oughtn't we?—that when I married her she was known as the Beautiful Statue."

34 "Oh dear!" said Mrs. Monarch ruefully.

35 "Of course I should want a certain amount of expression," I rejoined.

36 "Of *course!*"—and I had never heard such unanimity.

37 "And then I suppose you know that you'll get awfully tired."

38 "Oh we *never* get tired!" they eagerly cried.

39 "Have you had any kind of practice?"

40 They hesitated—they looked at each other. "We've been photographed—*immensely,*" said Mrs. Monarch.

41 "She means the fellows have asked us themselves," added the Major.

42 "I see—because you're so good-looking."

43 "I don't know what they thought, but they were always after us."

44 "We always got our photographs for nothing," smiled Mrs. Monarch.

45 "We might have brought some, my dear," her husband remarked.

46 "I'm not sure we have any left. We've given quantities away," she explained to me.

47 "With our autographs and that sort of thing," said the Major.

48 "Are they to be got in the shops?" I enquired as a harmless pleasantry.

49 "Oh yes, *hers*—they used to be."

50 "Not now," said Mrs. Monarch, with her eyes on the floor.

Their ingenuousness becomes a little embarrassing, but the artist's sarcasm, his cruelty in paragraph 42, angers the reader. Anger turns to outrage at the "harmless pleasantry" of paragraph 48, for the Monarch-baiting has gone too far. As if sensing danger, realizing their naivete is becoming unbelievable, James mercifully ends section I of the story.

Fifty paragraphs (well over one-third of the narrative) constitute the beginning. One scene, narrowly focused on the three main characters, has taken longer to read than would be needed to enact the scene. Selection? Pace? Both are just right. This is reflective, revealing narrative. The reader is allowed access to an embarrassment of mental riches. The "correct" language, the suggested insights, the tantalizing movements—all are as carefully conceived, selected, and presented as the details of a Hemingway bullfight episode. And, in their own way, they generate the same suspense—at a different level. Here is a man, the artist, daring to approach a beast—his own *bête noire*—himself. Armed only with the cape of ego, he executes his passes daringly, grazing the horns of his personal dilemma, working the episode toward a moment of truth which will reveal his mastery through spiritual strength or his cowardice through continued self-delusion. But the story is not done. Reaching a peak, James breaks the tension, withdraws, allows the reader a brief respite, and attacks again.

Section II occupies thirty-seven paragraphs. Chronologically they follow the first fifty of section I, but a slight change of tone sets them apart as if, in the recounting of section I, the artist has mellowed a bit, become more human, less defensive. His analysis of the Monarchs (and how like deposed royalty they are in this section) is that democratic, American, common-man approach to visiting royalty from economically poor but historically rich European countries. The American may state his contempt for the "useless" aristocracy, but let a Queen Marie of Roumania, a Prince Philip or Princess Margaret of England visit these shores and all contempt vanishes. Any news account is eagerly devoured, any parade route lined with enthusiastic welcoming crowds paying their unique, brash respect to the undemocratic heads of state who have deigned to pass their way. And the more faded, the more ruined those crowned heads, the warmer the reception.

II

51 I could fancy the "sort of thing" they put on the presentation copies of their photographs, and I was sure they wrote a beautiful hand. It was odd how quickly I was sure of everything that concerned them. If they were now so poor as to have to earn shillings and pence they could never have had much of a margin. Their good looks had been their capital, and they had good-humouredly made the most of the career that this resource marked out for them. It was in their faces, the blankness, the deep intellectual repose of the twenty years of country-house visiting that had given them pleasant intonations. I could see the sunny drawing-rooms, sprinkled with periodicals she didn't read, in which Mrs. Monarch had continuously sat; I could see the wet shrubberies in which she had walked, equipped to admiration

for either exercise. I could see the rich covers the Major had helped to shoot and the wonderful garments in which, late at night, he repaired to the smoking-room to talk about them. I could imagine their leggings and waterproofs, their knowing tweeds and rugs, their rolls of sticks and cases of tackle and neat umbrellas; and I could evoke the exact appearance of their servants and the compact variety of their luggage on the platforms of country stations.

52 They gave small tips, but they were liked; they didn't do anything themselves, but they were welcome. They looked so well everywhere; they gratified the general relish for stature, complexion and "form." They knew it without fatuity or vulgarity, and they respected themselves in consequence. They weren't superficial; they were thorough and kept themselves up—it had been their line. People with such a taste for activity had to have some line. I could feel how even in a dull house they could have been counted on for the joy of life. At present something had happened—it didn't matter what, their little income had grown less, it had grown least—and they had to do something for pocket-money. Their friends could like them, I made out, without liking to support them. There was something about them that represented credit—their clothes, their manners, their type; but if credit is a large empty pocket in which an occasional chink reverberates, the chink at least must be audible. What they wanted of me was to help to make it so. Fortunately they had no children—I soon divined that. They would also perhaps wish our relations to be kept secret: this was why it was "for the figure"—the reproduction of the face would betray them.

The Major Monarchs receive relatively warm treatment in paragraphs 51–52. The mercurial American ability to alternate rapidly between contempt and sentimentality pervades these lines. The realizations of ravaging time rest heavily on Mrs. Monarch's imagined words and actions in paragraph 50, triggering that alternation. The artist now sees the faded couple as representatives of a dusty past, of a romantically conceived way of life he never knew except vicariously in the writings he now illustrates. They are figures out of the portraits he never painted, representatives of a world he re-creates for books and magazines to be read by other people who also seek romantic association with that unattainable world. But, at the end of paragraph 52, the very real world of economic necessity reasserts itself; "support" and "credit" intrude themselves and the armor of cynicism, the self-protective sophistication, the jaded doubt reappear in the supposition that "They would also perhaps wish our relations to be kept secret: this was why it was 'for the figure'—the reproduction of the face would betray them." The parenthetical statement, "the wish being father to the thought" of paragraph 1, recalls itself to the reader. It does not seem to recall itself to the artist.

53 I liked them—I felt, quite as their friends must have done—they were so simple; and I had no objection to them if they would suit. But somehow with all their perfections I didn't easily believe in them. After all they were amateurs, and the ruling passion of my life was the detestation of the amateur. Combined with this was another perversity—an innate preference for the represented subject over the real one: the defect of the real one was so apt to be a lack of representation. I liked things that appeared; then one was sure. Whether they *were* or not was a subordinate and almost always a profitless question. There were other considerations, the first of which was that I already had two or three recruits in use, notably a young person with big feet, in alpaca, from Kilburn, who for a couple of years had come to me regularly for my illustrations and with whom I was still—perhaps ignobly—satisfied. I frankly explained to my visitors how the case stood, but they had taken more precautions than I supposed. They had reasoned out their opportunity, for Claude Rivet had told them of the projected *édition de luxe* of one of the writers of our day—the rarest of the novelists—who, long neglected by the multitudinous vulgar and dearly prized by the attentive (need I mention Philip Vincent?), had had the happy fortune of seeing, late in life, the dawn and then the full light of a higher criticism; an estimate in which on the part of the public there was something really of expiation. The edition preparing, planned by a publisher of taste, was practically an act of high reparation; the wood-cuts with which it was to be enriched were the homage of English art to one of the most independent representatives of English letters. Major and Mrs. Monarch confessed to me they had hoped I might be able to work *them* into my branch of the enterprise. They knew I was to do the first of the books, "Rutland Ramsay," but I had to make clear to them that my participation in the rest of the affair—this first book was to be a test—must depend on the satisfaction I should give. If this should be limited my employers would drop me with scarce common forms. It was therefore a crisis for me, and naturally I was making special preparations, looking about for new people, should they be necessary, and securing the best types. I admitted however that I should like to settle down to two or three good models who would do for everything.

The declarative "I liked them" of paragraph 53 has a hollow ring—not as if the artist lies to the reader but as if he deludes himself. Within the same line, the statement becomes a tempered "I had no objection to them" which is virtually negated by "if they would suit." The reader knows they *can't* suit, regardless of their suitability. Simultaneously, the reader knows they will be hired and *found* unsuitable. The rationalization for that eventuality begins immediately in the stated preference for the imitation, the *ersatz* that imagination can endow with the biases and prejudices of manufactured reality. Interwoven in the explanation is a specious treatment of the argument that literature is not a mirror of life, it is a controlled arrangement of selected details. The amateur

Englishman states his detestation of amateurs: "an innate preference for the represented subject over the real one." That representational man is clearly revealed in the self-satisfied "multitudinous vulgar and dearly prized by the attentive (need I mention Philip Vincent?)." The intellectual associations are as clear as the implication that an elite group can exist beyond blood lines. He belongs to the nobility of the intellectually aware.

[54]"Should we have often to—a—put on special clothes?" Mrs. Monarch timidly demanded.

[55]"Dear yes—that's half the business."

[56]"And should we be expected to supply our own costumes?"

[57]"Oh no; I've got a lot of things. A painter's models put on—or put off—anything he likes."

[58]"And you mean—a—the same?"

[59]"The same?"

[60]Mrs. Monarch looked at her husband again.

[61]"Oh she was just wondering," he explained, "if the costumes are in *general* use." I had to confess that they were, and I mentioned further that some of them—I had a lot of genuine greasy last-century things—had served their time, a hundred years ago, on living world-stained men and women; on figures not perhaps so far removed, in that vanished world, from *their* type, the Monarchs', *quoi!* of a breeched and bewigged age. "We'll put on anything that *fits,*" said the Major.

[62]"Oh I arrange that—they fit in the pictures."

The question of costumes supplies the artist shot to bring this high-flying pair to earth. "*Their* type" is of a "vanished world." The quiet dignity of Major Monarch asserts itself again in verbal ambiguity as he agrees to wear anything that "fits." The reader must decide whether or not the ambiguity is wasted on the artist. From his "attentive" position, is his answer sarcasm or reassurance or defense?

[63]"I'm afraid I should do better for the modern books. I'd come as you like," said Mrs. Monarch.

[64]"She has got a lot of clothes at home: they might do for contemporary life," her husband continued.

[65]"Oh I can fancy scenes in which you'd be quite natural." And indeed I could see the slipshod rearrangements of stale properties—the stories I tried to produce pictures for without the exasperation of reading them—whose sandy tracts the good lady might help to people. But I had to return to the fact that for this sort of work—the daily mechanical grind—I was already equipped: the people I was working with were fully adequate.

66 "We only thought we might be more like *some* characters," said Mrs. Monarch mildly, getting up.

67 Her husband also rose; he stood looking at me with a dim wistfulness that was touching in so fine a man. "Wouldn't it be rather a pull sometimes to have—a—to have—?" He hung fire; he wanted me to help him by phrasing what he meant. But I couldn't—I didn't know. So he brought it out awkwardly: "The *real* thing; a gentleman, you know, or a lady." I was quite ready to give a general assent—I admitted that there was a great deal in that. This encouraged Major Monarch to say, following up his appeal with an unacted gulp: "It's awfully hard—we've tried everything." The gulp was communicative; it proved too much for his wife. Before I knew it Mrs. Monarch had dropped again upon a divan and burst into tears. Her husband sat down beside her, holding one of her hands; whereupon she quickly dried her eyes with the other, while I felt embarrassed as she looked up at me. "There isn't a confounded job I haven't applied for—waited for—prayed for. You can fancy we'd be pretty bad first. Secretaryships and that sort of thing? You might as well ask for a peerage. I'd be *anything*—I'm strong; a messenger or a coalheaver. I'd put on a gold-laced cap and open carriage-doors in front of the haberdasher's; I'd hang about a station to carry portmanteaux; I'd be a postman. But they won't *look* at you; there are thousands as good as yourself already on the ground. *Gentlemen,* poor beggars, who've drunk their wine, who've kept their hunters!"

The Monarchs know what they are. In paragraph 67, with hesitating accuracy, the Major pronounces their state: "the *real* thing; a gentleman, you know, or a lady." Such a pronouncement could, conceivably, prove the artist's contention at the close of paragraph 52, but any such possibility is destroyed with the Major's impassioned avowal. He is not above any kind of work. Unfortunately, in a changing world, he is not the only destitute gentleman. Many exist: "*Gentlemen,* poor beggars, who've drunk their wine, who've kept their hunters!" is an exclamation wrung from a compassionate heart. Now the reader realizes Major Monarch would be a gentleman regardless of his occupation. What the man *is,* not what he *does,* makes him a gentleman.

68 I was as reassuring as I knew how to be, and my visitors were presently on their feet again while, for the experiment, we agreed on an hour. We were discussing it when the door opened and Miss Churm came in with a wet umbrella. Miss Churm had to take the omnibus to Maida Vale and then walk half a mile. She looked a trifle blowsy and slightly splashed. I scarcely ever saw her come in without thinking afresh how odd it was that, being so little in herself, she should yet be so much in others. She was a meagre little Miss Churm, but was such an ample heroine of romance. She was only a freckled cockney, but she could represent everything, from a fine lady to a shepherdess; she had the faculty as she might have had a fine voice or

long hair. She couldn't spell and she loved beer, but she had two or three "points," and practice, and a knack, and mother-wit, and a whimsical sensibility, and a love of the theatre, and seven sisters, and not an ounce of respect, especially for the *h*. The first thing my visitors saw was that her umbrella was wet, and in their spotless perfection they visibly winced at it. The rain had come on since their arrival.

69 "I'm all in a soak; there *was* a mess of people in the 'bus. I wish you lived near a stytion," said Miss Churm. I requested her to get ready as quickly as possible, and she passed into the room in which she always changed her dress. But before going out she asked me what she was to get into this time.

70 "It's the Russian princess, don't you know?" I answered; "the one with the 'golden eyes,' in black velvet, for the long thing in the *Cheapside*."

71 "Golden eyes? I *say!*" cried Miss Churm, while my companions watched her with intensity as she withdrew. She always arranged herself, when she was late, before I could turn round; and I kept my visitors a little on purpose, so that they might get an idea, from seeing her, what would be expected of themselves. I mentioned that she was quite my notion of an excellent model—she was really very clever.

72 "Do you think she looks like a Russian princess?" Major Monarch asked with lurking alarm.

73 "When I make her, yes."

74 "Oh if you have to *make* her—!" he reasoned, not without point.

75 "That's the most you can ask. There are so many who are not makeable."

76 "Well now, *here's* a lady"—and with a persuasive smile he passed his arm into his wife's—"who's already made!"

77 "Oh I'm not a Russian princess," Mrs. Monarch protested a little coldly. I could see she had known some and didn't like them. There at once was a complication of a kind I never had to fear with Miss Churm.

78 This young lady came back in black velvet—the gown was rather rusty and very low on her lean shoulders—and with a Japanese fan in her red hands. I reminded her that in the scene I was doing she had to look over some one's head. "I forget whose it is; but it doesn't matter. Just look over a head."

79 "I'd rather look over a stove," said Miss Churm; and she took her station near the fire. She fell into position, settled herself into a tall attitude, gave a certain backward inclination to her head and a certain forward droop to her fan, and looked, at least to my prejudiced sense, distinguished and charming, foreign and dangerous. We left her looking so while I went downstairs with Major and Mrs. Monarch.

80 "I believe I could come about as near it as that," said Mrs. Monarch.

81 "Oh you think she's shabby, but you must allow for the alchemy of art."

82 However, they went off with an evident increase of comfort founded on their demonstrable advantage in being the real thing. I could fancy them shuddering over Miss Churm. She was very droll about them when I went back, for I told her what they wanted.

83 "Well, if *she* can sit I'll tyke to book-keeping," said my model.

84 "She's very ladylike," I replied as an innocent form of aggravation.

85 "So much the worse for *you*. That means she can't turn round."

86 "She'll do for the fashionable novels."

87 "Oh yes, she'll *do* for them!" my model humorously declared. "Ain't they bad enough without her?" I had often sociably denounced them to Miss Churm.

The arrival of the foil character, Miss Churm (who would pronounce *charm* and her last name alike), underlines the point about inherent status. She may pose as nobility, but she is what she is—a composite of socially unacceptable characteristics. And, from his intellectual pinnacle, the artist can be quite superior to her. He can mold and shape her to his ends, making her "an ample heroine of romance" in literary terms as well as the artist's personal ones. That awful truth is amply proved in the closing line of section II. Miss Churm is, at the moment, an adequate Galatea to the artist's Pygmalion. And he is happy and companionable and comfortable with his creation. The reader knows, however, and suspects the artist is faintly disturbed by the undeniable fact that Galatea "ain't no lydy."

III

88 It was for the elucidation of a mystery in one of these works that I first tried Mrs. Monarch. Her husband came with her, to be useful if necessary—it was sufficiently clear that as a general thing he would prefer to come with her. At first I wondered if this were for "propriety's" sake—if he were going to be jealous and meddling. The idea was too tiresome, and if it had been confirmed it would speedily have brought our acquaintance to a close. But I soon saw there was nothing in it and that if he accompanied Mrs. Monarch it was—in addition to the chance of being wanted—simply because he had nothing else to do. When they were separate his occupation was gone and they never *had* been separate. I judged rightly that in their awkward situation their close union was their main comfort and that this union had no weak spot. It was a real marriage, an encouragement to the hesitating, a nut for pessimists to crack. Their address was humble—I remember afterwards thinking it had been the only thing about them that was really professional—and I could fancy the lamentable lodgings in which the Major would have been left alone. He could sit there more or less grimly with his wife—he couldn't sit there anyhow without her.

89 He had too much tact to try and make himself agreeable when he couldn't be useful; so when I was too absorbed in my work to talk he simply sat and waited. But I liked to hear him talk—it made my work, when not interrupting it, less mechanical, less special. To listen to him was to combine the excitement of going out with the economy of staying at home. There was only one hindrance—that I seemed

not to know any of the people this brilliant couple had known. I think he wondered extremely, during the term of our intercourse, whom the deuce I *did* know. He hadn't a stray sixpence of an idea to fumble for, so we didn't spin it very fine; we confined ourselves to questions of leather and even of liquor—saddlers and breeches-makers and how to get excellent claret cheap—and matters like "good trains" and the habits of small game. His lore on these last subjects was astonishing—he managed to interweave the station-master with the ornithologist. When he couldn't talk about greater things he could talk cheerfully about smaller, and since I couldn't accompany him into reminiscences of the fashionable world he could lower the conversation without a visible effort to my level.

90 So earnest a desire to please was touching in a man who could so easily have knocked one down. He looked after the fire and had an opinion on the draught of the stove without my asking him, and I could see that he thought many of my arrangements not half knowing. I remember telling him that if I were only rich I'd offer him a salary to come and teach me how to live. Sometimes he gave a random sigh of which the essence might have been: "Give me even such a bare old barrack as *this,* and I'd do something with it!" When I wanted to use him he came alone; which was an illustration of the superior courage of women. His wife could bear her solitary second floor, and she was in general more discreet; showing by various small reserves that she was alive to the propriety of keeping our relations markedly professional—not letting them slide into sociability. She wished it to remain clear that she and the Major were employed, not cultivated, and if she approved of me as a superior, who could be kept in his place, she never thought me quite good enough for an equal.

91 She sat with great intensity, giving the whole of her mind to it, and was capable of remaining for an hour almost as motionless as before a photographer's lens. I could see she had been photographed often, but somehow the very habit that made her good for that purpose unfitted her for mine. At first I was extremely pleased with her ladylike air, and it was a satisfaction, on coming to follow her lines, to see how good they were and how far they could lead the pencil. But after a little skirmishing I began to find her too insurmountably stiff; do what I would with it my drawing looked like a photograph or a copy of a photograph. Her figure had no variety of expression—she herself had no sense of variety. You may say that this was my business and was only a question of placing her. Yet I placed her in every conceivable position and she managed to obliterate their differences. She was always a lady certainly, and into the bargain was always the same lady. She was the real thing, but always the same thing. There were moments when I rather writhed under the serenity of her confidence that she *was* the real thing. All her dealings with me and all her husband's were an implication that this was lucky for *me.* Meanwhile I found myself trying to invent types that aproached her own, instead of making her own transform itself—in the clever way that was not impossible for instance to poor Miss Churm. Arrange as I would and take the precautions I

would, she always came out, in my pictures, too tall—landing me in the dilemma of having represented a fascinating woman as seven feet high, which (out of respect perhaps to my own very much scantier inches) was far from my idea of such a personage.

92 The case was worse with the Major—nothing I could do would keep *him* down, so that he became useful only for the representation of brawny giants. I adored variety and range, I cherished human accidents, the illustrative note; I wanted to characterise closely, and the thing in the world I most hated was the danger of being ridden by a type. I had quarreled with some of my friends about it; I had parted company with them for maintaining that one *had* to be, and that if the type was beautiful—witness Raphael and Leonardo—the servitude was only a gain. I was neither Leonardo nor Raphael—I might only be a presumptuous young modern searcher; but I held that everything was to be sacrificed sooner than character. When they claimed that the obsessional form could easily *be* character I retorted, perhaps superficially, "Whose?" It couldn't be everybody's—it might end in being nobody's.

The concern with status becomes more pronounced in section III. Paragraphs 88–89 reveal the Major's background while pointedly concealing the artist's; yet it is he who narrates the story. By the end of paragraph 89, the reader senses the artist's constant irritation with a man whom he "couldn't accompany into reminiscences of the fashionable world" but who could "lower the conversation without a visible effort to my level." Mrs. Monarch is even more unsettling, for "if she approved of me as a superior, who could be kept in his place, she never thought me quite good enough for an equal." A true Englishman would understand and accept the possibilities even if they were not actualities but erroneous suppositions growing out of a sensitive attitude. An expatriate American who had taken much of his native resentment to England could never accept them even though he might feel the same way toward Miss Churm—a reversed relationship he would find both fitting and proper.

Consequently, Mrs. Monarch becomes larger than life (paragraph 91) while the Major becomes a veritable giant (paragraph 92). Each possesses character, one that remains inviolable and constant. Paragraph 90 attaches itself to the foreshadowing of paragraph 67. If Miss Churm can be an ample heroine of romance, the artist is certainly the hero. In his procrustean determination, he is the expatriate of the 1920's, the beatnik of the 1950's, the protester of the 1960's. In avoiding "being ridden by a type," he *becomes* a type. He parts company with friends who maintain their point of view, never realizing he is escaping them before they can change him. Wherein lies his strength?

93 After I had drawn Mrs. Monarch a dozen times I felt surer even than before that the value of such a model as Miss Churm resided precisely in the fact that she had no positive stamp, combined of course with the other fact that what she did have was a curious and inexplicable talent for imitation. Her usual appearance was like a curtain which she could draw up at request for a capital performance. This performance was simply suggestive; but it was a word to the wise—it was vivid and pretty. Sometimes even I thought it, though she was plain herself, too insipidly pretty; I made it a reproach to her that the figures drawn from her were monotonously (*bêtement,* as we used to say) graceful. Nothing made her more angry; it was so much her pride to feel she could sit for characters that had nothing in common with each other. She would accuse me at such moments of taking away her "reputytion."

94 It suffered a certain shrinkage, this queer quantity, from the repeated visits of my new friends. Miss Churm was greatly in demand, never in want of employment, so I had no scruple in putting her off occasionally, to try them more at my ease. It was certainly amusing at first to do the real thing—it was amusing to do Major Monarch's trousers. They *were* the real thing, even if he did come out colossal. It was amusing to do his wife's back hair—it was so mathematically neat—and the particular "smart" tension of her tight stays. She lent herself especially to positions in which the face was somewhat averted or blurred; she abounded in ladylike back views and *profils perdus.* When she stood erect she took naturally one of the attitudes in which court-painters represent queens and princesses; so that I found myself wondering whether, to draw out this accomplishment, I couldn't get the editor of the *Cheapside* to publish a really royal romance, "A Tale of Buckingham Palace." Sometimes however the real thing and the make-believe came into contact; by which I mean that Miss Churm, keeping an appointment or coming to make one on days when I had much work in hand, encountered her invidious rivals. The encounter was not on their part, for they noticed her no more than if she had been the housemaid; not from intentional loftiness, but simply because as yet, professionally, they didn't know how to fraternise, as I could imagine they would have liked—or at least that the Major would. They couldn't talk about the omnibus—they always walked; and they didn't know what else to try—she wasn't interested in good trains or cheap claret. Besides, they must have felt—in the air—that she was amused at them, secretly derisive of their ever knowing how. She wasn't a person to conceal the limits of her faith if she had had a chance to show them. On the other hand Mrs. Monarch didn't think her tidy; for why else did she take pains to say to me—it was going out of the way, for Mrs. Monarch—that she didn't like dirty women?

95 One day when my young lady happened to be present with my other sitters—she even dropped in, when it was convenient, for a chat—I asked her to be so good as to lend a hand in getting tea, a service with which she was familiar and which was one of a class that, living as I did in a small way, with slender domestic resources, I often appealed to my models to render. They liked to lay hands on my property,

to break the sitting, and sometimes the china—it made them feel Bohemian. The next time I saw Miss Churm after this incident she surprised me greatly by making a scene about it—she accused me of having wished to humiliate her. She hadn't resented the outrage at the time, but had seemed obliging and amused, enjoying the comedy of asking Mrs. Monarch, who sat vague and silent, whether she would have cream and sugar, and putting an exaggerated simper into the question. She had tried intonations—as if she too wished to pass for the real thing—till I was afraid my other visitors would take offence.

96Oh they were determined not to do this, and their touching patience was the measure of their great need. They would sit by the hour, uncomplaining, till I was ready to use them; they would come back on the chance of being wanted and would walk away cheerfully if it failed. I used to go to the door with them to see in what magnificent order they retreated. I tried to find other employment for them—I introduced them to several artists. But they didn't "take," for reasons I could appreciate, and I became rather anxiously aware that after such disappointments they fell back upon me with a heavier weight. They did me the honour to think me most *their* form. They weren't romantic enough for the painters, and in those days there were few serious workers in black-and-white. Besides, they had an eye to the great job I had mentioned to them—they had secretly set their hearts on supplying the right essence for my pictorial vindication of our fine novelist. They knew that for this undertaking I should want no costume-effects, none of the frippery of past ages—that it was a case in which everything would be contemporary and satirical and presumably genteel. If I could work them into it their future would be assured, for the labour would of course be long and the occupation steady.

Is the artist's strength in the "talent for imitation" possessed by Miss Churm (paragraph 93)? In the appeal of the unrestrained (Miss Churm didn't "conceal the limits of her faith if she had had a chance to show them")? In the untidy? Certainly it is not in outright honesty, for he is amused by Miss Churm's retaliation against Mrs. Monarch's failure to notice her (paragraph 94). Nor is it in kindness or consideration as he suggests, for he reveals a basic unkindness by going to the door with the Monarchs "to see in what magnificent order they retreated" (paragraph 96).

97One day Mrs. Monarch came without her husband—she explained his absence by his having had to go to the City. While she sat there in her usual relaxed majesty there came at the door a knock which I immediately recognised as the subdued appeal of a model out of work. It was followed by the entrance of a young man whom I at once saw to be a foreigner and who proved in fact an Italian acquainted with no English word but my name, which he uttered in a way that made it seem to include all others. I hadn't then visited his country, nor was I proficient in his tongue;

but as he was not so meanly constituted—what Italian is?—as to depend only on that member for expression he conveyed to me, in familiar but graceful mimicry, that he was in search of exactly the employment in which the lady before me was engaged. I was not struck with him at first, and while I continued to draw I dropped few signs of interest or encouragement. He stood his ground however—not importunately, but with a dumb dog-like fidelity in his eyes that amounted to innocent impudence, the manner of a devoted servant—he might have been in the house for years—unjustly suspected. Suddenly it struck me that this very attitude and expression made a picture; whereupon I told him to sit down and wait till I should be free. There was another picture in the way he obeyed me, and I observed as I worked that there were others still in the way he looked wonderingly, with his head thrown back, about the high studio. He might have been crossing himself in Saint Peter's. Before I finished I said to myself "The fellow's a bankrupt orange-monger, but a treasure."

98 When Mrs. Monarch withdrew he passed across the room like a flash to open the door for her, standing there with the rapt pure gaze of the young Dante spell-bound by the young Beatrice. As I never insisted, in such situations, on the blankness of the British domestic, I reflected that he had the making of a servant—and I needed one, but couldn't pay him to be only that—as well as of a model; in short I resolved to adopt my bright adventurer if he would agree to officiate in the double capacity. He jumped at my offer, and in the event my rashness—for I had really known nothing about him—wasn't brought home to me. He proved a sympathetic though a desultory ministrant, and had in a wonderful degree the *sentiment de la pose*. It was uncultivated, instinctive, a part of the happy instinct that had guided him to my door and helped him to spell out my name on the card nailed to it. He had had no other introduction to me than a guess, from the shape of my high north window, seen outside, that my place was a studio and that as a studio it would contain an artist. He had wandered to England in search of fortune, like other itinerants, and had embarked, with a partner and a small green hand-cart, on the sale of penny ices. The ices had melted away and the partner had dissolved in their train. My young man wore tight yellow trousers with reddish stripes and his name was Oronte. He was sallow but fair, and when I put him into some old clothes of my own he looked like an Englishman. He was as good as Miss Churm, who could look, when requested, like an Italian.

His irritation grows; "her usual relaxed majesty" (paragraph 97) is scarcely an objective phrase. He is still the superior, but he is not yet the equal of the Monarchs. His need to be superior (as opposed to *the* superior) is pathetically revealed in this paragraph. The Italian is impressed, is obedient, is reverential. In short, he is a "treasure" because his reactions are the desired ones. He shares Miss Churm's ability to "look like," not "be."

By the end of section III, there has still been little action. On the surface, there is no real conflict except the unimportant minor clashes between Miss Churm and Mrs. Monarch. But beneath the surface, that steady, seething building of emotional steam continues. Frustrations and conflicts of a very true-to-life nature expand and grow. The pace was very slow in sections I and II where a single scene emerged. Panoramic treatment intensified the pace of section III. Section IV must, then, contain the climax and reveal any character change that might take place.

IV

99 I thought Mrs. Monarch's face slightly convulsed when, on her coming back with her husband, she found Oronte installed. It was strange to have to recognise in a scrap of a lazzarone a competitor to her magnificent Major. It was she who scented danger first, for the Major was anecdotically unconscious. But Oronte gave us tea, with a hundred eager confusions—he had never been concerned in so queer a process—and I think she thought better of me for having at last an "establishment." They saw a couple of drawings that I had made of the establishment, and Mrs. Monarch hinted that it never would have struck her he had sat for them. "Now the drawings you make from *us,* they look exactly like us," she reminded me, smiling in triumph; and I recognised that this was indeed just their defect. When I drew the Monarchs I couldn't anyhow get away from them—get into the character I wanted to represent; and I hadn't the least desire my model should be discoverable in my picture. Miss Churm never was, and Mrs. Monarch thought I hid her, very properly, because she was vulgar; whereas if she was lost it was only as the dead who got to heaven are lost—in the gain of an angel the more.

100 By this time I had got a certain start with "Rutland Ramsay," the first novel in the great projected series; that is I had produced a dozen drawings, several with the help of the Major and his wife, and I had sent them in for approval. My understanding with the publishers, as I have already hinted, had been that I was to be left to do my work, in this particular case, as I liked, with the whole book committed to me; but my connexion with the rest of the series was only contingent. There were moments when, frankly, it *was* a comfort to have the real thing under one's hand; for there were characters in "Rutland Ramsay" that were very much like it. There were people presumably as erect as the Major and women of as good a fashion as Mrs. Monarch. There was a great deal of country-house life—treated, it is true, in a fine fanciful ironical generalised way—and there was a considerable implication of knickerbockers and kilts. There were certain things I had to settle at the outset; such things for instance as the exact appearance of the hero and the particular bloom and figure of the heroine. The author of course gave me a lead, but there was a margin for interpretation. I took the Monarchs into my confidence, I told them frankly what I was about, I mentioned my embarrassments and alternatives. "Oh

take *him!*" Mrs. Monarch murmured sweetly, looking at her husband; and "What could you want better than my wife?" the Major enquired with the comfortable candour that now prevailed between us.

Paragraph 99 echoes paragraph 91 (compare "the gain of an angel the more" and "the servitude was only a gain"). The artist is unaware of the subtle shift, but the reader should not be. That gentle intrusion of the religious element is part of the basic character of the artist. He is not concerned with religion except when it serves his purpose; then, with unctuous ease, he employs it. His quiet hypocrisy has been revealed in many ways, but this is the most indirect. That a "comfortable candour" (paragraph 100) existed between the Monarchs and the artist indicates it further, for that same comfortable candor exists between him and Miss Churm (paragraphs 82–87), and he uses that intimate relationship to play his models against each other, enjoying whatever satisfactions that double-dealing affords him. Typically, he is either unaware of his conduct or prefers to avoid assessing it, but he does reveal it.

[101]I wasn't obliged to answer these remarks—I was only obliged to place my sitters. I wasn't easy in mind, and I postponed a little timidly perhaps the solving of my question. The book was a large canvas, the other figures were numerous, and I worked off at first some of the episodes in which the hero and the heroine were not concerned. When once I had set *them* up I should have to stick to them—I couldn't make my young man seven feet high in one place and five feet nine in another. I inclined on the whole to the latter measurement, though the Major more than once reminded me that *he* looked about as young as any one. It was indeed quite possible to arrange him, for the figure, so that it would have been difficult to detect his age. After the spontaneous Oronte had been with me a month, and after I had given him to understand several times over that his native exuberance would presently constitute an insurmountable barrier to our further intercourse, I waked to a sense of his heroic capacity. He was only five feet seven, but the remaining inches were latent. I tried him almost secretly at first, for I was really rather afraid of the judgement my other models would pass on such a choice. If they regarded Miss Churm as little better than a snare what would they think of the representation by a person so little the real thing as an Italian street-vendor of a protagonist formed by a public school?

Perhaps the explanation of the artist's conduct lies in the first sentence of paragraph 101: "I wasn't obliged to answer these remarks—I was only obliged to place my sitters." Obligations are subtle things. He had obligated himself to the Monarchs that first day when he decided he could use them. That they were not usable became immediately apparent, for he had seen them as types—his personal attitudes (paragraph 92) rather than their unsuitability thwarted him. He could neither change them conceptually for an illustration nor equal them for the satisfaction of his ego. In all, they represent those weaknesses in his character that are most difficult to analyze and accept with honesty.

His choice of Oronte as Rutland Ramsey reveals his closest approach to truth (paragraph 101), but he manages to evade that truth with the rationalization at the beginning of paragraph 102:

102 If I went a little in fear of them it wasn't because they bullied me, because they had got an oppressive foothold, but because in their really pathetic decorum and mysteriously permanent newness they counted on me so intensely. I was therefore very glad when Jack Hawley came home: he was always of such good counsel. He painted badly himself, but there was no one like him for putting his finger on the place. He had been absent from England for a year; he had been somewhere—I don't remember where—to get a fresh eye. I was in a good deal of dread of any such organ, but we were old friends; he had been away for months and a sense of emptiness was creeping into my life. I hadn't dodged a missile for a year.

It is a rationalization that is utterly hypocritical. And then the voice of conscience returns—a conscience that exists outside himself—Jack Hawley. Jack brings with him missiles, and the martyrdom of the artist approaches its climax.

103 He came back with a fresh eye, but with the same old black velvet blouse, and the first evening he spent in my studio we smoked cigarettes till the small hours. He had done no work himself, he had only got the eye; so the field was clear for the production of my little things. He wanted to see what I had produced for the *Cheapside,* but he was disappointed in the exhibition. That at least seemed the meaning of two or three comprehensive groans which, as he lounged on my big divan, his leg folded under him, looking at my latest drawings, issued from his lips with the smoke of the cigarette.

104 "What's the matter with you?" I asked.

105 "What's the matter with *you?*"

106 "Nothing save that I'm mystified."

107 "You are indeed. You're quite off the hinge. What's the meaning of this new fad?" And he tossed me, with visible irreverence, a drawing in which I happened to have depicted both my elegant models. I asked if he didn't think it good, and he replied that it struck him as execrable, given the sort of thing I had always represented myself to him as wishing to arrive at; but I let that pass—I was so anxious to see exactly what he meant. The two figures in the picture looked colossal, but I supposed this was *not* what he meant, inasmuch as, for aught he knew to the contrary, I

might have been trying for some such effect. I maintained that I was working exactly in the same way as when he last had done me the honour to tell me I might do something some day. "Well, there's a screw loose somewhere," he answered; "wait a bit and I'll discover it." I depended upon him to do so: where else was the fresh eye? But he produced at last nothing more luminous than "I don't know—I don't like your types." This was lame for a critic who had never consented to discuss with me anything but the question of execution, the direction of strokes and the mystery of values.

108"In the drawings you've been looking at I think my types are very handsome."

109"Oh they won't do!"

110"I've been working with new models."

111"I see you have. *They* won't do."

112"Are you very sure of that?"

113"Absolutely—they're stupid."

114"You mean *I* am—for I ought to get round that."

115"You *can't*—with such people. Who are they?"

116I told him, so far as was necessary, and he concluded heartlessly: "Ce sont des gens qu'il faut mettre à la porte."

117"You've never seen them; they're awfully good"—I flew to their defence.

118"Not seen them? Why all this recent work of yours drops to pieces with them. It's all I want to see of them."

119"No one else has said anything against it—the *Cheapside* people are pleased."

120"Every one else is an ass, and the *Cheapside* people the biggest asses of all. Come, don't pretend at this time of day to have pretty illusions about the public, especially about publishers and editors. It's not for *such* animals you work—it's for those you know, *coloro che sanno;* so keep straight for *me* if you can't keep straight for yourself. There was a certain sort of thing you used to try for—and a very good thing it was. But this twaddle isn't *in* it." When I talked with Hawley later about "Rutland Ramsay" and its possible successors he declared that I must get back into my boat again or I should go to the bottom. His voice in short was the voice of warning.

121I noted the warning, but I didn't turn my friends out of doors. They bored me a good deal; but the very fact that they bored me admonished me not to sacrifice them—if there was anything to be done with them—simply to irritation. As I look back at this phase they seem to me to have pervaded my life not a little. I have a vision of them as most of the time in my studio, seated against the wall on an old velvet bench to be out of the way, and resembling the while a pair of patient courtiers in a royal ante-chamber. I'm convinced that during the coldest weeks of the winter they held their ground because it saved them fire. Their newness was losing its gloss, and it was impossible not to feel them objects of charity. Whenever Miss Churm arrived they went away, and after I was fairly launched in "Rutland Ramsay" Miss Churm arrived pretty often. They managed to express to me tacitly that they supposed

I wanted her for the low life of the book, and I let them suppose it, since they had attempted to study the work—it was lying about the studio—without discovering that it dealt only with the highest circles. They had dipped into the most brilliant of our novelists without deciphering many passages. I still took an hour from them, now and again, in spite of Jack Hawley's warning: it would be time enough to dismiss them, if dismissal should be necessary, when the rigour of the season was over. Hawley had made their acquaintance—he had met them at my fireside—and thought them a ridiculous pair. Learning that he was a painter they tried to approach him, to show him too that they were the real thing; but he looked at them, across the big room, as if they were miles away: they were a compendium of everything he most objected to in the social system of his country. Such people as that, all convention and patent-leather, with ejaculations that stopped conversation, had no business in a studio. A studio was a place to learn to see, and how could you see through a pair of feather-beds?

The choice of Jack Hawley as a friend is consistent with the artist's previous choices. Jack "painted badly himself" (paragraph 102) and is, therefore, harmless enough. He serves as a critic, but he has always confined that criticism to "the question of execution, the direction of strokes and the mystery of values." Those are all safe topics that an outright dilettante could safely discuss in relation to illustrations for popular magazines. Now, with his "fresh eye," in his "black velvet blouse," and in his pompous satisfaction with his year's travel, he is quite prepared to deliver oracular judgments.

The artist almost pleads with Jack for truth, but Jack fails as miserably to provide it as he fails to paint well. When the artist suggests, "You mean I am [stupid]—for I ought to get round that," Jack supplies a rationalization that will satisfy him, allow him to continue on his downward path to success but deny him the harder, uphill road to accomplishment. He makes his decision at that moment, but he postpones putting it into action for the same reason he has done everything else: it is inconvenient to do so; it might prove painful.

The decay of social morality creates an awful stench, and the artist's behavior reeks to high heaven from paragraph 121 to the end of the story. He subjects the Monarchs to Hawley who "thought them a ridiculous pair" and gets close to the stateable theme of the story in his intensely ironic "A studio was a place to learn to see, and how could you see through a pair of feather-beds?" The reader is tempted to answer: "You can't when the blind lead the blind, but you should be grateful for feather-beds that protect you from the sharp edges of accident in your blind gropings." Such temptation indicates James' success at involving the reader in the story. Outrage is usually directed at characters the reader has identified with, and, in this case, we do so want the artist to *see* truth—not truth of the Monarchs, but truth of Self, for his Self is also the reader's Self.

122 The main inconvenience I suffered at their hands was that at first I was shy of letting it break upon them that my artful little servant had begun to sit to me for "Rutland Ramsay." They knew I had been odd enough—they were prepared by this time to allow oddity to artists—to pick a foreign vagabond out of the streets when I might have had a person with whiskers and credentials; but it was some time before they learned how high I rated his accomplishments. They found him in an attitude more than once, but they never doubted I was doing him as an organ-grinder. There were several things they never guessed, and one of them was that for a striking scene in the novel, in which a footman briefly figured, it occurred to me to make use of Major Monarch as the menial. I kept putting this off, I didn't like to ask him to don the livery—besides the difficulty of finding a livery to fit him. At last, one day late in the winter, when I was at work on the despised Oronte, who caught one's idea on the wing, and was in the glow of feeling myself go very straight, they came in, the Major and his wife, with their society laugh about nothing (there was less and less to laugh at); came in like country-callers—they always reminded me of that—who have walked across the park after church and are presently persuaded to stay to luncheon. Luncheon was over, but they could stay to tea—I knew they wanted it. The fit was on me, however, and I couldn't let my ardour cool and my work wait, with the fading daylight, while my model prepared it. So I asked Mrs. Monarch if she would mind laying it out—a request which for an instant brought all the blood to her face. Her eyes were on her husband's for a second, and some mute telegraphy passed between them. Their folly was over the next instant; his cheerful shrewdness put an end to it. So far from pitying their wounded pride, I must add, I was moved to give it as complete a lesson as I could. They bustled about together and got out the cups and saucers and made the kettle boil. I know they felt as if they were waiting on my servant, and when the tea was prepared I said: "He'll have a cup, please—he's tired." Mrs. Monarch brought him one where he stood, and he took it from her as if he had been a gentleman at a party squeezing a crush-hat with an elbow.

123 Then it came over me that she had made a great effort for me—made it with a kind of nobleness—and that I owed her a compensation. Each time I saw her after this I wondered what the compensation could be. I couldn't go on doing the wrong thing to oblige them. Oh it *was* the wrong thing, the stamp of the work for which they sat—Hawley was not the only person to say it now. I sent in a large number of the drawings I had made for "Rutland Ramsay," and I received a warning that was more to the point than Hawley's. The artistic adviser of the house for which I was working was of opinion that many of my illustrations were not what had been looked for. Most of these illustrations were the subjects in which the

Monarchs had figured. Without going into the question of what *had* been looked for, I had to face the fact that at this rate I shouldn't get the other books to do. I hurled myself in despair on Miss Churm—I put her through all her paces. I not only adopted Oronte publicly as my hero, but one morning when the Major looked in to see if I didn't require him to finish a *Cheapside* figure for which he had begun to sit the week before, I told him I had changed my mind—I'd do the drawing from my man. At this my visitor turned pale and stood looking at me. "Is *he* your idea of an English gentleman?" he asked.

124 I was disappointed, I was nervous, I wanted to get on with my work; so I replied with irritation: "Oh my dear Major—I can't be ruined for *you!*"

125 It was a horrid speech, but he stood another moment—after which, without a word, he quitted the studio. I drew a long breath, for I said to myself that I shouldn't see him again. I hadn't told him definitely that I was in danger of having my work rejected, but I was vexed at his not having felt the catastrophe in the air, read with me the moral of our fruitless collaboration, the lesson that in the deceptive atmosphere of art even the highest respectability may fail of being plastic.

But truth must be wanted. The artist rejects it utterly when he attempts to teach the Monarchs a lesson in pride (paragraph 122) and when he delivers his "horrid speech" (paragraph 124). He reveals his rejection in the selfish irony of paragraph 125 as he fails to understand his own motives.

126 I didn't owe my friends money, but I did see them again. They reappeared together three days later, and, given all the other facts, there was something tragic in that one. It was a clear proof they could find nothing else in life to do. They had threshed the matter out in a dismal conference—they had digested the bad news that they were not in for the series. If they weren't useful to me even for the *Cheapside* their function seemed difficult to determine, and I could only judge at first that they had come, forgivingly, decorously, to take a last leave. This made me rejoice in secret that I had little leisure for a scene; for I had placed both my other models in position together and I was pegging away at a drawing from which I hoped to derive glory. It had been suggested by the passage in which Rutland Ramsay, drawing up a chair to Artemisia's piano-stool, says extraordinary things to her while she ostensibly fingers out a difficult piece of music. I had done Miss Churm at the piano before—it was an attitude in which she knew how to take on an absolutely poetic grace. I wished the two figures to "compose" together with intensity, and my little Italian had entered perfectly into my conception. The pair were vividly before me, the piano had been pulled out; it was a charming show of blended youth and murmured love, which I had only to catch and keep. My visitors stood and looked at it, and I was friendly to them over my shoulder.

And now he is the young waiter of Hemingway's "A Clean, Well-Lighted Place" who said the old man had no reason to be in despair because he had money. The artist phrases it: "I didn't owe my friends money, but I did see them again" (paragraph 126). The cynicism of the monetary attitude, the devaluation of that golden word "friend"—these are the noxious vapors that asphyxiate the human soul.

127 They made no response, but I was used to silent company and went on with my work, only a little disconcerted—even though exhilarated by the sense that *this* was at least the ideal thing—at not having got rid of them after all. Presently I heard Mrs. Monarch's sweet voice beside or rather above me: "I wish her hair were a little better done." I looked up and she was staring with a strange fixedness at Miss Churm, whose back was turned to her. "Do you mind my just touching it?" she went on—a question which made me spring up for an instant as with the instinctive fear that she might do the young lady a harm. But she quieted me with a glance I shall never forget—I confess I should like to have been able to paint *that*—and went for a moment to my model. She spoke to her softly, laying a hand on her shoulder and bending over her; and as the girl, understanding, gratefully assented, she disposed her rough curls, with a few quick passes, in such a way as to make Miss Churm's head twice as charming. It was one of the most heroic personal services I've ever seen rendered. Then Mrs. Monarch turned away with a low sigh and, looking about her as if for something to do, stooped to the floor with a noble humility and picked up a dirty rag that had dropped out of my paint-box.

128 The Major meanwhile had also been looking for something to do, and, wandering to the other end of the studio, saw before him my breakfast-things neglected, unremoved. "I say, can't I be useful *here?*" he called out to me with an irrepressible quaver. I assented with a laugh that I fear was awkward, and for the next ten minutes, while I worked, I heard the light clatter of china and the tinkle of spoons and glass. Mrs. Monarch assisted her husband—they washed up my crockery, they put it away. They wandered off into my little scullery, and I afterwards found that they had cleaned my knives and that my slender stock of plate had an unprecedented surface. When it came over me, the latent eloquence of what they were doing, I confess that my drawing was blurred for a moment—the picture swam. They had accepted their failure, but they couldn't accept their fate. They had bowed their heads in bewilderment to the perverse and cruel law in virtue of which the real thing could be so much less precious than the unreal; but they didn't want to starve. If my servants were my models, then my models might be my servants. They would reverse the parts—the others would sit for the ladies and gentlemen and *they* would do the work. They would still be in the studio—it was an intense dumb appeal to me not to turn them out. "Take us on," they wanted to say—"we'll do *anything.*"

129 My pencil dropped from my hand; my sitting was spoiled and I got rid of my sitters, who were also evidently rather mystified and awestruck. Then, alone with

the Major and his wife I had a most uncomfortable moment. He put their prayer into a single sentence: "I say, you know—just let *us* do for you, can't you?" I couldn't—it was dreadful to see them emptying my slops; but I pretended I could, to oblige them, for about a week. Then I gave them a sum of money to go away, and I never saw them again. I obtained the remaining books, but my friend Hawley repeats that Major and Mrs. Monarch did me a permanent harm, got me into false ways. If it be true I'm content to have paid the price—for the memory. □

The artist reaches his moral nadir as he realizes he is "disconcerted at not having got rid of them after all, even though exhilarated by the sense that *this* was at least the ideal thing" (paragraph 127). James' parenthetical construction, you should notice, creates a sense of simultaneous reaction that is lost in the simple recasting of the sentence. This is the climax of the story. The character in whom change is revealed, the artist, is brilliantly illuminated now. He is a man of compromise—one who will choose between two possibilities by accepting the least desirable part of each.

Denouement conveys the moral comment beginning with the second sentence of paragraph 126. Had Hawthorne written this story (and he wrote one very like it), the moral comment would have been more explicit. But James wrote it (even though he owes a debt to Hawthorne) and the moral is implicit. Now that the Monarchs have been relegated to a satisfactorily compromised spot, they can be viewed realistically. Mrs. Monarch's "heroic personal service," their "doing for" the artist, present him with a realization about them: "They had accepted their failure, but they couldn't accept their fate." Perhaps that is what distinguishes "the real thing" from the spurious. The artist "obtained the remaining books" because he could not accept failure. In that victory, however, he accepted his fate. Portrait artist he desired to be; commercial book illustrator he became. Seemingly, it was fated to be so. But then, *he* wasn't "the real thing," was he? And how painful the near-realization was. He *saw* in that studio the glance, and it could not come from a feather-bed. His reaction: "I confess [note: *confess*] I should like to have been able to paint *that.*" But, of course, he never could, for *it* was the real thing too—not the unreal, not the romanticized look. Humility and arrogance are attitudes, and greatness is seldom—if ever—arrogant. The real thing—the lady, the gentleman—lack arrogance. Whenever they seemed guilty of it earlier in the story, he had ascribed it through interpretation of a look or general statement, not through an objective reporting of an overt action or statement.

But money, which he had earlier equated with a lady and gentleman, serves to buy him out of the uncomfortable situation. He gave them "a sum of money *to go away*"—subjecting them to their last, greatest indignity at his hands. It does not occur to him that *he* may have done *them* great harm.

Out of it all came something, however. The reader can only speculate what "false ways" the Monarchs had got the artist into, but the reader does not need to speculate on the irony of "my *friend* Hawley" (paragraph 129). A pathetic wistfulness attends the final line of the story.

A critic of Nathaniel Hawthorne, Henry James wrote a biography of that one American author to appear in the *English Men of Letters Series* (1879), and in one of his stories, "The Prophetic Pictures," Hawthorne presents a successful painter who

> . . . like all other men around whom an engrossing purpose wreathes itself, . . . was insulated from the mass of human kind. He had no aim—no pleasure—no sympathies—but what were ultimately connected with his art. Though gentle in manner and upright in intent and action, he did not possess kindly feelings; his heart was cold; no living creature could be brought near enough to keep him warm.

The moral of Hawthorne's story is that people disregard their prophetic fate and, as a result, deserve their destiny. His artist (who is, like James', never named but is, allegorically, a generic and professional representative) indulges in "reading other bosoms" but fails to see "the disorder of his own."

James knew the Hawthorne story, and its influence on "The Real Thing" is apparent. Critics of James often quote the author's statement in paragraph 128 as James' personal belief: "They had bowed their heads in bewilderment to the perverse and cruel law in virtue of which the real thing could be so much less precious than the unreal." *Precious* refers both to the esteemed and the economic—"precious freedom" and "precious gold." If this is James' comment, it is no less ambiguous than if it is merely the artist's. Which brings us back to aesthetic distance as an element of style. And only you, the individual reader, can decide whether James is too close to his material, too detached from it, or at the right distance. Your response indicates something about *your* style, however, for that is part of reading a story too.

One final word about style. Every author must decide what he wishes to achieve in a story. He must also be aware of the impact of the story upon the reader. If he strikes a balance between the two, he will probably write a story that is honest to the subject matter and fair to the reader. In such an accomplishment, he will have offered genuine emotion or *sentiment*. Unfortunately, authors do not always strike that balance. In attempting to elicit reader identification, they sometimes oversimplify, contrive emotionally charged scenes designed to reduce the reader to tears, or pepper their pages with such words as *passionate, heartbreaking, deep depression,* and so on. When this happens, the author is guilty of *sentimentality.* All three of the stories you have examined in this chapter are rich in the genuine emotion, sentiment. All three, in the hands of less adept stylists, could have descended to the most mawkish sort of sentimentality. That they did not is, perhaps, the best reason for being able to recognize style in an author's work, for all stories have *dramatic* elements (sentiment) that a lack of author restraint could reduce to the artificiality of *melodrama* (sentimentality) and the reader would drown in a hyperbolic pool of tears. Style allows the reader emotional release without emotional excess—which makes all good writing, if not poetry, at least poetic.

Suggested Activities. 1. Read "A Mother's Tale" (pp. 362–380) by James Agee and "Pig" (pp. 380–397) by Roald Dahl and compare the style of the two authors. Both stories are concerned with much the same subject and theme, but treatment and style distinguish each. In your comparison, if you prefer one, state and defend your preference.

2. Alfred Hayes' poem "The Slaughter-House" (p. 397) follows Dahl's "Pig." Comparing it with either "Pig" or Agee's "A Mother's Tale," explain why you agree or disagree with Shapiro and Beum's statement (p. 312) about aesthetic distance.

3. Compare "The Terrible Miss Dove" (pp. 398–406) by Frances Gray Patton with "Miss Brill" by Katherine Mansfield (pp. 138–144). Both are concerned with teachers and with loneliness. Decide if both are dramatic, melodramatic, or neither. If one is based on sentiment and one on sentimentality, decide why. How does the author's style create the distinction? Defend your decisions in a well-written paper.

A Mother's Tale

by James Agee

1 The calf ran up the hill as fast as he could and stopped sharp. "Mama!" he cried, all out of breath. "What *is* it! What are they *doing!* Where are they *going!"*

2 Other spring calves came galloping too.

3 They all were looking up at her and awaiting her explanation, but she looked out over their excited eyes. As she watched the mysterious and majestic thing they had never seen before, her own eyes became

even more than ordinarily still, and during the considerable moment before she answered, she scarcely heard their urgent questioning.

4 Far out along the autumn plain, beneath the sloping light, an immense drove of cattle moved eastward. They were at a walk, not very fast, but faster than they could imaginably enjoy. Those in front were compelled by those behind; those at the rear, with few exceptions, did their best to keep up; those who were locked within the herd could no more help moving than the particles inside a falling rock. Men on horses rode ahead, and alongside, and behind, or spurred their horses intensely back and forth, keeping the pace steady, and the herd in shape; and from man to man a dog sped back and forth incessantly as a shuttle, barking, incessantly, in a hysterical voice. Now and then one of the men shouted fiercely, and this like the shrieking of the dog was tinily audible above a low and awesome sound which seemed to come not from the multitude of hooves but from the center of the world, and above the sporadic bawlings and bellowings of the herd.

5 From the hillside this tumult was so distant that it only made more delicate the prodigious silence in which the earth and sky were held; and, from the hill, the sight was as modest as its sound. The herd was virtually hidden in the dust it raised, and could be known, in general, only by the horns which pricked this flat sunlit dust like little briars. In one place a twist of the air revealed the trembling fabric of many backs; but it was only along the near edge of the mass that individual animals were discernible, small in a driven frieze, walking fast, stumbling and recovering, tossing their armed heads, or opening their skulls heavenward in one of those cries which reached the hillside long after the jaws were shut.

6 From where she watched, the mother could not be sure whether there were any she recognized. She knew that among them there must be a son of hers; she had not seen him since some previous spring, and she would not be seeing him again. Then the cries of the young ones impinged on her bemusement: "Where are they going?"

7 She looked into their ignorant eyes.

8 "Away," she said.

9 "Where?" they cried. "Where? Where?" her own son cried again.

10 She wondered what to say.

11 "On a long journey."

12 "But where *to?*" they shouted. "Yes, where *to?*" her son exclaimed, and she could see that he was losing his patience with her, as he always did when he felt she was evasive.

13 "I'm not sure," she said.

14 Their silence was so cold that she was unable to avoid their eyes for long.

15 "Well, not *really* sure. Because, you see," she said in her most reasonable tone, "I've never seen it with my own eyes, and that's the only way to *be* sure; *isn't* it?"

16 They just kept looking at her. She could see no way out.

17 "But I've *heard* about it," she said with shallow cheerfulness, "from those who *have* seen it, and I don't suppose there's any good reason to doubt them."

18 She looked away over them again, and for all their interest in what she was about to tell them, her eyes so changed that they turned and looked, too.

19 The herd, which had been moving broadside to them, was being turned away, so slowly that like the turning of stars it could not quite be seen from one moment to the next; yet soon it was moving directly away from them, and even during the little while she spoke and they all watched after it, it steadily and very noticeably diminished, and the sounds of it as well.

20 "It happens always about this time of year," she said quietly while they watched. "Nearly all the men and horses leave, and go into the North and the West."

21 "Out on the range," her son said, and by his voice she knew what enchantment the idea already held for him.

22 "Yes," she said, "out on the range." And trying, impossibly, to imagine the range, they were touched by the breath of grandeur.

23 "And then before long," she continued, "everyone has been found, and brought into one place; and then . . . what you see, happens. All of them.

24 "Sometimes when the wind is right," she said more quietly, "you can hear them coming long before you can see them. It isn't even like a sound, at first. It's more as if something were moving far under the ground. It makes you uneasy. You wonder, why, what in the world can *that* be! Then you remember what it is and then you can really hear it. And then finally, there they all are."

25 She could see this did not interest them at all.

26 "But where are they *going?*" one asked, a little impatiently.

27 "I'm coming to that," she said; and she let them wait. Then she spoke slowly but casually.

28 "They are on their way to a railroad."

29 There, she thought; that's for that look you all gave me when I said I wasn't sure. She waited for them to ask; they waited for her to explain.

30 "A railroad," she told them, "is great hard bars of metal lying side by side, or so they tell me, and they go on and on over the ground as far as the eye can see. And great wagons run on the metal bars on wheels, like wagon wheels but smaller, and these wheels are made of solid metal too. The wagons are much bigger than any wagon you've ever seen, as big as, big as sheds, they say, and they are pulled along on the iron bars by a terrible huge dark machine, with a loud scream."

31 "Big as *sheds?*" one of the calves said skeptically.

32 "Big *enough,* anyway," the mother said. "I told you I've never seen it myself. But those wagons are so big that several of us can get inside at once. And that's exactly what happens."

33 Suddenly she became very quiet, for she felt that somehow, she could not imagine just how, she had said altogether too much.

34 "Well, *what* happens," the son wanted to know. "What do you mean, *happens.*"

35 She always tried hard to be a reasonably modern mother. It was probably better, she felt, to go on, than to leave them all full of imaginings and mystification. Besides, there was really nothing at all awful about what happened . . . if only one could know *why.*

36 "Well," she said, "it's nothing much, really. They just—why, when they all finally *get* there, why there are all the great cars waiting in a long line, and the big dark machine is up ahead . . . smoke comes out of it, they say . . . and . . . well, then, they just put us into the wagons, just as many as will fit in each wagon, and when everybody is in, why . . ." She hesitated, for again, though she couldn't be sure why, she was uneasy.

37 "Why then," her son said, "the train takes them away."

38 Hearing that word, she felt a flinching of the heart. Where had he picked it up, she wondered, and she gave him a shy and curious glance. Oh dear, she thought. I should never have even *begun* to explain. "Yes," she said, "when everybody is safely in, they slide the doors shut."

39 They were all silent for a little while. Then one of them asked thoughtfully, "Are they taking them somewhere they don't want to go?"

40 "Oh, I don't think so," the mother said. "I imagine it's very nice."

41 "*I* want to go," she heard her son say with ardor. "I want to go right now," he cried. "Can I, Mama? *Can* I? *Please?*" And looking into his eyes, she was overwhelmed by sadness.

42 "Silly thing," she said, "there'll be time enough for that when you're grown up. But what I very much hope," she went on, "is that instead of being chosen to go out on the range and to make the long journey, you will grow up to be very strong and bright so they will decide that you may stay here at home with Mother. And you, too,"

she added, speaking to the other little males; but she could not honestly wish this for any but her own, least of all for the eldest, strongest and most proud, for she knew how few are chosen.

43 She could see that what she said was not received with enthusiasm.

44 "But I want to go," her son said.

45 "Why?" she asked. "I don't think any of you realize that it's a great *honor* to be chosen to stay. A great privilege. Why, it's just the most ordinary ones are taken out onto the range. But only the very pick are chosen to stay here at home. If you want to go out on the range," she said in hurried and happy inspiration, "all you have to do is be ordinary and careless and silly. If you want to have even a chance to be chosen to stay, you have to try to be stronger and bigger and braver and brighter than anyone else, and that takes *hard work. Every day.* Do you see?" And she looked happily and hopefully from one to another. "Besides," she added, aware that they were not won over, "I'm told it's a very rough life out there, and the men are unkind.

46 "Don't you see," she said again; and she pretended to speak to all of them, but it was only to her son.

47 But he only looked at her. "Why do you want me to stay home?" he asked flatly; in their silence she knew the others were asking the same question.

48 "Because it's safe here," she said before she knew better; and realized she had put it in the most unfortunate way possible. "Not safe, not just that," she fumbled. "I mean . . . because here we *know* what happens, and what's going to happen, and there's never any doubt about it, never any reason to wonder, to worry. Don't you see? It's just *Home,"* and she put a smile on the word, "where we all know each other and are happy and well."

49 They were so merely quiet, looking back at her, that she felt they were neither won over nor alienated. Then she knew of her son that he, anyhow, was most certainly not persuaded, for he asked the question she most dreaded: "Where do they go on the train?" And hearing him, she knew that she would stop at nothing to bring that curiosity and eagerness, and that tendency toward skepticism, within safe bounds.

50 "Nobody knows," she said, and she added, in just the tone she knew would most sharply engage them, "Not for sure, anyway."

51 "What do you mean, *not for sure,"* her son cried. And the oldest, biggest calf repeated the question, his voice cracking.

52 The mother deliberately kept silent as she gazed out over the plain, and while she was silent they all heard the last they would ever hear of all those who were going away: one last great cry, as faint almost as a breath; the infinitesimal jabbing vituperation of the dog; the solemn muttering of the earth.

53 "Well," she said, after even this sound was entirely lost, "there was one who came back." Their instant, trustful eyes were too much for her. She added, "Or so they say."

54 They gathered a little more closely around her, for now she spoke very quietly.

55 "It was my great-grandmother who told me," she said. "She was told it by *her* great-grandmother, who claimed she saw it with her own eyes, though of course I can't vouch for that. Because of course I wasn't even dreamed of then; and Great-grandmother was so very, very old, you see, that you couldn't always be sure she knew quite *what* she was saying."

56 Now that she began to remember it more clearly, she was sorry she had committed herself to telling it.

57 "Yes," she said, "the story is, there was one, *just* one, who ever came back, and he told what happened on the train, and where the train went and what happened after. He told it all in a rush, they say, the last things first and every which way, but as it was finally sorted out and gotten into order by those who heard it and those they told it to, this is more or less what happened:

58 "He said that after the men had gotten just as many of us as they could into the car he was in, so that their sides pressed tightly together and nobody could lie down, they slid the door shut with a startling rattle and a bang, and then there was a sudden jerk, so strong they might have fallen except that they were packed so closely together, and the car began to move. But after it had moved only a little way, it stopped as suddenly as it had started, so that they all nearly fell down again. You see, they were just moving up the next car that was joined on behind, to put more of us into it. He could see it all between the boards of the car, because the boards were built a little apart from each other, to let in air."

59 *Car,* her son said again to himself. Now he would never forget the word.

60 "He said that then, for the first time in his life, he became very badly frightened, he didn't know why. But he was sure, at that moment, that there was something dreadfully to be afraid of. The others felt this same great fear. They called out loudly to those who were being put into the car behind, and the others called back, but it was no use; those who were getting aboard were between narrow white fences and then were walking up a narrow slope and the men kept jabbing them as they do when they are in an unkind humor, and there was no way to go but on into the car. There was no way to get out of the car, either: he tried, with all his might, and he was the one nearest the door.

61 "After the next car behind was full, and the door was shut, the

train jerked forward again, and stopped again, and they put more of us into still another car, and so on, and on, until all the starting and stopping no longer frightened anybody; it was just something uncomfortable that was never going to stop, and they began instead to realize how hungry and thirsty they were. But there was no food and no water, so they just had to put up with this; and about the time they became resigned to going without their suppers (for now it was almost dark), they heard a sudden and terrible scream which frightened them even more deeply than anything had frightened them before, and the train began to move again, and they braced their legs once more for the jolt when it would stop, but this time, instead of stopping, it began to go fast, and then even faster, so fast that the ground nearby slid past like a flooded creek and the whole country, he claimed, began to move too, turning slowly around a far mountain as if it were all one great wheel. And then there was a strange kind of disturbance inside the car, he said, or even inside his very bones. He felt as if everything in him was *falling,* as if he had been filled full of a heavy liquid that all wanted to flow one way, and all the others were leaning as he was leaning, away from this queer heaviness that was trying to pull them over, and then just as suddenly this leaning heaviness was gone and they nearly fell again before they could stop leaning against it. He could never understand what this was, but it too happened so many times that they all got used to it, just as they got used to seeing the country turn like a slow wheel, and just as they got used to the long cruel screams of the engine, and the steady iron noise beneath them which made the cold darkness so fearsome, and the hunger and the thirst and the continual standing up, and the moving on and on and on as if they would never stop."

62 "*Didn't* they ever stop?" one asked.

63 "Once in a great while," she replied. "Each time they did," she said, "he thought, Oh, now *at last! At last* we can get out and stretch our tired legs and lie down! *At last* we'll be given food and water! But they never let them out. And they never gave them food or water. They never even cleaned up under them. They had to stand in their manure and in the water they made."

64 "Why did the train stop?" her son asked; and with somber gratification she saw that he was taking all this very much to heart.

65 "He could never understand why," she said. "Sometimes men would walk up and down alongside the cars, and the more nervous and the more trustful of us would call out; but they were only looking around, they never seemed to do anything. Sometimes he could see many houses and bigger buildings together where people lived. Some-

times it was far out in the country and after they had stood still for a long time they would hear a little noise which quickly became louder, and then became suddenly a noise so loud it stopped their breathing, and during this noise something black would go by, very close, and so fast it couldn't be seen. And then it was gone as suddenly as it had appeared, and the noise became small, and then in the silence their train would start up again.

66 "Once, he tells us, something very strange happened. They were standing still, and cars of a very different kind began to move slowly past. Those cars were not red, but black with many glass windows like those in a house; and he says they were as full of human beings as the car he was in was full of our kind. And one of these people looked into his eyes and smiled, as if he liked him, or as if he knew only too well how hard the journey was.

67 "So by his account it happens to them, too," she said, with a certain pleased vindictiveness. "Only they were sitting down at their ease, not standing. And the one who smiled was eating."

68 She was still, trying to think of something; she couldn't quite grasp the thought.

69 "But didn't they *ever* let them out?" her son asked.

70 The oldest calf jeered. "Of *course* they did. He came back, didn't he? How would he ever come back if he didn't get out?"

71 "They didn't let them out," she said, "for a long, long time."

72 "How long?"

73 "So long, and he was so tired, he could never quite be sure. But he said that it turned from night to day and from day to night and back again several times over, with the train moving nearly all of this time, and that when it finally stopped, early one morning, they were all so tired and so discouraged that they hardly even noticed any longer, let alone felt any hope that anything would change for them, ever again; and then all of a sudden men came up and put up a wide walk and unbarred the door and slid it open, and it was the most wonderful and happy moment of his life when he saw the door open, and walked into the open air with all his joints trembling, and drank the water and ate the delicious food they had ready for him; it was worth the whole terrible journey."

74 Now that these scenes came clear before her, there was a faraway shining in her eyes, and her voice, too, had something in it of the far-away.

75 "When they had eaten and drunk all they could hold they lifted up their heads and looked around, and everything they saw made them happy. Even the trains made them cheerful now, for now they were no

longer afraid of them. And though these trains were forever breaking to pieces and joining again with other broken pieces, with shufflings and clashings and rude cries, they hardly paid them attention any more, they were so pleased to be in their new home, and so surprised and delighted to find they were among thousands upon thousands of strangers of their own kind, all lifting their voices in peacefulness and thanksgiving, and they were so wonder-struck by all they could see, it was so beautiful and so grand.

76 "For he has told us that now they lived among fences as white as bone, so many, and so spiderishly complicated, and shining so pure, that there's no use trying even to hint at the beauty and the splendor of it to anyone who knows only the pitiful little outfittings of a ranch. Beyond these mazy fences, through the dark and bright smoke which continually turned along the sunlight, dark buildings stood shoulder to shoulder in a wall as huge and proud as mountains. All through the air, all the time, there was an iron humming like the humming of the iron bar after it has been struck to tell the men it is time to eat, and in all the air, all the time, there was that same strange kind of iron strength which makes the silence before lightning so different from all other silence.

77 "Once for a little while the wind shifted and blew over them straight from the great buildings, and it brought a strange and very powerful smell which confused and disturbed them. He could never quite describe this smell, but he has told us it was unlike anything he had ever known before. It smelled like old fire, he said, and old blood and fear and darkness and sorrow and most terrible and brutal force and something else, something in it that made him want to run away. This sudden uneasiness and this wish to run away swept through every one of them, he tells us, so that they were all moved at once as restlessly as so many leaves in a wind, and there was great worry in their voices. But soon the leaders among them concluded that it was simply the way men must smell when there are a great many of them living together. Those dark buildings must be crowded very full of men, they decided, probably as many thousands of them, indoors, as there were of us, outdoors; so it was no wonder their smell was so strong and, to our kind, so unpleasant. Besides, it was so clear now in every other way that men were not as we had always supposed, but were doing everything they knew how to make us comfortable and happy, that we ought to just put up with their smell, which after all they couldn't help, any more than we could help our own. Very likely men didn't like the way we smelled, any more than we liked theirs. They passed along these ideas to the others, and soon everyone felt more calm, and then the wind changed

again, and the fierce smell no longer came to them, and the smell of our own kind was back again, very strong of course, in such a crowd, but ever so homey and comforting, and everyone felt easy again.

78 "They were fed and watered so generously, and treated so well, and the majesty and the loveliness of this place where they had all come to rest was so far beyond anything they had ever known or dreamed of, that many of the simple and ignorant, whose memories were short, began to wonder whether that whole difficult journey, or even their whole lives up to now, had ever really been. Hadn't it all been just shadows, they murmured, just a bad dream?

79 "Even the sharp ones, who knew very well it had all really happened, began to figure that everything up to now had been made so full of pain only so that all they had come to now might seem all the sweeter and the more glorious. Some of the oldest and deepest were even of a mind that all the puzzle and tribulation of the journey had been sent us as a kind of harsh trying or proving of our worthiness; and that it was entirely fitting and proper that we could earn our way through to such rewards as these, only through suffering, and through being patient under pain which was beyond our understanding; and that now at the last, to those who had borne all things well, all things were made known: for the mystery of suffering stood revealed in joy. And now as they looked back over all that was past, all their sorrows and bewilderment seemed so little and so fleeting that, from the simplest among them even to the most wise, they could feel only the kind of amused pity we feel toward the very young when, with the first thing that hurts them or they are forbidden, they are sure there is nothing kind or fair in all creation, and carry on accordingly, raving and grieving as if their hearts would break."

80 She glanced among them with an indulgent smile, hoping the little lesson would sink home. They seemed interested but somewhat dazed. I'm talking way over their heads, she realized. But by now she herself was too deeply absorbed in her story to modify it much. *Let* it be, she thought, a little impatient; it's over *my* head, for that matter.

81 "They had hardly before this even wondered that they were alive," she went on, "and now all of a sudden they felt they understood *why* they were. This made them very happy, but they were still only beginning to enjoy this new wisdom when quite a new and different kind of restiveness ran among them. Before they quite knew it they were all moving once again, and now they realized that they were being moved, once more, by men, toward still some other place and purpose they could not know. But during these last hours they had been so well that now they felt no uneasiness, but all moved forward calm and sure

toward better things still to come; he has told us that he no longer felt as if he were being driven, even as it became clear that they were going toward the shade of those great buildings; but guided.

82 "He was guided between fences which stood ever more and more narrowly near each other, among companions who were pressed ever more and more closely against each other; and now as he felt their warmth against him it was not uncomfortable, and his pleasure in it was not through any need to be close among others through anxiousness, but was a new kind of strong and gentle delight, at being so very close, so deeply of his own kind, that it seemed as if the very breath and heartbeat of each one were being exchanged through all that multitude, and each was another, and others were each, and each was a multitude, and the multitude was one. And quieted and made mild within this melting, they now entered the cold shadow cast by the buildings, and now with every step the smell of the buildings grew stronger, and in the darkening air the glittering of the fences was ever more queer.

83 "And now as they were pressed ever more intimately together he could see ahead of him a narrow gate, and he was strongly pressed upon from either side and from behind, and went in eagerly, and now he was between two fences so narrowly set that he brushed either fence with either flank, and walked alone, seeing just one other ahead of him, and knowing of just one other behind him, and for a moment the strange thought came to him, that the one ahead was his father, and that the one behind was the son he had never begotten.

84 "And now the light was so changed that he knew he must have come inside one of the gloomy and enormous buildings, and the smell was so much stronger that it seemed almost to burn his nostrils, and the smell and the somber new light blended together and became some other thing again, beyond his describing to us except to say that the whole air beat with it like one immense heart and it was as if the beating of this heart were pure violence infinitely manifolded upon violence: so that the uneasy feeling stirred in him again that it would be wise to turn around and run out of this place just as fast and as far as ever he could go. This he heard, as if he were telling it to himself at the top of his voice, but it came from somewhere so deep and so dark inside him that he could only hear the shouting of it as less than a whisper, as just a hot and chilling breath, and he scarcely heeded it, there was so much else to attend to.

85 "For as he walked along in this sudden and complete loneliness, he tells us, this wonderful knowledge of being one with all his race meant less and less to him, and in its place came something still more wonderful: he knew what it was to be himself alone, a creature separate

and different from any other, who had never been before, and would never be again. He could feel this in his whole weight as he walked, and in each foot as he put it down and gave his weight to it and moved above it, and in every muscle as he moved, and it was a pride which lifted him up and made him feel large, and a pleasure which pierced him through. And as he began with such wondering delight to be aware of his own exact singleness in this world, he also began to understand (or so he thought) just why these fences were set so very narrow, and just why he was walking all by himself. It stole over him, he tells us, like the feeling of a slow cool wind, that he was being guided toward some still more wonderful reward or revealing, up ahead, which he could not of course imagine, but he was sure it was being held in store for him alone.

86 "Just then the one ahead of him fell down with a great sigh, and was so quickly taken out of the way that he did not even have to shift the order of his hooves as he walked on. The sudden fall and the sound of that sigh dismayed him, though, and something within him told him that it would be wise to look up: and there he saw Him.

87 "A little bridge ran crosswise above the fences. He stood on this bridge with His feet as wide apart as He could set them. He wore spattered trousers but from the belt up He was naked and as wet as rain. Both arms were raised high above His head and in both hands He held an enormous Hammer. With a grunt which was hardly like the voice of a human being, and with all His strength, He brought this Hammer down into the forehead of our friend: who, in a blinding blazing, heard from his own mouth the beginning of a gasping sigh; then there was only darkness."

88 Oh, this is *enough!* it's *enough!* she cried out within herself, seeing their terrible young eyes. How *could* she have been so foolish as to tell so much!

89 "What happened then?" she heard, in the voice of the oldest calf, and she was horrified. This shining in their eyes: was it only excitement? no pity? no fear?

90 "What happened?" two others asked.

91 Very well, she said to herself. I've gone so far; now I'll go the rest of the way. She decided not to soften it, either. She'd teach them a lesson they wouldn't forget in a hurry.

92 "Very well," she was surprised to hear herself say aloud.

93 "How long he lay in this darkness he couldn't know, but when he began to come out of it, all he knew was the most unspeakably dreadful pain. He was upside down and very slowly swinging and turning, for he was hanging by the tendons of his heels from great frightful

hooks, and he has told us that the feeling was as if his hide were being torn from him inch by inch, in one piece. And then as he became more clearly aware he found that this was exactly what was happening. Knives would sliver and slice along both flanks, between the hide and the living flesh; then there was a moment of most precious relief; then red hands seized his hide and there was a jerking of the hide and a tearing of tissue which it was almost as terrible to hear as to feel, turning his whole body and the poor head at the bottom of it; and then the knives again.

94 "It was so far beyond anything he had ever known unnatural and amazing that he hung there through several more such slicings and jerkings and tearings before he was fully able to take it all in: then, with a scream, and a supreme straining of all his strength, he tore himself from the hooks and collapsed sprawling to the floor and, scrambling right to his feet, charged the men with the knives. For just a moment they were so astonished and so terrified they could not move. Then they moved faster than he had ever known men could—and so did all the other men who chanced to be in his way. He ran down a glowing floor of blood and down endless corridors which were hung with the bleeding carcasses of our kind and with bleeding fragments of carcasses, among blood-clothed men who carried bleeding weapons, and out of that vast room into the open, and over and through one fence after another, shoving aside many an astounded stranger and shouting out warnings as he ran, and away up the railroad toward the West.

95 "How he ever managed to get away, and how he ever found his way home, we can only try to guess. It's told that he scarcely knew, himself, by the time he came to this part of his story. He was impatient with those who interrupted him to ask about that, he had so much more important things to tell them, and by then he was so exhausted and so far gone that he could say nothing very clear about the little he did know. But we can realize that he must have had really tremendous strength, otherwise he couldn't have outlived the Hammer; and that strength such as his—which we simply don't see these days, it's of the olden time—is capable of things our own strongest and bravest would sicken to dream of. But there was something even stronger than his strength. There was his righteous fury, which nothing could stand up against, which brought him out of that fearful place. And there was his high and burning and heroic purpose, to keep him safe along the way, and to guide him home, and to keep the breath of life in him until he could warn us. He did manage to tell us that he just followed the railroad, but how he chose one among the many which branched out from that place, he couldn't say. He told us, too, that from time

to time he recognized shapes of mountains and other landmarks, from his journey by train, all reappearing backward and with a changed look and hard to see, too (for he was shrewd enough to travel mostly at night), but still recognizable. But that isn't enough to account for it. For he has told us, too, that he simply *knew* the way; that he didn't hesitate one moment in choosing the right line of railroad, or even think of it as choosing; and that the landmarks didn't really guide him, but just made him the more sure of what he was already sure of; and that whenever he *did* encounter human beings—and during the later stages of his journey, when he began to doubt he would live to tell us, he traveled day and night—they never so much as moved to make him trouble, but stopped dead in their tracks, and their jaws fell open.

96 "And surely we can't wonder that their jaws fell open. I'm sure yours would, if you had seen him as he arrived, and I'm very glad I wasn't there to see it, either, even though it is said to be the greatest and most momentous day of all the days that ever were or shall be. For we have the testimony of eyewitnesses, how he looked, and it is only too vivid, even to hear of. He came up out of the East as much staggering as galloping (for by now he was so worn out by pain and exertion and loss of blood that he could hardly stay upright), and his heels were so piteously torn by the hooks that his hooves doubled under more often than not, and in his broken forehead the mark of the Hammer was like the socket for a third eye.

97 "He came to the meadow where the great trees made shade over the water. 'Bring them all together!' he cried out, as soon as he could find breath. 'All!' Then he drank; and then he began to speak to those who were already there: for as soon as he saw himself in the water it was as clear to him as it was to those who watched him that there was no time left to send for the others. His hide was all gone from his head and his neck and his forelegs and his chest and most of one side and a part of the other side. It was flung backward from his naked muscles by the wind of his running and now it lay around him in the dust like a ragged garment. They say there is no imagining how terrible and in some way how grand the eyeball is when the skin has been taken entirely from around it: his eyes, which were bare in this way, also burned with pain, and with the final energies of his life, and with his desperate concern to warn us while he could; and he rolled his eyes wildly while he talked, or looked piercingly from one to another of the listeners, interrupting himself to cry out, '*Believe* me! Oh, *believe* me!' For it had evidently never occurred to him that he might not be believed, and must make this last great effort, in addition to all he had gone through for us, to *make* himself believed; so that he groaned with sorrow and

with rage and railed at them without tact or mercy for their slowness to believe. He had scarcely what you could call a voice left, but with this relic of a voice he shouted and bellowed and bullied us and insulted us, in the agony of his concern. While he talked he bled from the mouth, and the mingled blood and saliva hung from his chin like the beard of a goat.

98 "Some say that with his naked face, and his savage eyes, and that beard and the hide lying off his bare shoulders like shabby clothing, he looked almost human. But others feel this is an irreverence even to think; and others, that it is a poor compliment to pay the one who told us, at such cost to himself, the true ultimate purpose of Man. Some did not believe he had ever come from our ranch in the first place, and of course he was so different from us in appearance and even in his voice, and so changed from what he might ever have looked or sounded like before, that nobody could recognize him for sure, though some were sure they did. Others suspected that he had been sent among us with his story for some mischievous and cruel purpose, and the fact that they could not imagine what this purpose might be, made them, naturally, all the more suspicious. Some believed he was actually a man, trying—and none too successfully, they said—to disguise himself as one of us; and again the fact that they could not imagine why a man would do this, made them all the more uneasy. There were quite a few who doubted that anyone who could get into such bad condition as he was in, was fit even to give reliable information, let alone advice, to those in good health. And some whispered, even while he spoke, that he had turned lunatic; and many came to believe this. It wasn't only that his story was so fantastic; there was good reason to wonder, many felt, whether anybody in his right mind would go to such trouble for others. But even those who did not believe him listened intently, out of curiosity to hear so wild a tale, and out of the respect it is only proper to show any creature who is in the last agony.

99 "What he told, was what I have just told you. But his purpose was away beyond just the telling. When they asked questions, no matter how curious or suspicious or idle or foolish, he learned, toward the last, to answer them with all the patience he could and in all the detail he could remember. He even invited them to examine his wounded heels and the pulsing wound in his head as closely as they pleased. He even begged them to, for he knew that before everything else, he must be believed. For unless we could believe him, wherever could we find any reason, or enough courage, to do the hard and dreadful things he told us we must do!

100 "It was only these things, he cared about. Only for these, he came back."

101 Now clearly remembering what these things were, she felt her whole being quail. She looked at the young ones quickly and as quickly looked away.

102 "While he talked," she went on, "and our ancestors listened, men came quietly among us; one of them shot him. Whether he was shot in kindness or to silence him is an endlessly disputed question which will probably never be settled. Whether, even, he died of the shot, or through his own great pain and weariness (for his eyes, they say, were glazing for some time before the men came), we will never be sure. Some suppose even that he may have died of his sorrow and his concern for us. Others feel that he had quite enough to die of, without that. All these things are tangled and lost in the disputes of those who love to theorize and to argue. There is no arguing about his dying words, though; they were very clearly remembered:

103 " *'Tell them! Believe!'* "

104 After a while her son asked, "What did he tell them to do?"

105 She avoided his eyes. "There's a great deal of disagreement about that, too," she said after a moment. "You see, he was so very tired."

106 They were silent.

107 "So tired," she said, "some think that toward the end, he really *must* have been out of his mind."

108 "Why?" asked her son.

109 "Because he was so tired out and so badly hurt."

110 They looked at her mistrustfully.

111 "And because of what he told us to do."

112 "What did he tell us to do?" her son asked again.

113 Her throat felt dry. "Just . . . things you can hardly bear even to think of. That's all."

114 They waited. "Well, *what?*" her son asked in a cold, accusing voice.

115 " *'Each one is himself,'* " she said shyly. " *'Not of the herd. Himself alone.'* That's one."

116 "What else?"

117 " *'Obey nobody. Depend on none.'* "

118 "What else?"

119 She found that she was moved. " *'Break down the fences!'* " she said less shyly. " *'Tell everybody, everywhere.'* "

120 "Where?"

121 "Everywhere. You see, he thought there must be ever so many more of us than we had ever known."

122 They were silent. "What else?" her son asked.

123 "'*For if even a few do not hear me, or disbelieve me, we are all betrayed.*'"

124 "Betrayed?"

125 "He meant, doing as men want us to. Not for ourselves, or the good of each other."

126 They were puzzled.

127 "Because, you see, he felt there was no other way." Again her voice altered: "'*All who are put on the range are put onto trains. All who are put onto trains meet the Man With The Hammer. All who stay home are kept here to breed others to go onto the range, and so betray themselves and their kind and their children forever.*

128 "'*We are brought into this life only to be victims; and there is no other way for us unless we save ourselves.*'

129 "Do you understand?"

130 Still they were puzzled, she saw; and no wonder, poor things. But now the ancient lines rang in her memory, terrible and brave. They made her somehow proud. She began actually to want to say them.

131 "'*Never be taken,*'" she said. "'*Never be driven. Let those who can, kill Man. Let those who cannot, avoid him.*'"

132 She looked around at them.

133 "What else?" her son asked, and in his voice there was a rising valor.

134 She looked straight into his eyes. "'*Kill the yearlings,*'" she said very gently. "'*Kill the calves.*'"

135 She saw the valor leave his eyes.

136 "Kill us?"

137 She nodded. "'*So long as Man holds dominion over us,*'" she said. And in dread and amazement she heard herself add, "'*Bear no young.*'"

138 With this they all looked at her at once in such a way that she loved her child, and all these others, as never before; and there dilated within her such a sorrowful and marveling grandeur that for a moment she was nothing except her own inward whisper, "Why *I* am one alone. And of the herd, too. Both at once. All one."

139 Her son's voice brought her back: "Did they do what he told them to?"

140 The oldest one scoffed, "Would we be here, if they had?"

141 "They say some did," the mother replied. "Some tried. Not all."

142 "What did the men do to them?" another asked.

143 "I don't know," she said. "It was such a very long time ago."

144 "Do you believe it?" asked the oldest calf.

145 "There are some who believe it," she said.

146 "Do *you?*"

147 "I'm told that far back in the wildest corners of the range there are some of us, mostly very, very old ones, who have never been taken. It's said that they meet, every so often, to talk and just to think together about the heroism and the terror of two sublime Beings. The One Who Came Back, and The Man With The Hammer. Even here at home, some of the old ones, and some of us who are just old-fashioned, believe it, or parts of it anyway. I know there are some who say that a hollow at the center of the forehead—a sort of shadow of the Hammer's blow—is a sign of very special ability. And I remember how Great-grandmother used to sing an old, pious song, let's see now, yes, 'Be not like dumb-driven cattle, be a hero in the strife.' But there aren't many. Not any more."

148 "Do *you* believe it?" the oldest calf insisted; and now she was touched to realize that every one of them, from the oldest to the youngest, needed very badly to be sure about that.

149 "Of course not, silly," she said; and all at once she was overcome by a most curious shyness, for it occurred to her that in the course of time, this young thing might be bred to her. "It's just an old, old legend." With a tender little laugh she added, lightly, "We use it to frighten children with."

150 By now the light was long on the plain and the herd was only a fume of gold near the horizon. Behind it, dung steamed, and dust sank gently to the shattered ground. She looked far away for a moment, wondering. Something—it was like a forgotten word on the tip of the tongue. She felt the sudden chill of the late afternoon and she wondered what she had been wondering about. "Come, children," she said briskly, "it's high time for supper." And she turned away; they followed.

151 The trouble was, her son was thinking, you could never trust her. If she said a thing was so, she was probably just trying to get her way with you. If she said a thing wasn't so, it probably was so. But you never could be sure. Not without seeing for yourself. I'm going to go, he told himself; I don't care *what* she wants. And if it isn't so, why then I'll live on the range and make the great journey and find out what *is* so. And if what she told was true, why then I'll know ahead of time and the one *I* will charge is The Man With The Hammer. I'll put Him and His Hammer out of the way forever, and that will make me an even better hero than The One Who Came Back.

152 So when his mother glanced at him in concern, not quite daring to ask her question, he gave her his most docile smile, and snuggled his head against her, and she was comforted.

153 The littlest and youngest of them was doing double skips in his effort to keep up with her. Now that he wouldn't be interrupting her, and none of the big ones would hear and make fun of him, he shyly whispered his question, so warmly moistly ticklish that she felt as if he were licking her ear.

154 "What is it, darling?" she asked, bending down.

155 "What's a train?" □

Pig

by Roald Dahl

1 Once upon a time, in the City of New York, a beautiful baby boy was born into this world, and the joyful parents named him Lexington.

2 No sooner had the mother returned home from the hospital carrying Lexington in her arms than she said to her husband, "Darling, now you must take me out to a most marvellous restaurant for dinner so that we can celebrate the arrival of our son and heir."

3 Her husband embraced her tenderly and told her that any woman who could produce such a beautiful child as Lexington deserved to go absolutely any place she wanted. But was she strong enough yet, he enquired, to start running around the city late at night?

4 "No," she said, she wasn't. But what the hell.

5 So that evening they both dressed themselves up in fancy clothes, and leaving little Lexington in care of a trained infant's nurse who was costing them twenty dollars a day and was Scottish into the bargain, they went out to the finest and most expensive restaurant in town. There they each ate a giant lobster and drank a bottle of champagne between them, and after that, they went on to a nightclub, where they drank another bottle of champagne and then sat holding hands for several hours while they recalled and discussed and admired each individual physical feature of their lovely newborn son.

6 They arrived back at their house on the East Side of Manhattan at around two o'clock in the morning and the husband paid off the taxi-driver and then began feeling in his pockets for the key to the front door. After a while, he announced that he must have left it in the pocket of his other suit, and he suggested they ring the bell and get the nurse to come down and let them in. An infant's nurse at twenty dollars a day must expect to be hauled out of bed occasionally in the night, the husband said.

7 So he rang the bell. They waited. Nothing happened. He rang it again, long and loud. They waited another minute. Then they both

stepped back onto the street and shouted the nurse's name (McPottle) up at the nursery windows on the third floor, but there was still no response. The house was dark and silent. The wife began to grow apprehensive. Her baby was imprisoned in this place, she told herself. Alone with McPottle. And who was McPottle? They had known her for two days, that was all, and she had a thin mouth, a small disapproving eye, and a starchy bosom, and quite clearly she was in the habit of sleeping much too soundly for safety. If she couldn't hear the front-door bell, then how on earth did she expect to hear a baby crying? Why, this very second the poor thing might be swallowing its tongue or suffocating on its pillow.

8 "He doesn't use a pillow," the husband said. "You are not to worry. But I'll get you in if that's what you want." He was feeling rather superb after all the champagne, and now he bent down and undid the laces of one of his black patent-leather shoes, and took it off. Then, holding it by the toe, he flung it hard and straight right through the dining-room window on the ground floor.

9 "There you are," he said grinning. "We'll deduct it from McPottle's wages."

10 He stepped forward and very carefully put a hand through the hole in the glass and released the catch. Then he raised the window.

11 "I shall lift you in first, little mother," he said, and he took his wife around the waist and lifted her off the ground. This brought her big red mouth up level with his own, and very close, so he started kissing her. He knew from experience that women like very much to be kissed in this position, with their bodies held tight, and their legs dangling in the air, so he went on doing it for quite a long time, and she wiggled her feet, and made loud gulping noises down in her throat. Finally, the husband turned her round and began easing her gently through the open window into the dining-room. At this point, a police patrol car came nosing silently along the street toward them. It stopped about thirty yards away, and three cops of Irish extraction leaped out of the car and started running in the direction of the husband and wife, brandishing revolvers.

12 "Stick 'em up!" the cops shouted. "Stick 'em up!" But it was impossible for the husband to obey this order without letting go of his wife, and had he done this she would either have fallen to the ground or would have been left dangling half in and half out of the house, which is a terribly uncomfortable position for a woman; so he continued gallantly to push her upward and inward through the window. The cops, all of whom had received medals before for killing robbers, opened fire immediately, and although they were still running, and although the wife in particular was presenting them with a very small target

indeed, they succeeded in scoring several direct hits on each body—sufficient anyway to prove fatal in both cases.

13 Thus, when he was no more than twelve days old, little Lexington became an orphan.

2

14 The news of this killing, for which the three policemen subsequently received citations, was eagerly conveyed to all relatives of the deceased couple by newspaper reporters, and the next morning, the closest of these relatives, as well as a couple of undertakers, three lawyers, and a priest, climbed into taxis and set out for the house with the broken window. They assembled in the living-room, men and women both, and they sat around in a circle on the sofas and armchairs, smoking cigarettes and sipping sherry and debating what on earth should be done now with the baby upstairs, the orphan Lexington.

15 It soon became apparent that none of the relatives was particularly keen to assume responsibility for the child, and the discussions and arguments continued all through the day. Everybody declared an enormous, almost an irresistible desire to look after him, and would have done so with the greatest of pleasure were it not for the fact that their apartment was too small, or that they already had one baby and couldn't possibly afford another, or that they wouldn't know what to do with the poor little thing when they went abroad in the summer, or that they were getting on in years, which surely would be most unfair to the boy when he grew up, and so on and so forth. They all knew, of course, that the father had been heavily in debt for a long time and that the house was mortgaged and that consequently there would be no money at all to go with the child.

16 They were still arguing like mad at six in the evening when suddenly, in the middle of it all, an old aunt of the deceased father (her name was Glosspan) swept in from Virginia, and without even removing her hat and coat, not even pausing to sit down, ignoring all offers of a martini, a whisky, a sherry, she announced firmly to the assembled relatives that she herself intended to take sole charge of the infant boy from then on. What was more, she said, she would assume full financial responsibility on all counts, including education, and everyone else could go on back home where they belonged and give their consciences a rest. So saying, she trotted upstairs to the nursery and snatched Lexington from his cradle and swept out of the house with the baby clutched tightly in her arms, while the relatives simply sat and stared and smiled and looked relieved, and McPottle the nurse stood stiff with disapproval at the head of the stairs, her lips compressed, her arms folded across her starchy bosom.

17 And thus it was that the infant Lexington, when he was thirteen days old, left the City of New York and travelled southward to live with his Great Aunt Glosspan in the State of Virginia.

3

18 Aunt Glosspan was nearly seventy when she became guardian to Lexington, but to look at her you would never have guessed it for one minute. She was as sprightly as a woman half her age, with a small, wrinkled, but still quite beautiful face and two lovely brown eyes that sparkled at you in the nicest way. She was also a spinster, though you would never have guessed that either, for there was nothing spinsterish about Aunt Glosspan. She was never bitter or gloomy or irritable; she didn't have a moustache; and she wasn't in the least bit jealous of other people, which in itself is something you can seldom say about either a spinster or a virgin lady, although of course it is not known for certain whether Aunt Glosspan qualified on both counts.

19 But she was an eccentric old woman, there was no doubt about that. For the past thirty years she had lived a strange isolated life all by herself in a tiny cottage high up on the slopes of the Blue Ridge Mountains, several miles from the nearest village. She had five acres of pasture, a plot for growing vegetables, a flower garden, three cows, a dozen hens, and a fine cockerel.

20 And now she had little Lexington as well.

21 She was a strict vegetarian and regarded the consumption of animal flesh as not only unhealthy and disgusting, but horribly cruel. She lived upon lovely clean foods like milk, butter, eggs, cheese, vegetables, nuts, herbs, and fruit, and she rejoiced in the conviction that no living creature would be slaughtered on her account, not even a shrimp. Once, when a brown hen of hers passed away in the prime of life from being eggbound, Aunt Glosspan was so distressed that she nearly gave up egg-eating altogether.

22 She knew not the first thing about babies, but that didn't worry her in the least. At the railway station in New York, while waiting for the train that would take her and Lexington back to Virgina, she bought six feeding-bottles, two dozen diapers, a box of safety pins, a carton of milk for the journey, and a small paper-covered book called *The Care of Infants.* What more could anyone want? And when the train got going, she fed the baby some milk, changed its nappies after a fashion, and laid it down on the seat to sleep. Then she read *The Care of Infants* from cover to cover.

23 "There is no problem here," she said, throwing the book out the window. "No problem at all."

24 And curiously enough there wasn't. Back home in the cottage

everything went just as smoothly as could be. Little Lexington drank his milk and belched and yelled and slept exactly as a good baby should, and Aunt Glosspan glowed with joy whenever she looked at him, and showered him with kisses all day long.

4

25 By the time he was six years old, young Lexington had grown into a most beautiful boy with long golden hair and deep blue eyes the colour of cornflowers. He was bright and cheerful, and already he was learning to help his old aunt in all sorts of different ways around the property, collecting the eggs from the chicken house, turning the handle of the butter churn, digging up potatoes in the vegetable garden, and searching for wild herbs on the side of the mountain. Soon, Aunt Glosspan told herself, she would have to start thinking about his education.

26 But she couldn't bear the thought of sending him away to school. She loved him so much now that it would kill her to be parted from him for any length of time. There was, of course, that village school down in the valley, but it was a dreadful-looking place, and if she sent him there she knew they would start forcing him to eat meat the very first day he arrived.

27 "You know what, my darling?" she said to him one day when he was sitting on a stool in the kitchen watching her make cheese. "I don't really see why I shouldn't give you your lessons myself."

28 The boy looked up at her with his large blue eyes, and gave her a lovely trusting smile. "That would be nice," he said.

29 "And the very first thing I should do would be to teach you how to cook."

30 "I think I would like that, Aunt Glosspan."

31 "Whether you like it or not, you're going to have to learn some time," she said. "Vegetarians like us don't have nearly so many foods to choose from as ordinary people, and therefore they must learn to be doubly expert with what they have."

32 "Aunt Glosspan," the boy said, "what *do* ordinary people eat that we don't?"

33 "Animals," she answered, tossing her head in disgust.

34 "You mean *live* animals?"

35 "No," she said. "Dead ones."

36 The boy considered this for a moment.

37 "You mean when they die they *eat* them instead of *burying* them?"

38 "They don't wait for them to die, my pet. They kill them."

39 "How do they kill them, Aunt Glosspan?"

40 "They usually slit their throats with a knife."

41 "But what *kind* of animals?"

42 "Cows and pigs mostly, and sheep."

43 "Cows!" the boy cried. "You mean like Daisy and Snowdrop and Lily?"

44 "Exactly, my dear."

45 "But *how* do they eat them, Aunt Glosspan?"

46 "They cut them up into bits and they cook the bits. They like it best when it's all red and bloody and sticking to the bones. They love to eat lumps of cow's flesh with the blood oozing out of it."

47 "Pigs too?"

48 "They adore pigs."

49 "Lumps of bloody pig's meat," the boy said. "Imagine that. What else do they eat, Aunt Glosspan?"

50 "Chickens."

51 "Chickens!"

52 "Millions of them."

53 "Feathers and all?"

54 "No, dear, not the feathers. Now run along outside and get Aunt Glosspan a bunch of chives, will you, my darling?"

55 Shortly after that, the lessons began. They covered five subjects, reading, writing, geography, arithmetic, and cooking, but the latter was by far the most popular with both teacher and pupil. In fact, it very soon became apparent that young Lexington possessed a truly remarkable talent in this direction. He was a born cook. He was dextrous and quick. He could handle his pans like a juggler. He could slice a single potato into twenty paper-thin slivers in less time than it took his aunt to peel it. His palate was exquisitely sensitive, and he could taste a pot of strong onion soup and immediately detect the presence of a single tiny leaf of sage. In so young a boy, all this was a bit bewildering to Aunt Glosspan, and to tell the truth she didn't quite know what to make of it. But she was proud as proud could be, all the same, and predicted a brilliant future for the child.

56 "What a mercy it is," she said, "that I have such a wonderful little fellow to look after me in my dotage." And a couple of years later, she retired from the kitchen for good, leaving Lexington in sole charge of all household cooking. The boy was now ten years old, and Aunt Glosspan was nearly eighty.

5

57 With the kitchen to himself, Lexington straight away began experimenting with dishes of his own invention. The old favourites no

longer interested him. He had a violent urge to create. There were hundreds of fresh ideas in his head. "I will begin," he said, "by devising a chestnut soufflé." He made it and served it up for supper that very night. It was terrific. "You are a genius!" Aunt Glosspan cried, leaping up from her chair and kissing him on both cheeks. "You will make history!"

58 From then on, hardly a day went by without some new delectable creation being set up on the table. There was Brazil-nut soup, hominy cutlets, vegetable ragout, dandelion omelette, cream-cheese fritters, stuffed-cabbage surprise, stewed foggage, shallots *à la bonne femme,* beet-root mousse piquant, prunes Stroganoff, Dutch rarebit, turnips on horseback, flaming spruce-needle tarts, and many many other beautiful compositions. Never before in her life, Aunt Glosspan declared, had she tasted such food as this; and in the mornings, long before lunch was due she would go out onto the porch and sit there in her rocking-chair, speculating about the coming meal, licking her chops, sniffing the aromas that came wafting out through the kitchen window.

59 "What's that you're making in there today, boy?" she would call out.

60 "Try to guess, Aunt Glosspan."

61 "Smells like a bit of salsify fritters to me," she would say, sniffing vigorously.

62 Then out he would come, this ten-year-old child, a little grin of triumph on his face, and in his hands a big steaming pot of the most heavenly stew made entirely of parsnips and lovage.

63 "You know what you ought to do," his aunt said to him, gobbling the stew. "You ought to set yourself down this very minute with paper and pencil and write a cooking-book."

64 He looked across the table, chewing his parsnips slowly.

65 "Why not?" she cried. "I've taught you how to write and I've taught you how to cook and now all you've got to do is put the two things together. You write a cooking-book, my darling, and it'll make you famous the whole world over."

66 "All right," he said. "I will."

67 And that very day, Lexington began writing the first page of that monumental work which was to occupy him for the rest of his life. He called it *Eat Good and Healthy.*

6

68 Seven years later, by the time he was seventeen, he had recorded over nine thousand different recipes, all of them original, all of them delicious.

69 But now, suddenly, his labors were interrupted by the tragic death of Aunt Glosspan. She was afflicted in the night by a violent seizure, and Lexington, who had rushed into her bedroom to see what all the noise was about, found her lying on her bed yelling and cussing and twisting herself up into all manner of complicated knots. Indeed, she was a terrible sight to behold, and the agitated youth danced around her in his pyjamas, wringing his hands, and wondering what on earth he should do. Finally, in an effort to cool her down, he fetched a bucket of water from the pond in the cow field and tipped it over her head, but this only intensified the paroxysms, and the old lady expired within the hour.

70 "This is really too bad," the poor boy said, pinching her several times to make sure that she was dead. "And how sudden! How quick and sudden! Why only a few hours ago she seemed in the very best of spirits. She even took three large helpings of my most recent creation, devilled mushroomburgers, and told me how succulent it was."

71 After weeping bitterly for several minutes, for he had loved his aunt very much, he pulled himself together and carried her outside and buried her behind the cowshed.

72 The next day, while tidying up her belongings, he came across an envelope that was addressed to him in Aunt Glosspan's handwriting. He opened it and drew out two fifty-dollar bills and a letter. *Darling boy,* the letter said. *I know that you have never yet been down the mountain since you were thirteen days old, but as soon as I die you must put on a pair of shoes and a clean shirt and walk down to the village and find the doctor. Ask the doctor to give you a death certificate to prove that I am dead. Then take this certificate to my lawyer, a man called Mr. Samuel Zuckermann, who lives in New York City and who has a copy of my will. Mr. Zuckermann will arrange everything. The cash in this envelope is to pay the doctor for the certificate and to cover the cost of your journey to New York. Mr. Zuckermann will give you more money when you get there, and it is my earnest wish that you use it to further your researches into culinary and vegetarian matters, and that you continue to work upon the great book of yours until you are satisfied that it is complete in every way. Your loving aunt—Glosspan.*

73 Lexington, who had always done everything his aunt told him, pocketed the money, put on a pair of shoes and a clean shirt, and went down the mountain to the village where the doctor lived.

74 "Old Glosspan?" the doctor said. "My God, is *she* dead?"

75 "Certainly she's dead," the youth answered. "If you will come back home with me now I'll dig her up and you can see for yourself."

76 "How deep did you bury her?" the doctor asked.

77 "Six or seven feet down, I should think."

78 "And how long ago?"

79 "Oh, about eight hours."

80 "Then she's dead," the doctor announced. "Here's the certificate."

7

81 Our hero now set out for the City of New York to find Mr. Samuel Zuckermann. He travelled on foot, and he slept under hedges, and he lived on berries and wild herbs, and it took him sixteen days to reach the metropolis.

82 "What a fabulous place this is!" he cried as he stood at the corner of Fifty-seventh Street and Fifth Avenue, staring around him. "There are no cows or chickens anywhere, and none of the women looks in the least like Aunt Glosspan."

83 As for Mr. Samuel Zuckermann, he looked like nothing that Lexington had ever seen before.

84 He was a small spongy man with livid jowls and a huge magenta nose, and when he smiled, bits of gold flashed at you marvellously from lots of different places inside his mouth. In his luxurious office, he shook Lexington warmly by the hand and congratulated him upon his aunt's death.

85 "I suppose you knew that your dearly beloved guardian was a woman of considerable wealth?" he said.

86 "You mean the cows and the chickens?"

87 "I mean half a million bucks," Mr. Zuckermann said.

88 "How much?"

89 "Half a million dollars, my boy. And she's left it all to you." Mr. Zuckermann leaned back in his chair and clasped his hands over his spongy paunch. At the same time, he began secretly working his right forefinger in through his waistcoat and under his shirt so as to scratch the skin around the circumference of his navel—a favourite exercise of his, and one that gave him a peculiar pleasure. "Of course, I shall have to deduct fifty per cent for my services," he said, "but that still leaves you with two hundred and fifty grand."

90 "I am rich!" Lexington cried. "This is wonderful! How soon can I have the money?"

91 "Well," Mr. Zuckermann said, "luckily for you, I happen to be on rather cordial terms with the tax authorities around here, and I am confident that I shall be able to persuade them to waive all death duties and back taxes."

92 "How kind you are," murmured Lexington.

93 "I should naturally have to give somebody a small honorarium."

94 "Whatever you say, Mr. Zuckermann."

95 "I think a hundred thousand would be sufficient."

96 "Good gracious, isn't that rather excessive?"

97 "Never undertip a tax-inspector or a policeman," Mr. Zuckermann said. "Remember that."

98 "But how much does it leave for me?" the youth asked meekly.

99 "One hundred and fifty thousand. But then you've got the funeral expenses to pay out of that."

100 "*Funeral* expenses?"

101 "You've got to pay the funeral parlour. Surely you know that?"

102 "But I buried her myself, Mr. Zuckermann, behind the cowshed."

103 "I don't doubt it," the lawyer said. "So what?"

104 "I never used a funeral parlour."

105 "Listen," Mr. Zuckermann said patiently. "You may not know it, but there is a law in this state which says that no beneficiary under a will may receive a single penny of his inheritance until the funeral parlour has been paid in full."

106 "You mean that's a *law?"*

107 "Certainly it's a law, and a very good one it is, too. The funeral parlour is one of our great national institutions. It must be protected at all cost."

108 Mr. Zuckermann himself, together with a group of public-spirited doctors, controlled a corporation that owned a chain of nine lavish funeral parlours in the city, not to mention a casket factory in Brooklyn and a postgraduate school for embalmers in Washington Heights. The celebration of death was therefore a deeply religious affair in Mr. Zuckermann's eyes. In fact, the whole business affected him profoundly, almost as profoundly, one might say, as the birth of Christ affected the shopkeeper.

109 "You had no right to go out and bury your aunt like that," he said. "None at all."

110 "I'm very sorry, Mr. Zuckermann."

111 "Why, it's downright subversive."

112 "I'll do whatever you say, Mr. Zuckermann. All I want to know is how much I'm going to get in the end, when everything's paid."

113 There was a pause. Mr. Zuckermann sighed and frowned and continued secretly to run the tip of his finger around the rim of his navel.

114 "Shall we say fifteen thousand?" he suggested, flashing a big gold smile. "That's a nice round figure."

115 "Can I take it with me this afternoon?"

116 "I don't see why not."

117 So Mr. Zuckermann summoned his chief cashier and told him to

give Lexington fifteen thousand dollars out of the petty cash, and to obtain a receipt. The youth, who by this time was delighted to be getting anything at all, accepted the money gratefully and stowed it away in his knapsack. Then he shook Mr. Zuckermann warmly by the hand, thanked him for all his help, and went out of the office.

118 "The whole world is before me!" our hero cried as he emerged into the street. "I now have fifteen thousand dollars to see me through until my book is published. And after that, of course, I shall have a great deal more." He stood on the pavement, wondering which way to go. He turned left and began strolling slowly down the street, staring at the sights of the city.

119 "What a revolting smell," he said, sniffing the air. "I can't stand this." His delicate olfactory nerves, tuned to receive only the most delicious kitchen aromas, were being tortured by the stench of the diesel-oil fumes pouring out of the backs of the buses.

120 "I must get out of this place before my nose is ruined altogether," he said. "But first, I've simply got to have something to eat. I'm starving." The poor boy had had nothing but berries and wild herbs for the past two weeks, and now his stomach was yearning for solid food. I'd like a nice hominy cutlet, he told himself. Or maybe a few juicy salsify fritters.

121 He crossed the street and entered a small restaurant. The place was hot inside, and dark and silent. There was a strong smell of cooking-fat and cabbage water. The only other customer was a man with a brown hat on his head, crouching intently over his food, who did not look up as Lexington came in.

122 Our hero seated himself at a corner table and hung his knapsack on the back of his chair. This, he told himself, is going to be most interesting. In all my seventeen years I have tasted only the cooking of two people, Aunt Glosspan and myself—unless one counts Nurse McPottle, who must have heated my bottle a few times when I was an infant. But I am now about to sample the art of a new chef altogether, and perhaps, if I am lucky, I may pick up a couple of useful ideas for my book.

123 A waiter approached out of the shadows at the back, and stood beside the table.

124 "How do you do," Lexington said. "I should like a large hominy cutlet please. Do it twenty-five seconds each side, in a very hot skillet with sour cream, and sprinkle a pinch of lovage on it before serving—unless of course your chef knows of a more original method, in which case I should be delighted to try it."

125 The waiter laid his head over to one side and looked carefully

at his customer. "You want the roast pork and cabbage?" he asked. "That's all we got left."

126 "Roast what and cabbage?"

127 The waiter took a soiled handkerchief from his trouser pocket and shook it open with a violent flourish, as though he were cracking a whip. Then he blew his nose loud and wet.

128 "You want it or don't you?" he said, wiping his nostrils.

129 "I haven't the foggiest idea what it is," Lexington replied, "but I should love to try it. You see, I am writing a cooking-book and . . ."

130 "One pork and cabbage!" the waiter shouted, and somewhere in the back of the restaurant, far away in the darkness, a voice answered him.

131 The waiter disappeared. Lexington reached into his knapsack for his personal knife and fork. These were a present from Aunt Glosspan, given him when he was six years old, made of solid silver, and he had never eaten with any other instruments since. While waiting for the food to arrive, he polished them lovingly with a piece of soft muslin.

132 Soon the waiter returned carrying a plate on which there lay a thick greyish-white slab of something hot. Lexington leaned forward anxiously to smell it as it was put down before him. His nostrils were wide open now to receive the scent, quivering and sniffing.

133 "But this is absolute heaven!" he exclaimed. "What an aroma! It's tremendous!"

134 The waiter stepped back a pace, watching his customer carefully.

135 "Never in my life have I smelled anything as rich and wonderful as this!" our hero cried, seizing his knife and fork. "What on earth is it made of?"

136 The man in the brown hat looked around and stared, then returned to his eating. The waiter was backing away toward the kitchen.

137 Lexington cut off a small piece of the meat, impaled it on his silver fork, and carried it up to his nose so as to smell it again. Then he popped it into his mouth and began to chew it slowly, his eyes half closed, his body tense.

138 "This is fantastic!" he cried. "It is a brand-new flavour! Oh, Glosspan, my beloved Aunt, how I wish you were with me now so you could taste this remarkable dish! Waiter! Come here at once! I want you!"

139 The astonished waiter was now watching from the other end of the room, and he seemed reluctant to move any closer.

140 "If you will come and talk to me I will give you a present," Lexington said, waving a hundred-dollar bill. "Please come over here and talk to me."

141 The waiter sidled cautiously back to the table, snatched away the money, and held it up close to his face, peering at it from all angles. Then he slipped it quickly into his pocket.

142 "What can I do for you, my friend?" he asked.

143 "Look," Lexington said. "If you will tell me what this delicious dish is made of, and exactly how it is prepared, I will give you another hundred."

144 "I already told you," the man said. "It's pork."

145 "And what exactly is pork?"

146 "You never had roast pork before?" the waiter asked, staring.

147 "For heaven's sake, man, tell me what it is and stop keeping me in suspense like this."

148 "It's pig," the waiter said. "You just bung it in the oven."

149 *"Pig!"*

150 "All pork is pig. Didn't you know that?"

151 "You mean *this* is *pig's meat?"*

152 "I guarantee it."

153 "But . . . but . . . that's impossible," the youth stammered. "Aunt Glosspan, who knew more about food than anyone else in the world, said that meat of any kind was disgusting, revolting, horrible, foul, nauseating, and beastly. And yet this piece that I have here on my plate is without a doubt the most delicious thing that I have ever tasted. Now how on earth do you explain that? Aunt Glosspan certainly wouldn't have told me it was revolting if it wasn't."

154 "Maybe your aunt didn't know how to cook it," the waiter said.

155 "Is that possible?"

156 "You're damn right it is. Especially with pork. Pork has to be very well done or you can't eat it."

157 "Eureka!" Lexington cried. "I'll bet that's exactly what happened! She did it wrong!" He handed the man another hundred-dollar bill. "Lead me to the kitchen," he said. "Introduce me to the genius who prepared this meat."

158 Lexington was at once taken into the kitchen, and there he met the cook who was an elderly man with a rash on one side of his neck.

159 "This will cost you another hundred," the waiter said.

160 Lexington was only too glad to oblige, but this time he gave the money to the cook. "Now listen to me," he said, "I have to admit that I am really rather confused by what the waiter has just been telling me. Are you quite positive that the delectable dish which I have just been eating was prepared from pig's flesh?"

161 The cook raised his right hand and began scratching the rash on his neck.

162 "Well," he said, looking at the waiter and giving him a sly wink, "all I can tell you is that I *think* it was pig's meat."

163 "You mean you're not sure?"

164 "One can't ever be sure."

165 "Then what else could it have been?"

166 "Well," the cook said, speaking very slowly and still staring at the waiter. "There's just a chance, you see, that it might have been a piece of human stuff."

167 "You mean a man?"

168 "Yes."

169 "Good heavens."

170 "Or a woman. It could have been either. They both taste the same."

171 "Well—now you really do surprise me," the youth declared.

172 "One lives and learns."

173 "Indeed one does."

174 "As a matter of fact, we've been getting an awful lot of it just lately from the butcher's in place of pork," the cook declared.

175 "Have you really?"

176 "The trouble is, it's almost impossible to tell which is which. They're both very good."

177 "The piece I had just now was simply superb."

178 "I am glad you liked it," the cook said. "But to be quite honest, I think that was a bit of pig. In fact, I'm almost sure it was."

179 "You are?"

180 "Yes, I am."

181 "In that case, we shall have to assume that you are right," Lexington said. "So now will you please tell me—and here is another hundred dollars for your trouble—will you please tell me precisely how you prepared it?"

182 The cook, after pocketing the money, launched out upon a colourful description of how to roast a loin of pork, while the youth, not wanting to miss a single word of so great a recipe, sat down at the kitchen table and recorded every detail in his notebook.

183 "Is that all?" he asked when the cook had finished.

184 "That's all."

185 "But there must be more to it than that, surely?"

186 "You got to get a good piece of meat to start off with," the cook said. "That's half the battle. It's got to be a good hog and it's got to be butchered right, otherwise it'll turn out lousy whichever way you cook it."

187 "Show me how," Lexington said. "Butcher me one now so I can learn."

188 "We don't butcher pigs in the kitchen," the cook said. "That lot you just ate came from a packing-house over in the Bronx."

189 "Then give me the address!"

190 The cook gave him the address, and our hero, after thanking them both many times for all their kindnesses, rushed outside and leapt into a taxi and headed for the Bronx.

8

191 The packing-house was a big four-storey brick building, and the air around it smelled sweet and heavy, like musk. At the main entrance gates, there was a large notice which said VISITORS WELCOME AT ANY TIME, and thus encouraged, Lexington walked through the gates and entered a cobbled yard which surrounded the building itself. He then followed a series of signposts (THIS WAY FOR THE GUIDED TOURS), and came eventually to a small corrugated-iron shed set well apart from the main building (VISITORS WAITING-ROOM). After knocking politely on the door, he went in.

192 There were six other people ahead of him in the waiting-room. There was a fat mother with her two little boys aged about nine and eleven. There was a bright-eyed young couple who looked as though they might be on their honeymoon. And there was a pale woman with long white gloves, who sat very upright, looking straight ahead, with her hands folded on her lap. Nobody spoke. Lexington wondered whether they were all writing cooking-books, like himself, but when he put this question to them aloud, he got no answer. The grown-ups merely smiled mysteriously to themselves and shook their heads, and the two children stared at him as though they were seeing a lunatic.

193 Soon, the door opened and a man with a merry pink face popped his head into the room and said, "Next, please." The mother and the two boys got up and went out.

194 About ten minutes later, the same man returned. "Next, please," he said again, and the honeymoon couple jumped up and followed him outside.

195 Two new visitors came in and sat down—a middle-aged husband and a middle-aged wife, the wife carrying a wicker shopping-basket containing groceries.

196 "Next, please," said the guide, and the woman with the long white gloves got up and left.

197 Several more people came in and took their places on the stiff-backed wooden chairs.

198 Soon the guide returned for the third time, and now it was Lexington's turn to go outside.

199 "Follow me, please," the guide said, leading the youth across the yard toward the main building.

200 "How exciting this is!" Lexington cried, hopping from one foot to the other. "I only wish that my dear Aunt Glosspan could be with me now to see what I am going to see."

201 "I myself only do the preliminaries," the guide said. "Then I shall hand you over to someone else."

202 "Anything you say," cried the ecstatic youth.

203 First they visited a large penned-in area at the back of the building where several hundred pigs were wandering around. "Here's where they start," the guide said. "And over there's where they go in."

204 "Where?"

205 "Right there." The guide pointed to a long wooden shed that stood against the outside wall of the factory. "We call it the shackling-pen. This way, please."

206 Three men wearing long rubber boots were driving a dozen pigs into the shackling-pen just as Lexington and the guide approached, so they all went in together.

207 "Now," the guide said, "watch how they shackle them."

208 Inside, the shed was simply a bare wooden room with no roof, but there was a steel cable with hooks on it that kept moving slowly along the length of one wall, parallel with the ground, about three feet up. When it reached the end of the shed, this cable suddenly changed direction and climbed vertically upward through the open roof toward the top floor of the main building.

209 The twelve pigs were huddled together at the far end of the pen, standing quietly, looking apprehensive. One of the men in rubber boots pulled a length of metal chain down from the wall and advanced upon the nearest animal, approaching it from the rear. Then he bent down and quickly looped one end of the chain around one of the animal's hind legs. The other end he attached to a hook on the moving cable as it went by. The cable kept moving. The chain tightened. The pig's leg was pulled up and back, and then the pig itself began to be dragged backwards. But it didn't fall down. It was rather a nimble pig, and somehow it managed to keep its balance on three legs, hopping from foot to foot and struggling against the pull of the chain, but going back and back all the time until at the end of the pen where the cable changed direction and went vertically upward, the creature was suddenly jerked off its feet and borne aloft. Shrill protests filled the air.

210 "Truly a fascinating process," Lexington said. "But what was that funny cracking noise it made as it went up?"

211 "Probably the leg," the guide answered. "Either that or the pelvis."

212 "But doesn't that matter?"

213 "Why should it matter?" the guide asked. "You don't eat the bones."

214 The rubber-booted men were busy shackling the rest of the pigs, and one after another they were hooked to the moving cable and hoisted up through the roof, protesting loudly as they went.

215 "There's a good deal more in this recipe than just picking herbs," Lexington said. "Aunt Glosspan would never have made it."

216 At this point, while Lexington was gazing skyward at the last pig to go up, a man in rubber boots approached him quietly from behind and looped one end of a chain around the youth's own left ankle, hooking the other end to the moving belt. The next moment, before he had time to realize what was happening, our hero was jerked off his feet and dragged backwards along the concrete floor of the shackling-pen.

217 "Stop!" he cried. "Hold everything! My leg is caught!"

218 But nobody seemed to hear him, and five seconds later, the unhappy young man was jerked off the floor and hoisted vertically upward through the open roof of the pen, dangling upside down by one ankle, and wriggling like a fish.

219 "Help!" he shouted. "Help! There's been a frightful mistake! Stop the engines! Let me down!"

220 The guide removed a cigar from his mouth and looked up serenely at the rapidly ascending youth, but he said nothing. The men in rubber boots were already on their way out to collect the next batch of pigs.

221 "Oh save me!" our hero cried. "Let me down! Please let me down!" But he was now approaching the top floor of the building where the moving belt curled over like a snake and entered a large hole in the wall, a kind of doorway without a door; and there, on the threshold, waiting to greet him, clothed in a dark-stained yellow rubber apron, and looking for all the world like Saint Peter at the Gates of Heaven, the sticker stood.

222 Lexington saw him only from upside down, and very briefly at that, but even so he noticed at once the expression of absolute peace and benevolence on the man's face, the cheerful twinkle in the eyes, the little wistful smile, the dimples in his cheeks—and all this gave him hope.

223 "Hi there," the sticker said, smiling.

224 "Quick! Save me!" our hero cried.

225 "With pleasure," the sticker said, and taking Lexington gently by one ear with his left hand, he raised his right hand and deftly slit open the boy's jugular vein with a knife.

226 The belt moved on. Lexington went with it. Everything was still upside down and the blood was pouring out of his throat and getting into his eyes, but he could still see after a fashion, and he had a blurred impression of being in an enormously long room, and at the far end of the room there was a great smoking cauldron of water, and there were dark figures, half hidden in the steam, dancing around the edge of it, brandishing long poles. The conveyor-belt seemed to be travelling right over the top of the cauldron, and the pigs seemed to be dropping down one by one into the boiling water, and one of the pigs seemed to be wearing long white gloves on its front feet.

227 Suddenly our hero started to feel very sleepy, but it wasn't until his good strong heart had pumped the last drop of blood from his body that he passed on out of this, the best of all possible worlds, into the next. □

The Slaughter-House

Under the big 500-watted lamps, in the huge sawdusted
government inspected slaughter-house,
head down from hooks and clamps, run on trolleys over
troughs,
the animals die.
Whatever terror their dull intelligences feel
or what agony distorts their most protruding eyes
the incommunicable narrow skulls conceal.
Across the sawdusted floor,
ignorant as children, they see the butcher's slow
methodical approach
in the bloodied apron, leather cap above, thick square
shoes below,
struggling to comprehend this unique vision upside
down,
and then approximate a human scream
as from the throat slit like a letter
the blood empties, and the windpipe, like a blown valve,
spurts steam.

But I, sickened equally with the ox and lamb,
misread my fate,
mistake the butcher's love
who kills me for the meat I am
to feed a hungry multitude beyond the sliding doors.

I, too, misjudge the real
purpose of this huge shed I'm herded in: not for my love
or lovely wool am I here,
but to make some world a meal.
See, how on the unsubstantial air
I kick, bleating my private woe,
as upside down my rolling sight
somersaults, and frantically I try to set my world upright;
too late learning why I'm hung here,
whose nostrils bleed, whose life runs out from eye and
ear.

Alfred Hayes

The Terrible Miss Dove

by Frances Gray Patton

1 Miss Dove was waiting for the sixth grade to file in for its geography lesson. She stood behind her desk, straight as the long map pointer in her hand. And suddenly she had the feeling of not being really alone. Someone or something was moving about the room. Over there, near the sand table where the first grade's herd of rickety clay caribou grazed at the edge of the second grade's plateau, it paused and looked at her. But even when the presence glided, like the shadow of a drifting cloud, along the wall behind her; even when she heard—or almost heard—a new stick of chalk squeaking on the blackboard, Miss Dove did not turn around. She knew, of course, that nobody was there. Her imagination was playing tricks on her again. It was something, she had to admit, humiliatingly close to nerves. Miss Dove did not believe in nerves.

2 Through the open door she watched the sixth graders come out of the music room down the hall. They came out with a rush, as if for two minutes of freedom between classroom and classroom they were borne along upon some mass exhilaration. They always left the music room in that fashion, but this morning they managed to be noisier than usual. It was the season, she supposed. The spring day was warm, and the children were restless as the weather. There was a sharp sound among them, as of a plump posterior being spanked with a book; there was a voice saying, "Double dare, Randy!"; there was a breathless giggling.

3 But as they approached Miss Dove's room their disorder began to vanish. They pulled their excitement in, like a proud but well-broken

pony. One by one they stepped sedately across her doorsill. "Good morning, Miss Dove," they said, one by one, with the same proper lack of voice inflection, and went demurely to their places. At a nod from her they took their seats. Hands folded, eyes to the front, posture correct—they were ready for direction.

4 Jincey Webb, Miss Dove noticed without enthusiasm, had a permanent wave. Yesterday her carrot-colored mane had been neatly braided and pulled back from her serious, freckled face. Now it hung to her shoulders, a bushy mop of undulations and frizzy ringlets. It hung on her mind, too; that was plain to see. For Jincey's expression was one of utter and enviable complacency. It seemed doubtful that a long lifetime of repeated triumphs could again offer her an achievement so sublime with self-satisfaction.

5 Randy Baker, a pink boy of exceptional daring, wiggled his ears at Jincey. Miss Dove looked at him. Randy's pinkness paled. A glaze of innocence came over his round eyes. His ears grew very still.

6 Miss Dove kept looking at him, but she had stopped seeing him. Instead, she was seeing his brother Thomas, who had sat there at Randy's desk seven years before, with the same glaze over the mischief in his eyes. And then she saw Thomas on a raft in the Pacific. She did not see him as they had described him in the papers—skin and bones and haggard young face overgrown with a rough, wild beard. The Thomas she saw looked like Randy. He had braces on his teeth and a dimple in his chin. And he was all alone in the dismal gray mountains of the sea.

7 A wave of giddiness swept over her, but she did not sit down. It was nothing. It had been happening to her off and on all year, and it always passed. Miss Dove had a poor opinion of teachers who could not practice self-control.

8 For thirty years Miss Dove had taught geography in Cedar Grove Elementary School. She had been there before the brooding cedars had been chopped down by a city council that believed in progress and level playgrounds. She had seen principals and fads and theories come and go. But the school still squatted there, red brick, ugly, impervious. Inside it still smelled of wet raincoats and pickle sandwiches. Galahad still petted his charger on the left wall of the vestibule, and Washington still crossed the Delaware on the right. Every fall nervous six-year-olds had to be sent home in tears to put on dry drawers. Every spring there occurred the scandal of cigarette butts in the boys' basement. The same deplorable, old-fashioned words sprang up overnight like mushrooms on the cement walk. And now and then some hitherto graceless child could still surprise you with an act of loyalty or understanding.

The school had not changed much. Neither had human nature. Neither had Miss Dove.

9 Each June some forty-odd little girls and boys—transformed by the magic of organdy ruffles and white duck pants into a group picture of touching purity—were graduated from Cedar Grove. They went on to the wider world of junior high and, beyond that, to further realms of pleasure and pain. In the course of time they forgot much. They forgot dates and decimals and how to write business letters.

10 But they never forgot Miss Dove.

11 Years afterward the mention of the Euphrates River or the Arctic Circle or the Argentinian pampas would put them right back in the geography room. They would see again the big map with its flat blue ocean and its many-colored countries. (India was pink, they would recall, and China was orange, and the Italian boot was purple.) They would see Miss Dove lifting her long stick to point out the location of strange mountains and valleys. And they would feel again the wonder of a world far-flung and various and, like themselves, entirely under control. They would also feel a little thirsty.

12 "Remember Miss Dove?" they would smile.

13 But this green remembrance and the accident of her name's rhyming with a tender word should not deceive anybody about Miss Dove. She was no valentine. Miss Dove was a terror.

14 She had been young when she first started teaching. Her pupils would have hooted at the notion; they would have felt it more reasonable to believe Miss Dove had been born middle-aged with her mousy hair screwed into a knot at the back of her head and a white handkerchief pinned to her dark, bony bosom. Nevertheless, it is true. She had once been quite young.

15 Her father had died, leaving her little besides a library of travel books, an anemic violet-scented mother, and two young sisters yet in school. It had been up to Miss Dove. Older people had pitied her. She seemed too thin and pale and untried, they thought, to carry the burden alone. But Miss Dove never pitied herself. She loved responsibility.

16 The children of each grade came to her forty-five minutes a day, five days a week, six years of their lives. She saw them as a challenge. Their babyish shyness, their lisping pronunciation, their reckless forgetfulness—these evoked no compassion from Miss Dove. They were qualities to be nipped and pruned. Her classes were like a body of raw recruits that she was to toughen and charge with purpose. Miss Dove was the stuff that commanders are made of.

17 Other teachers had trouble keeping order, but not Miss Dove. Other teachers tried to make a game of their work—they played store and pasted gold stars on foreheads. They threatened and cajoled. Miss Dove

never raised her voice. She rarely smiled. She laid before the children the roster of her unalterable laws. And the laws were obeyed. Work was to be done on time. There was to be no whispering, no hair chewing, no wriggling. Coughing, if at all, was to be covered with a clean handkerchief. When one of these laws was chipped, Miss Dove merely looked at the offender. That was all. If a child felt obliged to disturb the class routine by leaving the room for a drink of water (Miss Dove loftily ignored any other necessity), he did so to the accompaniment of dead silence. The whole class would sit, idle and motionless, until he had returned. It was easier—even if you had eaten salt fish for breakfast—to remain and suffer.

18 Miss Dove managed to introduce a moral quality into the very subject she taught. The first graders, who studied the animals of different lands, repeated after her, "The yak is a very helpful animal." And they knew she expected them all to be yaks. Later they learned a more complicated sentence. "The camel," they recited in perfect unison, "is not a pretty beast, either in looks or disposition, but he is able to go many days without water." And they knew what was meant. "Above the fiftieth parallel," sixth graders wrote in their notebooks (keeping the margins even), "life requires hardihood."

19 Occasionally a group of progressive mothers would nearly rebel. "She's been teaching too long," they would cry. "Her pedagogy hasn't changed since we were in the third grade. She rules the children through fear." They would turn to the boldest one among them. "*You* go," they would say. "You go talk to her."

20 The bold one would go, but somehow she never did much talking. For under the level gaze of Miss Dove she would begin to feel—though she wore her handsomest tweeds and perhaps a gardenia for courage—that she was about ten years old and her petticoat was showing. Her throat would tickle. She would wonder desperately if she had a clean handkerchief to cough into.

21 And then there was the little matter of the state achievement tests. Cedar Grove always placed first in geography.

22 Occasionally, too, there would be an independent child who did not yield readily to group discipline. Miss Dove knew how to deal with him.

23 Once she had overheard two small boys talking about her at the drinking fountain. (They had no business at the fountain; it was their library period. But the librarian was lax.)

24 "I bet Miss Dove could lick Joe Louis," one of them had said.

25 "Who? That ole stick?" the other one had jeered. "I could beat her with my little finger."

26 He had glanced up then to see Miss Dove looking down at him.

She had looked at him for a long time. Her light gray eyes were expressionless. Her long nose was pink at the tip, but no pinker than usual. At last she had spoken.

27 "Thomas Baker," she had said in the tone of one making a pure observation, "you talk too much, don't you?"

28 "Yes, ma'am," Thomas had said in a tiny voice. He went off without getting any water. Seven years later he sweated when he thought of it. He could not know that Miss Dove also remembered. But she did.

29 Ever since Pearl Harbor Miss Dove had been troubled. She lived quite alone, for her sisters had married and her mother had departed for a place not on the map. (But decently, with every possible comfort. Miss Dove liked to remind herself of that.) And one evening while she was correcting papers she sensed, with that uncanny perception of the teacher, that something intruded upon her solitude. She turned quickly and looked about the room. A starched white curtain rustled in a puff of wind; her grandmother's rosewood whatnot cast a curious shadow on the polished floor; a finger of lamplight picked out the gilt titles of her father's old brown travel books. There was nothing else. But the red correction pencil was shaking in her fingers; for a moment her throat ached with a spasm of desolate, unaccountable grief, and —less familiar still—with a feeling of her own unworthiness. Miss Dove had never felt unworthy before in her life.

30 After that the thing happened frequently, until at last she saw who the intruders were. They were the children she had taught long ago.

31 War had scattered those children. There was a girl—a vain, silly little piece she had been—who was a nurse on Corregidor. At least, when last heard of she had been on Corregidor. One of the boys was dead in Tunisia. Others were on the Anzio beachhead, or in the jungles of New Guinea, or in the flak-brightened skies over Germany. But they came back to Miss Dove. She saw them as they had been at seven, at ten, at twelve. Only they had a beauty she had never seen in them then. They lifted their faces like starry morning flowers. Their limbs quivered with the unreasonable joy of childhood. And as Miss Dove looked at them they grew still. Their faces paled. Their eyes stopped dancing. They folded their little hands. They faded and were gone.

32 The child who came oftenest was Thomas Baker. The town paper had been full of Thomas. His ship had been bombed, his officers killed, and Thomas had taken over. A hundred men owed their lives to his presence of mind. For days he had floated on a raft with no food and only the water in his canteen. When they picked him up his tongue had protruded from his mouth, black and swollen with thirst. That was what got Miss Dove—he had run out of water.

33 The Thomas who came to stand before her now was a sturdy boy in knickers. He held his chin at a cocky angle, but the dimple in it trembled. He ran the tip of his tongue over his lips. He looked thirsty.

34 But they came only at night. When daylight returned Miss Dove could believe she had been imagining things. She would eat her customary boiled egg and her whole-wheat toast; she would take an extra vitamin pill with her orange juice; she would walk forth at her usual measured pace and assume her usual role of unshakable authority. The children at the school would seem plain and ordinary. They would have little in common with those graceful and evanescent figures that haunted her. And no intruders dared come into the geography room. Or they never had until this morning.

35 A boy in the back row cleared his throat. One by the window followed suit. Soon the whole room was dotted with the sound, a rough "h-hrmph," like frogs in a distant marsh. Miss Dove knew what the sound meant. It was the school's traditional signal—a kind of dare. She had heard other teachers speak of it in exasperation. It had never happened in her room before.

36 Slowly Randy Baker raised his hand. The sounds stopped. Silence like a caught breath hung on the room. Miss Dove could see a fine dew pop out on Randy's brow; his open palm was damp and gleaming.

37 "Yes, Randolph?" she said.

38 Randy stood up. Miss Dove's pupils always stood when they addressed her. He smoothed his round stomach with his hand. "I got a letter from Tom yestiddy," he said.

39 "*Received,* Randolph," said Miss Dove. "You received a letter from your brother *yesterday.* That was nice."

40 "Yes, ma'am," said Randy. He paused. He was clearly floundering. "He sent me a dollar he won playing poker in the convalescent hospital."

41 "I am sorry to hear that Thomas gambles," said Miss Dove, "but we are all very proud of his war record. If you have nothing more interesting to tell us you may take your seat, Randolph."

42 "H-hr-rmph!" went the boy behind Randy.

43 "He's been decorated," said Randy, "for bravery beyond the call of duty." The high words seemed to inspirit him. "He sent a message to the class."

44 "Did you bring the letter?" asked Miss Dove. "If so, you may read that part aloud."

45 Randy took an air-mail envelope from his hip pocket. Miss Dove noticed that Thomas' handwriting was as sprawling and untidy as ever. Somehow the observation pleased her.

46 The class stirred. The ghost of a titter rippled the air.

47 "Attention, please," said Miss Dove.

48 Randy opened the letter. The paper was smudged and crumpled. Obviously it had suffered many readings and many hands. Randy cleared his throat. The sound was not a link in the chain signal. Miss Dove could tell the difference. "It's sort of long," Randy demurred hopefully.

49 Miss Dove knew there was naughtiness afoot. The frog noises as well as Randy's hesitation had told her that. But she did not believe in avoiding an issue. She made a practice of facing impudence in the open—and facing it down.

50 "We can spare the time," she said.

51 Randy began to read. His voice was high and clear; it had the girlish sweetness that comes just before the breaking point.

52 "The funny thing about the world," Randy read, "is that it looks just like you think it does. When they flew me back to Cal. in a hospital plane I looked down and, heck, I might as well have been looking at those diagrams on the geography board back in dear (ha, ha!) ole Cedar Grove. I spotted a peninsula just as plain. A body of land almost entirely surrounded by water. I saw some atolls too. And they really are made in rings like doughnuts, with palm trees sprouting out of the cake part and blue water in the hole in the middle. The water is the color of that blue chalk I swiped once and drew the picture of Miss Dove on the sidewalk with. Remember?"

53 So it *was* Thomas who had drawn that caricature. She had always suspected him. "Proceed, Randolph," she said.

54 "You want to know if I was scared when the little yellow insects from"—Randy swallowed and went on—"from hell"—in his embarrassment he brought out the word with unnecessary force—"dive-bombed us. The answer is, you bet. But it came to me in a flash that I wasn't much scareder than I was that time ole lady Dove caught me bragging about how I could beat her up at the drinking fountain. 'I didn't run that time,' I told myself, 'so I won't run now.' Besides, there wasn't any place to run to."

55 The class laughed nervously.

56 "And later," read Randy, "when I was bobbing up and down like Crusoe on my raft, what do you guess I thought about? Well, it wasn't any pin-up girl. It was Miss Dove. I thought about that fishy stare she used to give us when we needed a drink of water. So to make my supply hold out I played I was back in the geography room. And even after the water was all gone I kept playing that. I'd think, 'The bell is bound to ring in a few minutes. You can last a little longer.' It took the same kind of guts in the Pacific it did in school. Tell that to the kids in Cedar Grove." Randy stopped abruptly.

57 "Is that the end?" asked Miss Dove.

58 Randy looked directly at her. For a fleeting moment she thought he was going to say yes. If he did, the incident would be closed, of course, for Miss Dove never questioned a child's word. That was why they generally told her the truth. He shook his head.

59 "No, ma'am," he said. "There's a little more." His face turned the color of a nearly ripe tomato. "He says here"—Randy gulped—"he says"—Randy took a deep breath—"he says: 'Give the terrible Miss Dove a kiss for me.' "

60 "Well, Randolph," said Miss Dove, "I am waiting."

61 There was an electric stillness that was followed, as the full meaning of her words penetrated the children's consciousness, by a gasp. Randy folded the letter and put it back into his pocket. Then he began to walk toward her. He walked with the deliberate stoicism of a martyr going to the chopping block. Miss Dove inclined her head and turned her cheek in his direction. He did not come any closer than he had to. He leaned forward stiffly from the waist and placed his puckered lips against her cheek. (*He smells like a last year's bird's nest,* thought Miss Dove. It was strange. However frequently a twelve-year-old boy was washed, he always smelled like a bird's nest.) Randy smacked. His kiss resounded, a small explosion in the room.

62 "Thank you, Randolph," said Miss Dove. "You may give Thomas my regards." She straightened up and faced the class. To her surprise, nobody was grinning.

63 Jincey Webb spoke. She did not raise her hand first for permission. She just spoke out. "It's like a medal," said Jincey softly. "It's like he pinned a medal on Miss Dove."

64 For a moment a lamp seemed to burn behind her face. Then over the light swept a shadow, a look of awe. It was as if Jincey had glimpsed some universal beauty—of sorrow, perhaps, or of nobility—too poignant for her youth to bear. She began to cry. She flopped her head down on her desk with her red hair falling forward and spreading out like a crinkly fan.

65 All the other girls were weeping too. All the boys were trying not to.

66 For the first time in her teaching career Miss Dove was at a loss. She wanted to make a speech. She wanted to say something beautiful and grateful about what life really meant to her, about the overwhelming generosity of children. No, not generosity. It was something better than that, something much harder to come by. It was justice. And Miss Dove did not know how to say what she felt. She had never thought it dignified to express emotion.

[67] But as she stood there waiting for the words to form in her mind, she realized that she was neglecting her duty. The first duty of a teacher was to preserve order.

[68] She fished a piece of string from a receptacle on her desk. She walked down the aisle to Jincey Webb. She took Jincey's hair, that marvel of art and nature, and bunched it in her hand. She tied it securely at the nape of Jincey's neck with the little bit of grocery string.

[69] "Now it will be out of your way," she said.

[70] At the sound of her voice, cool, precise and natural, the children rallied. They sat erect. They blew their noses on clean handkerchiefs. They folded their hands on their desks.

[71] "Get out your notebooks, class," she said.

[72] A transient mist came over her eyes. Through it, as through a prism, the children glowed. Freckles, cowlicks, pinafores and polo shirts seemed bathed in a rainbow iridescence. Her love flowed out to her children—to those opening their notebooks before her, and to those in the far places she had once helped them locate on the map. It did not flow tenderly like a mother's coddling love. It flowed on a fierce rush of pride and hope, as an old general's heart might follow his men into battle.

[73] She went to the blackboard and picked up a piece of chalk. "Above the fiftieth parallel—" wrote the terrible Miss Dove. □

CHAPTER VIII

Experiencing the Total Work

If you become a good reader—one who practices his craft all his life—you will probably be dissatisfied with your performance most of the time. And you will be sharing a dissatisfaction authors know too. Many excellent writers, near death, have lamented their inability to perfect their craft. Search as you may, you probably cannot find an author of any stature who will say, "I am satisfied with my ability. My work needs no improvement."

John Ciardi, himself a successful writer of many forms, has said:

> I think it was Bernard DeVoto who pointed out that the best reason for putting anything down on paper is that one may then change it. His remark not only suggests one sound theory of writing but identifies the writing process as a groping one. There is no end to that groping process, but in time the good writer will acquire not only a sense of *groping for* but a sense of having *groped to:* he begins to know when he has finally reached whatever he was reaching for.
>
> Ideally, there can be no real end to that groping. To reread is to revise. In the world as it is, however, one has to leave the writing at some point: either that or stay with it forever and never get on to anything else.°

And Ann Petry, another successful writer, has stated: "It is with reluctance that I speak of my own writing. I have never been satisfied with anything I have written and I doubt that I ever will be."°

Dissatisfaction with portions of human experience creates the author's need to write; dissatisfaction with an always imperfect craft forces him into constantly more ambitious undertakings. Dissatisfaction with

° "On Writing and Bad Writing," *Saturday Review,* December 15, 1962.

° "The Novel As Social Criticism," in *The Writer's Book,* ed. Helen Hull (New York, 1950, 1956).

less excellent work leads the reader to seek more satisfying material as his reading ability improves.

The stories in this chapter suggest some of the approaches taken by writers seeking the best way to tell a story. Some are slick stories, some are quality, others are a happy blend of the two. All are admirable examples of unique approaches to a story. As you read each one the first time, you will probably find yourself caught up in the narrative, reading along merely to see what happens next. Allow yourself that luxury. Then, when you have finished, turn back and analyze the story carefully, reading the accompanying discussions. Take it apart as mechanically as you can, seeking the magic and craft that combine to make it a satisfying literary experience.

In your reading, try to share Eudora Welty's conviction about beauty and sensitivity in the short story:

> The two things that cannot be imitated, beauty and sensitivity, are or may be kin to each other. But there is only one of them we can strive for. Sensitivity in ourselves. It is our technique. In the end, our technique is sensitivity, and beauty may be our reward.
>
> A short-story writer can try anything. He has tried anything—but presumably not everything. Variety is, has been, and no doubt will remain endless in possibilities, because the power and stirring of the mind never rests. It is what this power will try that will most pertinently define the short story. Not rules, not aesthetics, not problems and their solution. It is not rules as long as there is imagination; not aesthetics as long as there is passion; not success as long as there is intensity behind the effort that calls forth and communicates, that will try and try again.
>
> And at the other end of the stories is the reader. There is no use really to fear "the reader." The surly old bugaboo who wants his money's worth out of a magazine—yes, he is there (or I suspect it is a she, still wanting her money's worth and having yet to be convinced she's got it); but there is another reader too, perhaps with more at stake.
>
> Inescapably, this reader exists—the same as ourselves; the reader who is also a user of imagination and thought. This reader picks up a story, maybe our new story, and behold, sees it fresh, and meets it with a storehouse of hope and interest.
>
> And, reader and writer, we can wish each other well. Don't we after all want the same thing? A story of beauty and passion and truth.°

First, use your pencil lavishly. Mark transitions, character details, poetic devices, elements of setting, tone, atmosphere, and so on. Isolate descriptive passages that are well done and examine them for vocabulary, syntax, and their appeal to the five senses. Make a basic plot outline

° "The Reading and Writing of Short Stories," *Atlantic Monthly,* March 1949, p. 49.

and observe proportion through it. Decide how the author paced the story—and why. Compare panorama and scene. How effectively do they complement each other to create unity of plot? How is theme suggested, and how is it realized? What does style add to the story? Is it a distraction at any point? In short, be as clinical as you can. You will be amazed at the infinite number of small details you overlooked in your first hurried reading. And you will be surprised how an awareness of them gives meaning to the story, allowing you to understand it well rather than to think it means something of a generally vague nature.

As you isolate the small details, what you consider a so-so story may turn into an excellent one—as your reading goes from so-so to excellent. In the process, you will become aware of the meticulousness with which writers plot, develop characters, and weld descriptions to narrative flow. Concern yourself with their language (poetic aspects, expository processes, denotation, connotation). Observe symbols as they are used in the stories. Determine why an author chooses to focus on a scene at one point and employ panorama at another. Remember: there is no right or wrong way to tell a story. There may be a *best* way, however. See if you can discover how each author found his best way. Do not think yourself presumptuous if you feel you could tell the author how to improve his work.

Compare your analysis of each story with the one provided in this chapter. Between the two analyses, a relatively clear idea of structure should emerge for you. Even then, however, you will not have exhausted the story if it is a good one. And one way to distinguish between the good and the poor in literature is constant rereading. Poor material will not hold up under several readings—it grows monotonous. Good material is constantly rewarding, offering new facets of itself with each new examination.

Each of the stories in this chapter is structured on one of the four ingredients of fiction: narrative, description, character, and dialog. In each, all four elements are, of course, present; they are combined to create the total effect. But, in each story, one element predominates. As you read each story the first time, observe how the author makes one ingredient serve as the structural device. Attempt to understand why, for the choice of a structural device determines many things about the way an author will develop his work.

The Story of Narrative

Anyone who has read "The Squatter" (pp. 130–133) from Djuna Barnes' *Nightwood* will recognize the similarities between Jenny Petherbridge and Joan Harris in the following story structured on narrative, John Cheever's "Torch Song." Each character receives the same careful scrutiny from her fictional creator (another character's point of view). Each is thoroughly distasteful as a person; yet each is compelling in the same way snakes and accidents are. The reader may be repelled by them, but he is fascinated by their power to repel him.

Torch Song

by John Cheever

1 After Jack Lorey had known Joan Harris in New York for a few years, he began to think of her as The Widow. She always wore black, and he was always given the feeling, by a curious disorder in her apartment, that the undertakers had just left. This impression did not stem from malice on his part, for he was fond of Joan. They came from the same city in Ohio and had reached New York at about the same time in the middle thirties. They were the same age, and during their first summer in the city they used to meet after work and drink Martinis in places like the Brevoort and Charles', and have dinner and play checkers at the Lafayette.

2 Joan went to a school for models when she settled in the city, but it turned out that she photographed badly, so after spending six weeks learning how to walk with a book on her head she got a job as a hostess in a Longchamps. For the rest of the summer she stood by the hatrack, bathed in an intense pink light and the string music of heartbreak, swinging her mane of dark hair and her black skirt as she moved forward to greet the customers. She was then a big, handsome girl with a wonderful voice, and her face, her whole presence, always seemed infused with a gentle and healthy pleasure at her surroundings, whatever they were. She was innocently and incorrigibly convivial, and would get out of bed and dress at three in the morning if someone called her and asked her to come out for a drink, as Jack often did. In the fall, she got some kind of freshman executive job in a department store. They saw less and less of each other and then for quite a while stopped seeing each other altogether. Jack was living with a girl he had met at a party, and it never occurred to him to wonder what had become of Joan.

Paragraphs 1–2 establish the detached, sophisticated tone of the story. The background material is sketched in with panoramic skill and the first two sentences reveal the suspicions which are later to terrorize Jack. The narrative is told on Jack's authority from a third person limited omniscient point of view—only his observations and thoughts are recorded. Paragraph 2 states: "but it turned out she photographed badly . . . ," and the narrative then proceeds as a series of candid photographs snapped when Joan is least prepared for—if not totally unaware of—the camera. From the beginning, her robust health is contrasted with the black of her costume. A second contrast is also revealed: she is constantly cheerful and available; Jack is utterly self-centered and inconsiderate, if not a little jealous. He often calls Joan at 3:00 A.M. to have a drink. The implication that he is lonely, bored, and alone is strengthened throughout the story as he never consciously considers Joan's existence unless he needs companionship and does not know where else to find it.

[3]Jack's girl had some friends in Pennsylvania, and in the spring and summer of his second year in town he often went there with her for weekends. All of this—the shared apartment in the Village, the illicit relationship, the Friday-night train to a country house—were what he had imagined life in New York to be, and he was intensely happy. He was returning to New York with his girl one Sunday night on the Lehigh line. It was one of those trains that move slowly across the face of New Jersey, bringing back to the city hundreds of people, like the victims of an immense and strenuous picnic, whose faces are blazing and whose muscles are lame. Jack and his girl, like most of the other passengers, were overburdened with vegetables and flowers. When the train stopped in Pennsylvania Station, they moved with the crowd along the platform, toward the escalator. As they were passing the wide, lighted windows of the diner, Jack turned his head and saw Joan. It was the first time he had seen her since Thanksgiving, or since Christmas. He couldn't remember.

[4]Joan was with a man who had obviously passed out. His head was in his arms on the table, and an overturned highball glass was near one of his elbows. Joan was shaking his shoulders gently and speaking to him. She seemed to be vaguely troubled, vaguely amused. The waiters had cleared off all the other tables and were standing around Joan, waiting for her to resurrect her escort. It troubled Jack to see in these straits a girl who reminded him of the trees and the lawns of his home town, but there was nothing he could do to help. Joan continued to shake the man's shoulders, and the crowd pressed Jack past one after another of the diner's windows, past the malodorous kitchen, and up the escalator.

Paragraphs 3–4 reveal Jack's extreme egocentricity. What pleases him serves to guide his behavior. The small-town boy from Ohio pursues a romantically conceived life of free love and marginal vicariousness. He is a frequent weekend guest in a country house. Life is what he "imagined it to be"—not, certainly, what it is. As Jack sees Joan and realizes he can't even remember when he saw her last, he is "troubled" that she, a symbol of the *natural* past, is involved in the present sordid scene. He passes on, offering no help, making no assessment of her predicament. Panorama almost narrows to scene here, but, before it can, Jack moves away.

[5]He saw Joan again, later that summer, when he was having dinner in a Village restaurant. He was with a new girl, a Southerner. There were many Southern girls in the city that year. Jack and his belle had wandered into the restaurant because it was convenient, but the food was terrible and the place was lighted with candles. Halfway through dinner, Jack noticed Joan on the other side of the room, and when he had finished eating, he crossed the room and spoke to her. She was with a tall man who was wearing a monocle. He stood, bowed stiffly from the waist, and said to Jack, "We are very pleased to meet you." Then he excused himself and headed for the toilet. "He's a count, he's a Swedish count," Joan said. "He's on the radio, Friday afternoons at four-fifteen. Isn't it exciting?" She seemed to be delighted with the count and the terrible restaurant.

[6]Sometime the next winter, Jack moved from the Village to an apartment in the East Thirties. He was crossing Park Avenue one cold morning on his way to the office when he noticed, in the crowd, a woman he had met a few times at Joan's apartment. He spoke to her and asked about his friend. "Haven't you heard?" she said. She pulled a long face. "Perhaps I'd better tell you. Perhaps you can help." She and Jack had breakfast in a drugstore on Madison Avenue and she unburdened herself of the story.

[7]The count had a program called "The Song of the Fiords," or something like that, and he sang Swedish folk songs. Everyone suspected him of being a fake, but that didn't bother Joan. He had met her at a party and, sensing a soft touch, had moved in with her the following night. About a week later, he complained of pains in his back and said he must have some morphine. Then he needed morphine all the time. If he didn't get morphine, he was abusive and violent. Joan began to deal with those doctors and druggists who peddle dope, and when they wouldn't supply her, she went down to the bottom of the city. Her friends were afraid she would be found some morning stuffed in a drain. She got pregnant. She had an abortion. The count left her and moved to a flea bag near Times Square, but she was so impressed by then with his helplessness, so afraid that he would die without her, that she followed him there and shared his room and continued to buy his narcotics. He abandoned her again, and Joan waited a week for him to return before she went back to her place and her friends in the Village.

[8]It shocked Jack to think of that innocent girl from Ohio having lived with a brutal dope addict and traded with criminals, and when he got to his office that morning, he telephoned her and made a date for dinner that night. He met her at Charles'. When she came into the bar, she seemed as wholesome and calm as ever. Her voice was sweet, and reminded him of elms, of lawns, of those glass arrangements that used to be hung from porch ceilings to tinkle in the summer wind. She told him about the count. She spoke of him charitably and with no trace of bitterness, as if her voice, her disposition, were incapable of registering anything beyond simple affection and pleasure. Her walk, when she moved ahead of him toward their table, was light and graceful. She ate a large dinner and talked enthusiastically

about her job. They went to a movie and said goodbye in front of her apartment house.

Paragraphs 5–8 combine panorama and narrative frame to supply information Jack could not have had except for the chance meeting with the nameless woman. Coincidence is not suggested as such an encounter is narratively credible. Paragraph 5 supplies the initial material as Jack, now experiencing a fashionable alliance with a Southern belle, encounters Joan in a Village restaurant. His ennui is clearly indicated by "and the place was lighted by candles." What, in his recent past, would have seemed quite properly bohemian is now stale. His sophistication has been sharpened on the edges of the city and his concept of what is currently smart. Joan's escort is as much a movie prop as is Jack's belle, a similarity that escapes him. Jack relegates the count to commonness by sending him to the "toilet" rather than to the "men's room." Resentment of Joan's freshness is again apparent as Jack finds her "delighted with the count and the terrible restaurant." When the chance acquaintance recounts Joan's involvement with a dope addict, criminals, and abortion, Jack retains his "innocent" image of her by disregarding the abortion, thereby absolving Joan of deliberate wrongdoing and concentrating on others' abuse of her. His evening with her reestablishes the fresh image utterly. Home thoughts are safe in the symbol she is, and he forgets her again.

9 That winter, Jack met a girl he decided to marry. Their engagement was announced in January and they planned to marry in July. In the spring, he received, in his office mail, an invitation to cocktails at Joan's. It was for a Saturday when his fiancée was going to Massachusetts to visit her parents, and when the time came and he had nothing better to do, he took a bus to the Village. Joan had the same apartment. It was a walkup. You rang the bell above the mailbox in the vestibule and were answered with a death rattle in the lock. Joan lived on the third floor. Her calling card was in a slot on the mailbox, and above her name was written the name Hugh Bascomb.

10 Jack climbed the two flights of carpeted stairs, and when he reached Joan's apartment, she was standing by the open door in a black dress. After she greeted Jack, she took his arm and guided him across the room. "I want you to meet Hugh, Jack," she said.

11 Hugh was a big man with a red face and pale-blue eyes. His manner was courtly and his eyes were inflamed with drink. Jack talked with him for a little while and then went over to speak to someone he knew, who was standing by the mantelpiece. He noticed then, for the first time, the indescribable disorder of Joan's apartment. The books were in their shelves and the furniture was reasonably good,

but the place was all wrong, somehow. It was as if things had been put in place without thought or real interest, and for the first time, too, he had the impression that there had been a death there recently.

12 As Jack moved around the room, he felt that he had met the ten or twelve guests at other parties. There was a woman executive with a fancy hat, a man who could imitate Roosevelt, a grim couple whose play was in rehearsal, and a newspaperman who kept turning on the radio for news of the Spanish Civil War. Jack drank Martinis and talked with the woman in the fancy hat. He looked out of the window at the back yards and the ailanthus trees and heard, in the distance, thunder exploding off the cliffs of the Hudson.

13 Hugh Bascomb got very drunk. He began to spill liquor, as if drinking, for him, were a kind of jolly slaughter and he enjoyed the bloodshed and the mess. He spilled whiskey from a bottle. He spilled a drink on his shirt and then tipped over someone else's drink. The party was not quiet, but Hugh's hoarse voice began to dominate the others. He attacked a photographer who was sitting in a corner explaining camera techniques to a homely woman. "What did you come to the party for if all you wanted to do was to sit there and stare at your shoes?" Hugh shouted. "What did you come for? Why don't you stay at home?"

14 The photographer didn't know what to say. He was not staring at his shoes. Joan moved lightly to Hugh's side. "Please don't get into a fight now, darling," she said. "Not this afternoon."

15 "Shut up," he said. "Let me alone. Mind your own business." He lost his balance, and in struggling to steady himself he tipped over a lamp.

16 "Oh, your lovely lamp, Joan," a woman sighed.

17 "Lamps!" Hugh roared. He threw his arms into the air and worked them around his head as if he were bludgeoning himself. "Lamps. Glasses. Cigarette boxes. Dishes. They're killing me. They're killing me, for Christ's sake. Let's all go up to the mountains, for Christ's sake. Let's all go up to the mountains and hunt and fish and live like men, for Christ's sake."

18 People were scattering as if a rain had begun to fall in the room. It had, as a matter of fact, begun to rain outside. Someone offered Jack a ride uptown, and he jumped at the chance. Joan stood at the door, saying goodbye to her routed friends. Her voice remained soft, and her manner, unlike that of those Christian women who in the face of disaster can summon new and formidable sources of composure, seemed genuinely simple. She appeared to be oblivious of the raging drunk at her back, who was pacing up and down, grinding glass into the rug, and haranguing one of the survivors of the party with a story of how he, Hugh, had once gone without food for three weeks.

19 In July, Jack was married in an orchard in Duxbury, and he and his wife went to West Chop for a few weeks. When they returned to town, their apartment was cluttered with presents, including a dozen after-dinner coffee cups from Joan. His wife sent her the required note, but they did nothing else.

Paragraphs 9–18 constitute a *panoramic scene* (a scene in which focus never narrows to close examination but narrows enough to give a clearer impression than panorama does). Jack decides to marry a girl; he doesn't "fall in love" with her. His blasé approach suggests he has nothing better to do. For the same reason, he thinks of Joan and calls on her. The death image is established here as Jack sees the names on Joan's mailbox and must accept a reality: Joan is not a "trees and lawn" image which has no existence in his absence. She is "living," as she defines the word. His detachment is subtle as the third person singular pronoun of "he took a bus to the Village" gives way to the second person "you rang the bell." The death rattle opens the door as his symbol dies. Hugh is, obviously, a drunk, and Jack notices, "for the first time, the indescribable disorder of Joan's apartment." Jack has his life quite in order (is he not marrying in the approved fashion?) and he assesses Joan's life as being disordered. That "things had been put in place without thought or real interest" is an ironic statement indeed! For the first time, the death image actually asserts itself. Hugh's behavior is reprehensible, but Jack notices basic symbolic truths as Hugh declares the trappings of life (lamps, cigarette boxes) are "killing" him in the city where he is losing his manhood. The rain simile serves as transition for Jack's escape, but he notices Joan's composure, her refusal to be defeated. Her natural quality is apparent as her voice remains soft and simple.

A whitespace transition indicates nothing worth reporting between the party and Jack's marriage. Yet that period should have been an exciting, nervous time for Jack. He prefers, obviously, not to think about it.

[20]Late in the summer, Joan telephoned Jack at his office and asked if he wouldn't bring his wife to see her; she named an evening the following week. He felt guilty about not having called her, and accepted the invitation. This made his wife angry. She was an ambitious girl who liked a social life that offered rewards, and she went unwillingly to Joan's Village apartment with him.

[21]Written above Joan's name on the mailbox was the name Franz Denzel. Jack and his wife climbed the stairs and were met by Joan at the open door. They went into her apartment and found themselves among a group of people for whom Jack, at least, was unable to find any bearings.

[22]Franz Denzel was a middle-aged German. His face was pinched with bitterness or illness. He greeted Jack and his wife with that elaborate and clever politeness that is intended to make guests feel that they have come too early or too late. He insisted sharply upon Jack's sitting in the chair in which he himself had been sitting, and then went and sat on a radiator. There were five other Germans sitting around the room, drinking coffee. In a corner was another American couple, who

looked uncomfortable. Joan passed Jack and his wife small cups of coffee with whipped cream. "These cups belonged to Franz's mother," she said. "Aren't they lovely? They were the only things he took from Germany when he escaped from the Nazis."

23 Franz turned to Jack and said, "Perhaps you will give us your opinion on the American educational system. That is what we were discussing when you arrived."

24 Before Jack could speak, one of the German guests opened an attack on the American educational system. The other Germans joined in, and went on from there to describe every vulgarity that had impressed them in American life and to contrast German and American culture generally. Where, they asked one another passionately, could you find in America anything like the Mitropa dining cars, the Black Forest, the pictures in Munich, the music in Bayreuth? Franz and his friends began speaking in German. Neither Jack nor his wife nor Joan could understand German, and the other American couple had not opened their mouths since they were introduced. Joan went happily around the room, filling everyone's cup with coffee, as if the music of a foreign language were enough to make an evening for her.

25 Jack drank five cups of coffee. He was desperately uncomfortable. Joan went into the kitchen while the Germans were laughing at their German jokes, and he hoped she would return with some drinks, but when she came back it was with a tray of ice cream and mulberries.

26 "Isn't this pleasant?" Franz asked, speaking in English again.

27 Joan collected the coffee cups, and as she was about to take them back to the kitchen, Franz stopped her.

28 "Isn't one of those cups chipped?"

29 "No, darling," Joan said. "I never let the maid touch them. I wash them myself."

30 "What's that?" he asked, pointing at the rim of one of the cups.

31 "That's the cup that's always been chipped, darling. It was chipped when you unpacked it. You noticed it then."

32 "These things were perfect when they arrived in this country," he said.

33 Joan went into the kitchen and he followed her.

34 Jack tried to make conversation with the Germans. From the kitchen there was the sound of a blow and a cry. Franz returned and began to eat his mulberries greedily. Joan came back with her dish of ice cream. Her voice was gentle. Her tears, if she had been crying, had dried as quickly as the tears of a child. Jack and his wife finished their ice cream and made their escape. The wasted and unnerving evening enraged Jack's wife, and he supposed that he would never see Joan again.

Paragraphs 19–34 repeat the pattern of the previous panoramic scene. Jack acknowledges guilt for the first time, and he resents his wife who is "an ambitious girl who liked a social life that offered rewards." Franz has replaced Hugh. Jack is uncomfortable; Joan is happy. Even the blow in the kitchen does not disturb Joan (as Jack observes her), who retains a gentle voice and childlike quality. Unable to cope with the violence of the moment, Jack escapes.

35 Jack's wife got pregnant early in the fall, and she seized on all the prerogatives of an expectant mother. She took long naps, ate canned peaches in the middle of the night, and talked about the rudimentary kidney. She chose to see only other couples who were expecting children, and the parties that she and Jack gave were temperate. The baby, a boy, was born in May, and Jack was very proud and happy. The first party he and his wife went to after her convalescence was the wedding of a girl whose family Jack had known in Ohio.

36 The wedding was at St. James', and afterward there was a big reception at the River Club. There was an orchestra dressed like Hungarians, and a lot of champagne and Scotch. Toward the end of the afternoon, Jack was walking down a dim corridor when he heard Joan's voice. "Please don't darling," she was saying. "You'll break my arm. *Please* don't darling." She was being pressed against the wall by a man who seemed to be twisting her arm. As soon as they saw Jack, the struggle stopped. All three of them were intensely embarrassed. Joan's face was wet and she made an effort to smile through her tears at Jack. He said hello and went on without stopping. When he returned, she and the man had disappeared.

37 When Jack's son was less than two years old, his wife flew with the baby to Nevada to get a divorce. Jack gave her the apartment and all its furnishings and took a room in a hotel near Grand Central. His wife got her decree in due course, and the story was in the newspapers. Jack had a telephone call from Joan a few days later.

38 "I'm awfully sorry to hear about your divorce, Jack," she said. "She seemed like *such* a nice girl. But that wasn't what I called you about. I want your help, and I wondered if you could come down to my place tonight around six. It's something I don't want to talk about over the phone."

39 He went obediently to the Village that night and climbed the stairs. Her apartment was a mess. The pictures and the curtains were down and the books were in boxes. "You moving, Joan?" he asked.

40 "That's what I wanted to see you about, Jack. First, I'll give you a drink." She made two Old-Fashioneds. "I'm being evicted, Jack," she said. "I'm being evicted because I'm an immoral woman. The couple who have the apartment downstairs—they're charming people, I've always thought—have told the real-estate agent that I'm a drunk and a prostitute and all kind of things. Isn't that fantastic? This real-estate agent has always been so nice to me that I didn't think he'd believe them, but he's cancelled my lease, and if I make any trouble, he's threatened to take the matter up with the store, and I don't want to lose my job. This nice real-

estate agent won't even talk with me any more. When I go over to the office, the receptionist leers at me as if I were some kind of dreadful woman. Of course, there have been a lot of men here and we sometimes are noisy, but I can't be expected to go to bed at ten every night. Can I? Well, the agent who manages this building has apparently told all the other agents in the neighborhood that I'm an immoral and drunken woman, and none of them will give me an apartment. I went in to talk with one man—he seemed to be such a nice old gentleman—and he made me an indecent proposal. Isn't it fantastic? I have to be out of here on Thursday and I'm literally being turned out into the street."

41 Joan seemed as serene and innocent as ever while she described this scourge of agents and neighbors. Jack listened carefully for some sign of indignation or bitterness or even urgency in her recital, but there was none. He was reminded of a torch song, of one of those forlorn and touching ballads that had been sung neither for him nor for her but for their brothers and sisters by Marion Harris. Joan seemed to be singing her wrongs.

42 "They've made my life miserable," she went on quietly. "If I keep the radio on after ten o'clock, they telephone the agent in the morning and tell him I had some kind of orgy here. One night when Phillip—I don't think you've met Phillip; he's in the Royal Air Force; he's gone back to England—one night when Phillip and some other people were here, they called the police. The police came bursting in the door and talked to me as if I were I don't know what and then looked in the bedroom. If they think there's a man up here after midnight, they call me on the telephone and say all kinds of disgusting things. Of course, I can put my furniture into storage and go to a hotel, I guess. I guess a hotel will take a woman with my kind of reputation, but I thought perhaps you might know of an apartment. I thought—"

43 It angered Jack to think of this big, splendid girl's being persecuted by her neighbors, and he said he would do what he could. He asked her to have dinner with him, but she said she was busy.

44 Having nothing better to do, Jack decided to walk uptown to his hotel. It was a hot night. The sky was overcast. On his way, he saw a parade in a dark side street off Broadway near Madison Square. All the buildings in the neighborhood were dark. It was so dark that he could not see the placards the marchers carried until he came to a street light. Their signs urged the entry of the United States into the war, and each platoon represented a nation that had been subjugated by the Axis powers. They marched up Broadway, as he watched, to no music, to no sound but their own steps on the rough cobbles. It was for the most part an army of elderly men and women—Poles, Norwegians, Danes, Jews, Chinese. A few idle people like himself lined the sidewalks, and the marchers passed between them with all the self-consciousness of enemy prisoners. There were children among them dressed in the costumes in which they had, for the newsreels, presented the Mayor with a package of tea, a petition, a protest, a constitution, a check, or a pair of

tickets. They hobbled through the darkness of the loft neighborhood like a mortified and destroyed people, toward Greeley Square.

[45]In the morning, Jack put the problem of finding an apartment for Joan up to his secretary. She started phoning real-estate agents, and by afternoon she had found a couple of available apartments in the West Twenties. Joan called Jack the next day to say that she had taken one of the apartments and to thank him.

Paragraphs 35–36 bridge Jack's wife's pregnancy. Notice that he never considers her important enough to name. She is little more than a lamp or cigarette box in his life. However, his manhood is salvaged through the fertility rite of his wife's pregnancy. At the wedding, Joan is again in conflict with a man—as anonymous and unimportant as Jack's wife. Jack refuses involvement.

Jack dismisses two years of his life with a whitespace transition. Observe that at no point does he report an incident which might reflect discredit on him.

Paragraphs 37–45 reveal that Jack is divorced. Magnanimously, he "gave her the apartment and all its furnishings." That the "story was in the newspapers" indicates his wife enjoyed some social standing (the orchard in Duxbury indicated the same). Had she been as unimportant in New York City as Jack (his job is scarcely mentioned), there would have been no reason for a newspaper to consider the divorce newsworthy. Jack does not overtly report such details, however. And their omission reveals far more about Jack than he would care to reveal. Joan's call indicates a civilized woman. She immediately expresses her regret in a straightforward fashion and drops the subject, getting on with the reason for her call. In her account of reasons for eviction, Joan is transparent: on the one hand, she is frank; on the other, she twice persuades Jack to agree it is "fantastic" and she asks his approval of her late hours. Jack sees her again as "serene and innocent," equating her recital with a torch song. He does not seem to regard a torch song as one sung by a person seeking new masochistic experience. He is moved to gallantry (she is a "big, splendid girl") and protectiveness of a British, starched quality. He is much less moved by the remote people (Poles, Norwegians, Danes, Jews, Chinese) in the war parade. What would a gallant young man from Ohio know about the motives of foreigners? Jack's secretary solves Joan's housing problem.

[46]Jack didn't see Joan again until the following summer. It was a Sunday evening; he had left a cocktail party in a Washington Square apartment and had decided to walk a few blocks up Fifth Avenue before he took a bus. As he was

passing the Brevoort, Joan called to him. She was with a man at one of the tables on the sidewalk. She looked cool and fresh, and the man appeared to be respectable. His name, it turned out, was Pete Bristol. He invited Jack to sit down and join in a celebration. Germany had invaded Russia that weekend, and Joan and Pete were drinking champagne to celebrate Russia's changed position in the war. The three of them drank champagne until it got dark. They had dinner and drank champagne with their dinner. They drank more champagne afterward and then went over to the Lafayette and then to two or three other places. Joan had always been tireless in her gentle way. She hated to see the night end, and it was after three o'clock when Jack stumbled into his apartment. The following morning he woke up haggard and sick, and with no recollection of the last hour or so of the previous evening. His suit was soiled and he had lost his hat. He didn't get to his office until eleven. Joan had already called him twice, and she called him again soon after he got in. There was no hoarseness at all in her voice. She said that she had to see him, and he agreed to meet her for lunch in a sea-food restaurant in the Fifties.

47 He was standing at the bar when she breezed in, looking as though she had taken no part in that calamitous night. The advice she wanted concerned selling her jewelry. Her grandmother had left her some jewelry, and she wanted to raise money on it but didn't know where to go. She took some rings and bracelets out of her purse and showed them to Jack. He said that he didn't know anything about jewelry but that he could lend her some money. "Oh, I couldn't borrow money from you, Jack," she said. "You see, I want to get the money for Pete. I want to help him. He wants to open an advertising agency, and he needs quite a lot to begin with." Jack didn't press her to accept his offer of a loan after that, and the project wasn't mentioned again during lunch.

48 He next heard about Joan from a young doctor who was a friend of theirs. "Have you seen Joan recently?" the doctor asked Jack one evening when they were having dinner together. He said no. "I gave her a checkup last week," the doctor said, "and while she's been through enough to kill the average mortal—and you'll never know what she's been through—she still has the constitution of a virtuous and healthy woman. Did you hear about the last one? She sold her jewelry to put him into some kind of a business, and as soon as he got the money, he left her for another girl, who had a car—a convertible."

Paragraphs 46–48 present the cool, fresh Joan as a woman aware and involved but strangely detached. She seems almost an observer, even of the scenes in which she is an actress. She refuses his offer of a loan, since the money is for Pete. While Jack does not evaluate her reasoning, the reader must see an honesty in it. Jack's allowing the subject to die indicts him as dishonest. The doctor friend who completes the narrative of Pete ends it with casual irony in "a convertible."

49 Jack was drafted into the Army in the spring of 1942. He was kept at Fort Dix for nearly a month, and during this time he came to New York in the evening whenever he could get permission. Those nights had for him the intense keenness of a reprieve, a sensation that was heightened by the fact that on the train in from Trenton women would often press upon him dog-eared copies of *Life* and half-eaten boxes of candy, as though the brown clothes he wore were surely cerements. He telephoned Joan from Pennsylvania Station one night. "Come right over, Jack," she said. "Come right over. I want you to meet Ralph."

50 She was living in that place in the West Twenties that Jack had found for her. The neighborhood was a slum. Ash cans stood in front of her house, and an old woman was there picking out bits of refuse and garbage and stuffing them into a perambulator. The house in which Joan's apartment was located was shabby, but the apartment itself seemed familiar. The furniture was the same. Joan was the same big, easy-going girl. "I'm so glad you called me," she said. "It's so good to see you. I'll make you a drink. I was having one myself. Ralph ought to be here by now. He promised to take me to dinner." Jack offered to take her to Cavanagh's, but she said that Ralph might come while she was out. "If he doesn't come by nine, I'm going to make myself a sandwich. I'm not really hungry."

51 Jack talked about the Army. She talked about the store. She had been working in the same place for—how long was it? He didn't know. He had never seen her at her desk and he couldn't imagine what she did. "I'm terribly sorry Ralph isn't here," she said. "I'm sure you'd like him. He's not a young man. He's a heart specialist who loves to play the viola." She turned on some lights, for the summer sky had got dark. "He has this dreadful wife on Riverside Drive and four ungrateful children. He—"

52 The noise of an air-raid siren, lugubrious and seeming to spring from pain, as if all the misery and indecision in the city had been given a voice, cut her off. Other sirens, in distant neighborhoods, sounded, until the dark air was full of their noise. "Let me fix you another drink before I have to turn out the lights," Joan said, and took his glass. She brought the drink back to him and snapped off the lights. They went to the windows, and, as children watch a thunderstorm, they watched the city darken. All the lights nearby went out but one. Air-raid wardens had begun to sound their whistles in the street. From a distant yard came a hoarse shriek of anger. "Put out your lights, you Fascists!" a woman screamed. "Put out your lights you Nazi Fascist Germans. Turn out your lights. Turn out your lights." The last light went off. They went away from the window and sat in the lightless room.

53 In the darkness, Joan began to talk about her departed lovers, and from what she said Jack gathered that they had all had a hard time. Nils, the suspect count, was dead. Hugh Bascomb, the drunk, had joined the Merchant Marine and was missing in the North Atlantic. Franz, the German, had taken poison the night the Nazis bombed Warsaw. "We listened to the news on the radio," Joan said, "and

then he went back to his hotel and took poison. The maid found him dead in the bathroom the next morning." When Jack asked her about the one who was going to open an advertising agency, she seemed at first to have forgotten him. "Oh, Pete," she said after a pause. "Well, he was always very sick, you know. He was supposed to go to Saranac, but he kept putting it off and putting it off and—" She stopped talking when she heard steps on the stairs, hoping, he supposed, that it was Ralph, but whoever it was turned at the landing and continued to the top of the house. "I wish Ralph would come," she said, with a sigh. "I want you to meet him." Jack asked her again to go out, but she refused, and when the all-clear sounded, he said goodbye.

Paragraphs 49–53 find Jack in the Army, aware of death ("as though the brown clothes he wore were surely cerements") and alone. Joan is in the apartment that "Jack had found for her." He obviously feels he did find it; the secretary to whom he delegated the responsibility is forgotten. He reveals much of his reaction pattern here. The story is told on his authority; if he can manipulate such facts, how reliable are his observations as objective reportings elsewhere? As they wait for Ralph, Jack sees Joan still "big, easy-going." He cannot imagine her at work. In the dark, Joan speaks of the men in her life—at least the ones Jack has known. Their removal from Joan's life curiously coincided with their removal from *all* life.

54 Jack was shipped from Dix to an infantry training camp in the Carolinas and from there to an infantry division stationed in Georgia. He had been in Georgia three months when he married a girl from the Augusta boarding-house aristocracy. A year or so later, he crossed the continent in a day coach and thought sententiously that the last he might see of the country he loved was the desert towns like Barstow, that the last he might hear of it was the ringing of the trolleys on the Bay Bridge. He was sent into the Pacific and returned to the United States twenty months later, uninjured and apparently unchanged. As soon as he received his furlough, he went to Augusta. He presented his wife with the souvenirs he had brought from the islands, quarrelled violently with her and her family, and, after making arrangements for her to get an Arkansas divorce, left for New York.

Paragraph 54 chronicles Jack's war marriage, war years, and war divorce. All of the experiences left him "apparently unchanged." His insensitivity could not be as clearly indicated by chapters of hyperbole. Understatement here reduces him to the level of a clod.

55 Jack was discharged from the Army at a camp in the East a few months later. He took a vacation and then went back to the job he had left in 1942. He

seemed to have picked up his life at approximately the moment when it had been interrupted by the war. In time, everything came to look and feel the same. He saw most of his old friends. Only two of the men he knew had been killed in the war. He didn't call Joan, but he met her one winter afternoon on a crosstown bus.

56 Her fresh face, her black clothes, and her soft voice instantly destroyed the sense—if he ever had such a sense—that anything had changed or intervened since their last meeting, three or four years ago. She asked him up for cocktails and he went to her apartment the next Saturday afternoon. Her room and her guests reminded him of the parties she had given when she had first come to New York. There was a woman with a fancy hat, an elderly doctor, and a man who stayed close to the radio, listening for news from the Balkans. Jack wondered which of the men belonged to Joan and decided on an Englishman who kept coughing into a handkerchief that he pulled out of his sleeve. Jack was right. "Isn't Stephen brilliant?" Joan asked him a little later, when they were alone in a corner. "He knows more about the Polynesians than anyone else in the world."

Paragraphs 55–56 reestablish Jack's civilian life, an "unchanged" life. Death and war left *him* untouched, so his life is untouched. Joan's reappearance ("fresh face . . . black clothes . . . soft voice") reinforces the illusion. He goes to her apartment and meets the coughing Stephen.

57 Jack had returned not only to his old job but to his old salary. Since living costs had doubled and since he was paying alimony to two wives, he had to draw on his savings. He took another job, which promised more money, but it didn't last long and he found himself out of work. This didn't bother him at all. He still had money in the bank, and anyhow it was easy to borrow from friends. His indifference was the consequence not of lassitude or despair but rather of an excess of hope. He had the feeling that he had only recently come to New York from Ohio. The sense that he was very young and that the best years of his life still lay before him was an illusion that he could not seem to escape. There was all the time in the world. He was living in hotels then, moving from one to another every five days.

58 In the spring, Jack moved to a furnished room in the badlands west of Central Park. He was running out of money. Then, when he began to feel that a job was a desperate necessity, he got sick. At first, he seemed to have only a bad cold, but he was unable to shake it and he began to run a fever and to cough blood. The fever kept him drowsy most of the time, but he roused himself occasionally and went out to a cafeteria for a meal. He felt sure that none of his friends knew where he was, and he was glad of this. He hadn't counted on Joan.

59 Late one morning, he heard her speaking in the hall with his landlady. A few moments later, she knocked on his door. He was lying on the bed in a pair of pants and a soiled pajama top, and he didn't answer. She knocked again and walked in. "I've been looking everywhere for you, Jack," she said. She spoke softly. "When

I found out that you were in a place like this I thought you must be broke or sick. I stopped at the bank and got some money, in case you're broke. I've brought you some Scotch. I thought a little drink wouldn't do you any harm. Want a little drink?"

60 Joan's dress was black. Her voice was low and serene. She sat in a chair beside his bed as if she had been coming there every day to nurse him. Her features had coarsened, he thought, but there were still very few lines in her face. She was heavier. She was nearly fat. She was wearing black cotton gloves. She got two glasses and poured Scotch into them. He drank his whiskey greedily. "I didn't get to bed until three last night," she said. Her voice had once before reminded him of a gentle and despairing song, but now, perhaps because he was sick, her mildness, the mourning she wore, her stealthy grace, made him uneasy. "It was one of those nights," she said. "We went to the theatre. Afterward, someone asked us up to his place. I don't know who he was. It was one of those places. They're so strange. There were some meat-eating plants and a collection of Chinese snuff bottles. Why do people collect Chinese snuff bottles? We all autographed a lampshade, as I remember, but I can't remember much."

61 Jack tried to sit up in bed, as if there were some need to defend himself, and then fell back again, against the pillows. "How did you find me, Joan?" he asked.

62 "It was simple," she said. "I called that hotel. The one you were staying in. They gave me this address. My secretary got the telephone number. Have another little drink."

63 "You know you've never come to a place of mine before—never," he said. "Why did you come now?"

64 "Why did I come, darling?" she asked. "What a question! I've known you for thirty years. You're the oldest friend I have in New York. Remember that night in the Village when it snowed and we stayed up until morning and drank whiskey sours for breakfast? That doesn't seem like twelve years ago. And that night—"

65 "I don't like to have you see me in a place like this," he said earnestly. He touched his face and felt his beard.

66 "And all the people who used to imitate Roosevelt," she said, as if she had not heard him, as if she were deaf. "And that place on Staten Island where we all used to go for dinner when Henry had a car. Poor Henry. He bought a place in Connecticut and went out there by himself, one weekend. He fell asleep with a lighted cigarette and the house, the barn, everything burned. Ethel took the children out to California." She poured more Scotch into his glass and handed it to him. She lighted a cigarette and put it between his lips. The intimacy of this gesture, which made it seem not only as if he were deathly ill but as if he were her lover, troubled him.

67 "As soon as I'm better," he said, "I'll take a room at a good hotel. I'll call you then. It was nice of you to come."

68 "Oh, don't be ashamed of this room, Jack," she said. "Rooms never bother

me. It doesn't seem to matter to me where I am. Stanley had a filthy room in Chelsea. At least, other people told me it was filthy. I never noticed it. Rats used to eat the food I brought him. He used to have to hang the food from the ceiling, from the light chain."

69 "I'll call you as soon as I'm better," Jack said. "I think I can sleep now if I'm left alone. I seem to need a lot of sleep."

70 "You really *are* sick, darling," she said. "You must have a fever." She sat on the edge of his bed and put a hand on his forehead.

71 "How is that Englishman, Joan?" he asked. "Do you still see him?"

72 "What Englishman?" she said.

73 "You know. I met him at your house. He kept a handkerchief up his sleeve. He coughed all the time. You know the one I mean."

74 "You must be thinking of someone else," she said. "I haven't had an Englishman at my place since the war. Of course, I can't remember everyone." She turned and, taking one of his hands, linked her fingers in his.

75 "He's dead, isn't he?" Jack said. "That Englishman's dead." He pushed her off the bed, and got up himself. "Get out," he said.

76 "You're sick, darling," she said. "I can't leave you alone here."

77 "Get out," he said again, and when she didn't move, he shouted, "What kind of an obscenity are you that you can smell sickness and death the way you do?"

78 "You poor darling."

79 "Does it make you feel young to watch the dying?" he shouted. "Is that the lewdness that keeps you young? Is that why you dress like a crow? Oh, I know there's nothing I can say that will hurt you. I know there's nothing filthy or corrupt or depraved or brutish or base that the others haven't tried, but this time you're wrong. I'm not ready. My life isn't ending. My life's beginning. There are wonderful years ahead of me. There are, there are wonderful, wonderful, wonderful years ahead of me, and when they're over, when it's time, then I'll call you. Then, as an old friend, I'll call you and give you whatever dirty pleasure you take in watching the dying, but until then, you and your ugly and misshapen forms will leave me alone."

80 She finished her drink and looked at her watch. "I guess I'd better show up at the office," she said. "I'll see you later. I'll come back tonight. You'll feel better then, you poor darling." She closed the door after her, and he heard her light step on the stairs.

Paragraphs 57–80 trace Jack's disintegration. Unable to pick up life where he had left it before the war, he drifts from job to job, hotel to hotel, affluence to poverty, health to illness. Unable to mature, he feels everything is as it has always been, even deceiving himself when he begins to cough blood. At first, Joan seems unchanged—her black dress, her low, serene voice. Then, for the first time, Jack thinks he detects a change in her. And, as he detects it, it seems to intensify (paragraph

60). Her appearance unnerves him, but her explanation is plausible. There is something about her that touches his vanity as he declares he does not wish her to see him as he is.

As Joan speaks of new deaths, Jack remembers Stephen—the Englishman who also coughed. And he suddenly sees Joan as an "obscenity" that can "smell sickness and death." Terrified, he lashes out at her, hurting her as so many others have done. She leaves to go back to the job she has held successfully through the years.

81 Jack emptied the whiskey bottle into the sink. He began to dress. He stuffed his dirty clothes into a bag. He was trembling and crying with sickness and fear. He could see the blue sky from his window, and in his fear it seemed miraculous that the sky should be blue, that the white clouds should remind him of snow, that from the sidewalk he could hear the shrill voices of children shrieking, "I'm the king of the mountain, I'm the king of the mountain, I'm the king of the mountain." He emptied the ashtray containing his nail parings and cigarette butts into the toilet, and swept the floor with a shirt, so that there would be no trace of his life, of his body, when that lewd and searching shape of death came there to find him in the evening. □

Paragraph 81 creates a man crazed by terror. He empties the gift whiskey Joan brought. Packing, he removes all traces of himself from the room. Nail parings and cigarette butts go into the toilet; he seeks to erase all usable evidences of his presence by sweeping up his own dust. Black magic will not help Joan, the creature of death, when she comes to find him. The allusions are skillfully worked in here.

The advantage of narrative is apparent in this story. Were sharply defined scenes employed, the reader would have a clearer picture of Jack's mind. As it is, Jack may or may not be mad. He may or may not have been ordinary throughout the story. Was he merely imperceptive about Joan, or was he imperceptive about all people—himself most of all? Panoramic narrative keeps him always far enough out of range that the reader must decide for himself. And that final reader decision will reveal the theme of the story. Is this a "horror" story of Joan, the death-finder? Is it a story of a man who is so self-protective he must blame even his death on someone? Is it a statement of the meaningless futility of existence? Or is it all of these things?

"Torch Song" explores the character of Joan Harris carefully and thoroughly—from a biased and limited point of view. Simultaneously, it explores Jack Lorey's character from a narrower, less obvious point of view. Without a Jack Lorey to seek her motives, Joan Harris would be uninteresting, for it is only in the development and discovery of her unique sickness that she has reason to exist. Had a less egocentric character than Jack assessed her, she would immediately be unmasked as a tedious hostess to disaster. By juxtaposing her against an insensitive egocentric and revealing them in contrast, John Cheever creates two unforgettable characters. On first reading, you probably classified the story as character-structured. If so, your more careful analysis should have revealed narrative as the structural ingredient on which the story most heavily relies.

The eighty-one paragraphs cover a period of "a few years" (paragraph 1). They are countable as transitions: "spring and summer of his second year in town" (paragraph 3); "sometime the next winter" (paragraph 6); "in the spring" (paragraph 9); "The baby, a boy, was born in May" (paragraph 35); "When Jack's son was less than two years old" (paragraph 37); "Jack didn't see Joan until the following summer" (paragraph 46); "Jack was drafted into the Army in the spring of 1942" (paragraph 49); "Jack was discharged" (paragraph 55); and "In the spring" (paragraph 58). Thirteen years are chronicled as Jack's life is measured in affairs and war; Joan's, in deaths and embarrassing moments.

Character changes in Joan do not occur; realization and inordinate fear at the end of the thirteen meaningless years mark Jack's development. The reader knows little enough about either character at the end. They are clinically interesting, but their values, their human aspirations, their identifiable qualities are never revealed. Is Joan the "lewd and searching shape of death" Jack envisions in his sick terror? A veteran of some thirty-five years, two wives, and a war, is Jack the irresponsible, unrealistic illusionist of paragraph 57? Actually, the reader must accept the author's narrative for what it is: a chronicle of two unreal people in a very real New York. The panoramic sweep of the city blends with the sweep of time, and the reader becomes engrossed in narrative progression rather than in character development.

A plot outline will reveal the artful construction of the story:

I. Enveloping action (paragraphs 1–2).
   A. Point of view is established.
   B. Setting, background, main characters are established.

II. Generating circumstances—moments in time as Jack's life crosses Joan's.
   A. Jack's free love period (paragraphs 3–4).
      1. Sees Joan with drunk escort.
      2. Refuses involvement.

B. Jack's "romantic type" period (paragraphs 5–8).
   1. Sees Joan with count.
   2. Hears of her experience with dope addicts, criminals, abortion.
   3. Visits her.
C. Jack's engagement (paragraphs 9–18).
   1. Goes to Joan's for cocktails (Hugh).
   2. Notes recent-death atmosphere.
D. Jack's first marriage (paragraphs 19–34).
   1. Visits Joan (Franz).
   2. Hears Joan brutalized.
E. Jack's wife's pregnancy (paragraphs 35–36).
   1. Attends wedding of Ohio friend.
   2. Sees Joan brutalized by nameless man.
F. Jack's first divorce (paragraphs 37–45).
   1. Joan asks help in finding apartment (Philip).
   2. Jack's secretary locates apartment.
G. Jack's pre-induction days (paragraphs 46–48).
   1. Encounters Joan and Pete.
   2. Hears of her financial loss.
H. Jack's first month in Army (paragraphs 49–53).
   1. Visits Joan (Ralph).
   2. Joan recounts deaths of the count, Hugh, Franz, Pete.
I. Jack's wartime marriage and divorce (paragraph 54).
J. Jack's return to civilian life (paragraphs 55–56).
   1. Visits Joan.
   2. Meets Stephen who coughs.
K. Jack's job failures (paragraphs 57–80).
   1. Broke, Jack grows seriously ill.
   2. Joan finds him—her first visit.
   3. She reveals Henry's death.
   4. She mentions Stanley who was very ill.
   5. Jack demands to know what happened to Stephen.
   6. Jack sees Joan as a harbinger of death.

III. Climax (paragraph 81).
   A. Fearful, Jack prepares to flee.
   B. Overcome by terror, he removes traces of himself that might be used in black magic rites.

Jack's meaningless journey through the experiences of his life leaves him unable to assess the spiritual death that has slowly overtaken him. Instead, he collects a growing body of evidence that he interprets as he wishes. While his thoughts are explored, they are never profound. Is the reader to trust Jack's assessment of Joan's role in life, or is the reader to assume that Jack is a naive, unrealistic man who has mismanaged his own life without regret and, as he seems insensitive to his own affairs, cannot therefore be trusted to evaluate Joan's life? Or is the reader to accept Jack's evaluation as correct?

That decision on the part of the reader adds complication to the plot. At no single point in the outline can complication be labeled, for there is no stateable conflict between Jack and Joan. Is there conflict in Jack's life as he sees failure follow failure and remains immature? Is there conflict in Joan's life as she goes from disagreeable experience and death to new brutality and new death? No philosophical considerations are explored, but a conflict certainly exists as Jack's version of truth builds, slowly at first, then insistently, to create his terror. Open conflict occurs in the next to the last scene, but it is a conflict that has been subtly suggesting itself from the first sentence of paragraph 1. The climax, too, is deliberately unresolved by the author. Is Jack crazed by fever and running away to certain death, thus actually joining the long list of those who died after knowing Joan? (Did you notice she was never present at any death?) Or is Jack finally caught by the slow drift of his own life and, unable to stop the drift, disintegrating into madness? These questions are unanswered by the author. The reader must decide, and his decision creates conflict in him as he becomes the silent but transfixed spectator in the story. From that vantage point, the reader follows a narrative pattern of discovery as Jack builds a growing body of evidence from incidental experience.

The Story of Description

Descriptive structure is particularly effective for stories depicting action (sports stories, war stories) or the activities of a single character. Dialog, in both cases, becomes something of a problem to include naturally, and, as a result, the characters must react to their surroundings if the narrative flow is to be interesting. In such stories, characters are usually stock, for they are not the focal point. The reader of such stories is, ordinarily, less interested in character analysis than in character behavior. He wishes to see how a problem is met and defeated. If the plot revolves around a baseball game, for example, the reader expects descriptions of the stadium or field of action. He wants the background material which will allow him to accept the characters primarily as extensions of his concept of baseball players. He is primarily interested in the game and the characters' reactions to the game. Any conflicts the characters have must be related directly to the action at hand. And the reader expects the author to be an authority. Language and knowledge of the game are well-known to him; so he will reject a story by an author whose knowledge is inadequate, whose errors are obvious.

Geographical descriptions must also be accurate. To plant elm trees in south Florida or seagrape trees in Ohio is sure to alienate the reader. In writing about a city he has never visited, the author will study maps, guide books, picture postcards—anything to make his setting accurate. The reader will quickly spot an error if one slips in, and the author's authority will disappear as if by magic.

The setting of the next story, Jack London's "All Gold Cañon," is California, a state he knew and loved. His descriptions reveal that knowledge and love, for they are accurate and meticulous in their details. In 1897, London participated in the Alaskan gold rush as a prospector. When, in the story, he discusses panning procedures or methods of locating veins, authority pervades his lines. The reader does not question the author's knowledge; verisimilitude is born in accurate detail.

As you read the story the first time, notice how little you know about the prospector outside the confines of the immediate story. What his early life contributed, what his later life will be, are of no interest. His actions and behavior against the vivid background of gold-rush California *are* of interest. In physical appearance and mental activity, he might be any one of hundreds of prospectors. As a unique character, he is uninteresting, for he is a stock concept. As he behaves representatively of the classic concept of a prospector, he becomes interesting.

Observe the use of verbs and verbals in the course of narrative description. Nouns such as *coat* and *antler* assume movement in the forms London chooses to use: *coated* and *antlered* (paragraph 1). Such attention to language moves the narrative flow rapidly forward, allowing it no possibility of becoming static.

Two aspects of the short story as it developed in America are particularly noticeable in this story. The first is *local color,* an attention to the geographical local flavor of characters and their language ("Miss Tempy's Watchers," pp. 277–285, is a classic story of this type). The second is *naturalism,* a documentary technique wherein the author tries to create a scientific report about the characters and the world they live in. London is not an extreme naturalistic writer, however, for his words embody more than the denotative objectivity of such reports. His local color effects temper and soften the scientific.

Read the story first in its entirety.

All Gold Cañon

by Jack London

[1]It was the green heart of the cañon, where the walls swerved back from the rigid plan and relieved their harshness of line by making a little sheltered nook and filling it to the brim with sweetness and roundness and softness. Here all things rested. Even the narrow stream ceased its turbulent downrush long enough to form a quiet pool. Knee-deep in the water, with drooping head and half-shut eyes, drowsed a red-coated, many-antlered buck.

The first fifteen paragraphs constitute enveloping action. The scene is set, carefully and completely, and the main character is introduced. Conflict is at first merely suggested as the creatures in nature flee man. His actual conflict with nature begins to take shape in paragraph 15 when his gold pan is mentioned the second time. The California setting is suggested in the title, as London chooses to use the Spanish spelling *cañon* rather than *canyon.*

Space order serves as organizational structure for the description of the cañon. A verb-of-being in sentence 1 suggests the cañon exists timelessly. Notice the difference in tone if the sentence is rewritten to eliminate the expletive and verb-of-being, changing the scene into action from the beginning: "At the green heart of the cañon, the walls swerved back from the rigid plan," etc. The timeless quality is gone; *swerved* and *relieved* seem less forceful, removed from contrast with *was.* After the initial verb-of-being, movement stirs in the verbs, however, and the nouns and adjectives are verbal in tone. Notice *sheltered, turbulent downrush, quiet, drooping, half-shut, red-coated,* and *many-antlered.* The scene is alive with motion of a drowsy nature. And from the quiet pool in the center of the cañon, almost as if seeing the scene through the buck's half-shut eyes, the reader surveys the scene.

[2]On one side, beginning at the very lip of the pool, was a tiny meadow, a cool, resilient surface of green that extended to the base of the frowning wall. Beyond the pool a gentle slope of earth ran up and up to meet the opposing wall. Fine grass covered the slope—grass that was spangled with flowers, with here and there patches of color,—orange and purple and golden. Below, the cañon was shut in. There was no view. The walls leaned together abruptly, and the cañon ended in a chaos of rocks, moss-covered and hidden by a green screen of vines and creepers and boughs of trees. Up the cañon rose far hills and peaks, the big foothills, pine-covered and remote. And far beyond, like clouds upon the border of the sky, towered minarets of white, where the Sierra's eternal snows flashed austerely the blazes of the sun.

[3]There was no dust in the cañon. The leaves and flowers were clean and virginal. The grass was young velvet. Over the pool three cottonwoods sent their snowy fluffs fluttering down the quiet air. On the slope the blossoms of the wine-wooded manzanita filled the air with springtime odors, while the leaves, wise with experience, were already beginning their vertical twist against the coming aridity of summer. In the open spaces on the slope, beyond the farthest shadow reach of the manzanita, poised the mariposa lilies, like so many flights of jeweled moths suddenly arrested and on the verge of trembling into flight again. Here and there that woods harlequin, the madrone, permitting itself to be caught in the act of changing its pea-green trunk to madder red, breathed its fragrance into the air from great clusters of waxen bells. Creamy white were these bells, shaped like lilies of the valley, with the sweetness of perfume that is of the springtime.

Paragraph 2 employs verbs skillfully. A verb-of-being opens the description, but action verbs and verbals move the reader's eye from one image to another. Nor is sight alone invoked. The words *cool* and *resilient* activate the sense of touch. The eyes are thrilled with "orange and purple and golden." The nose can almost smell the sweet perfume as the walls lean together and trap the fragrance. Paragraph 3 appeals to sight, touch, taste, smell, and sound. No dust touches the reader's skin or grates between his tongue and teeth. The velvet grass moves him to luxury. The silent fall of cottonwood fluff is a velvet whisper as his nose is greeted by the winey fragrance of manzanita and madrone. Notice the vivid personification in this paragraph.

[4]There was not a sigh of wind. The air was drowsy with its weight of perfume. It was a sweetness that would have been cloying had the air been heavy and humid. But the air was sharp and thin. It was as starlight transmuted into atmosphere, shot through and warmed by sunshine, and flower-drenched with sweetness.

[5]An occasional butterfly drifted in and out through the patches of light and shade. And from all about rose the low and sleepy hum of mountain bees,—feasting sybarites that jostled one another good-naturedly at the board, nor found time for rough discourtesy. So quietly did the little stream drip and ripple its way through the cañon that it spoke only in faint and occasional gurgles. The voice of the stream was as a drowsy whisper, ever interrupted by dozings and silences, ever lifted again in the awakenings.

[6]The motion of all things was a drifting in the heart of the cañon. Sunshine and butterflies drifted in and out among the trees. The hum of the bees and the whisper of the stream were a drifting of sound. And the drifting sound and drifting color seemed to weave together in the making of a delicate and intangible fabric which was the spirit of the place. It was a spirit of peace that was not of death but of smooth-pulsing life, of quietude that was not silence, of movement that was not

action, of repose that was quick with existence without being violent with struggle and travail. The spirit of the place was the spirit of the peace of the living, somnolent with the easement and content of prosperity, and undisturbed by rumors of far wars.

[7] The red-coated, many-antlered buck acknowledged the lordship of the spirit of the place and dozed knee-deep in the cool, shaded pool. There seemed no flies to vex him, and he was languid with rest. Sometimes his ears moved when the stream awoke and whispered; but they moved lazily, with foreknowledge that it was merely the stream grown garrulous at discovery that it had slept.

Paragraphs 4–7 intensify the imagery, inducing lethargy and luxurious ease in the reader. (Compare these paragraphs with Keats' "To Autumn" and Chapter 1 of *Peyton Place,* p. 82. Notice the effects achieved by each author; notice the technique of each author as he achieves the effects.) Poetic devices are employed lavishly. Examine the last sentence of paragraph 4 for its poetic excellence. In paragraph 5, *bees* become *sybarites* as metaphor and allusion work together. Personification creates gentle onomatopoeia in the brook. Paragraph 6 almost achieves metered poetry form; you could easily arrange the lines into a free verse pattern. Anapests and iambs dominate the paragraph until the consonance and rhyme of the final spondee have moved the reader into near somnolence.

[8] But there came a time when the buck's ears lifted and tensed with swift eagerness for sound. His head was turned down the cañon. His sensitive, quivering nostrils scented the air. His eyes could not pierce the green screen through which the stream rippled away, but to his ears came the voice of a man. It was a steady, monotonous, singsong voice. Once the buck heard the harsh clash of metal upon rock. At the sound he snorted with a sudden start that jerked him through the air from water to meadow, and his feet sank into the young velvet, while he pricked his ears and again scented the air. Then he stole across the tiny meadow, pausing once and again to listen, and faded away out of the cañon like a wraith, soft-footed and without sound.

The transitional *But* which opens paragraph 8 is almost like the crack of a distant rifle. Observe the poetic change of pace: "‸But||there came|a time|when the buck's|ears lifted|and tensed|with swift|eagerness|for sound." The next sentence thrusts the passage into prose by shifting from active to passive voice, breaking the poetic flow. Notice the different pace if *was* is removed: "His head turned down the cañon"—violence overlays the scene as harsh imagery replaces the natural softness. *Pierce, harsh clash, metal, snorted,* and *jerked* move the reader toward the generating circumstances of the story. Conflict has intruded.

[9]The clash of steel-shod soles against the rocks began to be heard, and the man's voice grew louder. It was raised in a sort of chant and became distinct with nearness, so that the words could be heard:

Tu'n around an' tu'n yo' face
Untoe them sweet hills of grace
(D' pow'rs of sin yo' am scornin'!).
Look about an' look aroun'
Fling yo' sin-pack on d' groun'
(Yo will meet wid d' Lord in d' mornin'!).

[10]A sound of scrambling accompanied the song, and the spirit of the place fled away on the heels of the red-coated buck. The green screen was burst asunder, and a man peered out at the meadow and the pool and the sloping side hill. He was a deliberate sort of man. He took in the scene with one embracing glance, then ran his eyes over the details to verify the general impression. Then, and not until then, did he open his mouth in vivid and solemn approval: "Smoke of life an' snakes of purgatory! Will you just look at that! Wood an' water an' grass an' a side hill! A pocket hunter's delight an' a cayuse's paradise! Cool green for tired eyes! Pink pills for pale people ain't in it. A secret pasture for prospectors and a resting place for tired burros, by damn!"

Passive voice verbs, impersonal in nature, change the tone of narrative in paragraph 9. The unnatural quality of the dialectical spiritual he sings contrasts harshly with God's world of the first seven paragraphs. Paragraph 10 presents complete contrast at two levels. The "spirit of the place" flees as the "human" assumes command. He is a "deliberate sort of a man," earthy yet religious (notice his first statement). References to the cayuse and burro mark him as the stock prospector who thinks of his dumb companion. The indications of his profession are subtle ("pocket hunter's delight," "pasture for prospectors") and binding as London "pastures" the prospector, equating him with his burro. Virility permeates his "by damn!" in sharp contrast to the gentle poetry of "Pink pills for pale people."

[11]He was a sandy-complexioned man in whose face geniality and humor seemed the salient characteristics. It was a mobile face, quick-changing to inward mood and thought. Thinking was in him a visible process. Ideas chased across his face

like wind flaws across the surface of a lake. His hair, sparse and unkempt of growth, was as indeterminate and colorless as his complexion. It would seem that all the color of his frame had gone into his eyes, for they were startlingly blue. Also, they were laughing and merry eyes, within them much of the naïveté and wonder of the child; and yet, in an unassertive way, they contained much of calm self-reliance and strength of purpose founded upon self-experience and experience of the world.

12 From out the screen of vines and creepers he flung ahead of him a miner's pick and shovel and gold-pan. Then he crawled out himself into the open. He was clad in faded overalls and black cotton shirt, with hobnailed brogans on his feet, and on his head a hat whose shapelessness and stains advertised the rough usage of wind and rain and sun and camp smoke. He stood erect, seeing wide-eyed the secrecy of the scene and sensuously inhaling the warm, sweet breath of the cañon garden through nostrils that dilated and quivered with delight. His eyes narrowed to laughing slits of blue, his face wreathed itself in joy, and his mouth curled in a smile as he cried aloud: "Jumping dandelions and happy hollyhocks, but that smells good to me! Talk about your attar o' roses an' cologne factories! They ain't in it!"

13 He had the habit of soliloquy. His quick-changing facial expressions might tell every thought and mood, but the tongue, perforce, ran hard after, repeating, like a second Boswell.

14 The man lay down on the lip of the pool and drank long and deep of its water. "Tastes good to me," he murmured, lifting his head and gazing across the pool at the side hill, while he wiped his mouth with the back of his hand. The side hill attracted his attention. Still lying on his stomach, he studied the hill formation long and carefully. It was a practiced eye that traveled up the slope to the crumbling cañon wall and back and down again to the edge of the pool. He scrambled to his feet and favored the side hill with a second survey.

15 "Looks good to me," he concluded, picking up his pick and shovel and gold-pan.

The description in paragraphs 11–12 gains its effectiveness from the diction, almost academic in tone. *Geniality, salient,* and *mobile* contrast sharply with "overalls and hobnailed brogans." His idiom is a curious conglomerate of homespun hyperbole, gentility, and carelessness. Compare the poetic quality of *happy hollyhocks, cologne,* and *ain't.* Paragraph 13 provides further contrast. Compare the narrative statement "He had the habit of soliloquy" with "They ain't in it." The allusion to Boswell intensifies the description. In paragraph 14, the prospector replaces the buck, occupying the same vantage point. And the reader sees the cañon again as the man's gaze follows the path of earlier description. The line of dialog "Tastes good to me" serves as foreshadowing transition into the generating circumstances as he says, "Looks good to me" in paragraph 15.

[16]He crossed the stream below the pool, stepping agilely from stone to stone. Where the side hill touched the water he dug up a shovelful of dirt and put it into the gold-pan. He squatted down, holding the pan in his two hands and partly immersing it in the stream. Then he imparted to the pan a deft circular motion that sent the water sluicing in and out through the dirt and gravel. The larger and the lighter particles worked to the surface, and these, by a skillful dipping movement of the pan, he spilled out and over the edge. Occasionally, to expedite matters, he rested the pan and with his fingers raked out the large pebbles and pieces of rock.

[17]The contents of the pan diminished rapidly until only fine dirt and the smallest bits of gravel remained. At this stage he began to work very deliberately and carefully. It was fine washing, and he washed fine and finer, with a keen scrutiny and delicate and fastidious touch. At last the pan seemed empty of everything but water; but with a quick semicircular flirt that sent the water flying over the shallow rim into the stream, he disclosed a layer of black sand on the bottom of the pan. So thin was this layer that it was like a streak of paint. He examined it closely. In the midst of it was a tiny golden speck. He dribbled a little water in over the depressed edge of the pan. With a quick flirt he sent the water sluicing across the bottom, turning the grains of black sand over and over. A second tiny golden speck rewarded his effort.

[18]The washing had now become very fine,—fine beyond all need of ordinary placer mining. He worked the black sand, a small portion at a time, up the shallow rim of the pan. Each small portion he examined sharply, so that his eyes saw every grain of it before he allowed it to slide over the edge and away. Jealously, bit by bit, he let the black sand slip away. A golden speck, no larger than a pin point, appeared on the rim, and by his manipulation of the water it returned to the bottom of the pan. And in such fashion another speck was disclosed, and another. Great was his care of them. Like a shepherd he herded his flock of golden specks so that not one should be lost. At last, of the pan of dirt nothing remained but his golden herd. He counted it, and then, after all his labor, sent it flying out of the pan with one final swirl of water.

[19]But his blue eyes were shining with desire as he rose to his feet. "Seven," he muttered aloud, asserting the sum of the specks for which he had toiled so hard and which he had so wantonly thrown away. "Seven," he repeated, with the emphasis of one trying to impress a number on his memory.

Paragraphs 16–19 could stand alone as a "how to" essay in panning for gold. Process theme procedure is strictly observed in writing so exact that it might be considered technical were not narrative and descriptive words and phrases inserted. The reader is captured by the process; he is interested in counting specks also. The verisimilitude resulting from authorial accuracy causes the reader to identify with the prospector, and the story becomes a personal experience from this point on. Language such as *sluicing, flirt,* and *placer* is technically correct, and the words become vital and apparent as they are juxtaposed against such poetic lines as "Like a shepherd he herded his flock of golden specks so that no one should be lost." The biblical imagery of his dialog, his introductory spiritual, and this line all combine to establish him as a "good" man, and the reader identifies more completely with him. When he kills in self-defense later in the story, the act seems less brutal, more justifiable as a result of the care London lavishes on the story at this point.

[20]He stood still a long while, surveying the hillside. In his eyes was a curiosity, new aroused and burning. There was an exultance about his bearing and a keenness like that of a hunting animal catching the fresh scent of game.

[21]He moved down the stream a few steps and took a second panful of dirt.

[22]Again came the careful washing, the jealous herding of the golden specks, and the wantonness with which he sent them flying into the stream when he had counted their number.

[23]"Five," he muttered, and repeated, "five."

[24]He could not forbear another survey of the hill before filling the pan farther down the stream. His golden herds diminished. "Four, three, two, two, one," were his memory tabulations as he moved down the stream. When but one speck of gold rewarded his washing, he stopped and built a fire of dry twigs. Into this he thrust the gold-pan and burned it till it was blue-black. He held up the pan and examined it critically. Then he nodded approbation. Against such a color background he could defy the tiniest yellow speck to elude him.

[25]Still moving down the stream, he panned again. A single speck was his reward. A third pan contained no gold at all. Not satisfied with this, he panned three times again, taking his shovels of dirt within a foot of one another. Each pan proved empty of gold, and the fact, instead of discouraging him, seemed to give him satisfaction. His elation increased with each barren washing, until he arose, exclaiming jubilantly, "If it ain't the real thing, may God knock off my head with sour apples!"

[26]Returning to where he had started operations, he began to pan up the stream. At first his golden herds increased—increased prodigiously. "Fourteen, eighteen, twenty-one, twenty-six," ran his memory tabulations. Just above the pool he struck his richest pan,—thirty-five colors.

[27]"Almost enough to save," he remarked regretfully, as he allowed the water to sweep them away.

28 The sun climbed to the top of the sky. The man worked on. Pan by pan he went up the stream, the tally of the results steadily decreasing.

29 "It's just booful, the way it peters out," he exulted when a shovelful of dirt contained no more than a single speck of gold.

30 And when no specks at all were found in several pans, he straightened up and favored the hillside with a confident glance.

31 "Ah, ha! Mr. Pocket!" he cried out, as though to an auditor hidden somewhere above him beneath the surface of the slope. "Ah, ha! Mr. Pocket! I'm a-comin', I'm a-comin', an' I'm shorely gwine to get yer! You heah me, Mr. Pocket? I'm gwine to get yer as shore as punkins ain't cauliflowers!"

Paragraphs 20–30 generate suspense artfully as ignorance of the process moves the reader to disappointment which becomes pervasive as the old man burns the pan. Then, in paragraph 25, when the old man's piety and blasphemous levity penetrate the reader's consciousness, wild hope is regenerated and suspense builds again to paragraph 31. Here the prospector's *apostrophe* (direct address to an absent person, abstract idea, or personified thing in nature) creates exultation in the reader. He and the prospector have outwitted nature through clever detection. Only now is the reader aware of the intensity of the scene which has compelled his attention.

32 He turned and flung a measuring glance at the sun poised above him in the azure of the cloudless sky. Then he went down the cañon, following the line of shovel holes he had made in filling the pans. He crossed the stream below the pool and disappeared through the green screen. There was little opportunity for the spirit of the place to return with its quietude and repose, for the man's voice, raised in ragtime song, still dominated the cañon with possession.

33 After a time, with a greater clashing of steel-shod feet on rock, he returned. The green screen was tremendously agitated. It surged back and forth in the throes of a struggle. There was a loud grating and clanging of metal. The man's voice leaped to a higher pitch and was sharp with imperativeness. A large body plunged and panted. There was a snapping and ripping and rending, and amid a shower of falling leaves a horse burst through the screen. On its back was a pack, and from this trailed broken vines and torn creepers. The animal gazed with astonished eyes at the scene into which it had been precipitated, then dropped its head to the grass and began contentedly to graze. A second horse scrambled into view, slipping once on the mossy rocks and regaining equilibrium when its hoofs sank into the yielding surface of the meadow. It was riderless; on its back was a high-horned Mexican saddle, scarred and discolored by long usage.

Paragraph 32 allows a slacking of interest after the artfully built climax, and it passes transitionally over the period of the prospector's absence. The violent language of paragraph 33 prepares the reader for the reentry of the man and his horses. The Mexican saddle suggests the widely-traveled wanderer.

[34]The man brought up the rear. He threw off pack and saddle, with an eye to camp location, and gave the animals their freedom to graze. He unpacked his food and got out frying pan and coffeepot. He gathered an armful of dry wood, and with a few stones made a place for his fire.

[35]"My!" he said, "but I've got an appetite. I could scoff iron filings an' horseshoe nails an' thank you kindly, ma'am, for a second helpin'."

[36]He straightened up, and while he reached for matches in the pocket of his overalls his eyes traveled across the pool to the side hill. His fingers had clutched the matchbox, but they relaxed their hold and the hand came out empty. The man wavered perceptibly. He looked at his preparations for cooking and he looked at the hill.

[37]"Guess I'll take another whack at her," he concluded, starting to cross the stream.

[38]"They ain't no sense in it, I know," he mumbled apologetically. "But keepin' grub back an hour ain't goin' to hurt none, I reckon."

Paragraphs 34–38 are technically structured to resemble saṁvegha—the reader is led to expect a scene designed merely to show time passage. The colorful dialog of paragraph 35 lessens his disappointment, and he is delighted to discover he will participate in a second prospecting attempt.

[39]A few feet back from his first line of test pans he started a second line. The sun dropped down the western sky, the shadows lengthened, but the man worked on. He began a third line of test pans. He was crosscutting the hillside, line by line, as he ascended. The center of each line produced the richest pans, while the ends came where no colors showed in the pan. And as he ascended the hillside the lines grew perceptibly shorter. The regularity with which their length diminished served to indicate that somewhere up the slope the last line would be so short as to have scarcely length at all, and that beyond could come only a point. The design was growing into an inverted V. The converging sides of this V marked the boundaries of the gold-bearing dirt.

[40]The apex of the V was evidently the man's goal. Often he ran his eye along the converging sides and on up the hill, trying to divine the apex,—the point where the gold-bearing dirt must cease. Here resided "Mr. Pocket," for so the man familiarly addressed the imaginary point above him on the slope, crying out: "Come down out o' that, Mr. Pocket! Be right smart an' agreeable, an' come down!"

[41]"All right," he would add later, in a voice resigned to determination. "All

right, Mr. Pocket. It's plain to me I got to come right up an' snatch you out bald-headed. An' I'll do it! I'll do it!" he would threaten still later.

42 Each pan he carried down to the water to wash, and as he went higher up the hill the pans grew richer, until he began to save the gold in an empty baking-powder can which he carried carelessly in his hip pocket. So engrossed was he in his toil that he did not notice the long twilight of oncoming night. It was not until he tried vainly to see the gold colors in the bottom of the pan that he realized the passage of time. He straightened up abruptly. An expression of whimsical wonderment and awe overspread his face as he drawled, "Gosh darn my buttons! if I didn't plumb forget dinner!"

Paragraphs 39–42 are panoramic in movement, but the careful process of paragraphs 16–19 is a reader memory that overlays the panorama, suggesting a scene that is not written. The interspersed dialog intensifies verisimilitude and suspense as it strengthens the characterization. The growing riches of each pan creates mounting suspense.

43 He stumbled across the stream in the darkness and lighted his long-delayed fire. Flapjacks and bacon and warmed-over beans constituted his supper. Then he smoked a pipe by the smoldering coals, listening to the night noises and watching the moonlight stream through the cañon. After that he unrolled his bed, took off his heavy shoes, and pulled the blankets up to his chin. His face showed white in the moonlight, like the face of a corpse. But it was a corpse that knew its resurrection, for the man rose suddenly on one elbow and gazed across the hillside.

44 "Good night, Mr. Pocket," he called sleepily. "Good night."

45 He slept through the early gray of morning until the direct rays of the sun smote his closed eyelids, when he awoke with a start and looked about him until he had established the continuity of his existence and identified his present self with the days previously lived.

46 To dress he had merely to buckle on his shoes. He glanced at his fireplace and at his hillside, wavered, but fought down the temptation and started the fire.

47 "Keep yer shirt on, Bill; keep yer shirt on," he admonished himself. "What's the good of rushin'? No use in gettin' all het up an' sweaty. Mr. Pocket'll wait for you. He ain't a-runnin' away before you can get yer breakfast. Now, what you want, Bill, is something fresh in yer bill o' fare. So it's up to you to go an' get it."

48 He cut a short pole at the water's edge and drew from one of his pockets a bit of line and a draggled fly that had once been a royal coachman.

49 "Mebbe they'll bite in the early morning," he muttered as he made his first cast into the pool. And a moment later he was gleefully crying: "What'd I tell you, eh? What'd I tell you?"

50 He had no reel, nor any inclination to waste time, and by main strength, and swiftly, he drew out of the water a flashing ten-inch trout. Three more, caught in

rapid succession, furnished his breakfast. When he came to the steppingstones on his way to his hillside, he was struck by a sudden thought, and paused.

Paragraphs 43–50 come as something of a relief. The reader is so engrossed in the panning process that he too is hungry and tired. He relaxes with the prospector, and verisimilitude surrounds the dinner, the pipe, and the retirement preparations. The reader rests in the vicarious experiences. As stories structured on attention to description are usually written for men, the fishing half-scene is cleverly inserted. It places the suspense of fishing (under handicap, you notice) in tension with the reader's desire to return to panning. Thus is suspense carefully built. The details, though sketchy, are accurate and, therefore, lend further verisimilitude. A trout fisherman knows the royal coachman is a good trout fly.

[51]"I'd just better take a hike downstream a ways," he said. "There's no tellin' what cuss may be snoopin' around."

[52]But he crossed over on the stones, and with a "I really oughter take that hike," the need of the precaution passed out of his mind and he fell to work.

The end of paragraph 50 plus paragraphs 51–52 foreshadows the arrival of the claim jumper. Their casual insertion misleads the reader who, at this point, rests secure in the hidden remoteness of the cañon. Later, when the bushwhacker appears, the reader is prepared, however, because the possibility of the incident is planted here.

[53]At nightfall he straightened up. The small of his back was stiff from stooping toil, and as he put his hand behind him to soothe the protesting muscles, he said: "Now what d'ye think of that, by damn? I clean forgot my dinner again! If I don't watch out, I'll sure be degeneratin' into a two-meal-a-day crank."

[54]"Pockets is the damnedest things I ever see for makin' a man absent-minded," he communed that night, as he crawled into his blankets. Nor did he forget to call up the hillside, "Good night, Mr. Pocket! Good night!"

Paragraphs 53–54 are compressed panorama designed to heighten suspense and lend verisimilitude. A quick success would lack dramatic flair. The reader is here tantalized. Had London written the day's scene in detail, it would have been anticlimactic.

[55]Rising with the sun and snatching a hasty breakfast, he was early at work. A fever seemed to be growing in him, nor did the increasing richness of the test pans allay this fever. There was a flush in his cheek other than that made by the

heat of the sun, and he was oblivious to fatigue and the passage of time. When he filled a pan with dirt, he ran down the hill to wash it; nor could he forbear running up the hill again, panting and stumbling profanely, to refill the pan.

56 He was now a hundred yards from the water, and the inverted V was assuming definite proportions. The width of the pay dirt steadily decreased, and the man extended in his mind's eye the sides of the V to their meeting place far up the hill. This was his goal, the apex of the V, and he panned many times to locate it.

57 "Just about two yards above that manzanita bush an' a yard to the right," he finally concluded.

58 Then the temptation seized him. "As plain as the nose on your face," he said as he abandoned his laborious crosscutting and climbed to the indicated apex. He filled a pan and carried it down the hill to wash. It contained no trace of gold. He dug deep, and he dug shallow, filling and washing a dozen pans, and was unrewarded even by the tiniest golden speck. He was enraged at having yielded to the temptation, and cursed himself blasphemously and pridelessly. Then he went down the hill and took up the crosscutting.

Paragraphs 55–57 play on the anticlimax possibility. The discovery, desirable though it may be, is premature. Paragraph 58 establishes the prematurity and satisfies the reader by confirming his judgment. He has become the second person now. He is participating thoroughly.

59 "Slow an' certain, Bill; slow an' certain," he crooned. "Short cuts to fortune ain't in your line, an' it's about time you know it. Get wise, Bill; get wise. Slow an' certain's the only hand you can play; so go to it, an' keep to it, too."

Paragraph 59 creates greater sympathy for the prospector. The reader's "I told you so" attitude is rewarded.

60 As the crosscuts decreased, showing that the sides of the V were converging, the depth of the V increased. The gold trace was dipping into the hill. It was only at thirty inches beneath the surface that he could get colors in his pan. The dirt he found at twenty-five inches from the surface, and at thirty-five inches, yielded barren pans. At the base of the V, by the water's edge, he had found the gold colors at the grass roots. The higher he went up the hill, the deeper the gold dipped. To dig a hole three feet deep in order to get one test pan was a task of no mean magnitude; while between the man and the apex intervened an untold number of such holes to be dug. "An' there's no tellin' how much deeper it'll pitch," he sighed, in a moment's pause, while his fingers soothed his aching back.

Paragraph 60 builds suspense painfully as the logic of the location method overtakes the reader. The process theme is tempered here with suggestion to allow reader participation as he supplies the missing information. The lucid presentation to this point has given him the necessary information. Suspense is retained through this device.

61 Feverish with desire, with aching back and stiffening muscles, with pick and shovel gouging and mauling the soft brown earth, the man toiled up the hill. Before him was the smooth slope, spangled with flowers and made sweet with their breath. Behind him was devastation. It looked like some terrible eruption breaking out on the smooth skin of the hill. His slow progress was like that of a slug, befouling beauty with a monstrous trail.

Paragraph 61 contrasts the natural beauty and man's devastation of the land. Even action stories such as this may provide quite logical space for social comment. The recognition of the devastation also reveals new facets of the prospector's character.

62 Though the dipping gold trace increased the man's work, he found consolation in the increasing richness of the pans. Twenty cents, thirty cents, fifty cents, sixty cents, were the values of the gold found in the pans, and at nightfall he washed his banner pan, which gave him a dollar's worth of gold dust from a shovelful of dirt.

Paragraph 62 provides panoramic progression as he works toward the source of the gold, and time, as measured by days, becomes hazy. The reader is unsure if one day or several have elapsed in this paragraph. The physical expenditure of effort has assumed magnitude, and a subtle moral lesson is suggested: only hard work brings rewards. The reader is pleased to accept the implication, for he sees his own life as such a progression and identifies with the prospector more intensely as a result.

63 "I'll just bet it's my luck to have some inquisitive cuss come buttin' in here on my pasture," he mumbled sleepily that night as he pulled the blankets up to his chin.

64 Suddenly he sat upright. "Bill!" he called sharply. "Now, listen to me, Bill; d'ye hear! It's up to you, tomorrow mornin', to mosey round an' see what you can see. Understand? Tomorrow morning, an' don't you forget it!"

65 He yawned and glanced across at his side hill. "Good night, Mr. Pocket," he called.

66 In the morning he stole a march on the sun, for he had finished breakfast when its first rays caught him, and he was climbing the wall of the cañon where it crumbled away and gave footing. From the outlook at the top he found himself in the midst of loneliness.

[67]As far as he could see, chain after chain of mountains heaved themselves into his vision. To the east his eyes, leaping the miles between range and range and between many ranges, brought up at last against the white-peaked Sierras,—the main crest, where the backbone of the Western world reared itself against the sky. To the north and south he could see more distinctly the cross systems that broke through the main trend of the sea of mountains. To the west the ranges fell away, one behind the other, diminishing and fading into the gentle foothills that, in turn, descended into the great valley which he could not see.

[68]And in all that mighty sweep of earth he saw no sign of man nor of the handiwork of man, save only the torn bosom of the hillside at his feet. The man looked long and carefully. Once, far down his own cañon, he thought he saw in the air a faint hint of smoke. He looked again and decided that it was the purple haze of the hills made dark by a convolution of the cañon wall at its back.

Paragraphs 63–68 foreshadow the bushwhacker once again, this time with greater force. As the Sierras seem to come into existence in the skillful description built on expository principles, a faint hint of smoke lingers in the air and in the reader's mind. But the biblical quality of the language in the opening sentence of paragraph 68 allays reader fear. God qualities seem to reside in the old man.

[69]"Hey, you, Mr. Pocket!" he called down into the cañon. "Stand out from under! I'm a-comin', Mr. Pocket! I'm a-comin'!"

[70]The heavy brogans on the man's feet made him appear clumsy-footed, but he swung down from the giddy height as lightly and airily as a mountain goat. A rock, turning under his foot on the edge of the precipice, did not disconcert him. He seemed to know the precise time required for the turn to culminate in disaster, and in the meantime he utilized the false footing itself for the momentary earth contact necessary to carry him on into safety. Where the earth sloped so steeply that it was impossible to stand for a second upright, the man did not hesitate. His foot pressed the impossible surface for but a fraction of the fatal second and gave him the bound that carried him onward. Again, where even the fraction of a second's footing was out of the question, he would swing his body past by a moment's handgrip on a jutting knob of rock, a crevice, or a precariously rooted shrub. At last, with a wild leap and yell, he exchanged the face of the wall for an earth slide and finished the descent in the midst of several tons of sliding earth and gravel.

Paragraphs 69–70 negate any suspicion that the prospector may have been hasty in dismissing the smoke, for his sure-footedness on the heights makes him seem young, perceptive, and responsive to danger signals. He seems, further, to possess adequate reflexes to cope with any emergency. On the one hand, the foreshadowed encounter is submerged; on the other, the reflexes and quick thinking which are to save his life during that encounter are foreshadowed. The godlike quality of paragraph 68 resides in a body that is simian in physical ability. The demigods of the Greeks—Hercules and Achilles—were compounded of such mixed elements. And they, too, had the childish quality the old man exhibits as he speaks repeatedly to "Mr. Pocket." Why does Jack London lavish this subtle care in building a *stock* character? In many ways, the stock character is more difficult to create than any other kind. He must be the epitome of many concepts if the reader is to round him out in imagination. Remember: a stock character that is adequately realized in a story remains a stock character only in the plot. The reader rounds him out in his imagination, making him more complex than the rounded character who is confined by authorial limitations.

71 His first pan of the morning washed out over two dollars in coarse gold. It was from the center of the V. To either side the diminution in the values of the pans was swift. His lines of crosscutting holes were growing very short. The converging sides of the inverted V were only a few yards apart. Their meeting point was only a few yards above him. But the pay streak was dipping deeper and deeper into the earth. By early afternoon he was sinking the test holes five feet before the pans could show the gold trace.

72 For that matter, the gold trace had become something more than a trace; it was a placer mine in itself, and the man resolved to come back, after he had found the pocket, and work over the ground. But the increasing richness of the pans began to worry him. By later afternoon the worth of the pans had grown to three and four dollars. The man scratched his head perplexedly and looked a few feet up the hill at the mazanita bush that marked approximately the apex of the V. He nodded his head and said oracularly: "It's one o' two things, Bill; one o' two things. Either Mr. Pocket's spilled himself all out an' down the hill, or else Mr. Pocket's that damned rich you maybe won't be able to carry him all away with you. And that'd be hell, wouldn't it, now?" He chuckled at contemplation of so pleasant a dilemma.

73 Nightfall found him by the edge of the stream, his eyes wrestling with the gathering darkness over the washing of a five-dollar pan.

74 "Wisht I had an electric light to go on working," he said.

Paragraphs 71–74 carry the action forward, suggesting two possible complications: the pocket has spilled or it is too rich to be taken completely. As the pans increase in value, the suspense mounts steadily.

75 He found sleep difficult that night. Many times he composed himself and closed his eyes for slumber to overtake him; but his blood pounded with too strong desire, and as many times his eyes opened and he murmured wearily, "Wisht it was sunup."

76 Sleep came to him in the end, but his eyes were open with the first paling of the stars, and the gray of dawn caught him with breakfast finished and climbing the hillside in the direction of the secret abiding place of Mr. Pocket.

77 The first crosscut the man made, there was space for only three holes, so narrow had become the pay streak and so close was he to the fountainhead of the golden stream he had been following for four days.

78 "Be ca'm, Bill; be ca'm," he admonished himself as he broke ground for the final hole where the sides of the V had at last come together in a point.

79 "I've got the almighty cinch on you, Mr. Pocket, an' you can't lose me," he said many times as he sank the hole deeper and deeper.

80 Four feet, five feet, six feet, he dug his way down into the earth. The digging grew harder. His pick grated on broken rock. He examined the rock. "Rotten quartz" was his conclusion as, with the shovel, he cleared the bottom of the hole of loose dirt. He attacked the crumbling quartz with the pick, bursting the disintegrating rock asunder with every stroke.

81 He thrust his shovel into the loose mass. His eye caught a gleam of yellow. He dropped the shovel and squatted suddenly on his heels. As a farmer rubs the clinging earth from fresh-dug potatoes, so the man, a piece of rotten quartz held in both hands, rubbed the dirt away.

Paragraphs 75–81 build suspense swiftly as the pace of the story quickens. Notice the increased pace of language in paragraph 80 and the first three sentences of 81. Then an involved complex sentence, broken by an absolute phrase, slows the pace, almost making the reader hold his breath. Suspense is at a peak. Will the pocket be revealed?

82 "Sufferin' Sardanapolis!" he cried. "Lumps an' chunks of it! Lumps an' chunks of it!"

Paragraph 82 answers the question with artful, poetic dialog as the climax is created in one line.

83 It was only half rock he held in his hand. The other half was virgin gold. He dropped it into his pan and examined another piece. Little yellow was to be seen, but with his strong fingers he crumbled the rotten quartz away till both hands were filled with glowing yellow.

84 He rubbed the dirt away from fragment after fragment, tossing them into the gold-pan. It was a treasure hole. So much had the quartz rotted away that there was less of it than there was of gold. Now and again he found a piece to which no rock clung,—a piece that was all gold. A chunk where the pick had laid open the heart of the gold glittered like a handful of yellow jewels, and he cocked his head at it and slowly turned it around and over to observe the rich play of the light upon it.

85"Talk about yer Too Much Gold diggin's!" the man snorted contemptuously. "Why, this diggin' 'd make it look like thirty cents. This diggin' is All Gold. An' right here an' now I name this yere cañon 'All Gold Cañon,' b' gosh!"

Paragraphs 83–85 seem, at first, a little anticlimactic, but they suggest denouement also. The reader is rewarded with the historical allusion to the "Too Much Gold" strike—a measuring device indicating the great wealth of Bill's pocket. As Bill names the cañon, the reader is satisfied with the literary experience; he reads into the next paragraph feeling that a structural shadow has fallen on the experience.

86Still squatting on his heels, he continued examining the fragments and tossing them into the pan. Suddenly there came to him a premonition of danger. It seemed a shadow had fallen upon him. But there was no shadow. His heart had given a great jump up into his throat and was choking him. Then his blood slowly chilled and he felt the sweat of his shirt cold against his flesh.

This subtle manipulation of plot could be disastrous, but London has carefully foreshadowed the scene throughout the story. Light and shadow have frequently been discussed. "The spirit of the place" remains in the reader's memory. Bill's demi-god qualities have been established. His intuitive knowledge and patience as he tracked Mr. Pocket have been brought to full existence. The claim-jumper's arrival has been foreshadowed twice.

87He did not spring up nor look around. He did not move. He was considering the nature of the premonition he had received, trying to locate the source of the mysterious force that had warned him, striving to sense the imperative presence of the unseen thing that threatened him. There is an aura of things hostile, made manifest by messengers too refined for the senses to know; and this aura he felt, but knew not how he felt it. His was the feeling as when a cloud passes over the sun. It seemed that between him and life had passed something dark and smothering and menacing, a gloom, as it were, that swallowed up life and made for death,—his death.

88Every force of his being impelled him to spring up and confront the unseen danger, but his soul dominated the panic, and he remained squatting on his heels, in his hands a chunk of gold. He did not dare to look around, but he knew by now that there was something behind him and above him. He made believe to be interested in the gold in his hand. He examined it critically, turned it over and over, and rubbed the dirt from it. And all the time he knew that something behind him was looking at the gold over his shoulder.

89Still feigning interest in the chunk of gold in his hand, he listened intently, and he heard the breathing of the thing behind him. His eyes searched the ground in front of him for a weapon, but they saw only the uprooted gold, worthless to him now in his extremity. There was his pick, a handy weapon on occasion; but this was not such an occasion. The man realized his predicament. He was in a narrow hole that was seven feet deep. His head did not come to the surface of the ground. He was in a trap.

90 He remained squatting on his heels. He was quite cool and collected; but his mind, considering every factor, showed him only his helplessness. He continued rubbing the dirt from the quartz fragments and throwing the gold into the pan. There was nothing else for him to do. Yet he knew that he would have to rise up, sooner or later, and face the danger that breathed at his back. The minutes passed, and with the passage of each minute he knew that by so much he was nearer the time when he must stand up, or else,—and his wet shirt went cold against his flesh again at the thought,—or else he might receive death as he stooped there over his treasure.

Paragraphs 86–90 combine scene and stream-of-consciousness as all London's preparations focus down into the hole and into Bill's mind. The reader is caught by this new complication, this more painful suspense. Life is more important than gold. Through the paragraphs run many didactic reader considerations, unstated by the author, implicit in the scene.

91 Still he squatted on his heels, rubbing dirt from gold and debating in just what manner he should rise up. He might rise up with a rush and claw his way out of the hole to meet whatever threatened on the even footing above ground; or he might rise up slowly and carelessly, and feign casually to discover the thing that breathed at his back. His instinct and every fighting fiber of his body favored the mad, clawing rush to the surface. His intellect, and the craft thereof, favored the slow and cautious meeting with the thing that menaced and that he could not see. And while he debated, a loud, crashing noise burst on his ear. At the same instant he received a stunning blow on the left side of the back, and from the point of impact felt a rush of flame through his flesh. He sprang up in the air, but halfway to his feet collapsed. His body crumpled in like a leaf withered in sudden heat, and he came down, his chest across his pan of gold, his face in the dirt and rock, his legs tangled and twisted because of the restricted space at the bottom of the hole. His legs twitched convulsively several times. His body was shaken as with a mighty ague. There was a slow expansion of the lungs, accompanied by a deep sigh. Then the air was slowly, very slowly, exhaled, and his body as slowly flattened itself down into inertness.

Paragraph 91 focuses on the gunshot and Bill's collapse. The reader assumes Bill is dead, for the language is controlled to create that impression while suggesting Bill's crafty play-acting. His sense of the dramatic has been completely developed in his running soliloquy, a dramatic device (see paragraph 13). His sense of timing has been established in such scenes as his descent from the cañon wall. Language here focuses subtly on the reader's memory of those scenes. Notice, here, he receives a "stunning" blow—not a deadly one. He springs up but collapses (deliberation is suggested in the verbs). When his body crumples, it is "like a leaf withered in sudden heat." Wilted leaves are not dead; they revive when the heat passes. A sly humor rests in his convulsive twitchings and shakings "as with a mighty ague." In calm reflection, the reader can see Bill's dramatic flair almost trapping him as he interprets a death scene in his own way. Notice: "the air was slowly, very slowly, exhaled and his body as slowly flattened itself down into inertness." The passive voice states Bill did the action of exhaling; his body *flattened* itself—a conscious act. The first reading, however, is so shattering as climax follows climax that the reader fails to see the obvious.

92 Above, revolver in hand, a man was peering down over the edge of the hole. He peered for a long time at the prone and motionless body beneath him. After a while the stranger sat down on the edge of the hole so that he could see into it, and rested the revolver on his knee. Reaching his hand into a pocket, he drew out a wisp of brown paper. Into this he dropped a few crumbs of tobacco. The combination became a cigarette, brown and squat, with the ends turned in. Not once did he take his eyes from the body at the bottom of the hole. He lighted the cigarette and drew its smoke into his lungs with a caressing intake of the breath. He smoked slowly. Once the cigarette went out and he relighted it. And all the while he studied the body beneath him.

93 In the end he tossed the cigarette stub away and rose to his feet. He moved to the edge of the hole. Spanning it, a hand resting on each edge, and with the revolver still in the right hand, he muscled his body down into the hole. While his feet were yet a yard from the bottom he released his hands and dropped down.

Paragraphs 92–93 slow the pace and allow the reader time to hate the bushwhacker who makes himself even more hateful in his casual smoking scene.

94 At the instant his feet struck bottom he saw the pocket miner's arm leap out, and his own legs knew a swift, jerking grip that overthrew him. In the nature of the jump his revolver hand was above his head. Swiftly as the grip had flashed about his legs, just as swiftly he brought the revolver down. He was still in the air, his fall in process of completion, when he pulled the trigger. The explosion was deafening in the confined space. The smoke filled the hole so that he could see nothing. He

struck the bottom on his back, and like a cat's the pocket miner's body was on top of him. Even as the miner's body passed on top the stranger crooked in his right arm to fire; and even in that instant the miner, with a quick thrust of elbow, struck his wrist. The muzzle was thrown up, and the bullet thudded into the dirt of the side of the hole.

95 The next instant the stranger felt the miner's hand grip his wrist. The struggle was now for the revolver. Each man strove to turn it against the other's body. The smoke in the hole was clearing. The stranger, lying on his back, was beginning to see dimly. But suddenly he was blinded by a handful of dirt deliberately flung into his eyes by his antagonist. In that moment of shock his grip on the revolver was broken. In the next moment he felt a smashing darkness descend upon his brain, and in the midst of the darkness even the darkness ceased.

96 But the pocket miner fired again and again, until the revolver was empty. Then he tossed it from him and, breathing heavily, sat down on the dead man's legs.

Paragraphs 94–96 employ process theme narrative once again as the fight is carefully detailed in order of action. Point of view becomes apparent and logical in these paragraphs. Third person limited omniscient would have been inadequate. Even though it is Bill's story, he didn't see the cañon before his arrival; so those scenes would not have been possible. Such a point of view would have necessitated disclosure of Bill's survival in paragraph 91. The bushwhacker's thoughts could not be included as they are in paragraph 95 when "he felt a smashing darkness descend upon his brain." However, in these paragraphs, the point of view lessens in omniscience, allowing the reader to be a spectator in an exciting scene. The use of third person omniscient point of view is further justified as the reader almost feels the story is told on God's authority. The religious mood established in the opening scene, the biblical language, the triumph of right—all contribute to the prevailing tone.

97 The miner was sobbing and struggling for breath. "Measly skunk!" he panted; "a-campin' on my trail an' lettin' me do the work, an' then shootin' me in the back!"

98 He was half crying from anger and exhaustion. He peered at the face of the dead man. It was sprinkled with loose dirt and gravel, and it was difficult to distinguish the features.

99 "Never laid eyes on him before," the miner concluded his scrutiny. "Just a common an' ordinary thief, damn him! An' he shot me in the back! He shot me in the back!"

100 He opened his shirt and felt himself, front and back, on his left side.

101 "Went clean through, and no harm done!" he cried jubilantly. "I'll bet he aimed all right all right; but he drew the gun over when he pulled the trigger—the cuss! But I fixed 'm! Oh, I fixed 'm!"

102 His fingers were investigating the bullet hole in his side, and a shade of regret passed over his face. "It's goin' to be stiffer'n hell," he said. "An' it's up to me to get mended an' get out o' here."

103 He crawled out of the hole and went down the hill to his camp. Half an hour later he returned, leading his pack horse. His open shirt disclosed the rude bandages with which he had dressed his wounds. He was slow and awkward with his left-hand movements, but that did not prevent his using the arm.

104 The bight of the pack rope under the dead man's shoulders enabled him to heave the body out of the hole. Then he set to work gathering up his gold. He worked steadily for several hours, pausing often to rest his stiffening shoulder and to exclaim: "He shot me in the back, the measly skunk! He shot me in the back!"

105 When his treasure was quite cleaned up and wrapped securely into a number of blanket-covered parcels, he made an estimate of its value.

106 "Four hundred pounds, or I'm a Hottentot," he concluded. "Say two hundred in quartz an' dirt; that leaves two hundred pounds of gold. Bill! Wake up! Two hundred pounds of gold! Forty thousand dollars! An' it's yourn—all yourn!"

107 He scratched his head delightedly and his fingers blundered into an unfamiliar groove. They quested along it for several inches. It was a crease through his scalp where the second bullet had plowed.

108 He walked angrily over to the dead man.

109 "You would, would you?" he bullied. "You would, eh? Well, I fixed you good an' plenty, an' I'll give you decent burial, too. That's more 'n you'd have done for me."

110 He dragged the body to the edge of the hole and toppled it in. It struck the bottom with a dull crash, on its side, the face twisted up to the light. The miner peered down at it.

111 "An' you shot me in the back!" he said accusingly.

112 With pick and shovel he filled the hole. Then he loaded the gold on his horse. It was too great a load for the animal, and when he had gained his camp he transferred part of it to his saddle horse. Even so, he was compelled to abandon a portion of his outfit,—pick and shovel and gold-pan, extra food and cooking utensils, and divers odds and ends.

113 The sun was at the zenith when the man forced the horses at the screen of vines and creepers. To climb the huge bowlders the animals were compelled to uprear and struggle blindly through the tangled mass of vegetation. Once the saddle horse fell heavily, and the man removed the pack to get the animal on his feet. After it started on its way again the man thrust his head out from among the leaves and peered up at the side hill.

114 "The measly skunk!" he said.

The reader is in sympathy with Bill for many reasons as paragraphs 97–114 reveal him as the character the reader prefers to identify with.

His wonder at the bushwhacker's conduct is almost childlike in its naivete (paragraph 111). His "I fixed 'm!" is no more vindictive than is his "An' you shot me in the back!" He is like a child, incapable of understanding such behavior. That he gives the nameless man a "decent" burial further removes guilt from him. To round out Bill's kindness, London returns to the kindness-to-animals theme of paragraph 10.

115 There was a ripping and tearing of vines and boughs. The trees surged back and forth, marking the passage of the animals through the midst of them. There was a clashing of steel-shod hoofs on stone, and now and again an oath or a sharp cry of command. Then the voice of the man was raised in song:

Tu'n around an' tu'n yo' face
Untoe them sweet hills of grace
    (D' pow'rs of sin yo' am scornin'!).
Look about an' look aroun',
Fling yo' sin-pack on d' groun'
    (Yo' will meet wid d' Lord in d' mornin'!).

116 The song grew faint and fainter, and through the silence crept back the spirit of the place. The stream once more drowsed and whispered; the hum of the mountain bees rose sleepily. Down through the perfume-weighted air fluttered the snowy fluffs of the cottonwoods. The butterflies drifted in and out among the trees, and over all blazed the quiet sunshine. Only remained the hoof marks in the meadow and the torn hillside to mark the boisterous trail of the life that had broken the peace of the place and passed on. □

Paragraph 115 reverses the order of paragraphs 8–9. Paragraph 116 returns the setting to the description of paragraphs 1–6. The marks of man will be obliterated in a few weeks' time as nature effaces all signs of his presence.

Description moves the reader into the story, through the story, and out of the story. But the end completes a circle that suggests the story will be retold in the reader's memory many times.

The Story of Dialog

Stories structured on dialog are varied and interesting *if* the author has developed his ear and can perceive and translate to paper the subtle nuances of idiom and diction that characterize individual speech. Hemingway's "The Killers" is a classic example of the story structured exclusively on dialog, and, if you have never read it, you should, observing the speech peculiarities which distinguish the individual speakers.

As dialog is paramount in such stories, much narrative and description are deliberately omitted. That does not mean the reader has no sense of them; he has. They come through the suggestions in dialog in a curious fashion. As Hemingway is quite probably the most successful author of such stories, let him explain:

> People in a novel, not skillfully constructed *characters,* must be projected from the writer's assimilated experience, from his knowledge, from his head, from his heart and from all there is of him. If he ever has luck as well as seriousness and gets them out entire they will have more than one dimension and they will last a long time. A good writer should know as near everything as possible. Naturally he will not. A great enough writer seems to be born with knowledge. But he really is not; he has only been born with the ability to learn in a quicker ratio to the passage of time than other men and without conscious application, and with an intelligence to accept or reject what is already presented as knowledge. There are some things which cannot be learned quickly and time, which is all we have, must be paid heavily for their acquiring. They are the very simplest things and because it takes a man's life to know them the little new that each man gets from life is very costly and the only heritage he has to leave. Every novel which is truly written contributes to the total of knowledge which is there at the disposal of the next writer who comes, but the next writer must pay, always, a certain nominal percentage in experience to be able to understand and assimilate what is available as his birthright and what he must, in turn, take his departure from. If a writer of prose knows enough about what he is writing about he may omit things that he knows and the reader, if the writer is writing truly enough, will have a feeling of those things as strongly as though the writer had stated them. The dignity of movement of an ice-berg is due to only one-eighth of it being above water. A writer who omits things because he does not know them only makes hollow places in his writing.*

That "feeling of those things" is what we have called "scene," and a sense of scene is lacking in all too many published writers. The sense of "nowness" created by scene can usually be traced to an author's skillful use of dialog. If he has not mastered this element, his work will not seem to be happening at this moment as the reader reads.

H. H. Munro ("Saki") is adept at creating unique characters and revealing their weaknesses and strengths through dialog. As you read "The Open Window," observe the vocabularies, syntactical peculiarities, and conversational pacings of each character. You should also notice Saki's controlled use of narrative and description—a use confined to their contribution to the dialog. All of the elements of fiction work

**Death in the Afternoon* (New York, 1932), pp. 191–192.

harmoniously in this masterpiece of humor, but it is dialog which makes the story brilliant and unforgettable.

Read the story first in its entirety.

The Open Window

by "Saki" (H. H. Munro)

1"My aunt will be down presently, Mr. Nuttel," said a very self-possessed young lady of fifteen; "in the meantime you must try to put up with me."

Paragraph 1 combines dialog and narrative in balanced proportion to create scene, establish enveloping action, introduce the two main characters, and sketch one of them—all in only twenty-seven words. The importance of names is delightfully apparent in this story. The reader expects Mr. Nuttel to be a humorous character. In life, names mean relatively little; in fiction, they are a distinct aid in characterization. Not only does the reader agree that the "young lady" (notice, she is not "a girl") is "*very* self-possessed," he also finds her well-educated and articulate.

2Framton Nuttel endeavoured to say the correct something which should duly flatter the niece of the moment without unduly discounting the aunt that was to come. Privately he doubted more than ever whether these formal visits on a succession of total strangers would do much toward helping the nerve cure which he was supposed to be undergoing.

Paragraph 2 creates the character which Nuttel's name suggested. He is overly cautious, anxious to please. He is thoroughly introverted and a bit of a hypocrite.

3"I know how it will be," his sister had said when he was preparing to migrate to this rural retreat; "you will bury yourself down there and not speak to a living soul, and your nerves will be worse than ever from moping. I shall just give you letters of introduction to all the people I know there. Some of them, as far as I can remember, were quite nice."

The flashback seems logical and natural in paragraph 3 as a result of the transition sentence in the paragraph preceding it. Nuttel's stuffiness and concern with himself are further indicated in the diction of "preparing to migrate to this rural retreat." Nuttel's sister is perceptive, and her perception further establishes his self-interest.

4 Framton wondered whether Mrs. Sappleton, the lady to whom he was presenting one of the letters of introduction, came into the nice division.

Paragraph 4 suggests Framton's pessimism—if he wonders, he doubts. Mrs. Sappleton's name quickly sketches a picture of her also. It suggests a less than complimentary description.

5 "Do you know many of the people round here?" asked the niece, when she judged that they had had sufficient silent communion.

From paragraph 5, dialog occupies the major portion of the story, the necessary background having been given in paragraphs 1–4. Paragraph 5 places the young lady in command. It is she who judges the "silent communion" sufficient. This line serves two purposes: it is ironic, for they are not sharing ideas; it foreshadows her cleverness. She has assessed Framton. Her question is, of course, a standard, polite, conversational gambit.

6 "Hardly a soul," said Framton. "My sister was staying here, at the rectory, you know, some four years ago, and she gave me letters of introduction to some of the people here."

7 He made the last statement in a tone of distinct regret.

Framton's response in paragraph 6 is stock, but his tone definitely is not. And to indicate Framton's lack of good manners, thereby justifying any treatment he receives, Saki gives the narrative statement a paragraph (7). That the girl is "very self-possessed" indicates she is aware of nuance. That she deferred to Framton in paragraph 1 indicates she is sensitive. That she is capable of judging "sufficient silent communion" virtually proves her sensitivity. The "tone of distinct regret" would be obvious and distasteful to her as it is, certainly, a breach of good taste and an affront from one whose presence is, at best, intrusive.

8 "Then you know practically nothing about my aunt?" pursued the self-possessed young lady.

Her self-possession is reemphasized in paragraph 8 as she "pursues" her earlier question. Subtle foreshadowing exists here for the perceptive reader. The question is, of course, designed to suggest how elaborate her revenge may be.

9 "Only her name and address," admitted the caller. He was wondering whether Mrs. Sappleton was in the married or widowed state. An indefinable something about the room seemed to suggest masculine habitation.

Framton's reply (paragraph 9) lacks grace, but it serves precisely the purpose the niece seeks. His idle curiosity again indicates an insensitivity which prejudices the reader against him.

Should you scan Framton's and the niece's speech, you would observe she speaks in an iambic-anapestic pattern of interesting variation. His speech is unimaginative prose. While a reader is usually unaware of such speech patterns, an author deliberately establishes them. This is not to suggest conversation is written as poetry; a trained ear will simply make distinctions.

10 "Her great tragedy happened just three years ago," said the child; "that would be since your sister's time."

The dramatic launching-forth in paragraph 10 switches to irregular dactyls for effect; anapestic narrative breaks the line; the anapestic pattern is picked up at the end. The artful switch in poetic pace is reinforced as the "very self-possessed young lady of fifteen" becomes "the child."

11 "Her tragedy?" asked Framton; somehow, in this restful country spot, tragedies seemed out of place.

12 "You may wonder why we keep that window wide open on an October afternoon," said the niece, indicating a large French window that opened on to a lawn.

Paragraph 12 would delight an ancient Homer strumming his lyre to the alliterative *w*'s and assonantal *o*'s as they create their mournful magic. Her gesture ("indicating") may be of the head or hand; Saki is focusing on dialog, allowing the captivated reader to create whatever pleases him.

13 "It is quite warm for the time of the year," said Framton; "but has that window got anything to do with the tragedy?"

The prosaic Framton's response is logical; the narrative skill of the niece compels his question.

14 "Out through that window, three years ago to a day, her husband and her two young brothers went off for their day's shooting. They never came back. In crossing the moor to their favourite snipe-shooting ground they were all three engulfed in a treacherous piece of bog. It had been that dreadful wet summer, you know, and places that were safe in other years gave way suddenly without warning. Their bodies were never recovered. That was the dreadful part of it." Here the child's voice lost its self-possessed note and became falteringly human. "Poor aunt always thinks

that they will come back some day, they and the little brown spaniel that was lost with them, and walk in at that window just as they used to do. That is why the window is kept open every evening till it is quite dusk. Poor dear aunt, she has often told me how they went out, her husband with his white waterproof coat over his arm, and Ronnie, her youngest brother, singing, 'Bertie, why do you bound?' as he always did to tease her, because she said it got on her nerves. Do you know, sometimes on still, quiet evenings like this, I almost get a creepy feeling that they will all walk in through that window—"

"Out through | that window || three years ago | to a day" is as epic in structure as a line from *Beowulf:* "Wide-famed | was Be | owulf, || wide vaunt | ed his name." She understands the power of narrative poetry. The remainder of her speech can be written in poetic lines that, with some variation, follow the pattern. The poetic diction intensifies in such phrases as "gave way suddenly without warning." "They never came back" parallels "That was the dreadful part of it" almost as a refrain. Her narrative is organized to lead to a climax at the proper time. Until then, she dramatically shudders and breaks off (paragraph 15).

15 She broke off with a little shudder. It was a relief to Framton when the aunt bustled into the room with a whirl of apologies for being late in making her appearance.

16 "I hope Vera has been amusing you?" she said.

The aunt "bustled into the room" and, as one would expect, she is a "whirl of apologies" and aware of "making her appearance." A predictable and tiresome woman is rapidly sketched. Her prosaic question reveals the unimaginative woman completely. The reader is allowed access to the niece's name. It is, ironically, Vera ("truth").

17 "She has been very interesting," said Framton.

Framton's answer is predictably vague, recalling his caution in paragraph 2.

18 "I hope you don't mind the open window," said Mrs. Sappleton briskly; "my husband and brothers will be home directly from shooting, and they always come in this way. They've been out for snipe in the marshes to-day, so they'll make a fine mess over my poor carpets. So like you menfolks, isn't it?"

19 She rattled on cheerfully about the shooting and the scarcity of birds and the prospects for duck in the winter. To Framton it was all purely horrible. He made a desperate but only partially successful effort to turn the talk on to a less ghastly topic; he was conscious that his hostess was giving him only a fragment of her

attention, and her eyes were constantly straying past him to the open window and the lawn beyond. It was certainly an unfortunate coincidence that he should have paid his visit on this tragic anniversary.

20"The doctors agree in ordering me complete rest, an absence of mental excitement, and avoidance of anything in the nature of violent physical exercise," announced Framton, who laboured under the tolerably wide-spread delusion that total strangers and chance acquaintances are hungry for the least detail of one's ailments and infirmities, their cause and cure. "On the matter of diet they are not so much in agreement," he continued.

Mrs. Sappleton's speech (paragraph 18) is no surprise to Vera, but it is "purely horrible" to Framton. His dull introversion and egocentricity are presented with a delightful commentary on the delusions of those who enjoy poor health. If you have been uncertain of point of view, this paragraph reveals it as third person limited omniscient (Framton's) with the author's presence unconcealed.

21"No?" said Mrs. Sappleton, in a voice which replaced a yawn only at the last moment. Then she suddenly brightened into alert attention—but not to what Framton was saying.

22"Here they are at last!" she cried. "Just in time for tea, and don't they look as if they were muddy up to the eyes!"

Mrs. Sappleton is as rude as Framton (paragraph 21) and her trite phraseology ("muddy up to the eyes") establishes verisimilitude in her dialog.

23Framton shivered slightly and turned toward the niece with a look intended to convey sympathetic comprehension. The child was staring out through the open window with dazed horror in her eyes. In a chill shock of nameless fear Framton swung round in his seat and looked in the same direction.

24In the deepening twilight three figures were walking across the lawn toward the window; they all carried guns under their arms, and one of them was additionally burdened with a white coat hung over his shoulders. A tired brown spaniel kept close at their heels. Noiselessly they neared the house, and then a hoarse young voice chanted out of the dusk: "I said, Bertie, why do you bound?"

Paragraphs 23 and 24 complete Vera's account. The scansion of these paragraphs reveals them to be straight prose narrative. To repeat the epic treatment would destroy the effect of Vera's dialog.

25Framton grabbed wildly at his stick and hat; the hall-door, the gravel-drive, and the front gate were dimly-noted stages in his headlong retreat. A cyclist coming along the road had to run into the hedge to avoid imminent collision.

Paragraph 25 employs the same charming poetic prose used by Washington Irving in "The Legend of Sleepy Hollow." Observe the pompousness of the last line.

[26]"Here we are, my dear," said the bearer of the white mackintosh, coming in through the window; "fairly muddy, but most of it's dry. Who was that who bolted out as we came up?"

Although Mr. Sappleton is a minor character indeed, the accented "here," "my," and "we" reveal a great deal about him, further justifying and excusing Vera's amusement. She could hardly expect to be amused in such a routine household.

[27]"A most extraordinary man, a Mr. Nuttel," said Mrs. Sappleton; "could only talk about his illness, and dashed off without a word of good-bye or apology when you arrived. One would think he had seen a ghost."

Mrs. Sappleton's response is predictable. Her allusion to a ghost is artful in further establishing her lack of originality while adding an irony that Vera would, doubtless, enjoy.

[28]"I expect it was the spaniel," said the niece calmly; "he told me he had a horror of dogs. He was once hunted into a cemetery somewhere on the banks of the Ganges by a pack of pariah dogs and had to spend the night in a newly dug grave with the creatures snarling and grinning and foaming just above him. Enough to make anyone lose their nerve."

[29]Romance at short notice was her specialty. □

Vera returns to epic poetry: "he had a horror . . . ," "he was once hunted . . . ," "pack of pariah dogs." Only at the last minute does she avoid the trap of overacting; she employs a grammatical error (paragraph 28). "Romance [a verse narrative of extraordinary events] at short notice was [indeed] her specialty."

As the tone of "The Open Window" is humorous, a general statement of theme should, seemingly, encompass the humorous. Can you state such a theme or do the following seem more appropriate: "People usually get what they deserve," or "Imagination must create its own amusement among dull people"?

The Story of Character

Characters are created much as Athena was: they spring from the mind of the author at whatever stage of chronological age he envisions them. As a result of this "sudden birth," they are all stereotypes at first. As they progress through the intricacies of plot, additional dimensions are added to them; their mental, spiritual, and physical appearances change as they are refined through action and reaction. New facets of their being reflect the light of conversational or emotional focus. They emerge as unique characters of varying degrees of fullness.

The astute reader becomes something of a detective as he isolates clues to character, compiles a growing body of evidence, and arrives at a conclusion about it. His arrival at that conclusion usually coincides with his interpretation of the theme. If the author has been successful in creating the character, adding dimension, and chronicling a logical change, his intended theme and the reader's assumed theme will bear marked similarities even if they do not coincide. Absolute agreement between author and reader is improbable, for each reacts differently to experience; each holds attitudes and biases which may change slightly, but which remain relatively constant no matter how clever the author is. A reader's mind is not changed suddenly by one literary experience. The author knows he can illuminate areas for a reader; he cannot recondition a reader's thought processes.

If you understand this, you will also understand why a character does not "come to realize" anything. A character may find himself in a situation which begins abruptly, because a story starts within a reasonable distance of the climax. However, all of a character's past life, from infancy to his fictional present moment, determines his reactions and responses. As he experiences the incidents of the plot, past experience may demand that he react one way, present loyalties may insist that he violate belief and experience, and the resultant conflict constitutes new experience. When that new experience demands a decision of him, he may be torn between past and present, hope and reality, desire and actuality. At such a time, as a result of the totality of experience, including his present moment, the character decides what he will do or think. This is scarcely "coming to realize," as if God had touched him with wisdom. While experience may suddenly assume a pattern the character can interpret for the first time, the component parts of the realization have been his the whole time. He may decide to recognize them at his moment of intellectual climax.

Since fiction is a facsimile of life, it must follow the design of reality. If it does not, it is unsuccessful, for the reader soon realizes that "life is not like that." And he becomes indignant with the writer who underestimates his intelligence enough to try to make him think it is. His experience is a slow accretion, and he expects a fictional character's to be a gradual accumulation also. He expects to see the experience of the past brought into conflict with the experience of the present, to understand the complications growing from the meeting, and to share the logic of the character's final decision. He may not agree with the author about the outcome of the story, but he must agree that the outcome is logical.

As you read "Fulvous Yellow" by Stanley Kauffmann, notice the revelations growing one from another as the story unfolds. Notice, also, the lack of dominant scene. The story unfolds in the same way life does: the past runs into the present without elaborate drama. One ordinary event succeeds another until drama emerges—not suddenly and blindingly, but as a pervasive insidiousness that has been present from the beginning. Life seldom dramatizes itself in hyperbole; litotes is far more prevalent. The reader feels, as did Pan Student in "Boless," that life is, unfortunately, unresolvable. It simply flows on until death cancels it.

Structured in twelve scenes (which are numbered in roman numerals), "Fulvous Yellow" is deliberately paced through well-used, very average diction. When the word *fulvous* is inserted, it assumes dominance because it is unique diction. As the story is told from a third person limited omniscient point of view, the reader observes only Mr. Sprague's experience. The author limits the omniscience sharply, however, so the reader must evaluate Mr. Sprague's experience and his reactions. This involvement almost makes the reader serve as conscience for Mr. Sprague.

Read the story first in its entirety.

Fulvous Yellow

by Stanley Kauffmann

I [1]Mr. and Mrs. Sprague were a very nice middle-aged couple. They lived in Albany, New York, and they had managed to remain mentally alive. They read a lot of books, some of them not chosen by book clubs, owned a few nice paintings, and had quite a good collection of phonograph records, including "Scheherazade."

Paragraphs 1–8 constitute section I, narrative panorama including background and two half-scenes. The diction of paragraph 1 is calculated to establish the upper middle-class life and attitudes of the Spragues. As the story progresses and middle-class morality dominates Mr. Sprague's character, this paragraph becomes increasingly important. That the Spragues are "very nice" immediately indicates their lack of uniqueness. It is the safe description for people who are utterly undistinguished by either good or bad qualities. That they "had managed to remain mentally alive" indicates their conformity: this is what current fashion dictates. The term escapes exact definition and is, therefore, safe. Upper middle-class fashion dictates the possession of books (which probably accounts for the growth of book clubs) and, as book clubs have received criticism, "some of them not chosen by book clubs." They owned a few "nice" paintings ("nice" indicates their noncontroversial nature) and their records included "Scheherazade," the romantic quality of which appeals to those who wish to listen to "good music" without intellectual pain.

[2]They were proudest, however, of their son Everett. He was an unusual and talented boy. In six months down in New York City he had done well. He was already top assistant to one of the most important dress designers in the business.

[3]"Fashion stylists," Mrs. Sprague had corrected her husband once. "Ev says they don't call them dress designers any more."

[4]"Fashion stylists," Mr. Sprague agreed quickly.

That all of these possessions *were* possessions rather than accoutrements to their lives is apparent from the implication of their pride in ownership (paragraph 2): "They were proud*est* . . . of their son. . . ." He, too, is something of a possession. But he is a strayed possession. Fortunately, he has "done well," a safe statement open to whatever one's concept may be. That he is assistant to a "dress designer" indicates the Spragues *think* "dress designer" however often they deliberately use "fashion stylist." That Mr. Sprague "agreed quickly" suggests he wants to say the "correct" thing; it also implies an actual preference for the more acceptable term. However, his mind insists on "dress designer," the reason becoming clear as the story progresses.

[5]They were on their way down to New York now to visit Ev. They hadn't seen him in almost four months. When he had first got his New York job, he had come home every week end. Then his visits had slacked off to every two weeks. Then four months had gone by without his visiting them. But Mr. and Mrs. Sprague were not foolish or demanding parents. They understood that their son was in a new life, making new friends, finding new interests, and as long as his letters once a week told them that he was well and happy, they were reasonably content.

[6]Now Mr. Sprague had managed to get Friday off from the office and they were going down for a long week end. They hadn't told Ev in advance; they wanted it to be a surprise. They sent a wire just before they got on the train.

[7]"Make sure you send it to the new address," said Mrs. Sprague. "Remember, he moved last month."

[8]"I know that as well as you do," Mr. Sprague replied testily. Ev was as much his son as hers.

Paragraph 5 is gentle irony and subtle litotes. The Spragues were obviously not "foolish or demanding parents" because they were offered little choice. Ev's "making new friends, finding new interests" frightens their sense of security—"they were *reasonably* content." Their "surprise" visit may be prompted by many things; at least, they give Ev no chance to offer reasons for their not coming. Paragraph 7 foreshadows tensions to come; paragraph 8 reveals tensions in the present. That Ev is the son of both is unarguable. That his "nature" is equally divided is doubtful. One would ordinarily think of a boy as "his father's son" in middle-class terms.

II [9]They had lunch in the dining car. The steward put them at a table for four and then seated a big bald man next to Mr. Sprague. They fell into talk and the big bald man told them that he was on his way to his son's wedding in Brooklyn Heights. The Spragues agreed that that was fine and envied the bald man. Then they told him about Ev's progress in six short months.

[10]"What's your son's work?" asked the bald man, impressed.

[11]"He's a dress de—he's in fashion styling," Mr. Sprague said. "Always had an eye for color, and things like that."

[12]"Always," agreed his mother. "Ever since he was a very little boy."

[13]"Oh," said the man, with the hint of a wrinkle between his brows. "That's fine. Fine."

[14]Mr. Sprague noticed the wrinkle. "You know," he said with a laugh, "lots of people have the wrong idea about the fashion field. It takes ability and business sense just like any other business."

[15]"Oh, sure, I know," nodded the bald man quickly. "I saw an article about it in *Life*."

Generating circumstances occupy sections II–X. The dining car scene (paragraphs 9–15) focuses sharply on Mr. Sprague's conflict as point of view is definitely established. The bald man quickly touches the Spragues' weakest spot as they envy him. This is subtle foreshadowing. As it combines with "dress designer," the reader becomes uncomfortably aware of the problem. In paragraph 11, Mr. Sprague gently "explains" Ev's profession after stumbling over its accurate title. The hint of a wrinkle and the "Fine" response (notice the use is like the earlier "nice" and "doing well") suggest unspoken criticism. Mr. Sprague reacts immediately. The reader hears the falseness of his laugh in paragraph 14. What he does *not* say about the fashion field is far more revealing than his mild statement. The bald man's reference to *Life* magazine parallels "nice" and "fine." This scene reveals Mr. Sprague's conflict. *He* surely would show a "hint of a wrinkle" if their positions were reversed. A subtle irony is involved: the *Life* reference also suggests shrugged shoulders and a sympathetic "Well, that's life." Such sympathy would be even more difficult than outright accusation.

III [16]Ev wasn't at the station to meet them, but Mr. Sprague said that probably the wire hadn't given him time enough to get away. On an off chance, he called the apartment before he tried the office and was surprised to hear Ev answer.

[17]Ev was glad to hear his father's voice. Yes, he'd received the wire but he hadn't been able to meet the train. He had some things he had to finish up for Ty. Ty was his roommate. Also his boss. Why didn't they take a cab and come right over before they went to their hotel?

[18]It was a remodeled private house in the East Fifties, not far from the river. The card for Apt. 3 said "Emmet" with "Sprague" written in below it. Mr. Sprague gave the bell two pokes.

[19]Ev stood at the top of the stairs in a striped basque shirt and a pair of slacks. "Hello, Mother," he said. "Gosh, it's good to see you. What a wonderful surprise. Hello, Father."

[20]He used to call Mr. Sprague "Dad." Mr. Sprague thought he looked a little pale. Working too hard, probably.

Section III begins without transition. None is needed, for a numbness follows paragraph 15, a numbness the reader feels and shares with Mr. Sprague. This unwritten transition scene is similar to the unwritten one in "Miss Brill" (p. 144). Panorama opens this section and is more effective than stream-of-consciousness would be. Were the reader allowed full access to Mr. Sprague's thoughts, he would have to be told Mr. Sprague knew he was already making excuses for Ev—making them hopefully. His suspicion is reflected in the act of calling the apartment. The line "Mr. Sprague gave the bell two pokes" indicates restrained irritation—a restrained irritation that foreshadows the last line of the story. As focus is narrowed to scene, Ty is inserted as the reason for Ev's failure to meet his parents. At the apartment, Ev's "Father" hurts Mr. Sprague who interprets Ev's paleness as overwork. It is easier to equate the paleness with Ty than with Self if strain creates the pallor.

[21]The apartment was eye-filling. The furniture was low and modern, pearl gray and coral red. There were good reproductions of Picasso and Matisse and Utrillo in wide natural-wood frames. And there were small white-enameled wrought-iron gates between the living room and the tiny kitchen.

[22]Ev gave his parents each a glass of sherry and apologized for not having been up to Albany for so long. "But gosh, I've been busy," he said. He indicated the drawing board at the side of the room; there was a large colored sketch of a woman

in a coat tacked on it. "We're doing some rush work on a new line of casual clothes and Ty's given me some of the tougher things. But I don't mind. It's pretty exciting."

23 "Do you always work at home, Ev?" his mother asked.

24 "When I've got something really tough, yes. Because that office is a madhouse." He laughed. It was Mr. Sprague's boy's laugh, all right. "That's one advantage of living with your boss."

25 "It's certainly a nice place to work," said Mr. Sprague. He cleared his throat. "Ev—er, you mind if I ask? This is all pretty expensive, isn't it? And—"

26 "Oh, I pay my share," Ev replied. "Of the rent, anyway. Ty had the place for years before I moved in, of course, so I got the use of the furnishings for nothing. But when he saw the hole I was boarding in on Forty-fifth Street, he insisted on my coming in with him."

27 "He sounds like a very nice man," said his mother.

28 "Ty?" laughed Ev. "You'll love him. He ought to be along pretty soon. I phoned him when I got your wire and he said he'd come home early."

29 "By the way, Ev," said Mr. Sprague, "I've got regards for you. Or a bawling out, depending on how you look at it. Joanie Carson wants to be remembered, and she says she's not going to write to you again until you answer her last letter."

30 Ev laughed shortly. "Joanie Carson. That child."

31 "She still talks about you, Ev," said his mother.

32 "Does she?" said Ev.

The opening sentence of paragraph 21 probably seems very familiar to you. It might easily have been written by Sinclair Lewis and included in *Babbitt.* Mr. Sprague is a George F. Babbitt stereotype; Mrs. Sprague is a Myra Babbitt. If you have read the novel, you know Babbitt has as much difficulty understanding his son Ted as Mr. Sprague has accepting Ev's rejection. Paragraph 24 offers Mr. Sprague brief comfort as he finds Ev's laugh, at least, has not changed. Compare "It was Mr. Sprague's boy's laugh, all right" with "Ev was as much his son as hers." Mr. Sprague's suspicions grow as he realizes Ev is not able to afford the apartment. Mrs. Sprague's "He sounds like a very nice man" is a "safe" statement. Mr. Sprague's intrusion of Joanie Carson's message is an obvious gambit. Compare it with Mrs. Sprague's statement. Which is more calculated?

IV 33 Ty came in soon. He was a big man with a large, roundish face. He wore a beautiful gabardine suit and brown suède shoes. He had two boxes under his arm, and he gave one—a corsage box—to Mrs. Sprague.

34 "I'm so happy to meet Ev's parents," he said with a pleasant smile. "I hope you won't mind—I've brought you these, and I've taken the liberty of arranging things for this evening." He took a ticket envelope from his pocket. "There's a new

musical—a smash—but a friend of mine did the costumes and he got tickets for me. 'Ice to the Eskimos.' Have you heard of it?"

35 "Oh, yes," said Mr. Sprague, who kept up on things. "I read the review of it. We'd love to see it. That's very nice of you, Mr. Emmet."

36 Mrs. Sprague opened her box. "Orchids!" she exclaimed. "How lovely! Oh, Mr. Emmet, you shouldn't have—really."

37 Ty bowed, almost from the waist. "Pleasure, I assure you. It's only once that I'll meet Ev's parents for the first time. Talented Ev." He put his hand briefly on Ev's shoulder. "Which reminds me—this other box." He opened it as he spoke. "I was passing Quentin's at lunch time today—" He explained to the Spragues. "Quentin's a friend of mine who keeps a shop. Men's accessories. Really unusual things." From the box he took a silk muffler, a beautiful tawny yellow. "There, Ev. What do you think of it?"

38 "It's stunning," said Ev. "But—"

39 Ty proceeded to wind it around Ev's neck and to knot it. "It'll go nicely with your chocolate-brown jacket."

40 Ev shook his head. "Ty, as Mother says, you shouldn't have—really."

41 "Nonsense." Ty hushed him grandly. "Anniversary present. You know," he said to the Spragues, "it's a wonderful coincidence, your coming down today. It's just a month today that Ev's been living here."

42 "Yes," said Mr. Sprague, "that's right, I guess it is. I remember Ev's letter telling us about it came right on my birthday."

43 "But just the same, Ty," said Ev, stroking the silken scarf around his neck, "you're much too extravagant and generous."

44 Ty shrugged. "When I saw it in the window, I thought of you at once. It seemed your color somehow. A kind of—" he hesitated for a word, "—fulvous yellow."

45 "What kind?" asked Mr. Sprague.

46 "Fulvous," said Ty. "Tawny. Smoky yellow."

47 "Oh," said Mr. Sprague. He nodded thoughtfully. Then he sighed and got up. "Well, I suppose we ought to go on to our hotel."

Section IV introduces Ty physically in a tightly woven scene of narrow focus. His appearance is a bit dandified—one senses Mr. Sprague's disapproval and grudging envy. Ty's assumption of arrangements is apparent. Had Ev come home, Mr. Sprague would have been responsible for them. The orchids are designed to appeal to a middle-class woman. Ty is cosmopolitan enough to be perceptive. That perception extends to the muffler he presents to Ev. The obviousness of the "anniversary" gift could not be mistaken by any but a dolt. Ty's character is cleverly sketched in this scene. The conflict is no longer confined to Mr. Sprague's imagination. He and the reader recognize Ty's open challenge. Mrs. Sprague's unawareness stamps her as one who "kept up on things" only when they were spelled out. Timing is reemphasized when Mr. Sprague says Ev's letter came on his birthday. The implied accusation is pathetic. It becomes even more so as Ev, unaware or unconcerned, is entranced with his gift. Selfishness is indicated, but Mr. Sprague does not examine it. His refusal reveals far more than examination would have. "Fulvous" elicits a question from Mr. Sprague, one he probably would not have asked had he considered the implications. His "Oh," his thoughtful nod, his sigh—all reveal he knows he has lost a battle. And he retreats.

V [48]They agreed to meet in the hotel lobby to go out to dinner, and Ev put them in a cab. On the way to the hotel, which was not far, Mrs. Sprague held the flower box carefully and Mr. Sprague sat with his hands in his lap, one on each leg, palms down.

[49]After a while, Mrs. Sprague said, "It's a lovely apartment, don't you think?"

[50]"Very pretty," he replied.

[51]She looked at him. "Mr. Emmet's a nice man, don't you think?"

[52]The taxi stopped for a light. Then the light changed and they went on.

[53]"Very nice," said Mr. Sprague.

VI [54]That night Ty took the Spragues to a French restaurant where the headwaiter knew him quite well and where the specialty was little soufflé potatoes. At dinner Ty told them what a fine future he thought Ev had in designing. He said he felt no hesitancy in telling them, even at this early date, that he was training Ev for the time when they might operate a studio together.

[55]"I think there are really great things ahead for Ev," said Ty.

[56]Ev flushed happily and turned to his mother. "Gosh, Mother, wasn't I lucky to meet him? Some people have to struggle for years before they get a real break."

[57]"Not the ones like you, Ev," said Ty, patting his arm. "Not the ones with real talent."

[58]"Well, Ev," said his mother gently, "we've been bragging all over Albany about your wonderful progress."

[59]"Yes," said his father, "we have been."

[60]In the cab on the way to the theater Ty explained that their seats wouldn't be together; he'd had to take what he could get. But he and Ev would be sitting almost directly behind the Spragues. Mr. Sprague wanted to take the second row, but Ty insisted that his guests have the better seats.

[61]The show was loud and fast. The audience expected it to be funny, and where the show fell short of the mark, the audience's expectation filled up the gap and they laughed anyway. There was a scene in the first act in which a girl in a tight sweater threw herself on a bashful sailor's lap and made love to him. While the audience was howling, Mr. Sprague, vaguely disinterested, glanced around at the row behind. Ev was chuckling and Ty, his arm linked with Ev's, was smiling; the smile made his face seem larger.

62 Later, Ty wanted to take them to a supper club for drinks, but Mr. and Mrs. Sprague asked to be excused after their long day. Ty promised to pick them up in his car next morning at ten-thirty; they would drive out to his beach club on Long Island for lunch.

VII 63 The Spragues were in the lobby next morning promptly at ten-thirty. They had not wanted much breakfast, but the coffee was very good and Mr. Sprague had had a barbershop shave, complete with hot towel, which had refreshed him.

64 Ty came smiling through the revolving doors and behind him came Ev in his chocolate-brown jacket with the new muffler knotted about his neck. Mr. Sprague thought that Ty was right, the muffler went very well with the jacket.

65 "Good morning," beamed Ty. "A wonderful day. I'll get you some suits out at the club so you can take a dip."

66 "Goodness," laughed Mrs. Sprague, "do you think they'd have any to fit me?"

67 "Why, they must have," said Mr. Sprague. "Lots of fellows' mothers must come to visit them, don't they, Ev?"

68 "Sure, I suppose so," Ev nodded.

69 "It's a long time since Ev and I went swimming together," said Mr. Sprague. "Can you still do that shallow dive I taught you, Ev?"

70 Ty's car was a roadster and Mr. and Mrs. Sprague sat together in the little back seat. Mr. Sprague was busy most of the time keeping his hat on his head, but Ty wore a beret when he drove and Ev's hair never seemed the worse for wind. Mr. Sprague sat right behind his son and could see Ev's hair.

71 They got suits quickly enough at the club and Mrs. Sprague dabbled in the shallow end of the pool while the men swam. Mr. Sprague was very good for his age but he soon climbed up on the edge of the pool, puffing, and dangled his legs in the water. Ty swam over soon after and hoisted himself up next to Mr. Sprague.

72 "Those are nice trunks," said Mr. Sprague. Ty had Hawaiian trunks, yellow with a blue flower design.

73 "These?" smiled Ty. "They're Ev's idea. He picked them out for me. Said he liked them but didn't quite dare to wear them himself." Ev's trunks were a solid light blue. "Ev," he called, "let's see you dive."

74 Ev, swimming in toward the board, laughed and said, "Right. The professor will be happy to oblige."

75 "Where did he learn to dive, Mr. Sprague?" asked Ty.

76 "Oh, I taught him some," said Mr. Sprague, "and he was on the team at school."

77 Ev climbed to the board and walked to the end. He raised his arms and arched himself.

78 "Watch this, now," said Ty, watching.

79 Ev leaped into the air, then spread his arms wide in the sun and came sailing down. Just before he hit the water, he brought his hands together over his head.

80 Ty applauded. "Ah, perfect," he said. "That was perfect."

81 "Pretty good," said Mr. Sprague. "Knees might have been a little straighter."

82 They had lunch on the terrace overlooking the pool. Ty was dissatisfied with the salad dressing and asked the waiter to bring him oil and seasoning so that he could mix a dressing himself. "It seems a shame to invite you all the way out here and then just give you run-of-the-mill fare," he said to the Spragues.

83 "Wait till you taste this, Mother," said Ev. "You've never tasted anything like this salad dressing."

84 Mr. Sprague thought it was very good indeed, but he wasn't especially hungry. When he had finished lunch, he lit a pipe and said, "I thought maybe tonight we'd all have dinner and go up to the Stadium concert to hear Lily Pons. The ticket man in the hotel said he might get me tickets."

85 "Oh, I always love Lily Pons," said Mrs. Sprague. "So do you, Ev."

86 Ev glanced at Ty, then said, "Yes, Mother, I do. But I'm afraid I can't go tonight. I should have told you yesterday. I'm terribly sorry, but gosh, I didn't know that you were coming this week end."

87 "Oh," said Mrs. Sprague.

88 "It's my fault, Mrs. Sprague," Ty said. "You see, we were invited to this dinner party about a week ago and I accepted for us. Business friends, and some people from out of town. It's really rather important, but I suppose I could make excuses for you, Ev, if you wanted to go with your parents."

89 "Well—" said Ev.

90 "No, no," said Mr. Sprague, "I wouldn't want to interfere. I know how these things are, I'm a businessman myself. It's our fault for not letting you know far enough ahead. No, you go out to your party, Ev. Your mother and I will make out."

91 When they started back, Ty invited Mrs. Sprague to sit in front with him. Ev sat in back next to his father and they talked for a while of things in New York, then they talked a little about things in Albany. Then they just sat and enjoyed the ride.

Section V is a half-scene of both understatement and completely unstated material. The physical description of Mr. Sprague in paragraph 48 is one of weary defeat. Painful silence is indicated by "After a while." "Pretty" in paragraph 50 is superb litotes, the negative being implied. Examine it very carefully. "Nice" is interestingly shaded, denotatively and connotatively, in paragraph 53.

Whitespace transition introduces section VI. Notice "Ty took the Spragues"—not Ev *and* Ty. Paragraph 56 is revealing of the immature Ev's character. How like an engaged girl he seems! Paragraph 59 carries a stark implication: the present perfect seems oddly final. By paragraph 60, Ev's parents have become Ty's guests. Panorama sweeps the narrative through the musical, pausing to focus on the intimate gesture and

Ty's face which has become larger than life-size in Mr. Sprague's view. The Spragues plead weariness—a weariness of the soul, probably.

Section VII opens with a suggestion that the weariness was indeed not physical. Loss of appetite and the refreshment of the unusual barbershop shave suggest Mr. Sprague's emotional state. That Mr. Sprague is fair can be deduced from paragraph 64. A petty man would find the muffler unattractive. Ty is impressive again as he takes them to his club, and Mr. Sprague reclaims some small advantage as Ev's diving teacher. He loses it immediately with Ty's admonition to "Watch this, now." The indication: he has supplanted Mr. Sprague in this area too. The reactions in paragraphs 80–81 are revealing. Ty is satisfied; Mr. Sprague still wants improvement, wishes Ev to achieve greater things as a result of his own effort. These two paragraphs are masterful character portrayal. Mr. Sprague cannot dictate to his emotions; he is simply not hungry (paragraph 84). When Mr. Sprague assumes the position usurped by Ty, Ev glances at Ty (paragraph 86) for a cue. Ty chooses his words carefully to include "if you *wanted* to go with your parents." Ev's indecisive "Well—" decides Mr. Sprague. He will not interfere. He rationalizes for Ev, but he descends to obvious subterfuge with "Your mother and I will make out." Ev's inability or refusal to be humbled is, mercifully, passed over—making it more painful! Ty allows Mr. Sprague possession of Ev for a brief period (paragraph 91) but Mr. Sprague's defeat is complete. Desultory conversation gives way to silence. Irony resides in "Then they just sat and enjoyed the ride."

VIII [92]Ty dropped them at their hotel and Ev apologized for not being able to see them again that night. They said they understood perfectly. They all agreed to have dinner next day at three so that the Spragues could catch the five-o'clock train, and Mrs. Sprague thanked Ty for the pleasant day. Then Ev got into the front seat next to Ty and they drove off.

[93]Mr. Sprague watched them go. Mrs. Sprague said, "Well, do you want to see the man about Lily Pons?"

[94]"Oh," said Mr. Sprague, "sure."

[95]They went to the agency counter, but the man said he had only one seat left for that night and it wasn't a very good one. "I guess it's just as well that Ev went to his party," said Mrs. Sprague.

[96]"Yes," replied Mr. Sprague thoughtfully. He said, "Anyway, that Stadium's awfully far uptown."

[97]They rested for a while in their room, then went to an Italian restaurant which Ev had recommended. They couldn't understand most of the things on the menu and finally ordered meat balls and spaghetti.

[98]"What would you like to do tonight?" asked Mrs. Sprague.

99 "Oh, I don't know," he answered. "I don't much care. What would you like to do?"

100 "Would you like to go to the Music Hall?" she asked. "You always like to go to the Music Hall."

101 "Well, it's probably pretty crowded," he said. "What's playing there?"

102 "That life-of-a-composer picture," she said. "They say it's very good."

103 Mr. Sprague moved his spoon over close to his knife and lined it up exactly parallel. Then he pushed the knife ahead gently until the bottom was precisely level with the spoon. "Well," he said, "I don't know. I suppose we can see it up home."

104 "Sure," said Mrs. Sprague. "Sure we can."

105 They bought some papers and magazines after dinner and went back to their room. Later, when he undressed for bed, Mr. Sprague took his wallet out of his pocket, as was his custom, to put it in a drawer. He remembered a picture of Ev and himself that he carried in his wallet and found it. It had been snapped on an Adirondacks fishing trip about six years before. The boy was wearing high-top shoes and breeches and a plaid shirt open at the throat. He was grinning and squinting into the sun. In his hands he held the string of bass and pickerel he had caught that day.

106 When Mrs. Sprague came out of the bathroom, she scolded her husband for reading in the dark; and he went in and brushed his teeth.

IX 107 They waited in the lobby next day until half-past three before Mr. Sprague called the apartment. Ev answered sleepily. When he recognized his father's voice, he seemed to wake up. "Oh, gosh, Father," he said, "what time is it?"

108 Mr. Sprague told him.

109 "Good Lord," said Ev. "I had no idea. We were up terribly late. Gosh, I'm sorry, Father. I'm awfully sorry."

110 "Well," said Mr. Sprague, "those things happen."

111 "Are you still going to catch the five-o'clock?" Ev asked.

112 "I'm afraid we have to, Ev," answered Mr. Sprague.

113 "Then that spoils our dinner date," Ev said. "That's terrible."

114 "Oh, well," Mr. Sprague said, "we had a late breakfast. It doesn't matter."

115 "Well, at least we'll come over and take you to the train," Ev said. "We'll be right over."

116 Ty had dark circles under his eyes, but Ev looked all right. He had on a hound's-tooth jacket today, but he was still wearing the muffler.

117 Ty let go of Ev's arm to gesture apologetically. "A fine thing," he smiled ruefully, "a fine thing. And I wanted to make a good impression on you both. What ever are you going to think of me now?"

118 "Well," said Mr. Sprague, "as I told Ev, these things happen."

Section VIII combines narrative and half-scenes with understatement so controlled that it becomes agonizing. Mrs. Sprague thanks Ty for the pleasant day (paragraph 92). Mr. Sprague remains silent; he is no hypocrite. It is he who watches Ev and Ty drive off. Whatever Mrs. Sprague's failings, she is not insensitive to her husband. Her concern for him is very apparent as she suggests diversion and dismisses it as soon as he indicates a lack of interest. Her solicitousness is pathetic, and the reader sympathizes with her, feeling Mr. Sprague's insensitivity to her is justifiably comparable to Ev's to his father. As Mr. Sprague examines the picture in paragraph 105, he notes the plaid shirt, open at the throat —a radically different picture from the fulvous yellow mufflered throat of the last two days. Paragraph 106 reveals Mrs. Sprague's sensitivity again. Could she think he was "reading in the dark"?

Section IX brings the unstated conflict to its highest point. Ev does not meet them for dinner, does not call. And, when he and Ty arrive to drive the Spragues to the train, Ev looks "all right." Language is powerfully employed here. Notice the conjunction *but* in the second line of paragraph 116. Examine its effect.

X 119 They drove to the station, and Ty and Ev put them aboard the train. Ty shook hands with both of them, said how happy he'd been to meet them, and hoped they'd forgive them for oversleeping. Then Ev kissed his mother's cheek and shook hands with his father.

120 "Ev," said Mr. Sprague calmly, "please. I know how busy you are. But try to come up next Friday, won't you? I'd like to have one of our old-fashioned week ends. Real old walk and talk. Try. Won't you, Ev?"

121 "All right, Father," nodded Ev, "I'll try. I really will. It was awfully nice to see you again."

XI 122 Harlem, Hastings, Harmon. Change of engines. Mr. and Mrs. Sprague sat in the coach and didn't talk much. The train was really quite comfortably air-conditioned, but Mr. Sprague had buttoned his jacket to the top.

Section X reduces Mr. Sprague utterly. He pleads for one more chance to reclaim his son, but paragraph 121 reveals Ev's decision. The reader knows what it is; so does Mr. Sprague.

Full knowledge comes in section XI and chills Mr. Sprague. Notice the effective time transitions in the alliterative names of towns as geography separates Mr. Sprague even further from Ev.

XII 123 The waiter came through with the last call for dinner. Mrs. Sprague said, "We'd better have something, dear," and they went into the dining car. She ordered a sandwich and tea; he ordered a piece of pie and coffee.

124 The waiter brought their food. Mr. Sprague had been staring out the window,

but he picked up his fork automatically and turned his attention to the pumpkin pie. He stared at it a minute, then he prodded the viscous, flabby filling with his fork. Then he dropped his fork sharply.

125 His wife looked up anxiously, and after a moment, he spoke.

126 "Fulvous yellow," he said. □

The climax comes suddenly, violently in section XII as the "viscous, flabby filling" receives a stabbing. Symbolically, a viscous, flabby situation is murdered and Ty's large face is recalled as Mr. Sprague pronounces the symbol of defeat: "Fulvous yellow." He has not "come to realize" anything; he had spent a long weekend struggling to keep from admitting that which he suspected, that which the weekend had proved. In speaking the words that symbolize Ty's victory, Mr. Sprague accepts realization.

A difficult subject is handled with taste and discernment in the story. The characters "live," even the underdrawn ones. If you isolate the lines spoken by Ev or Mrs. Sprague or Ty, they reveal nothing. Refined through the point of view of Mr. Sprague, they are brilliant etchings of character dialog. Only a careful reader will discover the meaning of the story, however. The casual reader will decide arbitrarily that it is an indictment, that Mr. Sprague is a righteous and abused man. If a story is to assume full proportions, it must be intelligently and sensitively written. If it is to communicate fully, it must be intelligently and sensitively read. The good reader must learn to read carefully and well.

Suggested Assignments. 1. The following stories have much in common; yet in some ways they are completely different. Compare the effects achieved by each author as he finds the best way to tell his particular story.

2. Analyze one of the following stories, revealing your understanding of structural elements as they contribute to the dominant one.

3. Which of the stories seems more "important" and why? Defend your decision in a carefully considered essay.

The Use of Force

by William Carlos Williams

1 They were new patients to me, all I had was the name, Olson. Please come down as soon as you can, my daughter is very sick.

2 When I arrived I was met by the mother, a big startled looking

woman, very clean and apologetic who merely said, Is this the doctor? and let me in. In the back, she added. You must excuse us, doctor, we have her in the kitchen where it is warm. It is very damp here sometimes.

3 The child was fully dressed and sitting on her father's lap near the kitchen table. He tried to get up, but I motioned for him not to bother, took off my overcoat and started to look things over. I could see that they were all very nervous, eyeing me up and down distrustfully. As often, in such cases, they weren't telling me more than they had to, it was up to me to tell them; that's why they were spending three dollars on me.

4 The child was fairly eating me up with her cold, steady eyes, and no expression to her face whatever. She did not move and seemed, inwardly, quiet; an unusually attractive little thing, and as strong as a heifer in appearance. But her face was flushed, she was breathing rapidly, and I realized that she had a high fever. She had magnificent blonde hair, in profusion. One of those picture children often reproduced in advertising leaflets and the photogravure sections of the Sunday papers.

5 She's had a fever for three days, began the father and we don't know what it comes from. My wife has given her things, you know, like people do, but it don't do no good. And there's been a lot of sickness around. So we tho't you'd better look her over and tell us what is the matter.

6 As doctors often do I took a trial shot at it as a point of departure. Has she had a sore throat?

7 Both parents answered me together, No . . . No, she says her throat don't hurt her.

8 Does your throat hurt you? added the mother to the child. But the little girl's expression didn't change nor did she move her eyes from my face.

9 Have you looked?

10 I tried to, said the mother, but I couldn't see.

11 As it happens we had been having a number of cases of diphtheria in the school to which this child went during that month and we were all, quite apparently, thinking of that, though no one had as yet spoken of the thing.

12 Well, I said, suppose we take a look at the throat first. I smiled in my best professional manner and asking for the child's first name I said, come on, Mathilda, open your mouth and let's take a look at your throat.

13 Nothing doing.

14 Aw, come on, I coaxed, just open your mouth wide and let me

take a look. Look, I said opening both hands wide, I haven't anything in my hands. Just open up and let me see.

15 Such a nice man, put in the mother. Look how kind he is to you. Come on, do what he tells you to. He won't hurt you.

16 At that I ground my teeth in disgust. If only they wouldn't use the word "hurt" I might be able to get somewhere. But I did not allow myself to be hurried or disturbed but speaking quietly and slowly I approached the child again.

17 As I moved my chair a little nearer suddenly with one catlike movement both her hands clawed instinctively for my eyes and she almost reached them too. In fact she knocked my glasses flying and they fell, though unbroken, several feet away from me on the kitchen floor.

18 Both the mother and father almost turned themselves inside out in embarrassment and apology. You bad girl, said the mother, taking her and shaking her by one arm. Look what you've done. The nice man . . .

19 For heaven's sake, I broke in. Don't call me a nice man to her. I'm here to look at her throat on the chance that she might have diphtheria and possibly die of it. But that's nothing to her. Look here, I said to the child, we're going to look at your throat. You're old enough to understand what I'm saying. Will you open it now by yourself or shall we have to open it for you?

20 Not a move. Even her expression hadn't changed. Her breaths however were coming faster and faster. Then the battle began. I had to do it. I had to have a throat culture for her own protection. But first I told the parents that it was entirely up to them. I explained the danger but said that I would not insist on a throat examination so long as they would take the responsibility.

21 If you don't do what the doctor says you'll have to go to the hospital, the mother admonished her severely.

22 Oh yeah? I had to smile to myself. After all, I had already fallen in love with the savage brat, the parents were contemptible to me. In the ensuing struggle they grew more and more abject, crushed, exhausted while she surely rose to magnificent heights of insane fury of effort bred of her terror of me.

23 The father tried his best, and he was a big man but the fact that she was his daughter, his shame at her behavior and his dread of hurting her made him release her just at the critical times when I had almost achieved success, till I wanted to kill him. But his dread also that she might have diphtheria made him tell me to go on, go on though he himself was almost fainting, while the mother moved back and forth behind us raising and lowering her hands in an agony of apprehension.

[24] Put her in front of you on your lap, I ordered, and hold both her wrists.

[25] But as soon as he did the child let out a scream. Don't, you're hurting me. Let go of my hands. Let them go I tell you. Then she shrieked terrifyingly, hysterically. Stop it! Stop it! You're killing me!

[26] Do you think she can stand it, doctor! said the mother.

[27] You get out, said the husband to his wife. Do you want her to die of diphtheria?

[28] Come on now, hold her, I said.

[29] Then I grasped the child's head with my left hand and tried to get the wooden tongue depressor between her teeth. She fought, with clenched teeth, desperately! But now I also had grown furious—at a child. I tried to hold myself down but I couldn't. I know how to expose a throat for inspection. And I did my best. When finally I got the wooden spatula behind the last teeth and just the point of it into the mouth cavity, she opened up for an instant but before I could see anything she came down again and gripping the wooden blade between her molars she reduced it to splinters before I could get it out again.

[30] Aren't you ashamed, the mother yelled at her. Aren't you ashamed to act like that in front of the doctor?

[31] Get me a smooth-handled spoon of some sort, I told the mother. We're going through with this. The child's mouth was already bleeding. Her tongue was cut and she was screaming in wild hysterical shrieks. Perhaps I should have desisted and come back in an hour or more. No doubt it would have been better. But I have seen at least two children lying dead in bed of neglect in such cases, and feeling that I must get a diagnosis now or never I went at it again. But the worst of it was that I too had got beyond reason. I could have torn the child apart in my own fury and enjoyed it. It was a pleasure to attack her. My face was burning with it.

[32] The damned little brat must be protected against her own idiocy, one says to one's self at such times. Others must be protected against her. It is a social necessity. And all these things are true. But a blind fury, a feeling of adult shame, bred of a longing for muscular release are the operatives. One goes on to the end.

[33] In a final unreasoning assault I overpowered the child's neck and jaws. I forced the heavy silver spoon back of her teeth and down her throat till she gagged. And there it was—both tonsils covered with membrane. She had fought valiantly to keep me from knowing her secret. She had been hiding that sore throat for three days at least and lying to her parents in order to escape just such an outcome as this.

[34] Now truly she was furious. She had been on the defensive before

but now she attacked. Tried to get off her father's lap and fly at me while tears of defeat blinded her eyes. □

All Our Yesterdays

by Beb Vuyk

1 During that month it rained every day, but before evening fell it was dry again. Then the damp garden smelled of leaves and grass. The hospital was a rebuilt country house, surrounded by a park-like garden, where a famous painter had lived a hundred years ago in royal splendor. In spite of all the changes made by the scores of alterations for different purposes, it had retained much of the old in its sphere, a composure which is not of today and a naïve rusticity. It lay just outside the centrum on a busy highway, an enclave of rest in the town and in time.

2 Groves were cleared away and ponds were filled up, but the old driveway of royal palms had been spared, was asphalted, and led from the modern entrance building to the nurses' quarters, the former main building, bombastically ugly and yet with a gesture of grandeur. Though small courts had been formed by additions to the side wings, adequate lawns remained, partly overshadowed by trees, to preserve a feeling of space, of coolness and rusticity. Deer grazed there in the afternoons under tall trees.

3 She always lay alone in this white room. During the day the shutters remained closed, to open an hour before sundown, when the light had lost its glare and a gray shadow rose on the white of the walls, not cast and not directed, as if coming from inside. There are places where temporary things become lasting. From the tandem, through the dark tunnel of unconsciousness, she had been flung in this place, no longer in life and not yet in death. At night the door to the wide rear gallery stood open. From the dark room she could see into the gallery where some twenty meters from her bed, in the middle, a low-hanging lamp spread a soft circle over the table of the night nurses.

4 One night she had dreamed aloud, but when she wakened she could not remember what the dream was about. The night nurse was standing over her bed offering her something to drink.

5 "Are you afraid?" she asked. "There is no reason to be, everything is going to be all right. You have only to lie flat in the dark a few weeks longer."

6 "No, no, I am not afraid," she said hastily and was surprised about

the feeling of guilt that she recognized from her youth, when she had fibbed without being caught.

7 "Shall I give you something to make you sleep?"

8 "Oh, no," she answered almost offended and closed her eyes. "Thank you just the same, I'll fall asleep again."

9 But she did not go to sleep again. The nurse finished her rounds and sat down at the table under the lamp. She knitted for a while, went to help one of the patients in another room, and then put her knitting away and took up a newspaper.

* * *

10 The yellow light from a low-hanging lamp, under it a policeman sat reading the newspaper. She lay on a mat on the dirty floor and dreamed, screaming in the dream. She was sentenced and the judge was the Kempaitai captain with the pale face and the immobile eyes of a reptile. She told her story with Ann and Chris sitting next to her, they knew her lies and would bear her out.

11 Then Bennie was brought in. He did not wear a uniform any longer, but the old khaki shirt and trousers which he always had on when he went in the gardens. He looked calm and unsuspecting and greeted the judge unconstrainedly with a nod of his head. She had not been able to warn him, he was not taken prisoner together with them and had never been confronted with them. Now they had taken him from the prison camp and brought him here to testify.

12 She thought with dismay, he does not know the story I made up, he will betray us. His evidence will show that we are lying.

13 His face came nearer like a close-up in a film, a friendly, trustworthy face, the face of an honest and simple person. In his guilelessness he will betray us, she thought, he will tell the truth and his truth will be our death.

14 Then she saw his face begin to decay. The eyes sank deeper, the cheeks fell away, the teeth became bare. The image fell backward, she saw him from feet to head. His shirt was open, she could see his chest and how the flesh was already rotting, that the ribs were visible, that only a few shreds of dark flesh hung between the bars of the thorax.

15 She screamed, she heard herself screaming.

16 Someone touched her hand and said: "Are you afraid, do you want something to drink?"

17 The little policeman gave her the glass of water with trembling hands. Two others stood behind him.

18 "You frightened us," he said. "Were you dreaming?"

19 "Yes, about the Kempaitai."

20 She could see their faces, she nodded to both and repeated: "About the Kempaitai."

21 "Did they torture you?" asked the tallest one.

22 "Yes, with electricity, but it was not about that."

23 "You must not frighten us," said the small one earnestly.

24 She sat up straight on her mat and looked in their faces and recognized their fear. One of them squatted down next to her, took a little box from his pocket and rubbed some salve on her forehead.

25 "What is it?" she asked.

26 "*Obat matjan.*" The other offered some aspirin and got more water.

27 "Go to sleep again," said the tall one and added comfortingly as to a child, "tomorrow you will not be interrogated."

28 She lay down again and closed her eyes. Then they spoke Javanese to one another; a little later she heard the door close. When she looked up again the little policeman sat at the table under the low lamp—like a nurse who is watching a patient, she had thought then.

* * *

29 She was taken to the Roentgen room for an examination on a stretcher that was wheeled along the gallery. It was still early, but the light there outside her room was already unmercifully dazzling. Babus were mopping the long tiled gallery; nurses were moving swiftly from one section to the other; convalescing patients, their faces still sunken from illness, were walking with care in the garden. She closed her eyes and covered her face with her hands.

30 "That is better," said the nurse, "the light is too sharp for you."

31 She always made remarks that were intended to be friendly and were correct but which, for some reason or other, were not suited to the situation. After this trip the Roentgen room was dim, cool and mercifully quiet. They left her lying on the stretcher because the doctor had not yet arrived. She kept her eyes closed, especially when they gave her the injection, and she remained for a time in a state between the border of consciousness and moments of unconsciousness. Afterward the things around her became clearer again, though farther away and slightly shifted. The doctor stood next to her, before she was aware that he had come in.

32 "She has already had the shot," she heard the nurse saying, "but we did not know if we should shave off her hair or not."

33 He laid his hand on her neck. His fingers were as cold as the blade of a sword. Deathly cold like a sword, she thought. There was one word that expressed it exactly, but she could no longer remember it.

[34] Now there was nothing left but to die with dignity. This was the last command, die with dignity. At the same time she knew that she did not have to die, not at this moment in any case. The strain of fear was insupportable, though she knew with certainty that she was not going to die. More direct and more urgent than the fear of death was the fear to be lacking in dignity, to go to pieces, deteriorate under the torture, to shrink from the pain, to give in to a complaint, to beg with indignity.

* * *

[35] They had not closed her up in a cell, but in the *gudang* where the confiscated goods were kept. One evening a woman in one of the cells began to scream. She hardly knew her, only that she was the wife of the former mayor. On the way to the water closet, she had to pass the woman's cell, in the beginning a policeman always walked in back of her, later not, at least if there were no Japanese. Sometimes they exchanged a few words. The woman always stood in back of the observation hole, a white face, framed by tangled reddish hair that was completely shaved away on one side of her head. "They did that right away at the first interrogation," the woman had whispered to her. In the afternoon the woman's niece came to bring her food, the prisoners who were pending trial were allowed to receive their food from outside. Sometimes her little son came along, a cute, fat little fellow of about four. One afternoon Pak Ateng, the oldest policeman, opened the cell door, the woman came out and opened her arms and the little boy ran to her.

[36] She had seen it all from the window in the *gudang* and she had thought of her own children.

[37] "Who will take care of your little boys when we have beheaded you?" the Japanese captain had inquired a couple of days ago.

[38] It was nearly dark when she heard the screaming and she knew at once who it was. She had looked out of the window without seeing anything, her body rigid with the effort not to scream too. The inspector carried the woman out of the cell and laid her on a camp bed in the *gudang* and gave her a bromide. Then she wasn't screaming any more, but lay cramped, sobbing out loud. Later a doctor came with a Japanese lieutenant and they took her to the hospital. She was calm by then. She had sat on a bench and combed the long part of her hair over the shaved skull.

[39] "Whoever is accused of a capital crime gets his head shaven," the woman had said, "but they cannot prove anything on me. I took the radio to pieces and threw the broken parts in the river. Every afternoon I walked past the river with my little boy."

40 "You are sentenced to death," screamed the Japanese captain at her.

41 He threw the revolver on the table and pulled out his sword.

42 "The way you would like to be executed you may choose yourself, revolver or sword." And when she did not answer, she was more surprised than afraid at that moment, he had pulled her hair up in back and laid the blade of his sword on her neck. She felt the ice-cold of its thin edge penetrate her body.

43 "Then the coldness of death penetrated his body." It was a line from a poem, but she no longer knew of whom. It is not true, she thought, he is acting, that belongs to the nerve treatment. Nothing is going to happen!

44 She was not afraid and could think clearly. It was the coldness of the metal that penetrated to her spine and was reverberated from there that made her tremble. He brushed the sword upward along the back of her head and then pulled it away, holding it loosely in his hand.

45 "She has not been shaven yet," he said to the lieutenant. "I cannot cut off her head like that. Tomorrow. Then I'll call for her and take her to Bogor. It is really too difficult here—in Bogor we have all the necessary arrangements for it."

46 He won't come, she had thought. This is a case in the state of inquiry, no judgment has been pronounced. But he did come, in a light-yellow, open car with red upholstery inside that smelled like new leather. She had to sit next to him. He himself drove. They rode in the direction of Bogor. Acting, she thought, acting. She was not trembling any longer, but sat straight up, her body rigid, with a fixed smile. After ten minutes he turned into a side street, then she knew that they were going back.

47 He stopped near the guard.

48 "I'll give you one more chance tomorrow. We will interrogate you and then you must tell the truth."

49 She stood next to the car and he put out his arm and laid his fingers between two cervical vertebrae. "Watch out, here is where the cut comes," he had said.

50 The sun was shining, it was a warm day, but his fingers were as cold as his sword.

* * *

51 The doctor took his hand away. "We do not have to shave her hair for this Roentgen photo," he said. "Is everything ready, nurse? We will make the puncture first."

52 They had put her in a sitting position on the table. She had not sat up for days and it made her dizzy and still more unsure. The contours

of things shifted, but the voices remained clear and close. She felt his fingers between the vertebrae, but lower, much lower than then.

53 "Bend further forward," he had commanded and she obeyed.

54 She heard the needle push the cartilage and it was as if she felt the pain only much later that began to spread from the top of her skull, through thousands of little cells, like water seeping through sinter. She sat still, gripped in an icy rigidity from head to hips. She knew where she was, she knew the doctor and the assistant; if she had been asked she could have said their names without faltering. She knew what was happening to her and why and yet her reactions were only indirectly determined because of that.

55 "Don't you feel anything yet?" asked the doctor.

56 "No," she answered vaguely.

57 "No," repeated the doctor and it was the surprise in his voice that helped her gather the enormous exertion to bring up an answer against those other forces.

58 "Yes, now I do." This time she spoke calmly and clearly. The clarity only lasted a moment, for when the pain began to stream through her in full strength, she repeated several times: "It is terrible, terrible." Stammering, not about the pain, but about the indignity of this confession. □

CHAPTER IX

A Short Story Reader

With eyes red from weeping rather than from reading, many contemporary critics mourn the short story which, they wail, has either sickened irrecoverably or gone down to death. Fortunately, the form is both vitally alive and furiously active. It is not confined within the sterile walls of literary hospitals (schools and libraries), and perhaps for this reason the prophets of doom and faith-healing practitioners are often unaware that the ubiquitous invalid is robustly present at every coffee-break, business luncheon, and cocktail party in America. In abbreviated form, it passes from one person to another who, speaking of genre rather than of literary type, says, "You know, that reminds me of the story about . . ." and goes on to tell an anecdote such as

> A young bride went directly from her wedding to her new home in Boston where her bridegroom had been transferred. At a welcoming tea, a staid Boston matron observed loftily, "Here we regard breeding as everything." Lost in her own stars, the new wife replied, "In Ohio we think breeding is fun, but we don't think it's everything!"

As long as laughter greets such tales, the critics' wailing is wasted. The short story will continue. It may change its emphasis and direction from time to time. It may be simplified or grow more complex. But it will remain healthy and present as long as it continues to amuse the hearer or reader.

Concern may be shown for the lively corpse of the short story, but writers will certainly continue to write with the same knowledge and conviction Washington Irving revealed in 1824 when he said (in the preface to *Tales of a Traveller*):

> . . . As I know this to be a story-telling and a story-reading age, and that the world is fond of being taught by

apologue, I have digested the instruction I would convey into a number of tales. They may not possess the power of amusement, which the tales told by many of my contemporaries possess; but then I value myself on the sound moral which each of them contains. This may not be apparent at first, but the reader will be sure to find it out in the end. I am for curing the world by gentle alternatives, not by violent doses; indeed, the patient should never be conscious that he is taking a dose. . . .

I am not, therefore, for those barefaced tales which carry their moral on the surface, staring one in the face; they are enough to deter the squeamish reader. On the contrary, I have often hid my moral from sight, and disguised it as much as possible by sweets and spices, so that while the simple reader is listening with open mouth to a ghost or a love story, he may have a bolus of sound morality popped down his throat, and be never the wiser for the fraud. . . .

Irving would, doubtless, have chuckled knowingly had he heard the story of the Ohio bride. Like every author, he knew that the reader's discovery of theme, enjoyment of style, and recognition of Self are the curative ingredients of the story. Profitable amusement cloaks the dosage, making it palatable and easy to swallow. Readers today, as in 1824, insist on a *good* story, and there are thousands of writers who will happily supply one. Jack London, Franz Kafka, William Faulkner, and Washington Irving are somehow all of a piece in this respect, attempting to compound the pill that will be the reader's medicine for melancholy or that will reduce the fever of ennui. Each author has his own prescription; each patient finds his own specialist.

When W. Somerset Maugham died, *Time* declared in its obituary of that popular writer:

For this, the ability to write a readable story he was often described as a mere storyteller. Today, after Joyce and Freud, "storyteller" is somehow considered a term of denigration, and critics may reasonably question the depth of Maugham's insights. But he was able to do supremely well what storytellers are supposed to do —to dramatize character by putting that character into action, a specific action that displays in kinetic terms his or her faults and virtues.°

The truth of *Time's* assessment may create a temporary stumbling block for some readers. It makes reading sound easy and uncomplicated and casual, for amusement is pleasure, and pleasure should not be work. And yet, such a sport as surfing, to take a popular example, affords its limitless pleasure to the enthusiast only after he has willingly worked to learn to enjoy it. What beginner could learn to surf without a care-

° "W. Somerset Maugham (1874–1965)," December 24, 1965, p. 58.

ful examination of the surfboard and its function, an understanding of the methods of finding the right wave and riding it out, and an analysis of the styles of the most successful surfers? A great deal of concentration and work is required. The careful, serious surfer practices constantly to achieve his seemingly effortless form. The beginner must learn to understand his board—to understand it intimately, knowing every rough spot, every flaw in the grain. He learns to paddle the board before he learns to stand on it. Nor does he, initially, combine sea, board, and form into a total unit. He takes them one at a time, he learns to understand their independent features, and finally he combines all of his knowledge into the act of surfing. When, at last, he attains this degree of perfection, he knows all of the steps that went into it. He knows he didn't just buy a board, plop it in the water, and perform brilliantly because he had a general concept. The concept began his work—and work he did to learn the rules, to become proficient, to accomplish the hard job of amusing himself at surfing. After mastering each step of the process, he understood the total concept better. And the final performance was greater than any of the learned parts, but it wouldn't have been possible without them.

If you can understand why you must learn to play a game before you can become an expert player, you can understand the necessity of analyzing stories critically. After you've mastered the parts, the whole will be wonderful and amusing—but not before. J. Berg Esenwein, an author who learned his art of surfing with words, once observed:

> Do not forget that the whole is greater than the sum of all its parts. The completed result must possess a spirit all its own, it must be almost a living personality. And who will analyze *that* for us and lay bare its vital secret? At every stage of our inquiry we must feel how impossible it is to saw up a story and find anything more than lumber, or to nail and glue its parts together and have aught other than a grinning wooden clown. The story, the yarn, is the big thing. Unless the writer have a story to tell the telling of it foolish contradiction.°

Yet until, like the accomplished surfer, we learn to question the contribution of each element to the total achievement, we will never know the delight of "the big thing."

The stories that follow in this chapter are successful for a variety of reasons. As you read each, observe the author's methods. Isolate the

° *Writing the Short-Story: A Practical Handbook on the Rise, Structure, Writing, and Sale of the Modern Short-Story* (New York, 1909), p. 31.

underlying philosophy, the theme, and the stylistic features. The introductory story in each section and the accompanying questions will suggest approaches for your reading. Without any outside help, try to analyze the stories that follow the questioned stories, using the methods you have learned. The questions are intended to help you isolate elements and techniques you might have overlooked in your first reading. Answering the questions, therefore, will entail a second reading, and, as you carefully retrace your literary path, try to discover why you overlooked anything in your first reading. You will be delighted with your new ability to read with greater understanding and enjoyment as you continue to practice.

Theme and Style

Of theme, Katherine Anne Porter once said:

> . . . a short story [needs] *first a theme,* and then a point of view, a certain knowledge of human nature and strong feeling about it, and style—that is to say [one's] own special way of telling a thing that makes it precisely his own and no one else's. . . . The greater the theme and the better the style, the better the story, you might say.*

The theme of "The Unwanted" by Mary Elizabeth Counselman, the story which follows, is virtually stated in paragraph 84. While such outright statement of theme is not unusual, it is relatively rare. Ordinarily, the theme will be woven throughout a story, always unstated but implicit in the growing body of evidence within the narrative frame. Here, however, it is a necessary realization for the central character. Without its actual statement, she would be the same character the reader encountered in the opening paragraph, and, had the change not come about, there would be no story. The incident—for this story is one incident in one scene—would be meaningless had the census-taker been an insensitive realist.

As you read the story the first time, the focus will seem to be on the surface action. Conflicts abound in the story, however: first, between the census-taker and the one-armed mountaineer; then between the mountaineer and his wife; between the mountaineer and himself; and finally between the census-taker and herself. This last conflict provides the story's most subtle skein of conflict. Her perceptive eye and heart

* "No Plot, My Dear, No Story," *The Days Before* (New York, 1952), p. 134.

are obvious from the opening paragraphs, but she resists knowledge throughout the story, never recognizing her own resistance until it is thrust on her by the fear of a very real shotgun. Even then she does not arrive at a full realization, nor does the average reader. If you are prepared to notice the absence of any reference whatsoever to the census-taker's husband, the theme will be more readily understandable. On your first reading, you might miss the subtle depth of the story, but it is so constructed that you can achieve a satisfactory reading experience without that final realization. As you answer the questions, realization should become a bonus feature. Had the author made it more obvious, she would have weakened her story. As your perceptions are already growing, it is quite possible you may discover the depths of this story on one reading.

As you read, notice the skillful weaving of narrative flow, description, characterization, and dialog. The mountain dialect is suggested in a few carefully chosen words such as *ary* and *young'nes.* Grammar is violated only enough to establish the lack of formal education. In handling the dialect of a specific group, a writer's chief problem usually lies in overemphasis. Examine the dialect as you read—try to discover how restraint enhances the author's style.

The point of view is obviously first person in this story. How would omniscience have changed the story? *Could* it be written from that point of view? What would have happened to the story had an objective point of view been employed? Coherence is established in the chronology; unity is achieved as the census-taker's job enlists the reader's acceptance of material he would reject if the narrator were in another occupation. Notice how the gun, the bundled baby, and the lard bucket create unity in the story. How does the census-taker's thirst serve to intensify the story's mood? You will notice mood, tone, and atmosphere are interrelated here, but each is distinct. The tone of the narrative is one of gentle wonder. The central character is misplaced in geography, sophistication, and occupation. As a result, the incident is a little unreal in mood. How much does she imagine? How much is real? Do thirst and its promised but unrealized alleviation make her giddy? The atmosphere of the story grows out of the mood and the tone as they combine with the physical setting. The misty mountain air dims the action, blurring everything. Examine the technique carefully as you read. Writers who are much more famous than Mary Elizabeth Counselman might take a lesson from her.

Read the story first in its entirety, skipping over the questions. Then reread the story, trying to answer them.

The Unwanted

by Mary Elizabeth Counselman

[1]Trudging up the stony mountain road, with the relentless Alabama sun beating down on my head, I began to wish two things, in order of their intensity: I wished I had a big, cold, frosted-over glass of something—iced tea, lemonade, water, anything *wet*. And I wished I had never applied to my prolific Uncle Sam for this job as census-taker!

1. How are mood, tone, and atmosphere established in paragraph 1?
2. Examine the last sentence of paragraph 1. What does the author accomplish with it? (It has more than one function.)

[2]I sat down under a gnarled old tree, glaring up at the steep incline ahead of me, and decided that there are entirely too many citizens of the United States, and that they live too far apart. The district I was supposed to cover was a section of the Blue Ridge foothills, in which all the inhabitants were said to have one leg shorter than the other—from living on that sheer cliff of a mountain! Already I had covered the few scattered farms along this winding road that seemed determined to end at the gates of Heaven. Suspicious mountain eyes had peeked at me from every cranny of windworn little shacks, built of slab pine. Lean old hound dogs had run out at me, roaring annihilation, then leaping up to lick me all over the face. Small tow-headed children in flour-sack dresses scattered before me like chickens before a hawk.

[3]But they had to be counted, every blessed one of them. Uncle Sam loved them all, and most of them were on his personal relief-list, up here on Bent Mountain where nothing but honeysuckle and dogwood could be made to grow without a maximum of effort.

3. In paragraphs 2 and 3, the words resemble Humpty Dumpty's "portmanteaus" in *Through the Looking-Glass*—they serve more than one function. How do "gates of heaven" and "scattered before me like chickens" and "every blessed one" function at several levels?
4. Explain the significance of "Uncle Sam loved them all" in paragraph 3 and "And the Bureau of Vital Statistics could be wrong!" in paragraph 85. How are the two statements reconciled?

[4]I sat for a minute, panting and mopping the perspiration—no, sweat! This was nothing so Emily Post! Then I shifted my big leather folder to the other aching arm and started up the mountain once more. Just ahead, over the tops of scrub pine and oak, I could see a thin curl of smoke—indicating that I had either come

to another cabin, or had unfortunately stumbled on somebody's still. Pausing only to examine a blister on my heel, I climbed the hill toward that beckoning smoke-puff. If it was a farm, they would have water of sorts; if it was a still, I would take a drink of "white lightning," and nothing else would matter after that!

5. How is the character of the nameless census-taker established in paragraphs 1–4? Why is she nameless throughout the story if she is the main character?

5 Rounding a turn in the snake-like road, I came upon a typical mountain cabin, like any of a score of others I had stopped at this morning. Bright red peppers were hanging in strings from the rafters of a low front stoop, built onto the front of a slab-pine shack. There was the usual gourd-pole standing, gaunt and skeletal, in the yard. Martins darted in and out of the hanging gourd bird-houses, those professional hawk-warners for the chickens that clucked and scratched about the yard. Then, bubbling up clear and sweet as the one Moses struck from a rock, I saw a mountain spring just beyond the house. A gourd-dipper hung beside it, and a large watermelon lay chilling in its depths beside two brown crocks of milk or butter. With a faint moan I headed for this oasis—

6. Compare the hawk and chicken references in paragraphs 2 and 5. How do they differ in function?
7. Why is the Moses allusion employed in paragraph 5? Is *oasis* a successful word? Why?

6 And stopped short.

8. Why is paragraph 6 only three words long? Is it a complete paragraph?

7 A tall, spare mountaineer with a bushy red beard and a missing right arm had appeared, as though the rocky ground had sprouted him. His narrow blue eyes held an expression almost identical to the look of the rifle bore he held cradled in his left arm. It was pointed directly at my heart, which was pounding against my ribs like a trapped rabbit.

9. Paragraph 7 bears close study. Analyze it completely.

8 But I managed to smile. "Good morning, sir. I'm here to take the census. . . . Are you the head of the house?"

9 The blue eyes narrowed a fraction. Their owner spat. I heard the click of a cocked rifle as he frowned, as though puzzled at the word "census"; then, in a deep rusty drawl:

[10]"You ain't takin' nothin' around here, Ma'am. *Git!* Besides," he added with simple dignity, "we ain't got nary'ne. We're pore folks. . . ."

[11]I stifled a giggle, managing to keep my face straight with an effort—in spite of that deadly-looking weapon leveled at my chest.

[12]"No, no. I mean . . . The Government sent me to . . ."

[13]At the word, my unwilling host stiffened a bit more. His cold eyes flicked a look at my official folder, and he snorted.

[14]"We don't want no re-lief!" he snapped. "Them as can't do for theirselves—like them shif'less Hambys down the road!—you give *them* your re-lief! Me and Marthy can keep keer of one 'nother!"

[15]A grin of admiration crept over my face at sight of this one-armed, under-nourished old hellion, standing here on his little piece of unfertile land and defying the whole world to help or hinder him. This, I thought, is our American heritage. Pioneers like these hill people had made our nation what it is today. But some of them, like this old farmer, were still pioneering, still fighting to carve a living out of wilderness and weather. He didn't think of himself as a "citizen," didn't trade on it, and had probably never voted or paid taxes in his life. But he was an American, all right!

[16]"Look," I said gently. "All I'm supposed to do is take your name, and the names of all your family. For the files in Washington. They have to know how many people there are in the country. Every ten years, we . . ."

[17]The old codger—I couldn't decide how old he was; perhaps fifty, perhaps sixty—just looked at me.

[18]"How-come?" he asked simply. "How-come they want to know about *us?* Me and Marthy don't bother nobody. Don't ask favors. Don't aim fer nobody to push us around. We jest want to be let alone. Was anybody down in the bed, I reckon we'd holp 'em. Rest o' the time—*leave us be!*"

[19]I gulped, telling myself that here, again, was a typical American. It was obvious that my "basic questions" would be roundly resented by this two-fisted individualist, and certainly not answered unless I resorted to a sneak-approach.

10. Paragraphs 8–19 combine narrative, characterization, stream-of-consciousness, allusion, description, comparison and contrast, levels of diction, understatement, and hyperbole—in short, a large number of techniques and devices to advance the narrative by supplying necessary information and serve as transition. Examine them carefully, commenting on how they achieve their effect.

[20]I shrugged, and laid my folder down on a sawed-off stump.

[21]"All right, Mr. . . . er? I didn't catch the name?"

[22]"I don't aim to drop it," the old hellion answered dryly, but a twinkle of humor came into those rifle-eyes of his. The muzzle of his weapon lowered only a fraction.

He jerked his thumb toward the spring. "You dry? Git ye a drink, if you're a mind to. Then," he added politely but firmly, "I reckon you'll be on your way? Got a tin lizzie someplace?"

11. Examine paragraph 22. Why is it effective?

23"Parked down at Stoots General Store. I had to walk the rest of the way," I let my voice fall an octave, forlornly, hoping to play on his sympathy. After all, he was a citizen, and I was being paid, not to hike up and down these mountains, but to list the people living on them. "Think your . . . er, wife? . . . would mind if I sat down on that cool-looking porch for a minute and caught my breath? Folks who live in town," I added, grinning at him and trying flattery, "live from side to side. Not up and down, like you-all around these parts! I wouldn't last a week!"

24That drew a chuckle from him. But the rifle was still pointed in my general direction. Then I saw him stiffen, looking past my shoulder at someone. He frowned; shook his head slightly. But I turned too quickly—in time to see a frail, quiet-looking, little woman with graying hair and soft luminous dark eyes peeking out at me from the cabin doorway. She started to duck back out of sight, in obedience to the man's headshake. Then she seemed to think better of it, and stepped out into full view. There was a kind of a glow about her face, a warm happy look, that drew me at once.

25"Why, Jared!" she scolded in a mild sweet drawl. "Didn't you ast the lady to come in and set? *Shame* on you!" She winked at me cheerfully, a woman's wink, sharing the eccentricities of menfolk as our mutual cross. "I reckon you're jest plumb tuckered out, ain't you, ma'am? Why, come in! I'll send one of the childurn to the sprang to fetch ye a cold drink o' buttermilk. Don't nothin' cool me off like buttermilk, of a hot day!" she chattered on hospitably, then raised her voice. *"Tommee! Cleavydel!* . . . Now, where'd them young'uns git off to? Berry-pickin', I'll be bound! . . . *Raynell! Woodrow!"* she shouted again, then gave up, shaking her head and smiling.

12. Paragraph 25 contains the phrase "our mutual cross." Account for the growing body of biblical allusions in the story.

26I hesitated glancing back at the man with the rifle . . . and caught a peculiar look of alarm on his bearded face. He opened his mouth once as though about to protest, then sighed, and turned away to the spring.

27"I'll fetch the buttermilk," he offered gruffly. "I . . . I reckon Marthy would like a mite o' company now and then, at that. Man-person don't take no stock in visitin'!"

28"Well," I hesitated, as he strode out of earshot. "I'm not exactly here for a visit—" I eyed the little woman, whose bright eyes instantly took on a look of sensitive withdrawal.

29"Oh—! You . . . you ain't from County Welfare?" she faltered. "Jared, he's sot agin any kind of charity. Even the soldier kind. He lost that—'ere arm of his'n in the German war. Come back here to his pa's place and found it growed up in weeds, all his folks died off. Typhoid. I . . . I . . ." She flushed and lowered her eyes. "I was only a girl-baby when I first seen him, a-huntin' rabbits with that one arm. Took a shine to one another first sight, and I run off from my daddy to marry him. . . ."

13. What does "and I ran off from my daddy to marry him . . ." foreshadow?
14. What is the purpose of the last sentence of paragraph 29?

30She stopped, as if shocked at the flood of pent-up conversation that burst from her at sight of another woman. From what the old man had said, I sensed that she did not have the pleasure of much company, up here off the beaten trail. Church-going was about the only recreation most of these mountain women had, anyway; and there was something withdrawn about this household. I had sensed it before, though there was nothing I could put my finger on and call it "unusual." This middle-aged couple seemed a cross-section of the mountain families I had encountered today and yesterday, on my census-taking trek over the district assigned me. All were poor. All were suspicious, more or less, of the personal questions I had to ask. All had large families of children.

31I sat down on the porch and opened my folder, smiling, "No, no," I answered her question. "The Government makes a . . . a list of all the folks living in this country, and I'm here to ask you a few questions. About your family and your farm. . . . Your name is—?" I waited, pencil poised.

32The little gray woman's face cleared. "Oh!" She beamed. "I . . . I catch on now to what you . . . Our oldest boy told me about it, just yesterday. Said a lady was over to Baldy Gap, askin' questions for the Gover'mint. Likely 't'was you, yourself?" I nodded, beaming back at her. "Well, then!" she said eagerly. "I'll be happy and glad to answer ye. Jared," she lowered her voice apologetically, "he's a mite ill at strangers. Don't you take hurt by nothin' he says!"

15. How does paragraph 32 contribute to the total impression of the story? Does it make its main contribution at this point or elsewhere in the narrative?

33I sat back in the split-bottom rocker, thankful to get the business over with so smoothly. Their name, I learned, was Forney. Jared C. The "C" was just an initial; it didn't stand for anything. Jared's mother had simply thought it sounded well. Martha Ann was her name, aged forty-eight to her husband's sixty-seven. They had, she said brightly, eleven children. Woodrow was the oldest. The youngest, a baby in arms, was not yet named. He was simply called "the least one."

16. Examine the names in paragraph 33. Is there, for example, an ironic significance in Jared's initials? Who is "Martha" in the New Testament? Who is "Anne" in Christian tradition?

34 Smiling, I jotted down the names in my book, then asked Martha Forney to supply their birth dates. Rocking gently, she ticked them off with the fond memory of any mother. I stopped, frowning slightly at one apparent error in my figures. . . .

35 "Oh—I'm *sorry!* I must have got the names mixed." I laughed gaily. "I have the birthday of your youngest child listed as *second!* Nineteen-thirty-four. . . ."

36 Martha Forney turned toward me, her great luminous eyes glowing with matter-of-fact pride at having mothered this large brood.

37 "May tenth . . . 1934?" she corroborated the figures I had set down, then nodded happily. "Yes, that's right. That's when the least'ne come to us. Woodrow, he was the first. I reckon on account of Jared's arm and us needing a half-growed boy to help us around the place. But then," she burst out shyly, "I . . . I got to honin' for a *little* 'ne. One I could hold in my arms. . . . And the next morning', why, there he was! Nestled down in the bed on my side, a-kickin' the covers and cooin' like a turtledove. . . ."

17. Is Martha's poetic narrative in paragraph 37 believable? Why?

38 My jaws dropped. I blinked, peering at my cheery-voiced hostess with a look of shock. Then, I jumped. Jared Forney was looming over me, with a crock of buttermilk held in the crook of his one arm. His bearded face was like a thundercloud of anger, with flashes of lethal lightning darting from those cold blue eyes.

18. Comment on the poetic devices in paragraph 38.

39 With an ominous thump he set down the crock and towered above me, single fist clenched as though he seriously debated smashing it into my startled face.

40 "Marthy!" he snapped. "Git on into the house! . . . And you," he glared at me. "You jest *git!* You got no call to come sneakin' around our place, a-progin' into things that don't consarn you . . . and a-pokin' fun at them that's *afflicted!*"

41 Afflicted? I glanced at that stump of an arm, wondering if that was what he referred to. But the gentle, protective look he threw after his wife's meekly retreating figure made me wonder. Then suddenly I remembered those weirdly garbled figures on my census sheet, and thought I understood.

42 "Oh, I . . . I'm terribly sorry," I murmured. "I . . . just didn't understand. She . . . she was telling me about the children, their names, and when they were born. . . ."

43 "We got no young'nes," the old man cut me off, very quietly. "You mustn't mind Marthy. She's . . . not right in her head. And you oughtn't to be pesterin'

her, upsettin' her with all them questions!" he fired at me fiercely. "Ma'am, if there's anything important you want to ask, ask me! And then, I'll thank ye to git off'n my property and back where you belong!"

[44]"Yes, yes, of course," I nodded humbly, and managed to stammer out the last few questions about crops, acreage, and the rest, which the old fellow answered in a flat gruff voice. I scribbled down the information hurriedly, and was about to get to hell out of there, when I happened to glance back at the cabin door.

19. Comment on "and was about to get to hell out of there" in paragraph 44. Is it effective? How does it conflict with the Emily Post allusion in paragraph 4? How does it fit into the body of biblical allusion?

[45]The little gray-haired woman was standing just inside, half in shadow, half in clear mountain sunlight that slanted through the pines overhead. Her arms cuddled a wad of clothing close to her breast, and as she bent over it, crooning, I thought I saw a baby's small chubby hand wave from the folds of the cloth, playfully patting at her cheek.

[46]I whirled to face the old man, frowning. "I thought you had no children," I called his hand rather coolly; then decided that their offspring must be illegitimate, to account for his queer attitude. My face softened. "Everybody," I said kindly, "is entitled to his status as a citizen of this country, Mr. Forney. Your baby is, too. He's entitled to free education, the right to vote when he's twenty-one, the right to apply to certain benefits. . . ."

[47]My words broke off, like glass. Jared Forney was staring at me as if I had taken leave of my senses. His blue eyes darted toward his wife, then back to me with a shocked, amazed expression I shall never forget.

[48]"You . . . you see it?" he whispered sharply. "You see ary *baby?*"

[49]I gaped at him, then glanced back at the woman, at the cooing child in her arms. A soft rounded little cheek peeped out from the folds of the old dress, which she held lightly in her embrace, rocking it. I saw a tendril of curly blond hair, a flash of big innocent baby-eyes. I turned back to Jared Forney, deciding that he, and not his quiet gentle little wife, was the mental case. Anyone could mix the birth dates of eleven children, especially a vague, unlettered mountain woman like Mrs. Forney.

[50]"See *it?*" I echoed, puzzled. "See what, the baby? Of course I do! You weren't trying to hide it? Surely," I said softly, "you are not ashamed of a sweet little cherub like that? . . . And I've got to take his name and birth date," I added firmly. "That's the law, Mr. Forney. You could be fined and put in jail for withholding information from a census-taker."

20. Analyze the denotative and connotative language of paragraphs 45–50.

[51]The mild threat went right over his head. Jared Forney continued to stare at me, then back at his wife. He shook his head, muttering, then sat down weakly in a chair, mopping his forehead with a great red bandana, pulled from his overall pocket.

[52]"Well, I swahnee!" he whispered in a shaken voice. "Well, the Lord holp my time! Well . . . I . . . *swannee!*"

[53]I frowned at him impatiently, pencil raised. "Please, Mr. Forney," I pursued the advantage I seemed to have gained, for some reason I could not fathom. "If you have other children, you must tell me their names—or let your wife tell me. It doesn't matter . . . er . . . whether they are legally yours. . . ." I began.

[54]He jerked up his head, glaring at me. "Don't you say nothin' like that about Marthy!" he cut me short. "There ain't a finer, better woman in these hills than my old 'oman! Even if . . . even if she is a mite . . ." He gulped, casting another wary glance at the quiet figure with that baby in her arms. Then, swallowing twice, he called uncertainly: "W-woodrow? where are ye at, son? Cleavydel? Tom? Raynell. . . .?"

21. What has paragraph 54 in common with paragraph 29?

[55]Instantly, at his call, a group of children appeared from the shadowy pine coppice at our left. Sunlight, slanting golden through the quill-like leaves, made my eyes burn and smart, so that I could not see their faces clearly. But as they moved forward, in a smiling group, I made out the features of two young girls in their teens, a small boy of perhaps eleven, and a tall youth in his early twenties. They were all strong, healthy-looking children, in spite of a pronounced pallor that was unusual among these sun-tanned mountaineers. They were dressed in neat flour-sack shifts, or cut-down overalls, obviously having belonged to their father. All four were barefooted, and swinging lard-cans brimful of blackberries. I remember thinking it odd at the time that none of their faces and hands were stained with the dark purple juice . . . but perhaps they had removed these berry stains at the spring on their way to the cabin. What struck me as especially odd was their coloring.

22. What does paragraph 55 reveal about the census-taker? Examine the description and the stream-of-consciousness. How do they work together?

[56]The two girls were completely unalike, and would never have been taken for sisters. One was sturdy and dark, the other slim and blonde. The boys were as unlike each other as they were unlike the girls. One, the younger, had a pronounced Eurasian cast to his features, with small black slanted eyes in a mongoloid face. The older was a redhead, lanky, freckled, and grinning. All of them seemed in

high spirits, with a glow of such pure happiness in each face that I could not help glowing back at them.

57 "What a fine bunch of kids!" I commented to Mrs. Forney, with a faint look of reproach for her dour spouse.

58 Jared Forney gaped at me again, his face paling. He followed my gaze, squinting and shading his eyes against the sun, then shook his head.

59 "I *swannee!*" he gulped. "I . . . I . . . Ain't nobody but her ever really seen . . ."

23. Comment on Jared's progressive use of *swannee* from paragraph 52 through paragraph 59. Why is the *h* dropped after the first use of the word?

60 He broke off again, mopping his forehead once more and glancing sheepishly back at his wife.

61 "Well," I said briskly, "I'm sorry, but I've got to be getting along." I turned back to Mrs. Forney again, to ask pleasantly, "Do you have the children's birthdays listed in your family Bible? If you could get it for me, let me copy them. . . ."

62 Martha Forney glanced past me at her husband, a mild look of accusation.

63 "I . . . did have 'em wrote down," she said gently. "Hit was a peddler come by here, and I ast him if he'd write 'em for me. I never learned to read or write. . . ." She confessed timidly. "But I had all the dates in my head, and he wrote down what I told him. Then Jared," again she glanced at the hunched muttering figure, "he seen 'em and tore out the page. Said hit was a sin and a 'bomination to the Lord to write a lie in His Book. . . . But it was Him sent 'em! Every one! I . . . I know I never *birthed* ary one of 'em my own self, not like other women have kids. But . . . I . . ." She floundered, a vague bewildered look coming into her face as though she puzzled over an old familiar problem, still unsolved to her satisfaction. "I'm their maw. . . ."

24. Justify the illiterate Martha's quoting scripture in paragraph 63.

64 Then, suddenly, she turned to me. Those luminous dark eyes, alight with an innocent happiness and devotion, seemed to blot out the poverty and squalor of that small mountain farm, bathing it in a soft golden glow like the sunlight sifting through the trees overhead.

65 "Ma'am," she said abruptly, in a quiet voice like the murmur of a mountain brook, "Ma'am . . . *You* love kids, too, don't ye? You got ary young'nes of your own?"

25. Examine the poetic devices in paragraphs 64–65.

66 I said I had a little boy, aged six, whom I loved dearly . . . and added, politely, that I should be getting back to him before suppertime. Martha Forney nodded,

beaming. She shot a look of triumph at the old man, who was still muttering under his breath.

26. In paragraph 66, why does the census-taker fail to mention a husband? Is he dead? This must be speculation on your part. However, be sure to consider the actions the narrator has observed as Jared protects Martha against hurt.

67 "There, Jared!" she said happily. "You see? That's all there is to it. There's some as don't want young'nes," she added sadly. "For one reason or another, they don't *want* to bring a baby into the world. There's some as destroy. . . . But once they've started, once they've come just so far towards bein' borned, they *can't* go back—poor mites! All they ever want is . . . just to be wanted and loved, and mebbe needed, like Woodrow. Why, there must be thousands," she said softly, "a-pushin' and crowdin' *outside* some place, in hopes somebody'll let 'em come on ahead and be somebody's young'ne. Now, Woodrow, I reckon he waited for years out there, wherever it is they have to wait. He was a real big boy when I . . . I wanted a son. And," she sighed, happily, "that very evening, I heard somebody choppin' firewood out back o' the cabin. Thought it was Jared . . . but he was off a-huntin' possum! When he come back and found all that stovewood, he thought *I* done it—or some neighbor who was wantin' to shame him for leavin' me alone, without ary man-person to do for me. But . . . it was Woodrow! Jared, he ain't never been able to *see* his boy a-holpin' him around the place—just see what he *does*. He's learned," the little old woman chuckled, "to tell him and then go off some place. When he gits back, the chores is done. Woodrow," she spoke proudly with a note of deep fondness, "he's a right handy boy around a farm. Ain't hardly nothin' he can't turn his hand to! . . . and," her eyes saddened, "why there was somebody onct that didn't want a son like *him*, I jest can't understand!"

68 I had sat in wordless amazement, listening to all this. Now it was my turn to gape at Jared Forney, wracking my brain to figure out which of these two old mountain people was the insane one . . . or whether *I* was! Out of sheer desire to get my feet on solid earth again, I scribbled some figures on my census sheet, cleared my throat, and asked little Mrs. Forney pointblank:

69 "And . . . the baby's birthday? He's about . . . eight months old, isn't he? Some . . . er . . . some neighbor left them on your doorstep? They're foster-children, is that it?"

70 "No ma'am," Martha Forney said clearly. "They're *mine!* I . . . I caused 'em to git borned, jest by wishin' . . . and lovin'. Like an old hen settin' on another hen's eggs!" she chuckled with a matter-of-fact humor that made my scalp stir. "Of course they ain't . . . ain't *regular* young'nes. Jared, now, he ain't never seen 'em . . . exceptin' once when he was lickered up," she said in a tone of mild reproof for past sins. "Fell in a ditch full o' rain water, and liked to drowned! Hit was

Cleavydel holped him out . . . and he was that ashamed before his own daughter, he never has drunk another jugful! Oh, mebbe a nip now and then," she added with a tender tolerant grimace at her errant spouse. "But not, you know, *drinkin'*. Them kids have been the makin' of Jared," she said complacently. "Time was he'd beat me and go off to town for a week or more," she confided. "But now he knows the young'nes is lookin' up to him . . . even if *he* can't see *them!* . . . and he's as good a man as you'd find in these hills!"

27. Examine the dialog in paragraph 70. How many functions has it? How does it fulfill them?

71 I almost snickered, noting the sheepish, subdued, and even proud look on the old man's face. Here, indeed, was a fine and loving father. . . . But I still could not understand the origin of that smiling group of children before me, and of the baby in the woman's arms—the baby she said was born before those other three half-grown children!

72 "Er . . ." I tried again, helplessly. "Mrs. Forney . . . You mean they're adopted? I mean, not legally adopted, but . . . you say they were given to you by 'somebody who didn't want them,' as you call it? I . . . I'm afraid I don't quite . . ."

73 "They wasn't give to me," Martha Forney interrupted stoutly, with a fond smile from the baby to the group near the pine coppice. "I *taken 'em!* They was supposed to be born to some other woman, every last one of 'em! Some woman who didn't want 'em to be born. . . . But *I* did! You can do anything, if you're a mind to . . . and the Lord thinks it's right. So," she finished matter-of-factly, "Jared and me have got eleven young'nes. Nary one of 'em looks like us, except Woodrow's a redhead like Jared. But that's accidental, o'course. They look like their *real* ma and pa. . . . *John Henry!*" she raised her voice abruptly. "Where are you, son? . . . John Henry," she explained to me in a half-whisper, "he's kind of timid. *Ressie May!*" she called again, then sighed: "Folks can think up more reasons for not wantin' young'nes, seems like!"

74 I rubbed my eyes, staring at the group of children beside the cabin, waiting in a silent, good-humored group for whatever fond command their parents might issue next. As I looked, two more dim figures—for they all seemed dim, all at once, like figures in an old snapshot, faded by time—joined the others. One, a thin sad-eyed boy of seven, with a markedly Jewish cast to his features, smiled at me and ducked his head shyly, playing with a flower in his hand—a mountain daisy that, oddly enough, looked clumsy and solid in the misty fingers that held it. The second new figure—I started—was a little Negro girl. She giggled silently as my gaze fell on her, digging one bare black toe into the dust. On her face, too, was that blissful glow of complete happiness and security from all hurt.

75 "Ressie May's colored," Mrs. Forney whispered. "But she don't know it! To me, she's jest like all the rest o' my young'nes. . . ."

76 Suddenly Jared Forney leaped to his feet, glowering down at me.

77 "I ain't gonna have no more of this!" he thundered nervously. "They . . . they ain't there, and you both know it! You don't see nary young'ne, and neither does Marthy! I tell her over and over, it's all in her mind—from wantin' a passel o' kids we never could have! She's . . . sickly, Marthy is. She . . . Her paw alluz allowed she was a wood's-colt, her ownself, and tuck it out in beatin' her till she run off from him! All that's mixed up in her head, and now . . . well, she's a mite teched, as folks around here know. Her with her makelike young'nes named Woodrow, and Cleavydel, and . . . and some of 'em not even of our faith or color! I . . . I don't know where she gits all them berries she says the children pick, or how she does all them chores behindst my back—that she makes out like Woodrow done! But . . . if it made her any happier," he lowered his voice, speaking for my ears only, "I'd pretend the Devil was takin' the night with us!"

28. In paragraph 77, Jared uses the term *wood's-colt* (illegitimate child). Relate this to paragraphs 29 and 54. How does the progression explain Jared's inability to see the children? Can you justify his final statement in the paragraph?

78 My eyes misted, and I was about to nod in complete sympathy. But he wasn't having any. To this hard-bitten old rascal, I was against him, like the rest of the world, just another menace to his wife's peace of mind.

79 "And now," he snarled, "you *git!* You got no call to set there, makin' a mock of them as cain't help theirselves. And laughin', makin' out like you see them young'nes same as she. . . !"

80 "But . . . but I *do* see. . . !"

81 I broke off hastily. Jared Forney's rifle had appeared again as if by magic, cradled in that good arm of his . . . and pointed unwaveringly at my forehead. His left eye sighted along the barrel, drawing a bead on a spot just between my startled eyes . . . and I didn't stop to protest any longer. There was cold-blooded murder in that squinting blue eye, and a fierce proud protectiveness for that vague little wife of his that brooked no argument.

29. Paragraph 81 offers the final reference to Jared's blue eyes. Trace the many references. Why is the paragraph built so carefully?

82 I turned and ran, hugging my census-folder under my arm and not stopping to pick up a pencil that bounced from behind my ear. I ran, praying. Then I heard the click of a cocked rifle and just ran.

83 Only once did I so much as glance back over my shoulder at the humble little mountain cabin. When I did . . . well, it was only a bundle of old clothes that crooning woman was cuddling in her empty arms. There were four lard-buckets

brimful of blackberries *someone* had picked and set down just beyond the pine coppice. But the group of smiling, ill-assorted children had disappeared.

84 For me, that is, they had disappeared—perhaps because . . . I don't know. Because I didn't care enough, and it took that to make them live and to keep them alive. Perhaps it was only my devotion to my own little boy that made me see them at all, as Jared Forney's childless wife saw them. Rather sadly, I took out my census sheet, a few yards down the road, and scratched out the names of eleven children that no one—no one but Martha Forney—had wanted to live. Uncle Sam, I realized with a wry smile, might take a dim view of statistics such as those. Dream-children. Wish-children, born only of will and need . . . and love. The unwanted. The unborn. . . .

30. Explain why paragraph 84 is the climax of the story.

85 But for little old Mrs. Forney, their "mother" with the heart as big as all outdoors, I am quite certain that they are very much alive. And the Bureau of Vital Statistics could be wrong! ☐

Suggested Assignments. 1. In a three-paragraph paper, explain the theme of "The Unwanted" or discuss the most interesting features of the author's style as a result of your careful reading of the story.

2. Read the following stories with the same attention to detail that you gave to "The Unwanted." Constantly strive to improve your perceptions and understand the author's intentions. Constantly ask why a figure of speech, allusion, irony and so on are used. Observe repeated words throughout the story—why does the author tie one section of the story to another?

Adolph Hitler, Judy Mauritz, and the Clear Blue Sky of Japan

by Jerry Bumpus

1 It would be a big week. Monday was the talent show. Tuesday, Wednesday and Thursday would be pretty empty. Then Friday, the last day of the week, was Adolph Hitler Day. Anything could happen on Friday.

2 Eric sat at his desk looking over the top of his book. Outside the window the sky was blue and paled slightly by a haze of smoke and smog rising from the city. Mr Parks would be around soon to see that he was studying. He wondered how many bullet pills made a lethal dose. And Judy Mauritz was going to get him in trouble by whispering

to him in Mr Burke's science class. Mr Parks was the dormitory master and he was a jerk. Tall and skinny and pale. He had a way of staring at Eric that embarrassed him. The blue of the sky seemed to be all one piece. Was the sky in layers or sections? Flying in an airplane, a jet plane, you hit air pockets now and then. The plane would dip slightly. It was caused by the plane moving from one section of the sky to the next. Judy Mauritz told him she wasn't a virgin. Some guys down the hall in the dormitory began singing the school song in Japanese. Squares. When he got a chance, and he would get a chance, he was going to put a big fire cracker in the principal's desk, in the middle drawer. When the principal, Mr Bishoff, went into his office the desk would explode WHAM and the office would fill with dust and smoke and fire and Bishoff would be really sore.

3 Mr Parks came into his room without knocking. Eric knew it was Mr Parks and not one of the guys, but he didn't turn around or lift his head from his book.

4 Then out of the corner of his eye he saw Mr Parks's dark suit at the side of the desk. "Are you reading or are you looking out the window?"

5 Eric looked up at him. "Sir? I'm reading my history assignment. Gee, we sure do get big history assignments." Eric smiled.

6 Mr Parks just stared at him. Mr Parks's face was thin, his eyes were blue like the sky and cracked with tiny, wet black lines.

7 "Do you understand what you're reading, Eric?"

8 "Oh yes, sir. Some of it. But it's very tough stuff. Back in the States I didn't like history, but here at the Academy it's my favorite subject."

9 Mr Parks nodded his head, stared at him until Eric had to look away.

10 Eric's heart was pounding hard. It was the way Mr Parks looked at him. One of the guys who had lived a long time in the dormitory told Eric never to smart off to Mr Parks because he had a special kind of torture he used when he punished high school kids.

11 When Mr Parks wandered out of the room Eric stared out the window again. Flying through the sky in a four-engined jet plane. A Boeing 707. He had flown out here to Japan where his father was all the way from New York where his mother lived. He liked his father. He was a cool operator. Judy Mauritz had large breasts. Last night he had followed her into the girls' toilet on the second floor and she kissed him and let him put his hand inside her blouse.

12 His heart was pounding hard. Her breasts were the size of baseballs. Tomorrow after school, when everyone was out of the building, he would see if she was in the girls' toilet on the second floor.

13 He couldn't sit still. He got up and walked around the room. He wished he could turn on the radio. But Mr Parks was watching him

like a hawk since he caught him smoking in the basement of the dormitory. Eric was in trouble and was supposed to study all the time.

14 He lay down on the bed, lifted the corner of the photograph of his father on the wall and untaped one of the Benzedrine pills. He swallowed it and lay perfectly still. Tomorrow he would take a pill just before he went into the toilet with Judy. This time he would put his hand up her skirt. Then they would get into one of the stalls. He moaned, closing his eyes, and stretched himself out on the bed.

15 It was hell all day. Mr Burke crossed him in science class. Eric decided Mr Burke was a bum like the rest of them. After gym class he had been showing off a trick in the shower, all the guys staring at him, and the coach, Mr Flynn, caught him and told him if he ever caught him doing that again he would kick him out of gym class, and gym class was the only class Eric liked.

16 The afternoon was a drag and he stared at Judy and she looked at him now and then but her face didn't tell him anything. She had sent him a note in the morning asking him a question. He answered it by writing her a note and passing it to her. It said, "Dear Judy. Sex is sticky. I love you and want to meet you know where. Yours truly Eric." She wrote him a note and he was reading it—it said, "No"—when the study hall teacher came up behind him and snatched it out of his hands. It was about the fifth time he had gotten in trouble that day.

17 He stared hard at Judy, but now she didn't look at him. She had on a tight red skirt that showed the line of her underpants on her hips. He was dying, staring at her, and she had just written "No" on the piece of paper.

18 That night in the cafeteria he shoved a grade school kid and Mr Parks crowded him and said that if he didn't straighten up he would be scratched from doing his act in the talent show. So Eric was careful throughout dinner.

19 The auditorium was packed with kids and parents. The first prize was a transistor radio. It would be a neat thing to win because Eric already had one and he could sell it and use the money to get some more bullet pills or maybe even some hashish from a Jap who had the stuff.

20 One of the men on the school board was introducing the acts. Mary Delange played some long-hair stuff on the piano, Pete Rathskill sang some songs from *My Fair Lady,* and some junior high school kids sang duets, and then it was time for Eric's act.

21 It was listed on the program as "Eric May with some Modern Dance Steps popular in the United States."

22 He wore the new two-hundred dollar dark green Ivy League suit his father got him. He had on his silk vest, his narrow rep tie, and the neat high-heeled alligator ankle boots he bought on his mother's credit card the afternoon he flew out of New York. All the guys in the dormitory were completely dazzled by his clothes. They had never in their square lives seen anyone dressed like this.

23 Then he was on the stage and the curtain opened.

24 Above the row of footlights he could see a few faces in the big crowd. He bowed, the long forelock of hair falling down over his forehead, and gave them his smile.

25 "My name is Eric May, ladies and gents," he said, his voice clear and perfectly controlled, "and I'm here to entertain you." He paused, smiling. He heard some feet scuffling. "First, the Watusi."

26 The kid working the records on the p.a. system started the song spinning. The rhythm pounded and he swayed his slender hips slowly and unbuttoned his coat. He began dancing.

27 Let those square bastards see me now. They'll know I've got it. Something nobody else has got. All the teachers. Stiff Parks walks like a giraffe. I'd like to see him move like this. Judy's watching me. Tonight I could do it. I finish my act . . .

28 "Next, the Locomotion."

29 Tonight. We'll go down to the soccer field, to the trees down at the end. She'll have on that red skirt. Her legs. She'll open her mouth and she'll cry and whimper and she'll dig her fingernails into my back. Watch my feet, you stupid bastards. Watch my hips.

30 Then the Twist. Then the Bop. Then a bossa nova.

31 The audience was coughing and scooting their chairs around and Eric could hear people talking. They were probably grade school kids who didn't dig. Then he heard someone laugh out loud and he danced harder, faster.

32 "Next, another Twist."

33 When he finished that one the curtain closed on him and there was applause. He parted the curtain and stepped out on the apron of the stage for his bows. The jerk on the school board who was introducing the acts was standing out there. The man gave Eric the same look all adults gave him and Eric wanted to slug the bastard. But he didn't. He bowed several times until the applause stopped. The auditorium was completely silent. Everyone was staring at him. He smiled and said softly, "Thank you," and went back through the curtain.

34 He slipped around the side of the auditorium and went into the audience. He saw Judy, but she was sitting with her parents in the middle of a row of seats. During intermission.

35 He asked some of the guys who were in the Club how they liked his act and they said it was okay and he could tell they were really jealous. And the girls. They looked at him in a new way now. He gave them the smile and they smiled back and he could tell their eyes were wet and they wanted him to get close to them.

36 Intermission came. He found Judy, but she ignored him. "Hey, kid, how'd you like my act?"

37 She shrugged her shoulders.

38 He introduced himself to her parents. They were fat and had stupid faces. He tried talking to Judy some more, but she wouldn't be friendly.

39 And then she glanced at her father in a certain way and Eric understood. He gave her a secret wink. She was cool, all right. Later, baby. You bet. Later.

40 Tuesday and Wednesday were sheer dullsville. He daydreamed about a stage career. All those long-legged chorus girls. The girls in high school were now on his side. Even the girls in the junior and senior class who were older than he was. They could tell he wasn't as young as he looked. They could tell he knew what to do. He talked to some of the gals who were really important in high school. He didn't try anything too fast, but he could tell it wouldn't take much time and effort to get on nice terms with them.

41 Then Mr Burke kept him after school Thursday afternoon. It was a real pain because he had planned to take a bennie and go up to the girls' toilet on the second floor and see if there were any girls in there he could talk to privately. Wanda Peers, he was sure, would meet him there before many days went by. He could tell she was really hot for him.

42 "What's wong, Eric?" Mr Burke said.

43 "Nothing, sir." Eric smiled, showing his bright, even teeth.

44 "Drop that *sir* stuff. I want to talk to you man-to-man." Mr Burke had something wrong with him, Eric knew. The man blinked his eyes too much and he was always picking at his fingernails. He was a very nervous cat. He was very ugly and maybe that was his trouble. Eric felt sorry for ugly guys like Burke, even if they were usually the bastards who were out to give him a hard time.

45 "You don't concentrate on what's happening in class. You stare out the window . . ."

46 It went on and on and Eric looked at Mr Burke as if he were listening, but he knew everything the guy was going to say. He would fail science class. He would surely be kicked out of the Academy. He would become a problem to others and to himself. All the same old jazz.

47 "Why don't you *try?*" Mr Burke said and now it was time for Eric to do some talking.

48 While he answered all Mr Burke's questions, giving the answers he knew would go best with Burke, he was thinking of tomorrow. The guys he had let into the Club were ready for everything. They had let rumors spread and Eric was fairly certain Mr Burke had caught some of the rumors and that was one reason he was being called on the carpet this afternoon. All the girls were excited. Tomorrow would really be a day. Tomorrow would cinch it that he was the biggest guy in this one-horse school, and it would also, if everything went right, blow the top off everything.

49 Eric finished his spiel and he could tell Burke swallowed up every word of it.

50 "But surely," Mr Burke said, "your father would understand if you explained to him the way you've explained to me that you *want* to get letters from your mother."

51 Eric shook his head slowly, having a great deal of difficulty in keeping himself from bursting out into a horselaugh. Burke sure was falling for it hard. "I don't think my old man loves me," Eric said solemnly and Mr Burke turned his head away but not before Eric saw the man's eyes glistening. Eric smiled pleasantly.

52 Adolph Hitler Day began when certain members of the Club went around before school started, before the teachers were in their rooms, and wrote on the blackboards: "No work today. Hitler Day. Meet at noon in the auditorium."

53 In the first period of the morning a special announcement came around to all classes from Mr Bishoff, the principal. It said there would be *no* assembly today at noon in the auditorium.

54 Eric laughed out loud when the announcement was read in his class. Everyone, even the homeroom teacher, looked at him in a certain way that he understood, for most people by now knew he was the president and brains of the Hitler Club.

55 The morning classes were tense. The teachers were uneasy and their minds weren't on what they were doing. At eleven o'clock, before the last period before lunch, a loud explosion shook the building. It was the firecracker in the boys' toilet on the first floor.

56 Laughter and shouts started all over the building and a few people began stomping their feet and it spread until the building was shaking.

57 Eric took a bennie, grinning as Mr Burke stood in front of the class, and all the other members of the Club, in this classroom and in all the others in the school, he knew, were also taking the bennies he had given them.

58 "Stop it," Mr Burke shouted.

59 "Stop it, stop it, *stomp* it," Eric screamed above the noise and the

chant started in the room and was picked up throughout the high school.

60 Then Eric jumped up from his seat and yelled, "Come on," and waved his arm and ran out into the hall.

61 He ran to each room, stuck his head in the door and gave the signal and in a flash the halls were filled with kids. The teachers were shouting and waving their arms but they couldn't stop them. "They can't stop me, they can't stop me," he screamed.

62 They were stampeding down from the second floor, but he forced his way up the middle of all the kids. He saw Mr Bishoff grabbing hold of kids, trying to stop them, but the others kept going and yelling, "Stomp it, stomp it."

63 She was in the toilet, her eyes big. As soon as he closed the door she ran to him and began kissing him all over his face with her wet mouth. "I love you, Eric," she panted.

64 "Hurry up," he yelled and the echo pounded on the tile walls of the toilet.

65 He grabbed her breasts and squeezed them and her big eyes were like a dog's and she was drooling and rubbing his face with her hands. "Don't hurt me," she whispered.

66 He pulled up her tight red skirt with both hands, pushed her against the wall, and kissed her.

67 Nearly all the kids were out of the building by now and to the auditorium. "Hurry up," he said out loud.

68 He reached down to her underpants. "Don't," she said, her voice deep.

69 "Shut up," he said, gritting his teeth.

70 He tried to tear her underpants. She shoved him and yelled, "Stop it."

71 He hit her on the chin as hard as he could and was surprised when she didn't fall down. She stood there, her eyes even bigger than before, and he lunged against her, tripped her, and fell on top of her on the cold tile floor. He unzipped his trousers quickly. They wrestled on the floor, grunting and gasping for breath, and he got one hand on her neck and squeezed it as hard as he could. She stopped struggling, her eyes closed. Biting his lip, he pressed hard against her. Suddenly she raised both hands to his face and clawed his cheeks.

72 He reared up on his knees, away from her, and she hit him in the face. She scooted herself away from him and he stared at her, his mouth hanging open, his face aching.

73 He got up and ran out of the toilet. He was crying when he ran into the back door of the auditorium. He dabbed at his burning cheeks with the back of his hand and saw his own blood.

74 The auditorium was silent. Panting, he stopped behind the curtain and listened.

75 "It doesn't matter," he heard Bishoff's voice.

76 He knew what was happening. They had got over here to the auditorium and Bishoff had stopped them cold. He should have known it would happen, he told himself. He should have got here first. He sobbed and pushed the long forelock of hair back from his eyes.

77 "But I know who was the instigator of this . . . miserable display and you can be sure that *that* person is going to be leaving the Academy before another day passes."

78 That's *me.* The stupid old bastard.

79 He jerked the curtain aside and stepped out onto the stage. He held up his arm before him in stiff salute, his forelock down as he gave his head a jerk. *"Revolt,"* he shouted.

80 A few boys tried to shout the word in answer, but their voices were uncertain. The rest of them stared at Eric with large eyes, some of them starting to smile with glee. Then some of them started laughing.

81 *"Revolt,"* he shouted again, louder this time, and his voice echoed from the rear of the auditorium.

82 He heard Mr Bishoff's footsteps and felt the stage vibrating and he heard Bishoff mumbling and growling furiously.

83 He turned at the same time he realized his trousers were still unzipped and he sprawled facedown on the stage when Bishoff hit him between the shoulders.

84 He drew his legs up and clutched his knees against his face, and holding his breath he knew by the pain in his groin that they had pulled another square trick on him, this time using his body as the sticky, disgusting gimmick. □

A Glass of Blessings

by Glendon Swarthout

1 Cece was so hung her tongue clave to the roof of her mouth. She groaned. This roused Sandy and Paula who were nearly as hung. She had never been as bombed as last night, the Costume Ball in Cabin Class. Wearing the bikini she had bought in Cannes, holding high the clothesline to which were pinned damp nylon pants and a bra, she had pelvised down the stairway to flash bulbs and cheers as "Miss Drip Dry of 1958" and won first prize, a bottle of champagne she had promised The Group to uncork today.

2 Sandy swung out of the lower berth opposite and said they had missed lunch, which was unsensational since they always did, and of course the breakfast bit had anyway gone out with the Renaissance. Cece mumbled for an herb and Sandy stuck one between her lips and lit it for her. The three of them had thought her winning so keeno that they let themselves be talked into drinking Layaways and much later be herded down to the boys' cabin. She remembered necking up a storm with Jenk, but after that she drew a complete blank. Great with her because it must have been ultra-sordid.

3 Like vast snakes in their lairs the propeller shafts writhed and coiled and the cabin smelled like a wrestling team after some hot hammer locks. Cece absolutely abhorred squalor. Sandy was deterging a slip in the washbasin. That was the thing about Tourist Class, the squalor, the scaly people, professors and low-budget honeymooners and school-teachers and war wives going home to show off their S. Klein wardrobes, oh, and also being stuck down with the ship's viscera. She would never forgive her folks for sending her steerage.

4 Sitting in the upper berth Paula hit her head on the pipe again and asked Sandy to hand her the electric razor and said there was something under the door. Cece had not been as bombed since Rome, which had been mad, mad. They had run into Carl and Jenk at the American Express and drunk lunch at Doney's and dinner at Passetto and wound up around three A.M. with a horse-cab at the Fontana di Trevi. What was under the door was their customs declarations and a notice they were to be filled out and turned in to the Purser by eight that evening as they would dock in New York at approximately seven-thirty in the morning. Paula said she didn't know how, she was anyway too flaked out, and began to shave her legs. The floodlights on the fountain were out and she and Sandy went in wading while the boys, really bombed, tried to drive the cab into the fountain, actually getting the forelegs of the horse in the water and the animal whinnying and the cabman yelling and eventually some *carabinieri* or *cherubini* or whatever they were hauling them off to the tank. So she had never seen Keats' house or the Sistine Chapel but when she came to in the hotel that afternoon she found a dime between her toes.

5 Her legs dangling, accompanying herself with the razor, Paula was singing *Arrivederci, Roma,* off-key. Cece forced herself to sit up and agony out of the berth. *Arrivederci,* youth. Twenty, and what had she to look forward to? An Organization Man, three kids, and varicose veins. Possibly not even that because the summer after your junior year at Loftus was the either-or point. Either you were engaged and getting married at graduation so you pooped around home all summer building

a tan or you had no prospects so you sweat the folks into giving you the Grand Tour of Europe. Half-dressed, smoke from the cigarette watering her eyes, she leaned against a wall and took a fix on the bottle of champagne. Sandy said to bring the declarations and their purchase receipts, the boys could help them. Scrummaging in her luggage Paula said she had no receipts. Cece got her hair in a tail and fumbled a rubber band around it. Our trouble, she gloomed, is that we are the all-time unco-ordinated. Maybe because we average about one meal a day and lack calories. We shave legs and do washings on empty stomachs and we have no receipts. Thought for the day: when it's over do they give you a receipt for life? It was also like college. Concentrate as she might, she could recall nothing from any of her courses except the motley types who taught them and the beginning of some poem by some metaphysical poet which had really clicked with her: *When God at first made man, having a glass of blessings standing by, 'Let us,' said He, 'pour on him all we can.'* They lipsticked and found their handbags and, with Cece lugging the champagne, went out and down the passageway. She felt so grisly she was afraid any minute she would barf.

6 They opened the door into Cabin Class with the key Carl and Jenk had made for them by twisting a piece of coat hanger and, walking up a deck to the lobby, found the ship's photographer had already covered a bulletin board with developed shots taken at the Costume Ball.

7 "Cece, look!" Paula shrilled.

8 "Oh, no." Where had she raised the nerve to wear that bikini? She had a sensation alien to her. She wondered if it could be anything as childish as shame.

9 "Miss Fleshpot of 1958," Sandy said. "You going to buy one for the folks?"

10 "I am not. Let's tool before I'm recognized."

11 "With your clothes on?"

12 They decided, before going to the bar, to window-shop the ship's store, Galeries Mirabeau. The door between Cabin and First was open and they walked across the Grand Salon to the store, its windows crawling with gloves, scarves, perfume, men's ties and socks. Cece saw a man's red waistcoat with gold buttons in which her father would be really slick. She went in to price it and emerged grimacing.

13 "*Quanto costa?*" Sandy asked.

14 "Thirteen thousand francs. Around thirty dollars. I know I don't have it."

15 "I wish I could buy more perfume," Paula sighed.

16 Cece pressed her nose to the Galeries window. The vest was very

sharp. She could see how great her father would be wearing it, under a brown tweed jacket, say, how its red and gold and daring would contrast with the silver at his temples and, wanting it so much, swept a second time by the alien, childlike sensation, brought a sudden, oysterous lump to her throat, angering her.

17 "I really need another bottle of Canasta," Paula said.

18 "Get off my toe," Cece snapped.

19 Passing back into Cabin Class they went directly to the bar. Carl and Jenk were already there, beers before them, slouched at the corner table The Group had taken over on the first day out. Sandy and Paula went on while Cece paused to give the bottle of champagne to Emil, the bartender, to chill.

20 Going on she was stopped by the sight of the sea, which she had not taken time to look at since Southampton, blue and glittering and really oceanic, so perfect its undulance that it seemed to have been sprayed with a wave-set product from some cosmic container, so illimitable its beauty that she was absolutely clutched.

21 After Emil brought the girls beers they began to play bridge as they always did after missing lunch until second dinner sitting at eight, drinking and dealing and often, when they progressed from beer to liquor around five, singing school songs at the tops of their voices. One day, when an elderly couple had inadvertently usurped the corner table, The Group sat nearby making rude remarks until the couple left. From that point the other passengers avoided them as though they were leprous. Today the game soon disintegrated. The boys were hungover and needly. Jenk, who had another year at Dartmouth, threw in his cards every hand unless a slam were bid, and Carl, who had flunked out of Harvard in the spring, told Cece he had bought a print of her bikini shot and would arrange for old buddies of his to run it in the *Lampoon.*

22 "Help us with our declarations," Sandy said.

23 "List your loot, that's all," Carl said.

24 The girls spread out their declarations.

25 "I tell you about ol' Carl an' I in the canal in Amsterdam?" Jenk demanded. "It was one of those night tours with the canals all lit up. We're on this boat, see, an' this guide boring the hell out of everybody in three languages."

26 "How do they expect you to remember everything?" Paula complained.

27 "What is it, you're allowed five hundred worth of stuff duty-free?" Sandy asked.

28 The beer made cigarettes taste better to Cece, but it was no help psychologically.

29 "We're already drinking our tip money," Carl said.

30 "You're not," Sandy said.

31 "I forgot about tipping!" Paula wailed, opening her handbag and counting her money.

32 "You get off the boat, these jokers never see you again," Jenk said. "The hell with the French. They struck oil in Algeria."

33 Large Animal joined them. The Group had forgotten his name. He was big and smily and went to some Oriental place like Michigan State where he was going to graduate a veterinarian and specialize in Large Animals, such as cows and horses, as opposed to Small, such as dogs and cats.

34 "Anyway, we're on this boat in Amsterdam, ol' Carl an' I, an' we're bombed of course or we'd never go on a damn tour. The boat comes up this water gate an' the guide hollas out to open up an' the gate guy is out to lunch. So there we sit, about eighty passengers, an' dark as hell."

35 "Emil, *garçon,* beers, hey!" Carl called.

36 Large Animal was showing the girls his completed declaration. He was good for laughs and he made a date for Paula so they tolerated him. But he was a real cube.

37 "What's a Bavarian bird?" Sandy asked.

38 He tried to explain. He had done Europe on a shoestring and the bird, a gift for his mother, which he had bought in Lucerne, not Bavaria, was his only declarable purchase.

39 "Animal, I didn't know you had a human mother," Carl said. "I thought you were anyway dropped in some field."

40 "Funny," Cece said.

41 "Go bring it," Paula ordered him. The beer was getting to her. "I wanna see a Bavarian bird."

42 "Well, ol' Carl an' I climb out on the poop deck an' shinny up the canal wall to find the gate guy. But there's nobody in the gatehouse an' we don't have the faintest how to work the machinery."

43 Cece was listing gifts. English doeskin gloves for her sister, five dollars. Small bottle of *Numéro Cinq* for her mother, six. Her purchases for herself came to two hundred four. Her father had given her, besides the boat ticket, a thousand to spend for the six weeks. Fourteen dollars for gifts out of a thousand.

44 Emil brought the beers.

45 "I'll never know," Sandy said, "going into my last year of school, why I bought six cashmeres."

46 Cece wanted the red waistcoat bitterly.

47 Large Animal returned with his mother's gift. It was a small metal

canary perched in a large hand-painted cage. Under the tail a tiny key, when fully wound, caused the bird to sing for half an hour. A button at the base of the cage started and stilled it. He wound the key, pressed the button.

48 The bird tweeted.

49 Large Animal listened with rapture. The Group sat stunned. It was so hicky, in such bad taste, that they were speechless. Large Animal turned it off.

50 "Emil, *garçon,* Screwdrivers, hey!" Carl called.

51 "An' peanuts!" Paula called.

52 "So we see light across the street an' it's a bar or something so we can go in an' try to clue these jokers there's a boat can't get through the damn gate. 'Der boot iss schtuck!' we keep sayin'. Who knows any Dutch?"

53 Cece was counting her money. The francs and American and one traveler's cheque came to twenty-eight dollars and some cents. Her folks, driving in from Short Hills, would meet her at the pier, but even acing the dining and cabin stewards and Emil out of their tips would leave her short and, besides, she did not want to be that cruddy.

54 "Animal, I think it's absolutely charming and your mother will be made for it," Sandy told him, winking at the others.

55 Emil brought the Screwdrivers.

56 " 'Der boot iss schtuck!' we say but we can't get our message through to these jokers. Everybody's drinkin' this Dutch gin called Bols or something so what the hell, we have one."

57 "Are we playing bridge, hey?" Carl demanded.

58 Cece drank half her Screwdriver and had some peanuts. Jenk was anyway the bore of the world. Twenty years old and a beer belly and beer jowls and partly bald. To imagine kissing him was to barf. And what a beast.

59 "So we go on drinkin' Bols an' sayin' 'Der boot iss schtuck!' an' after a while we're so plowed we take off for the hotel. Could be that damn boat's still stuck in that damn canal!"

60 Large Animal had wandered off to the deck to look at the sea, leaving the Bavarian bird on the table.

61 "We heard that story the first day out," Cece said.

62 Paula pressed the button.

63 "And the second day out."

64 The bird tweeted.

65 "What's her problem?" Jenk asked injuredly.

66 "Paula, shut off that bird," Cece said.

67 "Oh, she's gone ape over a red vest in the store. For her father," Sandy explained.

68 "But I love it!" Cece wailed.

69 "Her father?" Carl tossed peanuts into his mouth. "What complex is that, hey? Oedipus or something?"

70 "Shut it off!" Cece commanded.

71 "The opposite," Sandy said, trying to remember her Psych. "Daughter for father. Electra, I think."

72 Cece was recounting her money. "Five to the cabin steward and ten in the dining room and maybe five for Emil."

73 "Who tips?" Jenk belched.

74 "How much is the jiving vest?" Carl asked.

75 Cece closed her eyes and chug-a-lugged her Screwdriver. She got spastic inside. "Sandy, my four cashmeres. I'll sell you the lot for twelve dollars."

76 "Cece, you know I don't have it."

77 "Paula, you can wear my size," Cece begged. "How about them for three apiece—they cost eighteen!"

78 "When you absolutely ruin the last afternoon of my summer?" Paula sniffed.

79 "*Voilá!*"

80 It was Emil bearing the champagne in a silver bucket. The Group cheered. He placed the bucket and glasses on the table beside the Bavarian bird.

81 "No," Cece said, swaying up. "Emil, wait. How much would that bottle be if I ordered it from you?"

82 "Twelf dollare. *Pourquoi?*"

83 "Would you buy it back from me for ten?"

84 "Bud no," Emil said. "*Maintenant* we nod need."

85 "You won't give me anything?"

86 "Bedder you drink."

87 "Then don't open it," Cece said, tossing her head. "We're not going to have it."

88 Emil shrugged, slipped the bottle into the ice.

89 The Group stared at her as though she had announced she were entering a convent or suggested they panel the world situation. She sank into her chair and put her head down on the table.

90 "How chintzy can you get?" Paula demanded.

91 "Why not have an auction in the cabin, Cece?" Sandy offered. "We'll put up signs and sell all your stuff. That should swing the vest."

92 "I didn't even get to see the Sistine Chapel!" Cece sobbed.

93 "Don't be so damn Michigan State," Carl said.

94 "I wanted to see where Keats died!"

95 Paula tweeted the bird.

96 "Thirty bucks, what the hell," Jenk said. "You anyway got tonight. Put on your bikini an' sell yourself. I'll pimp for you."

97 Cece reared, her cheeks flaming, struck the table a blow with her fist.

98 "Shut up all of you! That champagne is going home to my father because I've cheaped out on him! None of us saw Europe—we went on a bombing raid! We're selfish and unco-ordinated and I hate us, hate us, hate us!"

99 Her eyes awash she flung her head down on her arms again. She could hear them sweeping up cards and money and declarations.

100 Carl punctuated the bit: "Miss Drip of 1938."

101 Suddenly Cece understood they would leave her. She panicked completely. She would be the all-time isolate. Word of how gung-ho and preachy and childish she had been would circulate and there would be no Group for her anywhere. She stood. She made them wait until she unfoiled and uncorked the champagne. Against tears of terror she played out the scene by serving them herself. She cried that when this bottle was killed she would buy more. She laughed that her father was anyway past the red vest phase. So terrific was she, so her real self again, that she won: they stayed, and by second sitting they were singing and absolutely stoned. □

Social Comment

Social comment exists in almost every short story. It may be as obvious as Montressor's human need for revenge in Poe's "The Cask of Amontillado" or as subtle as the symbolic reason for war in Ray Bradbury's "The Scythe" (p. 22). In many short stories, social comment is implicit, existing not because the author is concerned with it, but because the story reflects such comment automatically through the plot. In other stories, social comment is the most important element of the plot, which is chosen to promote the social observation. Still other stories combine a social comment and a plot to work together, revealing character at a primary level of interest and comment at an equally important level.

Such a story is "The World Outside" by Barbara Holland. You will notice that, without reading the story, you expect it to present two views: the world from an interior location and a view of that interior location itself. You may expect the title to be symbolic, the story detailing the inner struggle of a character against conflicts from an external source. You might expect it to be very realistic, the story concerned with concrete, geographical locations. You might expect it to be a combination of these possibilities, and you would be right in this case. Character, setting, dialog, and narrative are combined to create a fictional account of two worlds in conflict, a woman in conflict with herself because of those worlds. Her problem is common to many women; the story gains pertinence from the sharing.

Wilson R. Thornley, in an essay for beginning writers, once observed: "A good short story begins with careful author observation of scene and character and ends in a significant appraisal of life." * As you read "The World Outside," you should see the author's "appraisal of life" emerging. And it should serve to sharpen your own appraisal which is a constantly changing, expanding awareness.

The World Outside

by Barbara Holland

1Margery held the balloon and waited for the blackness to clear from in front of her eyes. Oxygen starvation. There were two dozen balloons to blow up, and this was the last. She tied off its end and added it to the heap in the basket.

1. How do the words "oxygen starvation" establish the tone of the story in paragraph 1?

2Very good. She was pleased. Under the swaying heap of balloons were small favors—tin trucks and trains, cap pistols and harmonicas and bags of marbles. Pray there would be enough. She had no idea how many little boys Peter had invited.

2. The two sentences "Very good. She was pleased" establish what about Margery's character?

3The balloons stirred restlessly in the draft as Margery moved away to check over the room once more. It looked nice, she thought—but then, it always did. It was a pleasant room, pleasantly shaped. The house had been built in a day when builders gave thought to the proportions of walls and ceilings and windows and doors.

3. How is Margery's complacency indicated in paragraph 3?

4Of course, as soon as the children came it would be a shambles. Caps would bang and balloons pop and the floor would be drifted with colored papers and cake crumbs and ribbons. No matter. It was Peter's house too.

* "Launching the Young Writer," a special supplement from *Scholastic Magazines, Inc.*, 1962.

4. Are you convinced that paragraph 4 is an honest appraisal?

5 But now, before the party, the dark, polished floors glowed in a vine-filtered light from the windows, curtains moved in the breeze and roses and lilies bloomed in the copper vase.

5. Compare paragraphs 4 and 5. Why are the contrasts so sharp?

6 Margery's neighbors envied her the shine and quiet of her house. They reassured each other with the thought that they themselves had more important things to do than to be forever washing and waxing. But it wasn't cleanliness Margery loved; it was the house. She had lived here all her life. She had been born in the front bedroom; and when she married, her parents had given the house to her and Bob and moved to a small apartment in town. She tended the house with devotion, as if it were the family itself—her own family and her mother's before that—as if it were the tangible shape of family love and safety.

6. Examine the point of view of paragraph 6. What do you question?

7 Most of the furniture had been her mother's. It was old, but Margery was good with furniture and knew how to steady a wobbling table and recane raveling chairs. Care and polish gave the sturdy old things a self-satisfied glow, as if they knew that they were loved.

7. What creates the effectiveness of paragraph 7?

8 Now she straightened a pillow, touched the roses with her fingertips and went out through the silent dining room. White candles stood reflected on the dark table. The fruit on the big, painted plate was real; but the glass decanters on the sideboard, now that no one could afford to fill them with liqueurs, were filled with colored water. It was Margery's one concession to fakery. She could not bear to put away the pretty bottles.

8. What does Margery's "one concession to fakery" suggest?

9 She looked once more at the cake waiting in the kitchen and crossed to the screened porch. Over it was another porch that opened from the back bedroom, and she and Bob slept there in the summer, listening to the wind in the apple tree and the soft thump of apples falling through the dark.

10 There would be games in the garden to start the party off. Pin the Tail on the Donkey. She would get Peter to make the donkey; it would keep him from exploding

with impatience. Foot races, she thought—someone could use a cap pistol for the starting gun. She had prizes for the winners—goldfish and turtles from the ten-cent store.

[11]The sun was hot. She moved across the lawn to look at the pear tree. It was weighted with pears, and she reached up to touch one, proud of it.

9. Paragraphs 9–11 are designed to reveal character and trace physical movement. Examine the way they work. What is the significance of the fruit?

[12]Suddenly there were yells and a loud cry of "Catch it! Catch it!" Something struck the trunk of the pear tree and bounced off. She jumped away. A football bounced again on the ground and lay still.

[13]"Why didn't you *catch* it, you dummy?" cried the voice.

[14]There was scuffling behind her rose-covered back fence, and then a boy appeared. He was tearing frantically at the roses. Petals showered down. "Ouch, damn it!" A length of rose was ripped loose, and another.

10. Compare the dialog and the action of paragraphs 12–14. Violence is created in several ways—explain how. Why does the reader understand Margery's reaction, even though it is unstated?

[15]"Stop that!" called Margery.

[16]"I'm bleeding," yelled the boy. He scrambled over the fence and fell into the yard. More rose tendrils came down with him. Two other boys came over behind him, widening the gap he had made.

[17]"Just a minute," said Margery. She picked up the ball and held it. "Will you boys just look at what you've done to the roses?"

[18]They glared at her, sullen, defensive.

[19]"We want our ball," said the first one.

[20]"Well, then, why not come up the driveway and get it like gentlemen?" Margery's voice was steady, but her heart was beating hard.

[21]They said nothing.

[22]"Are you boys from around here?"

[23]"Yeah. Give us the ball, lady, and we'll get out."

[24]"Yeah, give us the ball. It's our ball."

11. Explain the contrasts in revealed character in paragraphs 15–24. Notice the control of language.

[25]They moved closer. All three were dirty and tangled, and there was a quality of menace in their movements and the way their feet touched the grass.

12. Explain the effect of paragraph 25. How is it achieved? Is the "menace" merely physical?

26Margery, standing in her own garden, was scared. The biggest boy was almost as tall as she was. His thick hair fell over his forehead to his eyes. He seemed balanced between fear and rage, like a wild animal met suddenly in the woods. If she made a quick move, he might run away, frightened—or, frightened, he might spring at her throat.

27Without moving his eyes from her, he took a stone from his bulging pocket and tossed it into the air a few times. Then he turned and threw it with incredible force at the house. It bounded off the screen of the porch. The others snickered.

28They aren't people at all, thought Margery. Not even savages—savages have dignity. They're like magic things without hearts, like something in a fairy story that has to be killed with a silver bullet. How could you talk to them?

29She felt her own house standing behind her, and gathering up her courage, she said, "First put back those roses you tore down. Then you can have your ball."

13. What do paragraphs 26–29 indicate about Margery's reading habits?

30The smallest of the three darted forward. He snatched the ball from her hands and ran. The other two put out their tongues and blew rude noises at her, then whirled and pounded away down the driveway. As the last boy skidded around the corner of the house, he grabbed a pale Patricia lily and jerked it from its stem. Screams of laughter floated back.

31Margery leaned against the pear tree. Her knees were limp.

32The screen door creaked and Peter ran out. "Hey, Mom, who were those kids?"

33She smiled at him and started to touch his shoulder, but her hand was trembling, so she tucked it behind her against the bark of the tree. "I don't know, Petey. Have you ever seen them before? They said they lived in the neighborhood."

34"I guess so. I think they live over there by Wilsons'. You know where those houses are?"

35"Oh. Yes, I suppose they do."

36When Margery was growing up, all the houses in the neighborhood had been like her own—big and roomy, with angular lines softened by sleeping porches and elm trees, with gardens full of snowball bushes and sundials and birdbaths. The women made applesauce and pies for their large families from the windfall apples, and birds rejoiced among the cherries and scattered them, half eaten, in the grass. In the winter the children went sledding on Hillcrest Place all day long, until their mittens were armor-plated with snow and their mothers called them in through the gathering dark to warm and lighted houses.

37 But as fortunes declined and taxes rose, parts of the gardens were sold, leaving the big houses looking surprised on small plots, like a person standing on a shrinking rock while the tide rises around his feet. The zoning regulations were changed, and in the old back yards and side yards little box-shaped houses appeared. These houses had no gardens and no dining rooms. They each had one enormous window in the living room, through which anyone could see the husband in his undershirt watching television. These people, the new people, had big families too. The women came out in flowered wrappers to sit on their doorsteps, each with a baby slung over one shoulder. The older children ran wild.

14. How do paragraphs 30–35 function structurally against paragraphs 36–37?

38 "Do you play with any of those kids, Peter?" Margery asked.

39 He shook his head. "They don't play fair," he said. "And they're mean. You know what one of them did to Arnie Rattner's cat, Mom? He took the cat and he—"

40 "Don't tell me, Pete. I don't want to hear about it. I'm sure it's bad." She walked over to the back fence. "What a mess!" she said sadly. She lifted the fallen tendrils into place. Then she knelt and began to collect the torn petals and leaves. Her garden seemed vulnerable now, and no longer quite a safe place to be. Maybe we'll have to get a higher fence, she thought. Maybe even a gate for the driveway.

41 "Mom, how long is it now?" Peter had followed her.

42 She looked at her watch. "It is now one forty-five. That makes two hours and fifteen minutes to go. And you still have to make the donkey for Pin the Tail—remember?"

43 "Oh, I forgot! Will you show me?"

44 She threw the leaves over the fence and crossed the grass, with Peter prancing at her side. She held the screen door for him, and together they went back into the quiet house. Margery felt its safety close around them, like a fortress against the world and the forces of anger and confusion at large there.

15. What does Margery's refusal to listen to the cat incident (paragraph 40) indicate about her? Compare the lines with her thoughts about the fence and gate.
16. What does her action of throwing the leaves over the fence (paragraph 44) reveal about her to the sensitive reader?

45 Promptly at four the guests began to stream in. Peter's best friends banged on the screen or simply walked in; the boys he knew less well rang politely and stood waiting, wrapped and ribboned presents held stiffly. "Here!" they would say, fierce with embarrassment, and shove the gifts at Peter.

46 Once inside, restraint vanished. They greeted each other with yells and punches.

They ran through the house and slid on the rugs. They chased one another upstairs, their voices scaling higher. Peter yelled almost steadily with excitement.

47 Margery kept trying to count them, but they were fluid. They ran in circles, waving Peter's birthday presents. Ben Bradley hit Brian MacAllister for saying crayons were for girls. Margery put the vase of flowers on the mantelpiece, out of reach. Johnny Pierce was popping balloons with his fingernails, and little Carter Frailey, who was really too young, began to cry.

48 Margery herded them outside to organize the games. She was already hoarse from shouting over the din. But these were Peter's own friends. Most of them she knew by name; she knew who their mothers and fathers were. They ran and shouted, but when she called and held up the blindfold, they came. They respected clumps of lilies and veered away from the borders of daisies and petunias. They were normal children, normally raised. They did not menace.

17. Why is paragraph 48 included? What does it reveal of character?

49 Pin the Tail was a great success, and Ben, who won, was struck into silence by the prize of two small green turtles. "I thought it would be handkerchiefs, or something dumb," he murmured, bending over them. The others crowded around to poke them curiously, but Ben shouted them away. "Don't touch them!" he said. "It's bad for turtles to be touched." Margery answered a stream of questions: Would they get bigger? Did they really eat flies? Could they breathe under water? The goldfish, awarded for the sack race, were something of an anticlimax.

18. Examine the brief dialog of paragraph 49. How effective is it?

50 Then food. The boys quieted over the more important business of eating and destroyed enormous quantities of cake and ice cream. Then they popped the rest of the balloons, scattering fragments of colored rubber over the floor and furniture. They opened their favors, and the toot of harmonicas and crack of cap pistols reduced Carter Frailey to tears again. Margery comforted him with more ice cream.

19. Examine "The boys . . . destroyed enormous quantities of cake" (paragraph 50). What does "destroyed" reveal?

51 Restless, they streamed back outside. Margery sat amid the wreckage and listened to their voices as they raced up the driveway and through the back yard, and from the shouts and tinny bangs decided they were climbing the cherry tree and dropping down onto the garage roof. The more noise, the better the party, she thought. She began to gather up paper plates.

52 At six they swarmed back in again and finished the cake, and then some were fetched by their mothers and some went home on bikes.

53 The house was quiet. Margery, alone, collected bits of broken balloons into a paper bag. When Peter came in, looking pale and drained, she asked, "Everybody gone?"

54 "Yup."

55 "It was a good party, wasn't it?"

56 "Uh-huh. Look, Mom, I got a robot man."

57 "My goodness, who gave you that?"

58 "I forget." He carried it upstairs to his room.

59 Margery closed the draperies and remembered, with a tightening in her stomach, the three boys in the garden.

20. What does "amid the wreckage" (paragraph 51) contribute?
21. Comment on the diction in paragraphs 53 and 59.

60 When Bob came home he swatted his wife with the evening paper and kissed her. "Good party?" he asked.

61 "Very. Nothing broken, everything eaten."

62 "No birthday cake for supper?"

63 "Not a crumb."

64 "Good." He held her gently, and Margery closed her eyes. Just themselves, just the family. All the little boys, the outsiders, were gone, leaving the three of them enclosed in their house like sea animals locked in the safety of their shells.

65 "Leggo," she murmured. "I must go start food."

22. Examine the dialog in paragraphs 60–65. Is it effective?

66 She pressed the light switch at the door to the dining room.

67 The light went on. There was a crash and a howl. Margery screamed.

68 A little boy stood by the sideboard, his feet in a spreading puddle of golden water. A glass decanter lay at his feet. He was clutching its stopper.

69 "Where did you come from?" asked Bob.

70 The child started to cry.

71 "I didn't mean to scream," said Margery. "I thought he was one of the boys from the garden."

72 "What boys? What garden?"

73 "I'll explain later."

74 "I was drinking the whisky," wailed the child.

75 In the other decanters the port-colored and chartreuse-colored and crème-de-menthe-colored waters had gone down an inch or more.

76 Margery laughed unsteadily. "I hope it was good. You were at Peter's birthday party, weren't you?"

77 He nodded.

78 He was not one of the boys from the garden. He was the same breed, but

smaller. One of their younger brothers, Margery thought—ragged and wild. But not yet dangerous.

23. Explain paragraph 78.

79"Did Peter invite you?" asked Bob.

80The boy shifted his feet. "I saw the other kids go in," he muttered. "I heard them playing and stuff. So I came too. You going to tell my father?"

81"We're going to walk you home," said Bob.

82Peter came in. "What was all that screaming? Oh, hello."

83"Pete, do you know this boy?"

84"You live down on Hillcrest Place, don't you? You came to the party. His name's Joe," he reported to his parents.

85"Well, we're taking Joe home," said Bob. "He seems to have been left over."

86Fireflies were out, and the street lights threw leafy shadows across the sidewalk. Peter dashed ahead and came skittering back, excited all over again by the unexpected. But Joe seemed sucked down into a heavy silence. He trudged along between Margery and Bob, scuffing his shoes. Although neither of them touched him, Margery felt as if they were pushing him along the sidewalk one step at a time.

87Five years ago Hillcrest Place had been woods, but now the area was covered with regular rows of small houses. The narrow strips of ground between them were patchy with dying grass; the bulldozers had left no topsoil, and not even weeds grew in the yellow clay. The houses had not taken root either. They seemed set down lightly on top of the ground, like the little colored houses in a Monopoly game.

24. How does paragraph 86 achieve its effect? Notice all the elements. How does paragraph 87 grow out of paragraph 86?

88Joe's house was dark. From a cord around his neck he produced a key and silently handed it to Bob.

89"Where's your mother, Joe?" asked Margery. The darkness and emptiness of Joe's house leaked out through its walls.

25. Is paragraph 89 believable? Explain.

90"My mother's away."

91"Away where?"

92"I dunno. It's okay—I can take care of myself!"

93"Where's your father?" asked Bob.

94"Working. He always works."

95Margery and Bob exchanged a look that in the dark was more felt than seen.

96 "Well," said Bob, "I'm leaving your father a note telling him where to find you. You're coming home with us."

97 "I can take care of myself," Joe mumbled again, but without conviction. He seemed relieved.

98 Peter, who had been watching Joe with deepening respect, walked beside him on the way home. "You can play with my robot," he offered.

26. Is the point of view violated in paragraph 98? Defend your answer.

99 Margery fed them sandwiches and soup at the kitchen table and sat with them, shelling peas and taking quick, secret looks at her guest.

100 Joe was one of those children whose skin seems both dark and pale—the paleness deep, the dark an overtone. Shadows ran up his thin wrists and down along the hollows of his neck, under his ears. Motherhood moved uneasily within her. Dirt, she told herself. He needs a bath, that's all. Poor kid, poor little animal. She felt as if the boys in the garden had come back and thrown in something more complicated than a football, done something more ruinous than climb through her roses.

27. Explain the complexities of paragraph 100.

101 "Now, you two run along upstairs and play quietly in Peter's room," she told them when they had finished. "I'll call you when your father comes, Joe."

102 She and Bob ate by candlelight at the polished table in the dining room.

103 "He seems a nice little kid," said Bob. "Quiet. Wonder if his mother's gone for good?"

104 "Poor mite, with his key around his neck."

105 "Peter doesn't travel much with that bunch, does he? The boys from the new houses?"

106 She shook her head. "He says they're rough."

107 "I expect they are."

28. What does the dialog of paragraphs 105–107 suggest?

108 Margery looked around her dining room and felt, for the first time, guilty of her own wealth. They were not rich; they had no servants, no private income, and she did all her own housework and gardening. But she did have this grace of life, this pride and sureness, that made her house what it was. And she had inherited them, just as certainly as one might inherit a fortune or a diamond necklace. If she had been born in Joe's house, or had been a sister to the boys in the garden, she would not have been Margery, but someone else.

109 It was a simple thought. She had read it often enough. But its reality surprised her.

29. Why does paragraph 108 seem artificial until paragraph 109 is added?

110 By the time Joe's father arrived it was after nine, and Margery had almost decided to put the boys to bed together.

111 Bob invited him in. He stood in the hallway, a tired, honest man, uncertain whether or not to be angry.

30. Who makes the judgment offered in paragraph 111?

112 Margery came forward, smiling. "Can we offer you a cup of coffee?"

113 He shook his head. "Where's my boy?"

114 "Upstairs. He'll be right down. He came to Peter's birthday party," she explained, unable to stop smiling, "and we invited him to stay for supper."

115 The man nodded. He doesn't believe me, she thought. Why should he?

116 "I was wondering," she went on bravely, "while his mother's away—I mean, until she comes back—maybe Joe could come over here to play with Peter in the evenings. Until you get home from work. We'd be happy to have him."

117 "The lady next door looks after him," said Joe's father. "Mrs. Riera. She keeps an eye on him."

118 "Of course. I see. Well . . ."

119 Joe and Peter came tumbling down the stairs. "Daddy, hey, Daddy!" called Joe. "Come on up and see Peter's train. Can I have a train for Christmas? It has signal lights and a whistle and everything." He pulled on his father's hand. "And he got a robot for his birthday that really walks!"

31. What does paragraph 119 reveal? Is the reader prepared for it? Was it foreshadowed?

120 "We have to get home," said his father. "It's late. You been here long enough." And he turned grudgingly to Margery and Bob. "Thank you," he said hesitantly.

121 "So long," said Peter. "See you."

122 "Yeah. See you," said Joe.

123 "Come back, Joe," said Margery. "Come back any time."

124 Joe and his father crossed the lighted porch and went down the steps into the dark. Margery stood at the screen door, listening as their footsteps faded away. Then she turned slowly back into the light of her own house, which was no longer a fortress and no longer a safe place to hide from the sorrows and confusion out-

side. No higher fence for the garden or gate for the driveway could ever make it safe again. □

32. Trace the growth of the idea in the last paragraph. Did Margery "come to realize" it or had she realized but refused to accept it elsewhere in the story?
33. State the theme of this story.
34. Is the story sincere? Defend your answer.
35. Describe Margery's physical appearance. Where did you get your picture?
36. In a carefully phrased sentence, state the social problem that lies at the heart of this story. How is it distinguished from the theme?

Suggested Assignments. 1. Compare Margery and Bailey's wife ("A Good Man Is Hard to Find," pp. 184–198) as mothers. In a brief paper, detail your reasons for thinking one is more "true to life" than the other. Remember: you will be concerned with the author's presentation rather than with the women as people. As people, they don't actually exist. If you have to think about this for a while, you are becoming an attentive reader.

2. The following two stories are based on a similar subject and deal with social problems, though the authors make their social comments on two different levels of subtlety. While one story may interest you more, decide which is the better story—and why.

The Echo and the Nemesis

by Jean Stafford

1 Sue Ledbetter and Ramona Dunn became friends through the commonplace accident of their sitting side by side in a philosophy lecture three afternoons a week. There were many other American students at Heidelberg University that winter—the last before the war—but neither Sue nor Ramona had taken up with them. Ramona had not because she scorned them; in her opinion, they were Philistines, concerned only with drinking beer, singing German songs, and making spectacles of themselves on their bicycles and in their little rented cars. And Sue had not because she was self-conscious and introverted and did not make friends easily. In Ramona's presence, she pretended to deplore her compatriots' escapades, which actually she envied desperately. Sometimes on Saturday nights she lay on her bed unable to read or daydream and in an agony

of frustration as she listened to her fellow-lodgers at the Pension Kirchenheim laughing and teasing and sometimes bursting into song as they played bridge and Monopoly in the cozy veranda café downstairs.

2 Soon after the semester opened in October, the two girls fell into the habit of drinking their afternoon coffee together on the days they met in class. Neither of them especially enjoyed the other's company, but in their different ways they were lonely, and as Ramona once remarked, in her high-falutin way, "From time to time, I need a rest from the exercitation of my intellect." She was very vain of her intellect, which she had directed to the study of philology, to the exclusion of almost everything else in the world. Sue, while she had always taken her work seriously, longed also for beaux and parties, and conversation about them, and she was often bored by Ramona's talk, obscurely gossipy, of the vagaries of certain Old High Franconian verbs when they encountered the High German consonant shift, or of the variant readings of passages in Layamon's *Brut,* or the linguistic influence Eleanor of Aquitaine had exerted on the English court. But because she was well-mannered she listened politely and even appeared to follow Ramona's exuberant elucidation of Sanskrit "a"-stem declensions and her ardent plan to write a monograph on the word "ahoy." They drank their coffee in the Konditorei Luitpold, a very noisy café on a street bent like an elbow, down behind the cathedral. The din of its two small rooms was aggravated by the peripheral racket that came from the kitchen and from the outer shop, where the cakes were kept. The waiters, all of whom looked cross, hustled about at a great rate, slamming down trays and glasses and cups any which way before the many customers, who gabbled and rattled newspapers and pounded on the table for more of something. Over all the to-do was the blare of the radio, with its dial set permanently at a station that played nothing but stormy choruses from *Wilhelm Tell.* Ramona, an invincible expositor, had to shout, but shout she did as she traced words like "rope" and "calf" through dozens of languages back to their Indo-Germanic source. Sometimes Sue, somewhat befuddled by the uproar, wanted by turns to laugh and to cry with disappointment, for this was not at all the way she had imagined that she would live in Europe. Half incredulously and half irritably, she would stare at Ramona as if in some way she were to blame.

3 Ramona Dunn was fat to the point of parody. Her obesity fitted her badly, like extra clothing put on in the wintertime, for her embedded bones were very small and she was very short, and she had a foolish gait, which, however, was swift, as if she were a mechanical doll whose engine raced. Her face was rather pretty, but its features were so small that it was all but lost in its billowing surroundings, and it was covered by a

thin, fair skin that was subject to disfiguring affections, now hives, now eczema, now impetigo, and the whole was framed by fine, pale hair that was abused once a week by a *Friseur* who baked it with an iron into dozens of horrid little snails. She habitually wore a crimson tam-o'-shanter with a sportive spray of artificial edelweiss pinned to the very top of it. For so determined a bluestocking, her eccentric and extensive wardrobe was a surprise; nothing was ever completely clean or completely whole, and nothing ever matched anything else, but it was apparent that all these odd and often ugly clothes had been expensive. She had a long, fur-lined cape, and men's tweed jackets with leather patches on the elbows, and flannel shirts designed for hunters in the State of Maine, and high-necked jerseys, and a waistcoat made of unborn gazelle, dyed Kelly green. She attended particularly to the dressing of her tiny hands and feet, and she had gloves and mittens of every color and every material, and innumerable pairs of extraordinary shoes, made for her by a Roman bootmaker. She always carried a pair of field glasses, in a brass-bound leather case that hung over her shoulder by a plaited strap of rawhide; she looked through the wrong end of them, liking, for some reason that she did not disclose, to diminish the world she surveyed. Wherever she went, she took a locked pigskin satchel, in which she carried her grammars and lexicons and the many drafts of the many articles she was writing in the hope that they would be published in learned journals. One day in the café, soon after the girls became acquainted, she opened up the satchel, and Sue was shocked at the helter-skelter arrangement of the papers, all mussed and frayed, and stained with coffee and ink. But, even more, she was dumfounded to see a clear-green all-day sucker stuck like a bookmark between the pages of a glossary to "Beowulf."

4 Sue knew that Ramona was rich, and that for the last ten years her family had lived in Italy, and that before that they had lived in New York. But this was all she knew about her friend; she did not even know where she lived in Heidelberg. She believed that Ramona, in her boundless erudition, was truly consecrated to her studies and that she truly had no other desire than to impress the subscribers to *Speculum* and the *Publications of the Modern Language Association*. She was the sort of person who seemed, at twenty-one, to have fought all her battles and survived to enjoy the quiet of her unendangered ivory tower. She did not seem to mind at all that she was so absurd to look at, and Sue, who was afire with ambitions and sick with conflict, admired her arrogant self-possession.

5 The two girls had been going to the Konditorei Luitpold three times a week for a month or more, and all these meetings had been

alike; Ramona had talked and Sue had contributed expressions of surprise (who would have dreamed that "bolster" and "poltroon" derived from the same parent?), or murmurs of acquiescence (she agreed there might be something in the discreet rumor that the Gothic language had been made up by nineteenth-century scholars to answer riddles that could not otherwise be solved), or laughter, when it seemed becoming. The meetings were neither rewarding nor entirely uninteresting to Sue, and she came to look upon them as a part of the week's schedule, like the philosophy lectures and the seminar in Schiller.

6 And then, one afternoon, just as the weary, mean-mouthed waiter set their cake down before them, the radio departed from its custom and over it came the "Minuet in G," so neat and winning and surprising that for a moment there was a general lull in the café, and even the misanthropic waiter paid the girls the honor, in his short-lived delight, of not slopping their coffee. As if they all shared the same memories that the little sentimental piece of music awoke in her, Sue glanced around smiling at her fellows and tried to believe that all of them—even the old men with Hindenburg mustaches and palsied wattles, and even the Brown Shirts fiercely playing chess—had been children like herself and had stumbled in buckled pumps through the simple steps of the minuet at the military command of a dancing teacher, Miss Conklin, who had bared her sinewy legs to the thigh. In some public presentation of Miss Conklin's class, Sue had worn a yellow bodice with a lacing of black velvet ribbon, a bouffant skirt of chintz covered all over with daffodils, and a cotton-batting wig that smelled of stale talcum powder. Even though her partner had been a sissy boy with nastily damp hands and white eyelashes, and though she had been grave with stage-fright, she had had moments of most thrilling expectation, as if this were only the dress rehearsal of the grown-up ball to come.

7 If she had expected all the strangers in the café to be transported by the "Minuet" to a sweet and distant time, she had not expected Ramona Dunn to be, and she was astonished and oddly frightened to see the fat girl gazing with a sad, reflective smile into her water glass. When the music stopped and the familiar hullabaloo was re-established in the room, Ramona said, "Oh, I don't know of anything that makes me more nostalgic that that tinny little tune! It makes me think of Valentine parties before my sister Martha died."

8 It took Sue a minute to rearrange her family portrait of the Dunns, which heretofore had included, besides Ramona, only a mother and a father and three brothers. Because this was by far the simplest way, she had seen them in her mind's eye as five stout, scholarly extensions of Ramona, grouped together against the background of Vesuvius. She had

imagined that they spent their time examining papyri and writing Latin verses, and she regretted admitting sorrow into their lives, as she had to do when she saw Ramona's eyes grow vague and saw her, quite unlike her naturally greedy self, push her cake aside, untouched. For a moment or two, the fat girl was still and blank, as if she were waiting for a pain to go away, and then she poured the milk into her coffee, replaced her cake, and began to talk about her family, who, it seemed, were not in the least as Sue had pictured them.

9 Ramona said that she alone of them was fat and ill-favored, and the worst of it was that Martha, the most beautiful girl who ever lived, had been her twin. Sue could not imagine, she declared, how frightfully good-looking all the Dunns were—except herself, of course: tall and dark-eyed and oval-faced, and tanned from the hours they spent on their father's boat, the San Filippo. And they were terribly gay and venturesome; they were the despair of the croupiers at the tables on the Riviera, the envy of the skiers at San Bernardino and of the yachtsmen on the Mediterranean. Their balls and their musicales and their dinner parties were famous. All the brothers had unusual artistic gifts, and there was so much money in the family that they did not have to do anything but work for their own pleasure in their studios. They were forever involved in scandals with their mistresses, who were either married noblewomen or notorious dancing girls, and forever turning over a new leaf and getting themselves engaged to lovely, convent-bred princesses, whom, however, they did not marry; the young ladies were too submissively Catholic, or too stupid, or their taste in painting was vulgar.

10 Of all this charming, carefree brood, Martha, five years dead, had been the most splendid, Ramona said, a creature so slight and delicate that one wanted to put her under a glass bell to protect her. Painters were captivated by the elegant shape of her head, around which she wore her chestnut hair in a coronet, and there were a dozen portraits of her, and hundreds of drawings hanging in the big bedroom where she had died and which now had been made into a sort of shrine for her. If the Dunns were odd in any way, it was in this devotion to their dead darling; twice a year Mrs. Dunn changed the nibs in Martha's pens, and in one garden there grew nothing but anemones, Martha's favorite flower. She had ailed from birth, pursued malevolently by the disease that had melted her away to the wick finally when she was sixteen. The family had come to Italy in the beginning of her mortal languor in the hope that the warmth and novelty would revive her, and for a while it did, but the wasting poison continued to devour her slowly, and for years she lay, a touching invalid, on a balcony overlooking the Bay of Naples. She lay on a blond satin chaise longue, in a quaint

peignoir made of leaf-green velvet, and sometimes, as she regarded her prospect of sloops and valiant skiffs on the turbulent waves, the cypress trees, white villas in the midst of olive groves, and the intransigent smoldering of Vesuvius, she sang old English airs and Irish songs as she accompanied herself on a lute. If, in the erratic course of her illness, she got a little stronger, she asked for extra cushions at her back and half sat up at a small easel to paint in water colors, liking the volcano as a subject, trite as it was, and the comic tourist boats that romped over the bay from Naples to Capri. If she was very unwell, she simply lay smiling while her parents and her sister and her brothers attended her, trying to seduce her back to health with their futile offerings of plums and tangerines and gilt-stemmed glasses of Rhine wine and nosegays bought from the urchins who bargained on the carriage roads.

11 When Martha died, Ramona's own grief was despair, because the death of a twin is a foretaste of one's own death, and for months she had been harried with premonitions and prophetic dreams, and often she awoke to find that she had strayed from her bed, for what awful purpose she did not know, and was walking barefoot, like a pilgrim, down the pitch-black road. But the acute phase of her mourning had passed, and now, although sorrow was always with her, like an alter ego, she had got over the worst of it.

12 She paused in her narrative and unexpectedly laughed. "What a gloom I'm being!" she said, and resumed her monologue at once but in a lighter tone, this time to recount the drubbing her brother Justin had given someone when he was defending the honor of a dishonorable soprano, and to suggest, in tantalizing innuendoes, that her parents were not faithful to each other.

13 Sue, whose dead father had been an upright, pessimistic clergyman and whose mother had never given voice to an impure thought, was bewitched by every word Ramona said. It occurred to her once to wonder why Ramona so frowned upon the frolics of the other American students when her beloved relatives were so worldly, but then she realized that the manners of the *haut monde* were one thing and those of undergraduates another. How queer, Sue thought, must seem this freakish bookworm in the midst of it all! And yet such was the ease with which Ramona talked, so exquisitely placed were her fillips of French, so intimate and casual her allusions to the rich and celebrated figures of international society, that Ramona changed before Sue's eyes; from the envelope of fat emerged a personality as *spirituelle* and knowing as any practicing sophisticate's. When, in the course of describing a distiller from Milan who was probably her mother's lover, she broke off and pressingly issued Sue an invitation to go with her a month

from then, at the Christmas holiday, to San Bernardino to meet her brothers for a fortnight of skiing, Sue accepted immediately, not stopping to think, in the heady pleasure of the moment, that the proposal was unduly sudden, considering the sketchy nature of their friendship. "My brothers will adore you," she said, giving Sue a look of calm appraisal. "They are eclectic and they'll find your red hair and brown eyes irresistibly naive." As if the plan had long been in her mind, Ramona named the date they would leave Heidelberg; she begged permission, in the most gracious and the subtlest possible way, to let Sue be her guest, even to the extent of supplying her with ski equipment. When the details were settled—a little urgently, she made Sue promise "on her word of honor" that she would not default—she again took up her report on Signor da Gama, the distiller, who was related by blood to the Pope and had other distinctions of breeding as well to recommend him to her mother, who was, she confessed, something of a snob. "Mama," she said, accenting the ultima, "thinks it is unnecessary for anyone to be badly born."

14 The Konditorei Luitpold was frequented by teachers from the Translators' Institute, and usually Ramona rejoiced in listening to them chattering and expostulating, in half a dozen European languages, for she prided herself on her gift of tongues. But today her heart was in Sorrento, and she paid no attention to them, not even to two vociferous young Russians at a table nearby. She disposed of the roué from Milan (Sue had read Catullus? Signor da Gama had a cottage at Sirmio not far from his reputed grave) and seemed to be on the point of disclosing her father's delinquencies when she was checked by a new mood, which made her lower her head, flush, and, through a long moment of silence, study the greasy hoops the rancid milk had made on the surface of her coffee.

15 Sue felt as if she had inadvertently stumbled upon a scene of deepest privacy, which, if she were not careful, she would violate, and, pretending that she had not observed the hiatus at all, she asked, conversationally, the names of Ramona's brothers besides Justin.

16 The two others were called Daniel and Robert, but it was not of them, or of her parents, or of Martha, that Ramona now wanted to speak but of herself, and haltingly she said that the "Minuet in G" had deranged her poise because it had made her think of the days of her childhood in New York, when she had been no bigger than her twin and they had danced the minuet together, Ramona taking the dandy's part. A friend of the family had predicted that though they were then almost identical, Ramona was going to be the prettier of the two. Now Sue was shocked, for she had thought that Ramona must always have

been fat, and she was nearly moved to tears to know that the poor girl had been changed from a swan into an ugly duckling and that it was improbable, from the looks of her, that she would ever be changed back again. But Sue was so young and so badly equipped to console someone so beset that she could not utter a word, and she wished she could go home.

17 Ramona summoned the waiter and ordered her third piece of cake, saying nervously, after she had done so, "I'm sorry. When I get upset, I have to eat to calm myself. I'm awful! I ought to kill myself for eating so much." She began to devour the cake obsessively, and when she had finished it down to the last crumb and the last fragment of frosting, she said, with shimmering eyes, "Please let me tell you what it is that makes me the unhappiest girl in the world, and maybe you can help me." Did Sue have any idea what it was like to be ruled by food and half driven out of one's mind until one dreamed of it and had at last no other ambition but to eat incessantly with an appetite that grew and grew until one saw oneself, in nightmares, as nothing but an enormous mouth and a tongue, trembling lasciviously? Did she know the terror and the remorse that followed on the heels of it when one slyly sneaked the lion's share of buttered toast at tea? Had she ever desired the whole of a pudding meant for twelve and hated with all her heart the others at the dinner table? Sue could not hide her blushing face or put her fingers in her ears or close her eyes against the tortured countenance of that wretched butterball, who declared that she had often come within an ace of doing away with herself because she was so fat.

18 Leaning across the table, almost whispering, Ramona went on, "I didn't come to Heidelberg for its philologists—they don't know any more than I do. I have exiled myself. I would not any longer offend that long-suffering family of mine with the sight of me." It had been her aim to fast throughout this year, she continued, and return to them transformed, and she had hoped to be thinner by many pounds when she joined her brothers at Christmastime. But she had at once run into difficulties, because, since she was not altogether well (she did not specify her illness and Sue would not have asked its name for anything), she had to be under the supervision of a doctor. And the doctor in Heidelberg, like the doctor in Naples, would not take her seriously when she said her fatness was ruining her life; they had both gone so far as to say that she was *meant* to be like this and that it would be imprudent of her to diet. Who was bold enough to fly in the face of medical authority? Not she, certainly.

19 It appeared, did it not, to be a dilemma past solution, Ramona asked. And yet this afternoon she had begun to see a way out, if Sue

would pledge herself to help. Sue did not reply at once, sensing an involvement, but then she thought of Ramona's brothers, whom she was going to please, and she said she would do what she could.

20 "You're not just saying that? You are my friend? You know, of course, that you'll be repaid a hundredfold." Ramona subjected Sue's sincerity to some minutes of investigation and then outlined her plan, which seemed very tame to Sue after all these preparations, for it consisted only of Ramona's defying Dr. Freudenburg and of Sue's becoming a sort of unofficial censor and confessor. Sue was to have lunch with her each day, at Ramona's expense, and was to remind her, by a nudge or a word now and again, not to eat more than was really necessary to keep alive. If at any time Sue suspected that she was eating between meals or late at night, she was to come out flatly with an accusation and so shame Ramona that it would never happen again. The weekends were particularly difficult, since there were no lectures to go to and it was tempting not to stir out of her room at all but to gorge throughout the day on delicacies out of tins and boxes that she had sent to herself from shops in Strasbourg and Berlin. And since, in addition to fasting, she needed exercise, she hoped that Sue would agree to go walking with her on Saturdays and Sundays, a routine that could be varied from time to time by a weekend trip to some neighboring town of interest.

21 When Sue protested mildly that Ramona had contradicted her earlier assertion that she would not dare dispute her doctor's word, Ramona grinned roguishly and said only, "Don't be nosy."

22 Ramona had found an old ladies' home, called the Gerstnerheim, which, being always in need of funds, welcomed paying guests at the midday meal, whom they fed for an unimaginably low price. Ramona did not patronize it out of miserliness, however, but because the food was nearly inedible. And it was here that the girls daily took their Spartan lunch. It was quite the worst that Sue had ever eaten anywhere, for it was cooked to pallor and flaccidity and then was seasoned with unheard-of condiments, which sometimes made her sick. The bread was sour and the soup was full of pasty clots; the potatoes were waterlogged and the old red cabbage was boiled until it was blue. The dessert was always a basin of molded farina with a sauce of gray jelly that had a gray taste. The aged ladies sat at one enormously long table, preserving an institutional silence until the farina was handed around, and, as if this were an alarm, all the withered lips began to move simultaneously and from them issued high squawks of protest against the dreary lot of being old and homeless and underfed. Sue could not help admiring Ramona, who ate her plate of eel and celeriac as if she really preferred

it to tuna roasted with black olives and who talked all the while of things quite other than food—of Walther von der Vogelweide's eccentric syntax, of a new French novel that had come in the mail that morning, and of their trip to Switzerland.

23 Justin and Daniel and Robert were delighted that Sue was coming, Ramona said, and arrangements were being made in a voluminous correspondence through the air over the Alps. Sue had never been on skis in her life, but she did not allow this to deflate her high hopes. She thought only of evenings of lieder (needless to say, the accomplished Dunns sang splendidly) and hot spiced wine before a dancing fire, of late breakfasts in the white sun and brilliant conversation. And of what was coming afterward! The later holidays (Ramona called them *villeggiatura*), spent in Sorrento! The countesses' garden parties in Amalfi and the cruises on the Aegean Sea, the visits to Greece, the balls in the princely houses of Naples! Ramona could not decide which of her brothers Sue would elect to marry. Probably Robert, she thought, since he was the youngest and the most affectionate.

24 It was true that Sue did not quite believe all she was told, but she knew that the ways of the rich are strange, and while she did not allow her fantasies to invade the hours assigned to classes and study, she did not rebuff them when they came at moments of leisure. From time to time, she suddenly remembered that she was required to give something in return for Ramona's largess, and then she would say how proud she was of her friend's self-discipline or would ask her, like a frank and compassionate doctor, if she had strayed at all from her intention (she always had; she always immediately admitted it and Sue always put on a show of disappointment), and once in a while she said that Ramona was looking much thinner, although this was absolutely untrue. Sometimes they took the electric tram to Neckargemünd, where they split a bottle of sweet Greek wine. Occasionally they went to Mannheim, to the opera, but they never stayed for a full performance; Ramona said that later in the year Signor da Gama would invite them to his house in Milan and then they could go to the Scala every night. Once they went for a weekend to Rothenburg, where Ramona, in an uncontrollable holiday mood, ate twelve cherry tarts in a single day. She was tearful for a week afterward, and to show Sue how sorry she was, she ground out a cigarette on one of her downy wrists. This dreadful incident took place in the Luitpold and was witnessed by several patrons, who could not conceal their alarm. Sue thought to herself, Maybe she's cuckoo, and while she did not relinquish any of her daydreams of the festivities in Italy, she began to observe Ramona more closely.

25 She could feel the turmoil in her when they went past bakeshop

windows full of cream puffs and cheesecake and petits fours. Ramona, furtively glancing at the goodies out of the corner of her eye, would begin a passionate and long-winded speech on the present-day use of Latin in Iceland. When, on a special occasion, they dined together at the Ritterhalle, she did not even look at the menu but lionheartedly ordered a single dropped egg and a cup of tea and resolutely kept her eyes away from Sue's boiled beef and fritters. When drinking cocktails in the American bar at the Europäischer Hof, she shook her head as the waiter passed a tray of canapés made of caviar, anchovy, lobster, foie gras, and Camembert, ranged fanwise around a little bowl of ivory almonds. But sometimes she did capitulate, with a piteous rationalization—that she had not eaten any breakfast or that she had barely touched her soup at the Gerstnerheim and that therefore there would be nothing wrong in her having two or perhaps three or four of these tiny little sandwiches. One time Sue saw her take several more than she had said she would and hide them under the rim of her plate.

26 As the date set for their departure for Switzerland drew nearer, Ramona grew unaccountable. Several times she failed to appear at lunch, and when Sue, in a friendly way, asked for an explanation, she snapped, "None of your business. What do you think you are? My nurse?" She was full of peevishness, complaining of the smell of senility in the Gerstnerheim, of students who sucked the shells of pistachio nuts in the library, of her landlady's young son, who she was sure rummaged through her bureau drawers when she was not at home. Once she and Sue had a fearful row when Sue, keeping up her end of the bargain, although she really did not care a pin, told her not to buy a bag of chestnuts from a vendor on a street corner. Ramona shouted, for all the world to hear, "You are sadly mistaken, Miss Ledbetter, if you think you know more than Dr. Augustus Freudenburg, of the Otto-Ludwigs Clinic!" And a little after that she acquired the notion that people were staring at her, and she carried an umbrella, rain or shine, to hide herself from them. But, oddest of all, when the skis and boots and poles that she had ordered for Sue arrived, and Sue thanked her for them, she said, "I can't think what use they'll be. Obviously there never is any snow in this ghastly, godforsaken place."

27 There was an awful afternoon when Ramona was convinced that the waiter at the Luitpold had impugned her German, and Sue found herself in the unhappy role of intermediary in a preposterous altercation so bitter that it stopped just short of a bodily engagement. When the girls left the café—at the insistence of the management—they were silent all the way to the cathedral, which was the place where they usually

took leave of each other to go their separate ways home. They paused a moment there in the growing dark, and suddenly Ramona said, "Look at me!" Sue looked at her. "I say!" said Ramona. "In this light you look exactly like my sister. How astonishing! Turn a little to the left, there's a dear." And when Sue had turned as she directed, a whole minute—but it seemed an hour to Sue—passed before Ramona broke from her trance to cry, "How blind I've been! My brothers would be shocked to death if they should see you. It would kill them!"

28 She put out her hands, on which she wore white leather mittens, and held Sue's face between them and studied it, half closing her eyes and murmuring her amazement, her delight, her perplexity at her failure until now to see this marvelous resemblance. Once, as her brown eyes nimbly catechized the face before her, she took off her right mitten and ran her index finger down Sue's nose, as if she had even learned her sister's bones by heart, while Sue, unable to speak, could only think in panic, What does she mean *if* they should see me?

29 Ramona carried on as if she were moon-struck, making fresh discoveries until not only were Sue's and Martha's faces identical but so were their voices and their carriage and the shape of their hands and feet. She said, "You must come to my room and see a picture of Martha right now. It's desperately weird."

30 Fascinated, Sue nodded, and they moved on through the quiet street. Ramona paused to look at her each time they went under a street light, touched her hair, begged leave to take her arm, and called her Martha, Sister, Twin, and sometimes caught her breath in an abortive sob. They went past the lighted windows of the *Bierstuben,* where the shadows of young men loomed and waved, and then turned at the Kornmarkt and began to climb the steep, moss-slick steps that led to the castle garden. As they went through the avenue of trees that lay between the casino and the castle, Ramona, peering at Sue through the spooky mist, said, "They would have been much quicker to see it than I," so Sue knew, miserably and for sure, that something had gone wrong with their plans to go to San Bernardino. And then Ramona laughed and broke away and took off her tam-o'-shanter, which she hurled toward the hedge of yew, where it rested tipsily.

31 "I could vomit," she said, standing absolutely still.

32 There was a long pause. Finally, Sue could no longer bear the suspense, and she asked Ramona if her brothers knew that she and Ramona were not coming.

33 "Of course they know. They've known for two weeks, but you're crazy if you think the reason we're not going is that you look like Martha. How beastly vain you are!" She was so angry and she trembled

so with her rage that Sue did not dare say another word. "It was Freudenburg who said I couldn't go," she howled. "He has found out that I have lost ten pounds."

34 Sue had no conscious motive in asking her, idly and not really caring, where Dr. Freudenburg's office was; she had meant the guileless question to be no more than a show of noncommittal and courteous interest, and she was badly frightened when, in reply, Ramona turned on her and slapped her hard on either cheek, and then opened her mouth to emit one hideous, protracted scream. Sue started instinctively to run away, but Ramona seized and held her arms, and began to talk in a lunatic, fast monotone, threatening her with lawsuits and public exposure if she ever mentioned the name Freudenburg again *or* her brothers *or* her mother and father *or* Martha, that ghastly, puling, pampered hypochondriac who had totally wrecked her life.

35 Sue felt that the racket of her heart and her hot, prancing brain would drown out Ramona's voice, but it did nothing of the kind, and they stood there, rocking in their absurd attitude, while the fit continued. Sue was sure that the police and the townsfolk would come running at any moment and an alarm would be sounded and they would be arrested for disturbing the peace. But if anyone heard them, it was only the shades of the princes in the castle.

36 It was difficult for Sue to sort out the heroes and the villains in this diatribe. Sometimes it appeared that Ramona's brothers and her parents hated her, sometimes she thought they had been glad when Martha died; sometimes Dr. Freudenburg seemed to be the cause of everything. She had the impression that he was an alienist, and she wondered if now he would send his patient to an institution; at other times she thought the Doctor did not exist at all. She did not know whom to hate or whom to trust, for the characters in this *Walpurgisnacht* changed shape by the minute and not a one was left out—not Signor da Gama or the ballet girls in Naples or the old ladies at the Gerstnerheim or the prehistoric figures of a sadistic nurse, a base German governess, and a nefarious boy cousin who had invited Ramona to misbehave when she was barely eight years old. Once she said that to escape Dr. Freudenburg she meant to order her father to take her cruising on the San Filippo; a minute later she said that that loathsome fool Justin had wrecked the boat on the coast of Yugoslavia. She would go home to the villa in Sorrento and be comforted by her brothers, who had always preferred her to everyone else in the world—except that they hadn't! They had always despised her. Freudenburg would write to her father and he would come to fetch her back to that vulgar, parvenu house, and there, in spite of all her efforts to outwit them, they would make

her eat and eat until she was the laughing stock of the entire world. What *were* they after? Did they want to indenture her to a sideshow?

37 She stopped, trailed off, turned loose Sue's arm, and stood crestfallen, like a child who realizes that no one is listening to his tantrum. Tears, terribly silent, streamed down her round cheeks.

38 Then, "It isn't true, you know. They aren't like that, they're good and kind. The only thing that's true is that I eat all the time," and softly, to herself, she repeated, "All the time." In a mixture of self-hatred and abstracted bravado, she said that she had supplemented all her lunches at the Gerstnerheim and had nibbled constantly, alone in her room; that Dr. Freudenburg's recommendation had been just the opposite of what she had been saying all along.

39 Unconsolable, Ramona moved on along the path, and Sue followed, honoring her tragedy but struck dumb by it. On the way through the courtyard and down the street, Ramona told her, in a restrained and rational voice, that her father was coming the next day to take her back to Italy, since the experiment of her being here alone had not worked. Her parents, at the counsel of Dr. Freudenburg, were prepared to take drastic measures, involving, if need be, a hospital, the very thought of which made her blood run cold. "Forgive me for that scene back there," she said. "You grow wild in loneliness like mine. It would have been lovely if it had all worked out the way I wanted and we had gone to Switzerland."

40 "Oh, that's all right," said Sue, whose heart was broken. "I don't know how to ski anyway."

41 "Really? What crust! I'd never have bought you all that gear if I had known." Ramona laughed lightly. They approached the garden gate of a tall yellow house, and she said, "This is where I live. Want to come in and have a glass of kirsch?"

42 Sue did not want the kirsch and she knew she should be on her way home if she were to get anything hot for supper, but she was curious to see the photograph of Martha, and since Ramona seemed herself again, she followed her down the path. Ramona had two little rooms, as clean and orderly as cells. In the one where she studied, there was no furniture except a long desk with deep drawers and a straight varnished chair and a listing bookcase. She had very few books, really, for one so learned—not more than fifty altogether—and every one of them was dull: grammars, dictionaries, readers, monographs reprinted from scholarly journals, and treatises on semantics, etymology, and phonetics. Her pens and pencils lay straight in a lacquered tray, and a pile of notebooks sat neatly at the right of the blotter, and at the

left there was a book open to a homily in Anglo-Saxon which, evidently, she had been translating. As soon as they had taken off their coats, Ramona went into the bedroom and closed the door; from beyond it Sue could hear drawers being opened and quickly closed, metal clashing, and paper rustling, and she imagined that the bureaus were stocked with contraband—with sweets and sausages and cheese. For the last time, she thought of Daniel and Justin and Robert, of whom she was to be forever deprived because their sister could not curb her brutish appetite.

43 She wandered around the room and presently her eye fell on a photograph in a silver frame standing in a half-empty shelf of the bookcase. It could only be Martha. The dead girl did not look in the least like Sue but was certainly as pretty as she had been described, and as Sue looked at the pensive eyes and the thoughtful lips, she was visited by a fugitive feeling that this was really Ramona's face at which she looked and that it had been refined and made immaculate by an artful photographer who did not scruple to help his clients deceive themselves. For Martha wore a look of lovely wonder and remoteness, as if she were all disconnected spirit, and it was the same as a look that sometimes came to Ramona's eyes and lips just as she lifted her binoculars to contemplate the world through the belittling lenses.

44 Sue turned the photograph around, and on the back she read the penned inscription "Martha Ramona Dunn at sixteen, Sorrento." She looked at that ethereal face again, and this time had no doubt that it had once belonged to Ramona. No wonder the loss of it had left her heartbroken! She sighed to think of her friend's desperate fabrication. In a sense, she supposed the Martha side of Ramona Dunn *was* dead, dead and buried under layers and layers of fat. Just as she guiltily returned the picture to its place, the door to the bedroom opened and Ramona, grandly gesturing toward her dressing table, cried, "Come in! Come in! Enter the banquet hall!" She had emptied the drawers of all their forbidden fruits, and arrayed on the dressing table, in front of her bottles of cologne and medicine, were cheeses and tinned fish and pickles and pressed meat and cakes, candies, nuts, olives, sausages, buns, apples, raisins, figs, prunes, dates, and jars of pâté and glasses of jelly and little pots of caviar, as black as ink. "Don't stint!" she shouted, and she bounded forward and began to eat as if she had not had a meal in weeks.

45 "All evidence must be removed by morning! What a close shave! What if my father had come without telling me and had found it all!" Shamelessly, she ranged up and down the table, cropping and lowing

like a cow in a pasture. There were droplets of sweat on her forehead and her hands were shaking, but nothing else about her showed that she had gone to pieces earlier or that she was deep, deeper by far than anyone else Sue had ever known.

46 Sucking a rind of citron, Ramona said, "You must realize that our friendship is over, but not through any fault of yours. When I went off and turned on you that way, it had nothing to do with you at all, for of course you don't look any more like Martha than the man in the moon."

47 "It's all right, Ramona," said Sue politely. She stayed close to the door, although the food looked very good. "I'll still be your friend."

48 "Oh, no, no, there would be nothing in it for you," Ramona said, and her eyes narrowed ever so slightly. "Thank you just the same. I am exceptionally ill." She spoke with pride, as if she were really saying "I am exceptionally talented" or "I am exceptionally attractive."

49 "I didn't know you were," said Sue. "I'm sorry."

50 "*I'm* not sorry. It is for yourself that you should be sorry. You have such a trivial little life, poor girl. It's not your fault. Most people do."

51 "I'd better go," said Sue.

52 "Go! Go!" cried Ramona, with a gesture of grand benediction. "I weep not."

53 Sue's hand was on the knob of the outer door, but she hesitated to leave a scene so inconclusive. Ramona watched her as she lingered; her mouth was so full that her cheeks were stretched out as if in mumps, and through the food and through a devilish, mad grin she said, "Of *course* you could never know the divine joy of being twins, provincial one! Do you know what he said the last night when my name was Martha? The night he came into that room where the anemones were? He pretended that he was looking for a sheet of music. Specifically for a sonata for the harpsichord by Wilhelm Friedrich Bach."

54 But Sue did not wait to hear what he, whoever he was, had said; she ran down the brown-smelling stairs and out into the cold street with the feeling that Ramona was still standing there before the food, as if she were serving herself at an altar, still talking, though there was no one to listen. She wondered if she ought to summon Dr. Freudenburg, and then decided that, in the end, it was none of her business. She caught a trolley that took her near her pension, and was just in time to get some hot soup and a plate of cold meats and salad before the kitchen closed. But when the food came, she found that she had no appetite at all. "What's the matter?" asked Herr Sachs, the fresh young waiter. "Are you afraid to get fat?" And he looked absolutely flabbergasted when, at this, she fled from the café without a word. □

The Three Fat Women of Antibes

by W. Somerset Maugham

1 One was called Mrs. Richman and she was a widow. The second was called Mrs. Sutcliffe; she was American and she had divorced two husbands. The third was called Miss Hickson and she was a spinster. They were all in the comfortable forties and they were all well off. Mrs. Sutcliffe had the odd first name of Arrow. When she was young and slender she had liked it well enough. It suited her, and the jests it occasioned, though too often repeated, were very flattering; she was not disinclined to believe that it suited her character too: it suggested directness, speed and purpose. She liked it less now that her delicate features had grown muzzy with fat, that her arms and shoulders were so substantial and her hips so massive. It was increasingly difficult to find dresses to make her look as she liked to look. The jests her name gave rise to now were made behind her back, and she very well knew that they were far from obliging. But she was by no means resigned to middle age. She still wore blue to bring out the colour of her eyes and, with the help of art, her fair hair had kept its lustre. What she liked about Beatrice Richman and Frances Hickson was that they were both so much fatter than she, it made her look quite slim; they were both of them older and much inclined to treat her as a little young thing. It was not disagreeable. They were good-natured women, and they chaffed her pleasantly about her beaux; they had both given up the thought of that kind of nonsense, indeed Miss Hickson had never given it a moment's consideration, but they were sympathetic to her flirtations. It was understood that one of these days Arrow would make a third man happy.

2 "Only you mustn't get any heavier, darling," said Mrs. Richman.

3 "And for goodness' sake make certain of his bridge," said Miss Hickson.

4 They saw for her a man of about fifty, but well preserved and of distinguished carriage, an admiral on the retired list and a good golfer, or a widower without encumbrances, but in any case with a substantial income. Arrow listened to them amiably, and kept to herself the fact that this was not at all her idea. It was true that she would have liked to marry again, but her fancy turned to a dark slim Italian with flashing eyes and a sonorous title or to a Spanish don of noble lineage; and not a day more than thirty. There were times when, looking at herself in her mirror, she was certain she did not look any more than that herself.

5 They were great friends, Miss Hickson, Mrs. Richman and Arrow

Sutcliffe. It was their fat that had brought them together and bridge that had cemented their alliance. They had met first at Carlsbad, where they were staying at the same hotel and were treated by the same doctor who used them with the same ruthlessness. Beatrice Richman was enormous. She was a handsome woman, with fine eyes, rouged cheeks and painted lips. She was very well content to be a widow with a handsome fortune. She adored her food. She liked bread and butter, cream, potatoes and suet puddings, and for eleven months of the year ate pretty well everything she had a mind to, and for one month went to Carlsbad to reduce. But every year she grew fatter. She upbraided the doctor, but got no sympathy from him. He pointed out to her various plain and simple facts.

6 "But if I'm never to eat a thing I like life isn't worth living," she expostulated.

7 He shrugged his disapproving shoulders. Afterwards she told Miss Hickson that she was beginning to suspect he wasn't so clever as she had thought. Miss Hickson gave a great guffaw. She was that sort of woman. She had a deep bass voice, a large flat sallow face from which twinkled little bright eyes; she walked with a slouch, her hands in her pockets, and when she could do so without exciting attention smoked a long cigar. She dressed as like a man as she could.

8 "What the deuce should I look like in frills and furbelows?" she said. "When you're as fat as I am you may just as well be comfortable."

9 She wore tweeds and heavy boots and whenever she could went about bareheaded. But she was as strong as an ox and boasted that few men could drive a longer ball than she. She was plain of speech, and she could swear more variously than a stevedore. Though her name was Frances she preferred to be called Frank. Masterful, but with tact, it was her jovial strength of character that held the three together. They drank their waters together, had their baths at the same hour, they took their strenuous walks together, pounded about the tennis court with a professional to make them run, and ate at the same table their sparse and regulated meals. Nothing impaired their good humour but the scales, and when one or other of them weighed as much on one day as she had the day before neither Frank's coarse jokes, the *bonhomie* of Beatrice nor Arrow's pretty kittenish ways sufficed to dispel the gloom. Then drastic measures were resorted to, the culprit went to bed for twenty-four hours and nothing passed her lips but the doctor's famous vegetable soup which tasted like hot water in which a cabbage had been well-rinsed.

10 Never were three women greater friends. They would have been independent of anyone else if they had not needed a fourth at bridge. They

were fierce, enthusiastic players, and the moment the day's cure was over they sat down at the bridge table. Arrow, feminine as she was, played the best game of the three, a hard, brilliant game, in which she showed no mercy and never conceded a point or failed to take advantage of a mistake. Beatrice was solid and reliable. Frank was dashing; she was a great theorist, and had all the authorities at the tip of her tongue. They had long arguments over the rival systems. They bombarded one another with Culbertson and Sims. It was obvious that not one of them ever played a card without fifteen good reasons, but it was also obvious from the subsequent conversation that there were fifteen equally good reasons why she should not have played it. Life would have been perfect, even with the prospect of twenty-four hours of that filthy soup when the doctor's rotten (Beatrice) bloody (Frank) lousy (Arrow) scales pretended one hadn't lost an ounce in two days, if only there had not been this constant difficulty of finding someone to play with them who was in their class.

11 It was for this reason that on the occasion with which this narrative deals Frank invited Lena Finch to come and stay with them at Antibes. They were spending some weeks there on Frank's suggestion. It seemed absurd to her, with her common sense, that immediately the cure was over Beatrice who always lost twenty pounds should by giving way to her ungovernable appetite put it all on again. Beatrice was weak. She needed a person of strong will to watch her diet. She proposed then that on leaving Carlsbad they should take a house at Antibes where they could get plenty of exercise, everyone knew that nothing slimmed you like swimming, and as far as possible could go on with the cure. With a cook of their own they could at least avoid things that were obviously fattening. There was no reason why they should not all lose several pounds more. It seemed a very good idea. Beatrice knew what was good for her, and she could resist temptation well enough if temptation was not put right under her nose. Besides, she liked gambling, and a flutter at the Casino two or three times a week would pass the time very pleasantly. Arrow adored Antibes, and she would be looking her best after a month at Carlsbad. She could just pick and choose among the young Italians, the passionate Spaniards, the gallant Frenchmen and the long-limbed English who sauntered about all day in bathing trunks and gay-coloured dressing gowns. The plan worked very well. They had a grand time. Two days a week they ate nothing but hard-boiled eggs and raw tomatoes, and they mounted the scales every morning with light hearts. Arrow got down to eleven stone and felt just like a girl; Beatrice and Frank by standing in a certain way just avoided the thirteen. The machine they had bought registered kilogrammes, and they got

extraordinarily clever at translating these in the twinkling of an eye to pounds and ounces.

12 But the fourth at bridge continued to be the difficulty. This person played like a foot, the other was so slow that it drove you frantic, one was quarrelsome, another was a bad loser, a third was next door to a crook. It was strange how hard it was to find exactly the player you wanted.

13 One morning when they were sitting in pyjamas on the terrace overlooking the sea, drinking their tea (without milk or sugar) and eating a rusk prepared by Dr. Hudebert and guaranteed not to be fattening, Frank looked up from her letters.

14 "Lena Finch is coming down to the Riviera," she said.

15 "Who's she?" asked Arrow.

16 "She married a cousin of mine. He died a couple of months ago, and she's just recovering from a nervous breakdown. What about asking her to come here for a fortnight?"

17 "Does she play bridge?" asked Beatrice.

18 "You bet your life she does," boomed Frank in her deep voice. "And a damned good game too. We should be absolutely independent of outsiders."

19 "How old is she?" asked Arrow.

20 "Same age as I am."

21 "That sounds all right."

22 It was settled. Frank, with her usual decisiveness, stalked out as soon as she had finished her breakfast to send a wire, and three days later Lena Finch arrived. Frank met her at the station. She was in deep but not obtrusive mourning for the recent death of her husband. Frank had not seen her for two years. She kissed her warmly and took a good look at her.

23 "You're very thin, darling," she said.

24 Lena smiled bravely.

25 "I've been through a good deal lately. I've lost a lot of weight."

26 Frank sighed, but whether from sympathy with her cousin's sad loss, or from envy, was not obvious.

27 Lena was not, however, unduly depressed, and after a quick bath was quite ready to accompany Frank to Eden Roc. Frank introduced the stranger to her two friends and they sat down in what was known as the Monkey House. It was an enclosure covered with glass overlooking the sea, with a bar at the back, and it was crowded with chattering people in bathing costumes, pyjamas or dressing gowns, who were seated at the tables having drinks. Beatrice's soft heart went out to the lorn widow, and Arrow, seeing that she was pale, quite ordinary to look

at and probably forty-eight, was prepared to like her very much. A waiter approached them.

28 "What will you have, Lena dear?" Frank asked.

29 "Oh, I don't know, what you all have, a dry Martini or a White Lady."

30 Arrow and Beatrice gave her a quick look. Everyone knows how fattening cocktails are.

31 "I daresay you're tired after your journey," said Frank kindly.

32 She ordered a dry Martini for Lena and a mixed lemon and orange juice for herself and her two friends.

33 "We find alcohol isn't very good in all this heat," she explained.

34 "Oh, it never effects me at all," Lena answered airily. "I like cocktails."

35 Arrow went very slightly pale under her rouge (neither she nor Beatrice ever wet their faces when they bathed, and they thought it absurd of Frank, a woman of her size, to pretend she liked diving), but she said nothing. The conversation was gay and easy, they all said the obvious things with gusto, and presently they strolled back to the villa for luncheon.

36 In each napkin were two little antifat rusks. Lena gave a bright smile as she put them by the side of her plate.

37 "May I have some bread?" she asked.

38 The grossest indecency would not have fallen on the ears of those three women with such a shock. Not one of them had eaten bread for ten years. Even Beatrice, greedy as she was, drew the line there. Frank, the good hostess, recovered herself first.

39 "Of course, darling," she said, and turning to the butler asked him to bring some.

40 "And some butter," said Lena in that pleasant easy way of hers.

41 There was a moment's embarrassed silence.

42 "I don't know if there's any in the house," said Frank, "but I'll enquire. There may be some in the kitchen."

43 "I adore bread and butter, don't you?" said Lena, turning to Beatrice.

44 Beatrice gave a sickly smile and an evasive reply. The butler brought a long crisp roll of French bread. Lena slit it in two and plastered it with the butter which was miraculously produced. A grilled sole was served.

45 "We eat very simply here," said Frank. "I hope you won't mind."

46 "Oh, no, I like my food very plain," said Lena as she took some butter and spread it over her fish. "As long as I can have bread and butter and potatoes and cream I'm quite happy."

47 The three friends exchanged a glance. Frank's great sallow face

sagged a little, and she looked with distaste at the dry, insipid sole on her plate. Beatrice came to the rescue.

48 "It's such a bore, but we can't get cream here," she said. "It's one of the things one has to do without on the Riviera."

49 "What a pity," said Lena.

50 The rest of the luncheon consisted of lamb cutlets with the fat carefully removed so that Beatrice should not be led astray, and spinach boiled in water, with stewed pears to end up with. Lena tasted her pears and gave the butler a look of enquiry. That resourceful man understood her at once, and though powdered sugar had never been served at that table before, handed her without a moment's hesitation a bowl of it. She helped herself liberally. The other three pretended not to notice. Coffee was served, and Lena took three lumps of sugar in hers.

51 "You have a very sweet tooth," said Arrow in a tone which she struggled to keep friendly.

52 "We think saccharine so much more sweetening," said Frank, as she put a tiny tablet of it into her coffee.

53 "Disgusting stuff," said Lena.

54 Beatrice's mouth drooped at the corners, and she gave the lump sugar a yearning look.

55 "Beatrice!" boomed Frank sternly.

56 Beatrice stifled a sigh and reached for the saccharine.

57 Frank was relieved when they could sit down to the bridge table. It was plain to her that Arrow and Beatrice were upset. She wanted them to like Lena, and she was anxious that Lena should enjoy her fortnight with them. For the first rubber Arrow cut with the newcomer.

58 "Do you play Vanderbilt or Culbertson?" she asked her.

59 "I have no conventions," Lena answered in a happy-go-lucky way, "I play by the light of nature."

60 "I play strict Culbertson," said Arrow acidly.

61 The three fat women braced themselves to the fray. No conventions indeed! They'd learn her. When it came to bridge even Frank's family feeling was forgotten, and she settled down with the same determination as the others to trim the stranger in their midst. But the light of nature served Lena very well. She had a natural gift for the game and great experience. She played with imagination, quickly, boldly, and with assurance. The other players were in too high a class not to realize very soon that Lena knew what she was about, and since they were all thoroughly good-natured, generous women, they were gradually mollified. This was real bridge. They all enjoyed themselves. Arrow and Beatrice began to feel more kindly towards Lena, and Frank, noticing this, heaved a fat sigh of relief. It was going to be a success.

62 After a couple of hours they parted, Frank and Beatrice to have a round of golf, and Arrow to take a brisk walk with a young Prince Roccamare whose acquaintance she had lately made. He was very sweet and young and good-looking. Lena said she would rest.

63 They met again just before dinner.

64 "I hope you've been all right, Lena, dear," said Frank. "I was rather conscience-stricken at leaving you with nothing to do all this time."

65 "Oh, don't apologize. I had a lovely sleep, and then I went down to Juan and had a cocktail. And d'you know what I discovered? You'll be so pleased. I found a dear little teashop where they've got the most beautiful thick fresh cream. I've ordered half a pint to be sent every day. I thought it would be my little contribution to the household."

66 Her eyes were shining. She was evidently expecting them to be delighted.

67 "How very kind of you," said Frank, with a look that sought to quell the indignation that she saw on the faces of her two friends. "But we never eat cream. In this climate it makes one so bilious."

68 "I shall have to eat it all myself then," said Lena cheerfully.

69 "Don't you ever think of your figure?" Arrow asked with icy deliberation.

70 "The doctor said I must eat."

71 "Did he say you must eat bread and butter and potatoes and cream?"

72 "Yes. That's what I thought you meant when you said you had simple food."

73 "You'll get simply enormous," said Beatrice.

74 Lena laughed gaily.

75 "No, I shan't. You see, nothing ever makes me fat. I've always eaten everything I wanted to, and it's never had the slightest effect on me."

76 The stony silence that followed this speech was only broken by the entrance of the butler.

77 "*Mademoiselle est servie,*" he announced.

78 They talked the matter over late that night, after Lena had gone to bed, in Frank's room. During the evening they had been furiously cheerful and they had chaffed one another with a friendliness that would have taken in the keenest observer. But now they dropped the mask. Beatrice was sullen, Arrow was spiteful and Frank was unmanned.

79 "It's not very nice for me to sit there and see her eat all the things I particularly like," said Beatrice plaintively.

80 "It's not very nice for any of us," Frank snapped back.

81 "You should never have asked her here," said Arrow.

82 "How was I to know?" cried Frank.

83 "I can't help thinking that if she really cared for her husband she would hardly eat so much," said Beatrice. "He's only been buried two months. I mean, I think you ought to show some respect for the dead."

84 "Why can't she eat the same as we do?" asked Arrow viciously. "She's a guest."

85 "Well, you heard what she said. The doctor told her she must eat."

86 "Then she ought to go to a sanatorium."

87 "It's more than flesh and blood can stand, Frank," moaned Beatrice.

88 "If I can stand it you can stand it."

89 "She's your cousin, she's not our cousin," said Arrow. "I'm not going to sit there for fourteen days and watch that woman make a hog of herself."

90 "It's so vulgar to attach all this importance to food," Frank boomed, and her voice was deeper than ever. "After all the only thing that counts really is spirit."

91 "Are you calling *me* vulgar, Frank?" asked Arrow with flashing eyes.

92 "No, of course she isn't," interrupted Beatrice.

93 "I wouldn't put it past you to go down in the kitchen when we're all in bed and have a good square meal on the sly."

94 Frank sprang to her feet.

95 "How dare you say that, Arrow! I'd never ask anybody to do what I'm not prepared to do myself. Have you known me all these years and do you think me capable of such a mean thing?"

96 "How is it you never take off any weight then?"

97 Frank gave a gasp and burst into a flood of tears.

98 "What a cruel thing to say! I've lost pounds and pounds."

99 She wept like a child. Her vast body shook, and great tears splashed on her mountainous bosom.

100 "Darling, I didn't mean it," cried Arrow.

101 She threw herself on her knees and enveloped what she could of Frank in her own plump arms. She wept and the mascara ran down her cheeks.

102 "D'you mean to say I don't look thinner?" Frank sobbed. "After all I've gone through!"

103 "Yes, dear, of course you do," cried Arrow through her tears. "Everybody's noticed it."

104 Beatrice, though naturally of a placid disposition, began to cry gently. It was very pathetic. Indeed, it would have been a hard heart that failed to be moved by the sight of Frank, that lion-hearted woman, crying her eyes out. Presently, however, they dried their tears and had

a little brandy and water, which every doctor had told them was the least fattening thing they could drink, and then they felt much better. They decided that Lena should have the nourishing food that had been ordered her, and they made a solemn resolution not to let it disturb their equanimity. She was certainly a first-rate bridge player, and after all it was only for a fortnight. They would do whatever they could to make her stay enjoyable. They kissed one another warmly and separated for the night feeling strangely uplifted. Nothing should interfere with the wonderful friendship that had brought so much happiness into their three lives.

105 But human nature is weak. You must not ask too much of it. They ate grilled fish while Lena ate macaroni sizzling with cheese and butter; they ate grilled cutlets and boiled spinach while Lena ate *pâté de foie gras;* twice a week they ate hard-boiled eggs and raw tomatoes, while Lena ate peas swimming in cream and potatoes cooked in all sorts of delicious ways. The chef was a good chef, and he leapt at the opportunity afforded him to send up one dish more rich, tasty and succulent than the other.

106 "Poor Jim," sighed Lena, thinking of her husband, "he loved French cooking."

107 The butler disclosed the fact that he could make half a dozen kinds of cocktail, and Lena informed them that the doctor had recommended her to drink burgundy at luncheon and champagne at dinner. The three fat women persevered. They were gay, chatty and even hilarious (such is the natural gift that women have for deception), but Beatrice grew limp and forlorn, and Arrow's tender blue eyes acquired a steely glint. Frank's deep voice grew more raucous. It was when they played bridge that the strain showed itself. They had always been fond of talking over their hands, but their discussions had been friendly. Now a distinct bitterness crept in, and sometimes one pointed out a mistake to another with quite unnecessary frankness. Discussion turned to argument and argument to altercation. Sometimes the session ended in angry silence. Once Frank accused Arrow of deliberately letting her down. Two or three times Beatrice, the softest of the three, was reduced to tears. On another occasion Arrow flung down her cards and swept out of the room in a pet. Their tempers were getting frayed. Lena was the peacemaker.

108 "I think it's such a pity to quarrel over bridge," she said. "After all, it's only a game."

109 It was all very well for her. She had had a square meal and half a bottle of champagne. Besides, she had phenomenal luck. She was winning all their money. The score was put down in a book after each

session and hers mounted up day after day with unfailing regularity. Was there no justice in the world? They began to hate one another. And though they hated her too they could not resist confiding in her. Each of them went to her separately and told her how detestable the others were. Arrow said she was sure it was bad for her to see so much of women so much older than herself. She had a good mind to sacrifice her share of the lease and go to Venice for the rest of the summer. Frank told Lena that with her masculine mind it was too much to expect that she could be satisfied with any one so frivolous as Arrow and so frankly stupid as Beatrice.

110 "I must have intellectual conversation," she boomed. "When you have a brain like mine you've got to consort with your intellectual equals."

111 Beatrice only wanted peace and quiet.

112 "Really I hate women," she said. "They're so unreliable; they're so malicious."

113 By the time Lena's fortnight drew to its close the three fat women were barely on speaking terms. They kept up appearances before Lena, but when she was not there made no pretenses. They had got past quarrelling. They ignored one another, and when this was not possible treated each other with icy politeness.

114 Lena was going to stay with friends on the Italian Riviera, and Frank saw her off by the same train as that by which she had arrived. She was taking away with her a lot of their money.

115 "I don't know how to thank you," she said, as she got into the carriage. "I've had a wonderful visit."

116 If there was one thing that Frank Hickson prided herself on more than on being a match for any man it was that she was a gentlewoman, and her reply was perfect in its combination of majesty and graciousness.

117 "We've all enjoyed having you here, Lena," she said. "It's been a real treat."

118 But when she turned away from the departing train she heaved such a vast sigh of relief that the platform shook beneath her. She flung back her massive shoulders and strode home to the villa.

119 "Ouf!" she roared at intervals. "Ouf!"

120 She changed into her one-piece bathing suit, put on her espadrilles and a man's dressing gown (no nonsense about it) and went to Eden Roc. There was still time for a bathe before luncheon. She passed through the Monkey House, looking about her to say good morning to anyone she knew, for she felt on a sudden at peace with mankind, and then stopped dead still. She could not believe her eyes. Beatrice was sitting at one of the tables, by herself; she wore the pyjamas she had bought

at Molyneux's a day or two before, she had a string of pearls around her neck, and Frank's quick eyes saw that she had just had her hair waved; her cheeks, her eyes, her lips were made up. Fat, nay vast, as she was, none could deny that she was an extremely handsome woman. But what was she doing? With the slouching gait of the Neanderthal man which was Frank's characteristic walk she went up to Beatrice. In her black bathing dress Frank looked like the huge cetacean which the Japanese catch in the Torres Straits and which the vulgar call a sea cow.

121 "Beatrice, what are you doing?" she cried in her deep voice.

122 It was like the roll of thunder in the distant mountains. Beatrice looked at her coolly.

123 "Eating," she answered.

124 "Damn it, I can see you're eating."

125 In front of Beatrice was a plate of *croissants* and a plate of butter, a pot of strawberry jam, coffee and a jug of cream. Beatrice was spreading butter thick on the delicious hot bread, covering this with jam, and then pouring the thick cream over all.

126 "You'll kill yourself," said Frank.

127 "I don't care," mumbled Beatrice with her mouth full.

128 "You'll put on pounds and pounds."

129 "Go to hell!"

130 She actually laughed in Frank's face. My God, how good those *croissants* smelt.

131 "I'm disappointed in you, Beatrice. I thought you had more character."

132 "It's your fault. That blasted woman. You would have her down. For a fortnight I've watched her gorge like a hog. It's more than flesh and blood can stand. I'm going to have one square meal if I bust."

133 The tears welled up to Frank's eyes. Suddenly she felt very weak and womanly. She would have liked a strong man to take her on his knee and pet her and cuddle her and call her little baby names. Speechless, she sank down on a chair by Beatrice's side. A waiter came up. With a pathetic gesture she waved towards the coffee and *croissants.*

134 "I'll have the same," she sighed.

135 She listlessly reached out her hand to take a roll, but Beatrice snatched away the plate.

136 "No you don't," she said, "You wait till you get your own."

137 Frank called her a name which ladies seldom apply to one another in affection. In a moment the waiter brought her *croissants,* butter, jam and coffee.

138 "Where's the cream, you fool?" she roared like a lioness at bay.

139 She began to eat. She ate gluttonously. The place was beginning

to fill up with bathers coming to enjoy a cocktail or two after having done their duty by the sun and the sea. Presently Arrow strolled along with Prince Roccamare. She had on a beautiful silk wrap which she held tightly around her with one hand in order to look as slim as possible, and she bore her head high so that he should not see her double chin. She was laughing gaily. She felt like a girl. He had just told her (in Italian) that her eyes made the blue of the Mediterranean look like pea soup. He left her to go into the men's room to brush his sleek black hair, and they arranged to meet in five minutes for a drink. Arrow walked on to the women's room to put a little more rouge on her cheeks and a little more red on her lips. On her way she caught sight of Frank and Beatrice. She stopped. She could hardly believe her eyes.

140 "My God!" she cried. "You beasts. You hogs." She seized a chair "Waiter."

141 Her appointment went clean out of her head. In the twinkling of an eye the waiter was at her side.

142 "Bring me what these ladies are having," she ordered.

143 Frank lifted her great heavy head from her plate.

144 "Bring me some *pâté de foie gras,"* she boomed.

145 "Frank!" cried Beatrice.

146 "Shut up."

147 "All right, I'll have some too."

148 The coffee was brought, and the hot rolls and cream and the *pâté de foie gras,* and they set to. They spread the cream on the *pâté* and they ate it. They devoured great spoonfuls of jam. They crunched the delicious crisp bread voluptuously. What was love to Arrow then? Let the Prince keep his palace in Rome and his castle in the Apennines. They did not speak. What they were about was much too serious. They ate with solemn, ecstatic fervour.

149 "I haven't eaten potatoes for twenty-five years," said Frank in a far-off brooding tone.

150 "Waiter," cried Beatrice, "bring fried potatoes for three."

151 *"Très bien, madame."*

152 The potatoes were brought. Not all the perfumes of Arabia smelt so sweet. They ate them with their fingers.

153 "Bring me a dry Martini," said Arrow.

154 "You can't have a dry Martini in the middle of a meal, Arrow," said Frank.

155 "Can't I? You wait and see."

156 "All right then. Bring me a double dry Martini," said Frank.

157 "Bring three double dry Martinis," said Beatrice.

158 They were brought and drunk at a gulp. The women looked at

one another and sighed. The misunderstandings of the last fortnight dissolved, and the sincere affection each had for the other welled up again in their hearts. They could hardly believe that they had ever contemplated the possibility of severing a friendship that had brought them so much solid satisfaction. They finished the potatoes.

159 "I wonder if they've got any chocolate éclairs," said Beatrice.

160 "Of course they have."

161 And of course they had. Frank thrust one whole into her huge mouth, swallowed it and seized another, but before she ate it she looked at the other two and plunged a vindictive dagger into the heart of the monstrous Lena.

162 "You can say what you like, but the truth is she played a damned rotten game of bridge, really."

163 "Lousy," agreed Arrow.

164 But Beatrice suddenly thought she would like a meringue. □

Diction, Idiom, and Violence

"The Mugging" by Edward L. Perry is a dramatic—if not melodramatic—story structured on one incident containing four scenes. The word *dramatic,* like *emotion,* suggests the genuine; the word *melodramatic,* like *emotional,* suggests the spurious, the author's dishonest attempt to pander to the reader rather than to be true to the materials of the story. Using a first person point of view, Perry achieves verisimilitude as a result of carefully controlled language. Realistic slang is tempered with naive clichés to create a character whose development is traced through the narrative. The reader's attention is focused on the narrative flow, but the power of the story does not lie in the surface plot. Read the story first in its entirety as a casual reader might. Then reread it, trying to answer the questions.

The Mugging

by Edward L. Perry

1 It was Tony's idea. We had just come out of the flicker. Me, him, and my deb Jane. It had cost us our last coin, and the picture had been lousy. It's late, close to midnight. And we have to figure a way to make some dough. Fast. Then we spot this crud.

1. The idiom of the first person narrator establishes the tone of the story in the first paragraph. How?

[2]He's standing in front of the flicker, goggling at the young chicks who come out. He's a fat, greasy slob with blubber hanging over his belt, but he's dressed to kill. Loud sport coat and flashy cufflinks. Real gold ones.

[3]But you don't notice these things much. You only notice his face. It's a round white blot, with small, restless pig-eyes that strip you naked. There's beads of sweat on his upper lip, and he keeps mopping his forehead with a handkerchief. When a young chick walks by, he gives them a sickly grin and leans towards them like a dog sniffing at a bone.

[4]I'd seen his type before; so I know what's churning around in that brain of his. He likes chicks. Real young ones.

[5]Then he spots Jane, and he starts mopping his forehead like there's a furnace burning inside of him. I don't blame him. Jane's really decked out tonight. She's wearing a thin white skirt, so tight across the hips that their firmness is brought out in sharp relief, and a red blouse opened at the throat with a plunging V neck-line. She's young and cute.

2. The second, third, and fourth paragraphs reveal the "crud" in description and limited characterization. How do they also reveal the character of the narrator? What do they reveal about him?
3. The fifth paragraph is physical description of Jane. What does it reveal about the narrator?
4. The first five paragraphs are the beginning of the story. Do they effectively capture your attention, guaranteeing that you will finish the story? If so, how?
5. Isolate every descriptive line devoted to Jane. How do these work to create her character? As they are reported by Jake, how do they reveal him?

[6]We walk to the end of the street and stop. Tony takes out a weed and lights up. He nods in Fatboy's direction.

[7]"Let's take him," he says.

[8]I don't think much of the idea and I say so.

[9]"What's wrong with you, man?" he wants to know. "That fat guy looks really loaded. Did you get a look at them clothes?"

[10]"I don't like his looks. He acts like a Horn Bug."

[11]"You mean one of those sex maniacs? Man, what are you talking about, huh? He's just trying to pick up something. That's all."

[12]"I still don't like it," I say.

[13]"He's big. Real big." But I know Tony is going to talk me into it. He always does. I look at Jane. "What do you think?"

[14]"I don't know—" she says slowly. "I don't like the way he looked at me. It sure gave me the creeps."

15 Tony exhales slowly and flips the butt into the gutter.

16 "Listen, man," he says, "the streets're emptying fast. And—and this crud is a pushover."

17 "I don't know, Tony. I just—"

18 "Listen, man. I wouldn't take no chances if I didn't know we could handle him. Now would I, huh?"

19 "No—no I guess not." I'm looking at Jane as I say this. She knows Tony is talking me into it, and she's scared. Real scared. Her face has gone pale, and she keeps shifting her weight from one foot to the other. She's new at this racket, but she'll do anything I ask her. I see how helpless she looks and I want to tell Tony to go to hell. But I ain't got the guts. He'd think I was scared, punking out.

20 "You sure we can handle him, Tony?"

21 "Easy, man, easy!"

22 I'm not looking at Jane now, but I hear her gulp hard. She reaches out and puts her hand on my arm. Her hand is shaking.

23 "You want to do it, Jane?" I ask.

24 For a moment she hesitates; then she nods her head slowly. But when she speaks, her voice trembles. "If you say so, Jake. I'll do anything you want."

25 Tony rubs his hands together. "Good, man. Then it's all settled, huh?"

26 "Yeah," I say, "I guess so."

27 "Now here's how we'll do it. Jane, you go back up the street and let Fatboy pick you up. Give him the eye, see. Then you waltz him up the street to a good dark alley. Me and Jake'll follow. Once you get him in the alley, we'll rush in, work lover boy over, and scram with the loot. It's simple."

28 I take out a butt and light up. I'm shaking like a leaf, but I try to laugh it off. Tell myself I'm getting chicken since I met Jane. We've done this kind of jig before. Lots of times. Nothing has ever gone wrong.

29 "Okay," Jane says in a small voice, "but promise you'll be right behind me and him. He scares me."

30 "We will be, kid." I promise, and I mean it. She gets up on tiptoes and kisses me right in front of Tony. It's a sweet one.

31 I lean back against the lamppost and watch her walk up the street and I get that sick feeling all over again. Something about Fatboy scares me, too.

32 The streets are deserted, now. Only Jane and Fatboy are in sight. He's watching her come towards him, and he starts mopping his forehead like mad. Yeah, man. He's getting all steamed up. He don't see Tony and me. We watch her make contact. She's young. Sixteen. But she knows the ropes. She stops, and for a moment they stand there talking. Then I see Fatboy reach over and hook his finger in the V of her blouse. I can hear him giggle and I want to kick his guts out.

33 "Easy, man, easy," Tony mutters, and I realize I've been cussing Fatboy out loud.

34 The crud wraps one arm around Jane's waist, and they start down the street away from us. I can see by the way she's lagging back that she's scared to death of the crud.

6. Examine the dialog. Read it without expository matter. In isolation, is it realistic? If not, why not? If it is, why?
7. Why is whitespace transition used as Jane walks toward Fatboy?
8. In the narrative line "I can see by the way she's lagging back that she's scared to death of the crud" two separate levels of idiom are employed. Why?

35 "Let's go, Tony," I say, and start up the street.

36 He grabs me by the arm. "Not yet, stupid! What's wrong with you, huh? You want to mess it up?"

37 I force myself to relax. I know he's right. We got to wait. If we're seen now Fatboy will catch on. I start puffing my weed like mad, but it don't do no good. I'm really keyed up.

38 Jane and Fatboy comes to an alley at the end of the block. They duck inside.

39 "Let's take him!" Tony says, and he don't have to repeat it a second time. We start up the street. Fast. I wanta run. I'm cold, freezing up. The alley's a hundred miles off. Seems like we're never going to reach it.

9. How many uses of hyperbole can you find in the story? How effective is hyperbole here? Compare hyperbole and understatement in this story for their various effects.

40 "Walk normal!" Tony snaps. "Walk normal!"

41 That's easy for him to say. It ain't his girl in the alley. Time's flying. I don't want to get there too late.

42 Next thing I know this police car pulls up to the curb and two bulls pile out of it.

43 "Hold up there, you two!" a graveled voice orders.

44 "What's the beef, copper?" Tony wants to know.

45 "You'll find out, kid. Over against the wall."

46 "Listen, copper—" I begin.

47 "You heard me, move!"

48 Something in his voice leaves no room for argument. We move against the side of the building. Palms out. The bull runs his hands up and down my body, searching. I'm clean.

49 "Where've you been?" Graveled Voice wants to know.

50 "To the flicker. We just got out."

51 "Yeah?"

52 "Sure, man. There ain't no law against that, is there?"

53 "How about the other one?" Graveled Voice asks.

54 "Clean as a whistle," the other bull reports. "Reckon we ought to take them in?"

10. Metaphor abounds in the story. Is it effective? Why? Both slang and cliché are especially poetic in paragraphs 40–54. Explain their effectiveness.

55 Suddenly, I feel like I'm going to faint. My knees are shaking so hard I have to lean against the building to support myself. I'm tough. I don't like cops. I never did and I've let 'em know it. But not tonight. I keep thinking about what's going on in the alley, and I start pleading because the police station is a mile off and if they take us all the way there—

56 "Look, man, we've just come out of the flicker. Honest!"

57 Graveled Voice looks thoughtful. "Take that one on back to the theatre and check their alibi," he says after awhile.

58 The other bull starts down the street in the direction we've just covered. He takes Tony with him. I want to cry out.

59 Graveled Voice takes out a weed and lights up. He ain't in no hurry. He looks me over through narrowed eyes.

60 "You're mighty jumpy, kid. Anything wrong?"

61 I force a smile. "No—no, nothing's wrong. Why?"

62 "Just wondered."

63 I laugh uneasily. No. Nothing's wrong, I think. Nothing's wrong unless Fatboy is a Horn Bug. Nothing's wrong if we can just get to the alley in time. I cast a glance towards it. I can't see nothing. Just an empty street. No sound. Nothing. I turn my attention to the bull.

64 "Who are you looking for?" I ask. I couldn't care less.

65 "Couple of punks robbed a store down the block."

66 "It wasn't us," I say quickly.

67 The bull looks at his weed, studying it. "We'll find out soon enough, kid."

68 My eyes go back to the alley. Then I feel sweat popping out all over me and I start digging my fingers into the brick wall until they hurt like hell.

69 Fatboy has come out of the alley. For a moment, he stands on the street looking over his shoulder at something he's left behind. I see something fall out of his pocket and land on the sidewalk. He don't seem to notice. Then he catches sight of me and the bull and he starts cruising down the street in the opposite direction. Fast.

70 My tongue feels fuzzy, and I try to open my mouth to speak, but can't. I watch Fatboy disappear from sight. I don't even see Tony and the bull who was with him come back.

71 "They've got an alibi," the bull says. "The girl at the ticket window remembered this one."

72 "Okay, kids, get on home," we're told.

11. Are the policemen round, foil, or stock characters? What is their function in the story? Does their arrival seem contrived or coincidental or natural? Why?

73 But I'm not listening. My feet start moving up the street. Tony's right behind me. The bulls climb back into the car. I walk faster, then break into a run. To hell with them!

74 We come to the alley. Tony leans down and picks something up off the sidewalk, the something Fatboy dropped. He holds it up to the street lamp. It's a shiv. The blade is covered with blood! For a moment Tony's eyes hold mine. Then we make a dive for the alley. I feel sick and I want to vomit. I know what we're going to find. □

12. Why is the final line of the story effective? Explain in technical terms.
13. Is the point of view of this story the best choice?
14. Why is the story told in the historical present tense? Would it have been as effective in the simple past tense? Why?
15. Suspense is generated through what obvious methods? How does the language contribute to the sense of suspense?
16. Conflict exists at more than one level in this story. Explain.
17. What sentence contains the climax? Why?
18. Where in the story is the climax sentence foreshadowed?
19. What line in the story is synechdoche? Why is it effective?
20. Clichés are used effectively in the story. Examine several to see why they are acceptable here.
21. State the theme of the story.
22. Is the title effective? Explain.

Suggested Assignment. Sherwood Anderson's influence on the twentieth-century American short story has been considerable. He once said:

. . . Having, from a conversation overheard or in some other way, got the tone of a tale, I was like a woman who has just become impregnated. Something was growing inside me. At night when I lay in my bed I could feel the heels of the tale kicking against the walls of my body. Often as I lay thus every word of the tale came to me quite clearly but when I got out of bed to write it down the words would not come. . . .

. . . the words used by the tale-teller were as the colors used by the painter. Form was another matter. It grew out of the materials of the tale and the teller's reaction to them. It was the tale trying to take form that kicked about inside the tale-teller at night when he wanted to sleep.

And words were something else. Words were the surfaces, the clothes of the tale. I thought I had begun to get something a little clearer now. I had smiled to myself a little at the sudden realization of how little native American words had been used by American story-writers. When most American writers wanted to be very American they went in for slang. Surely we American scribblers had paid long and hard for the English blood in our veins. . . .

Would the common words of our daily speech in shops and offices do the trick? Surely the Americans among whom one sat talking had felt everything the Greeks had felt, everything the English had felt? Deaths came to them, the tricks of fate assailed their lives. I was certain none of them lived felt or talked as the average American novel made them live feel and talk. . . .°

Anderson's attitudes are definite, his ideas defensible. Henry James would probably have agreed with him. So would Hemingway and McCullers. As you read the following stories, decide which of the two authors might be in disagreement. Be able to defend your choice in a paper pinpointing examples to support your reasoning.

You should notice, as you read, that violence takes many forms. For instance, how many kinds of violence can you find in each of the stories? The physical violence is, perhaps, more obvious, but it is, certainly, less interesting than the other forms.

Little Memento

by John Collier

1 A young man who was walking fast came out of a deep lane onto a wide hilltop space, where there was a hamlet clustered about a green. The setting encompassed a pond, ducks, the Waggoner Inn, with white paint and swinging sign; in fact, all the fresh, clean, quiet, ordinary appurtenances of an upland Somerset hamlet.

2 The road went on, and so did the young man, over to the very brink of the upland, where a white gate gave upon a long garden well furnished with fruit trees, and at the end of it a snug little house sheltered by a coppice and enjoying a view over the vast vale below. An old man of astonishingly benevolent appearance was pottering about in the garden. He looked up as the walker, Eric Gaskell, approached his gate.

° *A Story Teller's Story* (New York, 1924), p. 362.

3 "Good morning," said he. "A fine September morning!"

4 "Good morning," said Eric Gaskell.

5 "I have had my telescope out this morning," said the old man. "I don't often get down the hill these days. The way back is a little too steep for me. Still, I have my view and my telescope. I think I know all that goes on."

6 "Well, that's very nice," said Eric.

7 "It is," said the old man. "You are Mr. Gaskell?"

8 "Yes," said Eric. "I know. We met at the vicarage."

9 "We did," said the old man. "You often take your walk this way. I see you go by. Today I thought, 'Now this is the day for a little chat with young Mr. Gaskell!' Come in."

10 "Thanks," said Eric. "I will, for a spell."

11 "And how," said the old man, opening his gate, "do you and Mrs. Gaskell like Somerset?"

12 "Enormously," said Eric.

13 "My housekeeper tells me," said the old man, "that you come from the East Coast. Very bracing. Her niece is your little maid. You don't find it too dull here? Too backward? Too old-fashioned?"

14 "We like that part of it best," said Eric, sitting with his host on a white seat under one of the apple trees.

15 "In these days," said the old man, "young people like old-fashioned things. That's a change from my day. Now most of us who live about here are old codgers, you know. There's Captain Felton, of course, but the Vicar, the Admiral, Mr. Coperus, and the rest—all old codgers. You don't mind that?"

16 "I like it," said Eric.

17 "We have our hobbies," said the old man. "Coperus is by way of being an antiquarian; the Admiral has his roses."

18 "And you have your telescope," said Eric.

19 "Ah, my telescope," said the old man. "Yes, yes, I have my telescope. But my principal pastime—what I really plume myself on—is my museum."

20 "You have a museum?" said Eric.

21 "Yes, a museum," said the old man. "I should like you to have a look at it and tell me what you think."

22 "I shall be delighted," said Eric.

23 "Then come right in," said the old man, leading him toward the house. "I seldom have the chance of showing my collection to a newcomer. You must bring Mrs. Gaskell one of these days. Does she find enough entertainment in this quiet part, would you say?"

24 "She loves it," said Eric. "She can't see too much of the country here. She drives out almost every day."

25 "All by herself in that little red roadster of hers," said the old man. "Does she like the house?"

26 "Well, I don't know," said Eric. "She did when we chose it last spring. She liked it very much."

27 "It is a very nice house," said the old man.

28 "She finds it a little oppressive lately, I'm afraid," said Eric. "She says she has to get out to breathe."

29 "It is the difference in the air," said the old man. "After living on the East Coast."

30 "Probably it's that," said Eric.

31 By this time they had reached the front door. The old man ushered Eric in. They entered a very snug, trim little room, the furniture all well polished and everything meticulously arranged. "This is my little sitting-room," the old man said. "My dining-room, too, these days. The drawing-room and the little study beyond I have given over entirely to my museum. Here we are."

32 He threw open a door. Eric stepped in, looked around, and stared in amazement. He had been expecting the usual sort of thing: a neat cabinet or two with Roman coins, flint implements, a snake in alcohol, perhaps a stuffed bird or some eggs. But this room and the study, seen through the connecting doorway, were piled high with the most broken, battered, frowzy, gimcrack collection of junk he had ever seen in his life. What was oddest of all was that no item in this muddle of rubbish had even the excuse of a decent antiquity. It was as if several cartloads of miscellaneous material had been collected from the village dump and spilled over the tables, sideboards, chairs, and floors of these two rooms.

33 The old man observed Eric's astonishment with the greatest good humour. "You are thinking," said he, "that this collection is not the sort of thing one usually finds in a museum. You are right. But let me tell you, Mr. Gaskell, that every object here has a history. These pieces are pebbles rolled and broken by the stream of time as it flows over the villages in our quiet little district. Taken together, they are a—a record. Here is a souvenir from the War: a telegram to the Bristows in Upper Medlum, saying their boy was killed. It was years before I could get that from poor Mrs. Bristow. I gave her a pound for it."

34 "Very interesting," said Eric.

35 "That wheelbarrow," said the old man, pointing out a splintered wreck, "was the cause of two deaths. It rolled down a bank into the lane here just as a car was coming along. It was in all the papers. 'Local Tragedy.' "

36 "Extraordinary!" said Eric.

37 "It all makes up life," said the old man. "Here is a belt dropped by one of the Irish haymakers when they fought the gipsies. This hat

belonged to the man who had Church Farm, near you. He won a prize in the Irish Sweep and drank himself to death, poor fellow! These are bricks from my gardener's cottage. It burned down, you know, and nobody knows how the fire started. This is a snake which somehow got into the church during service last year. Captain Felton killed it. He's a very handsome man, don't you think?"

38 "Yes. I suppose so. I hardly know him."

39 "That's funny. I thought you and Mrs. Gaskell were very great friends of Captain Felton."

40 "What gave you that idea?"

41 "Perhaps it was just my fancy. Here is a rather sad exhibit. These horns came from a bull that Farmer Lawson put into my meadow. Somebody left the gate open; it got out and gored a man on the road."

42 "We scarcely know Captain Felton," said Eric. "We met him when first we came here, but—"

43 "Quite, quite," said the old man. "Here is an anonymous letter. We have them now and then in this district, as in most places. Mr. Coperus gave me this."

44 "Are they usually well founded, the hints in your local brand of anonymous letters?" asked Eric.

45 "I believe they are," said the old man. "Someone seems to know what goes on. Here's something that I fear won't last very long: a giant puffball from the graveyard. They grow larger there than anywhere else. Feel how light it is."

46 He thrust it toward Eric. Eric had been fumbling with his pipe and tobacco pouch and now put them down to take the puffball. "Very light," said he. "Wonderful."

47 "Come through here," cried the old man eagerly. "I was forgetting my boots." Eric followed him, still carrying the giant fungus. "These boots," said the old man, "came off a tramp found drowned in a pond. That little pond near Captain Felton's house."

48 "What does Felton do?" asked Eric.

49 "He has an income," said the old man. "He amuses himself."

50 "What is his amusement?" said Eric very casually.

51 "I'm afraid," said the old man, with a twinkle, "that Captain Felton is rather one for the ladies."

52 "Indeed?" said Eric.

53 "There are stories," said the old man. "The Captain is very discreet, but—you know how it is. That big crystal up there—that was found in the quarry half a mile down our little road here. Well now, that quarry has been out of use for many years. You can drive into it from the road, and I'm told the Captain finds it a very secluded rendezvous. Dear me,

I ought not to gossip. But the fact is the shepherd boys have been known to look over the top, and of course stories get around. People love to chuckle over such matters. I'm afraid that some day one of the worthy gentlemen whose domestic relations the Captain has, so to speak, trespassed upon will look over the top and—well, there are some very large stones lying about. Here is a cat I had stuffed. Now there is a very extraordinary story connected with this cat."

54 "Tell me," said Eric, "is Felton here now or is he away?"

55 "He's here," said the old man. "I saw his car go by only an hour ago. It's a red car. One doesn't often see a red car, though as a matter of fact another red one came by just after his."

56 "I—I think I must be off," said Eric.

57 "Must you go?" said the old man. "I was just going to tell you about this unhappy cat."

58 "Another time," said Eric.

59 "Another time then," said the old man. "I shall always be delighted. Let me see you to the gate."

60 Eric hurried through the gate.

61 "You are not going back the way you came?" said the old man. "It's quicker."

62 "No. No. I have to go round this way," said Eric.

63 "That will lead you past the Captain's quarry," said the old man. "Well, goodbye. Come again soon."

64 He watched Eric stride rapidly down the road and even climbed a bank to watch him farther. When he saw him leave the road and strike over the face of the down, toward the up lip of the quarry, he went placidly back to his museum.

65 There he took up Eric's pipe and tobacco pouch and fondled them with infinite affection. It was quite a long time before he could bring himself to place them carefully on a shelf and return to his pottering in the garden.□

Rashōmon

by Ryūnosuke Akutagawa

1 It was a chilly evening. A servant of a samurai stood under the Rashōmon, waiting for a break in the rain.

2 No one else was under the wide gate. On the thick column, its crimson lacquer rubbed off here and there, perched a cricket. Since the Rashōmon stands on Sujaku Avenue, a few other people at least, in

sedge hat or nobleman's headgear, might have been expected to be waiting there for a break in the rain storm. But no one was near except this man.

[3] For the past few years the city of Kyōto had been visited by a series of calamities, earthquakes, whirlwinds, and fires, and Kyōto had been greatly devastated. Old chronicles say that broken pieces of Buddhist images and other Buddhist objects, with their lacquer, gold, or silver leaf worn off, were heaped up on roadsides to be sold as firewood. Such being the state of affairs in Kyōto, the repair of the Rashōmon was out of the question. Taking advantage of the devastation, foxes and other wild animals made their dens in the ruins of the gate, and thieves and robbers found a home there too. Eventually it became customary to bring unclaimed corpses to this gate and abandon them. After dark it was so ghostly that no one dared approach.

[4] Flocks of crows flew in from somewhere. During the daytime these cawing birds circled round the ridgepole of the gate. When the sky overhead turned red in the afterlight of the departed sun, they looked like so many grains of sesame flung across the gate. But on that day not a crow was to be seen, perhaps because of the lateness of the hour. Here and there the stone steps, beginning to crumble, and with rank grass growing in their crevices, were dotted with the white droppings of crows. The servant, in a worn blue kimono, sat on the seventh and highest step, vacantly watching the rain. His attention was drawn to a large pimple irritating his right cheek.

[5] As has been said, the servant was waiting for a break in the rain. But he had no particular idea of what to do after the rain stopped. Ordinarily, of course, he would have returned to his master's house, but he had been discharged just before. The prosperity of the city of Kyōto had been rapidly declining, and he had been dismissed by his master, whom he had served many years, because of the effects of this decline. Thus, confined by the rain, he was at a loss to know where to go. And the weather had not a little to do with his depressed mood. The rain seemed unlikely to stop. He was lost in thoughts of how to make his living tomorrow, helpless incoherent thoughts protesting an inexorable fate. Aimlessly he had been listening to the pattering of the rain on the Sujaku Avenue.

[6] The rain, enveloping the Rashōmon, gathered strength and came down with a pelting sound that could be heard far away. Looking up, he saw a fat black cloud impale itself on the tips of the tiles jutting out from the roof of the gate.

[7] He had little choice of means, whether fair or foul, because of his helpless circumstances. If he chose honest means, he would undoubtedly

starve to death beside the wall or in the Sujaku gutter. He would be brought to this gate and thrown away like a stray dog. If he decided to steal . . . His mind, after making the same detour time and again, came finally to the conclusion that he would be a thief.

8 But doubts returned many times. Though determined that he had no choice, he was still unable to muster enough courage to justify the conclusion that he must become a thief.

9 After a loud fit of sneezing he got up slowly. The evening chill of Kyōto made him long for the warmth of a brazier. The wind in the evening dusk howled through the columns of the gate. The cricket which had been perched on the crimson-lacquered column was already gone.

10 Ducking his neck, he looked around the gate, and drew up the shoulders of the blue kimono which he wore over his thin underwear. He decided to spend the night there, if he could find a secluded corner sheltered from the wind and rain. He found a broad lacquered stairway leading to the tower over the gate. No one would be there, except the dead, if there were any. So, taking care that the sword at his side did not slip out of the scabbard, he set foot on the lowest step of the stairs.

11 A few seconds later, halfway up the stairs, he saw a movement above. Holding his breath and huddling cat-like in the middle of the broad stairs leading to the tower, he watched and waited. A light coming from the upper part of the tower shone faintly upon his right cheek. It was the cheek with the red, festering pimple visible under his stubbly whiskers. He had expected only dead people inside the tower, but he had only gone up a few steps before he noticed a fire above, about which someone was moving. He saw a dull, yellow, flickering light which made the cobwebs hanging from the ceiling glow in a ghostly way. What sort of person would be making a light in the Rashōmon . . . and in a storm? The unknown, the evil terrified him.

12 As quietly as a lizard, the servant crept up to the top of the steep stairs. Crouching on all fours, and stretching his neck as far as possible, he timidly peeped into the tower.

13 As rumor had said, he found several corpses strewn carelessly about the floor. Since the glow of the light was feeble, he could not count the number. He could only see that some were naked and others clothed. Some of them were women, and all were lolling on the floor with their mouths open or their arms outstretched showing no more signs of life than so many clay dolls. One would doubt that they had ever been alive, so eternally silent they were. Their shoulders, breasts, and torsos stood out in the dim light; other parts vanished in shadow. The offensive smell of these decomposed corpses brought his hand to his nose.

14 The next moment his hand dropped and he stared. He caught sight

of a ghoulish form bent over a corpse. It seemed to be an old woman, gaunt, gray-haired, and nunnish in appearance. With a pine torch in her right hand, she was peeping into the face of a corpse which had long black hair.

15 Seized more with horror than curiosity, he even forgot to breathe for a time. He felt the hair of his head and body stand on end. As he watched, terrified, she wedged the torch between two floor boards and, laying hands on the head of the corpse, began to pull out the long hairs one by one, as a monkey kills the lice of her young. The hair came out smoothly with the movement of her hands.

16 As the hair came out, fear faded from his heart, and his hatred toward the old woman mounted. It grew beyond hatred, becoming a consuming antipathy against all evil. At this instant if anyone had brought up the question of whether he would starve to death or become a thief—the question which had occurred to him a little while ago—he would not have hesitated to choose death. His hatred toward evil flared up like the piece of pine wood which the old woman had stuck in the floor.

17 He did not know why she pulled out the hair of the dead. Accordingly, he did not know whether her case was to be put down as good or bad. But in his eyes, pulling out the hair of the dead in the Rashōmon on this stormy night was an unpardonable crime. Of course it never entered his mind that a little while ago he had thought of becoming a thief.

18 Then, summoning strength into his legs, he rose from the stairs and strode, hand on sword, right in front of the old creature. The hag turned, terror in her eyes, and sprang up from the floor, trembling. For a small moment she paused, poised there, then lunged for the stairs with a shriek.

19 "Wretch! Where are you going?" he shouted, barring the way of the trembling hag who tried to scurry past him. Still she attempted to claw her way by. He pushed her back to prevent her . . . they struggled, fell among the corpses, and grappled there. The issue was never in doubt. In a moment he had her by the arm, twisted it, and forced her down to the floor. Her arms were all skin and bones, and there was no more flesh on them than on the shanks of a chicken. No sooner was she on the floor than he drew his sword and thrust the silver-white blade before her very nose. She was silent. She trembled as if in a fit, and her eyes were open so wide that they were almost out of their sockets, and her breath came in hoarse gasps. The life of this wretch was his now. This thought cooled his boiling anger and brought a calm pride and satisfaction. He looked down at her, and said in a somewhat calmer voice:

20 "Look here, I'm not an officer of the High Police Commissioner. I'm a stranger who happened to pass by the gate. I won't bind you or do anything against you, but you must tell me what you're doing up here."

21 Then the old woman opened her eyes still wider, and gazed at his face intently with the sharp red eyes of a bird of prey. She moved her lips, which were wrinkled into her nose, as though she were chewing something. Her pointed Adam's apple moved in her thin throat. Then a panting sound like the cawing of a crow came from her throat:

22 "I pull the hair . . . I pull out the hair . . . to make a wig."

23 Her answer banished all unknown from their encounter and brought disappointment. Suddenly she was only a trembling old woman there at his feet. A ghoul no longer: only a hag who makes wigs from the hair of the dead—to sell, for scraps of food. A cold contempt seized him. Fear left his heart, and his former hatred entered. These feelings must have been sensed by the other. The old creature, still clutching the hair she had pulled off the corpse, mumbled out these words in her harsh broken voice:

24 "Indeed, making wigs out of the hair of the dead may seem a great evil to you, but these that are here deserve no better. This woman, whose beautiful black hair I was pulling, used to sell cut and dried snake flesh at the guard barracks, saying that it was dried fish. If she hadn't died of the plague, she'd be selling it now. The guards liked to buy from her, and used to say her fish was tasty. What she did couldn't be wrong, because if she hadn't, she would have starved to death. There was no other choice. If she knew I had to do this in order to live, she probably wouldn't care."

25 He sheathed his sword, and, with his left hand on its hilt, he listened to her meditatively. His right hand touched the big pimple on his cheek. As he listened, a certain courage was born in his heart—the courage which he had not had when he sat under the gate a little while ago. A strange power was driving him in the opposite direction of the courage which he had had when he seized the old woman. No longer did he wonder whether he should starve to death or become a thief. Starvation was so far from his mind that it was the last thing that would have entered it.

26 "Are you sure?" he asked in a mocking tone, when she finished talking. He took his right hand from his pimple, and, bending forward, seized her by the neck and said sharply:

27 "Then it's right if I rob you. I'd starve if I didn't."

28 He tore her clothes from her body and kicked her roughly down on the corpses as she struggled and tried to clutch his leg. Five steps, and

he was at the top of the stairs. The yellow clothes he had wrested off were under his arm, and in a twinkling he had rushed down the steep stairs into the abyss of night. The thunder of his descending steps pounded in the hollow tower, and then it was quiet.

29 Shortly after that the hag raised up her body from the corpses. Grumbling and groaning, she crawled to the top stair by the still flickering torchlight, and through the gray hair which hung over her face, she peered down to the last stair in the torch light.

30 Beyond this was only darkness . . . unknowing and unknown. ☐

Irony and Conflict

Pauline C. Smith's "The People Next Door" is structured on artful use of understatement and irony. The reader's attention is diverted from the theme to the narrative in such a fashion that he feels he is being entertained by a pleasantly ghoulish tale. However, you will notice as you read the story the second time that the conflict is not between the people next door. It is in the lives of Ed and Evelyn. Understatement creates the irony in all of the dialog.

After your first reading for pleasure, examine the story for its theme. The psychological detail in the story is accurate and revealing. It has to be, for readers always delight in finding an author's errors. John Keasler, humorist of *The Miami News,* presents a delightful case in point in the following article from that paper:

Shuffle, Deal

"Write About What You Know!"

That was the title of an article I just read which gave advice to would-be writers of fiction. I have read similar articles in writer's magazines for several years, and the device is certainly sound—if, perhaps, not carried quite far enough.

The point is excellent. Again, as far as it goes. It says there is probably a gripping human drama right around the pickle works there, so why attempt to ferret out the motivations of an Armenian archduke who secretly wants to be an acrobat.

Quite true. And, yet, for one reason or another, the aspiring writer of fiction almost always thinks the plots are anywhere save where he is. Take my steamboat.

I wrote my steamboat story for the same reason, from the same crucible of white-hot creativity, which has prompted almost every author. Ole Wolfie snarling at the door.

Literary Gem

It was my first published short story, an event of great moment which happened 17 years ago. My bride-to-be was laboring on a Florida newspaper. I had moved North, to the Atlanta Journal, and the theory was that I would accumulate enough wealth so we could meet the altar deadline, Dec. 27.

Things were not going according to plan. My system of regular savings seemed faulty, somehow. (I am still attempting to iron the bugs out of it.) An ill-advised faith in two small pair had run into three deuces, furthermore, and I was broke. The date loomed closer.

I was staying at a hotel out on Peachtree named the Robert Fulton, after the steamboat inventor of the same name. A large painting of a steamboat was in the lobby. While sitting about the lobby whimpering in desperation, a solution suddenly came.

I would write and sell a short story! About what? Hmm. Then—as my eyes fell on the painting the answer was clear. About a steamboat, obviously.

So I did. It was about a poker game on an early Mississippi steamboat and the name of it was "No-Limit Bluff." There was this noble riverboat gambler, see, and he was out to get even with the bad guys who framed his kindly old father and swiped the plantation and—I can't go on.

Jackpot!

I mailed it off to one of the best of the low-class magazines and, to my utter consternation and complete delight, it passed that most discerning literary test. It sold.

My bride and I returned to Atlanta the same month the story appeared. The story brought me one letter. It came from the magazine's editor—who had been deluged with letters concerning my masterpiece.

The reason? The year I used in the story was, as practically all his readers pointed out, 45 years before the invention of the steamboat.

Write about what you know is excellent advice, if you add a codicil: If you don't know it, for Pete's sake look it up.

If, then, you can assume the psychological approach is sound, "The People Next Door" could be merely a case history—or little more than a comment on an interesting neighborhood occurrence—or simply escape literature. As you read, however, notice the use of such symbols as the newspaper, the knitting needles, and color in the yarn Evelyn works with. How does the use of the color red remind you of the same color in "Some of the Time, All of the Time" (p. 206)? As the answer becomes apparent, you will discover you are reading something more important than mere escape fiction.

The People Next Door

by Pauline C. Smith

1 "Well, how are you getting along with your new neighbor?" Ed asked.

2 Evelyn looked down at the knitting in her lap. "All right," she said.

3 "I talked with her a few minutes before dinner, while I was out in the yard. They used to live in California, she said. Seemed like a nice, ordinary woman."

1. Is there irony in Ed's statement in paragraph 3? Examine it carefully. The theme begins to emerge at this point.

4 Evelyn held up the wool, inspected it. "She did?"

2. How is the wool used effectively as a symbol in the story? You become aware of it here and it assumes growing importance.

5 "You like her all right, don't you?"

6 "I guess so."

7 "It gives you someone for company during the day. Keeps you from thinking about yourself too much," he persisted.

8 "I don't see her much. Sometimes I talk to her when she's hanging the wash on the line."

3. In paragraph 8 the clothesline is introduced. It is important. Remember: every detail in a good short story has relevance. If it does not, the author is merely padding, thereby losing effect. In a good short story, if a rope is mentioned, it will be used later in the story to tie something or someone, serve as a noose, be an obstacle for falling over, and so on.

9 "Well, it's good for you," he said briskly, the clinical look taking over his face.

10 Evelyn picked up the wool again and clicked the needles. The knitting was a form of prescription.

11 "She hangs out her washing as if she was angry at it," she said. "She puts the clothespins on the shirts as if she were stabbing them."

4. Explain "as if she *was* angry" and "as if she *were* stabbing" in paragraph 11.

12 "Evie!" His tone was sharp.

13 "Well, she does," Evelyn persisted. "Maybe it's because there's so many shirts. Fourteen of them. Two clean shirts every day. Perhaps her husband has a phobia about clean shirts."

14 Ed rattled his newspaper as he lowered it.

15 "Evie," he said, "you mustn't imagine things! You mustn't try to find phobias and neuroses in everything anybody does. It isn't healthy. I should think you'd have had enough of analyzing and being analyzed all this last year since your breakdown."

5. Evelyn's "breakdown" is not directly mentioned until paragraph 15. Find the foreshadowing words in the first fourteen paragraphs.

16 Evie thought of the washing erupting convulsively onto the line as the woman next door hung up each garment with controlled violence.

17 "Maybe she's tired of washing and ironing so many shirts every week," she said. "Maybe she's sick to death of it. Maybe that's why she seems to be stabbing the shirts with the clothespins."

18 "Evie, you're almost well now!" Ed was speaking with forced calm. "You can't afford to let your imagination run away about every simple little thing. It isn't healthy. You'll have a relapse."

19 "I'm sorry, Ed." She picked up the wool again. "I won't imagine things."

20 "That's a good girl." He relaxed. "She tell you what her husband does?"

21 "He's a salesman," Evelyn said, needles clicking. "He sells cutlery to restaurants—knives and cleavers and things."

6. Why is the salesman's occupation included in the dialog?

22 "You see?" Ed remarked. "Salesmen have to be neat. That's why he wears so many shirts."

23 "Is it?" Evelyn studied the sweater. The gray wool was very unexciting. She decided she would work a little pattern into it—red, maybe. "Have you ever seen him?"

7. In paragraph 23, the colors gray and red are introduced. Explain the choices. Remember, the psychology of this story is sound and accurate.

24 "No." Ed removed his glasses and polished them. "Have you?"

8. What does Ed's action in paragraph 24 indicate? How is the ironic tone of the story intensified here?

25 "Every morning. He leaves for work a little while after you do. His car is parked in their driveway, right by our kitchen window. I see him while I'm doing the breakfast dishes."

26 Ed turned the pages of his newspaper to the sport section.

27 "What's he like?"

28 "He's very tall and thin. His mouth is thin, like a knife. He wears gray all the time. He makes me think of a gray snake."

9. Paragraph 28 is packed with careful detail. Explain all of the techniques and devices—there are many!

29 "Evie!" Ed's voice was angry now. "Stop that!"

30 "All right." She stood up. "I guess I'll go to bed now."

31 In her bedroom, she stood for a moment at the window. There was a light on next door—one window was an orange oblong. She got into bed, took a nembutal, and fell asleep.

32 Over the clean suds of dishwater each morning she saw the man next door appear, stride quickly to his car and get in with his sample case—tall, his features as sharp as the knives he sold, his eyes hooded. Then the car would start, rattle off and he would be gone.

10. The descriptive phrase "orange oblong" is clever technique. Explain the allusion and symbol as they are created through alliteration and assonance. Why are alliteration and assonance used here?
11. Explain the whitespace transition. Why was the transitional phrase "Next morning" not used after paragraph 31?
12. Explain the "knives" and "hooded" allusions in paragraph 32. Why is the car onomatopoetic?

33 Through her brief appearances in the back yard, Evelyn grew to know the woman; by her long strides to the refuse can where she would clatter the lid off, throw in her paper-wrapped bundle with an over-arm motion, clang the lid back; by her short, fierce tussle with a garment on the clothesline; by her soliloquy as she talked to herself, the words inaudible but the tone clear—sometimes a grumbling complaint and sometimes a violently fierce monolog. Evelyn grew to know her, she felt, quite well. And sometimes at night she would hear sounds from next door. Not very loud sounds; not conversation. Muffled sounds. You would have to use imagination to say they were sounds of anger, or perhaps of pain. And she had promised Ed not to let herself imagine things . . .

34 When the car had been sitting in the driveway for two days, she mentioned it to Ed. He lowered his paper.

35 "Oh?" he said politely. "Is he sick?"

36 "Maybe he is. I haven't seen her, either."

37 "You'd better go over, hadn't you? Maybe they're both sick."

38 "No. I don't want to go over there."

39 He glanced at his paper, then at his wife. "Why not? You've talked to her. It would be the kind thing to do."

40 Evelyn bent over her occupational therapy, the knitting on her lap. "She might think I was snooping."

13. Examine paragraph 33. Explain every technique you can find in it. How is characterization established? Explain the repetition of the word *stride* in both paragraphs 32 and 33. What does your answer tell you about Ed and Evelyn's ability to live together with some harmony?
14. Explain the whitespace transition *plus* the word *When* (paragraphs 33–34). Why is the double transition used?
15. Ed's paper is mentioned in paragraphs 14, 26, 34, 39, 56, 58, 72, and 82. Examine the eight references. What is their purpose? Are they effective? (Do not underestimate the use of the paper. Is it a symbol?)
16. Explain the irony of "She might think I was snooping" in paragraph 40.

41 Aggravation and indulgence struggled in Ed's face. At last, he said mildly, "I don't think she'd think that."

42 "She might."

43 Through one more day without backyard clangor, Evelyn listened and watched while the house next door slept.

44 On the next day the woman next door emerged to hang out her washing. She no longer moved with a controlled fury. She handled the pieces of wash, even the shirts, as if they were fabric, inanimate and impersonal—no longer as if she wrestled a hated opponent.

17. Does paragraph 44 employ personification or metonomy? Why is the distinction important to you as a reader?

45 Stepping to the dividing fence, Evelyn rested her hands on the palings. She leaned over. "I see your husband's car in the driveway . . ." she began.

46 The words seemed to filter slowly through the other woman's mind, to arrange themselves in her brain to make a sense which startled her. She looked at the car, then back at Evelyn.

47 "He took a trip." Her expression was suddenly veiled and withdrawn. She wet her lips with the tip of her tongue. "He's gone off to a convention. It was too far to drive. He took the train and left the car for me."

48 "Oh, that's it," Evie said politely. "We were afraid he was sick."

49 "No, he's not sick. He's not sick at all."

18. Compare the use of "at all" in paragraph 49 with its use in paragraph 84. What literary device is employed? Do you think such careful attention to detail can be accidental with the author?

50 Abruptly the woman backed away, spare-lipped mouth moving as if to utter further words of explanation that would reduce the unusual to the commonplace. Then she turned, stepped through her back door and locked it behind her.

51 "The man next door is out of town," Evelyn told Ed that evening.

52 He smiled. "So you went over, after all."

53 "No."

54 "Oh? You talked to her, though?"

55 "Yes. I talked to her." Evelyn bent over the knitting. "She took the car and went away this afternoon."

56 Rustling the paper, Ed settled to read.

57 "She wasn't gone long. When she came back, she had two big dogs in the car with her."

58 He lowered the paper. "She did?"

59 "Two big thin dogs," described Evelyn. "She tied them in the back yard using the clothesline to tie them to the clothes pole. She had a big wash this morning and after it dried, she went and got the dogs and tied them with the clothesline."

19. Explain the whitespace transition between paragraphs 50–51.
20. Compare the use of the word *thin* in paragraphs 28 and 59. What do you conclude?
21. Examine the implications of paragraph 59. How do the references begin to make a pattern?

60 "Maybe she's scared while her husband's gone. And she got them for watchdogs."

61 "Maybe."

62 Now Evelyn felt ready to give up the nembutal she had used to get her to sleep all these months. Pushing the little bottle of sleeping tablets far back on the bedside table, she lay down. She thought of the woman next door, the dogs and the car in the driveway . . . the woman, the dogs and the car . . .

63 At last, she rose to pace through the darkened house.

64 Standing at the kitchen window, she looked out at the night to see a button of light cross the yard next door. Her eyes followed it. She heard a plop, a snarl and a growl—then the gulping, snuffling sound of hunger being satisfied. The light made an arc and moved back to the house and was lost.

22. Compare the use of light in paragraphs 31 and 64. Explain.
23. How effective is onomatopoeia in paragraph 64?

65 For a long time she stood at the window, then she went to her bedroom, took a nembutal and fell asleep . . .

66 "She doesn't like the dogs," Evelyn told Ed several days later.

67 "She doesn't have to. They're watchdogs, not pets."

68 "She walks them every day. She unties their ropes from the clothes pole and goes off with them. When she comes back, she's tired and the dogs are tired. Then after dark she gives them a big dinner."

69 Evie thought of them, the slip-slap drag of the animals, their lolling tongues —the fatigued tread of the woman, her face drained of everything but lassitude. Of the way she re-tied them to the clothes pole, knotting, knotting and re-knotting the ropes while they lay, eyes closed, panting, satiated.

24. Why are ellipsis marks used instead of a whitespace transition at the end of paragraph 65? Why is a final period not used?
25. Consider the combination of narrative and description in paragraph 69. How effective is it?

70 "What does she say about her husband? Seems to me that convention is lasting awfully long."

71 "She doesn't say anything. She just walks the dogs. Walks them and feeds them."

72 Ed laid down his paper. "Evie," he said, "Don't you talk with her any more?"

73 Holding the needles tightly, Evelyn looked at him. "I don't see her to talk with her. She just walks the dogs. She doesn't hang anything on her line any more because she doesn't have any line. She doesn't seem to do anything in the yard except untie the dogs and tie them up again."

74 "Well, that's too bad. I wanted you to have some company. Maybe you could walk . . ."

75 "No! I don't want to walk with her or the dogs." Evelyn dropped the knitting on the chair as she left for bed . . .

26. Explain the difference in the ellipsis marks after paragraphs 65 and 75.

76 Filled with torpor, the dogs were quiet now, lazy, growing fat as they ambled reluctantly at the end of their rope leashes, to crawl back and lie somnolent.

27. Is there a reason for the separated alliteration in *satiated* (last word of paragraph 69) and *somnolent* (paragraph 76)?

77 Evelyn was knitting quietly. The sweater was almost finished; the drab, uninteresting sweater with the bright little pattern of scarlet she had added. "She took the dogs away in the car today," she told Ed on Friday.

28. Explain everything you can about paragraph 77.

[78]Ed looked at her over his glasses. "She did?"

[79]"And she came back alone. Then she went in the house, got two suitcases, came out, put them in the car and drove off."

[80]"Maybe that's why she took the dogs away—she's going on a trip."

[81]"She's going on a trip all right."

[82]"Or perhaps the upkeep was too high." Ed yawned, and polished his glasses, fitted them carefully on his nose. "She shouldn't have exercised them so much. It made them too hungry." He opened his paper and placed it across his knees. "Must have cost her plenty to feed the brutes."

[83]Evie pulled the needles from the yarn and folded the sweater. She stood. The thing was a pattern, its design all finished.

[84]"I don't think it did," she said. "I don't think it cost her hardly anything at all." □

29. Explain everything you can about paragraph 83. How does paragraph 77 become a part of this explanation?
30. Compare the use of the phrase "at all" in paragraphs 49 and 84. How does the repetition create irony? Explain the ambiguity in the final sentence.
31. Where in this story is the climax?
32. Compare the inability to communicate in this story and in "Some of the Time, All of the Time" (p. 206).
33. Explain the irony of the title, "The People Next Door."
34. Actually, the murder of the husband next door is a *subplot* (a sequence of events within the main plot). What, then, is the plot of this story? Why is it effective to focus on the subplot and understate the main plot?
35. Describe the setting of the story. Can you find textual evidence for your description or did you supply it for the author?
36. Describe Ed and Evelyn physically. Why did the author fail to supply this description?

Suggested Assignments. 1. According to Maurice Baudin, Jr.:

When one has said that the short story is a work of fiction embodying a central motif, somewhere between a few hundred and ten thousand words (too long for a suicide note and too short for a novel), then one has said everything, short of discussion. But is there no preferred method of narration, no style of writing, no favored subject matter that will assure one story of superiority to another? The answer is no.*

As you read the following stories, assess the authors' methods of narration, subject matter, and style. All concern human violence in one way or another. Irony and conflict are central in each presentation. As you read, decide whether or not you agree with Baudin. Be prepared to defend your decision from an objective point of view.

2. Remembering that short stories can be roughly classified as pulp, slick, or quality, in a paper of moderate length compare the following three stories, revealing why you think each falls into its own category.

The Squaw

by Bram Stoker

1 Nurnberg at the time was not so much exploited as it has been since then. Irving had not been playing *Faust,* and the very name of the old town was hardly known to the great bulk of the travelling public. My wife and I being in the second week of our honeymoon, naturally wanted someone else to join our party, so that when the cheery stranger, Elias P. Hutcheson, hailing from Isthmian City, Bleeding Gulch, Maple Tree County, Neb., turned up at the station at Frankfort, and casually remarked that he was going on to see the most all-fired old Methuselah of a town in Yurrup, and that he guessed that so much travelling alone was enough to send an intelligent, active citizen into the melancholy ward of a daft house, we took the pretty broad hint and suggested that we should join forces. We found, on comparing notes afterwards, that we had each intended to speak with some diffidence or hesitation so as not to appear too eager, such not being a good compliment to the success of our married life; but the effect was entirely marred by our both beginning to speak at the same instant—stopping simultaneously and then going on together again. Anyhow, no matter how, it was done; and Elias P. Hutcheson became one of our party. Straightway Amelia and I found the pleasant benefit; instead of quarrelling, as we had been doing, we found that the re-

* "Introduction," *Contemporary Short Stories, Representative Selections, Volume 1,* ed. Maurice Baudin, Jr. (New York, 1953), p. x.

straining influence of a third party was such that we now took every opportunity of spooning in odd corners. Amelia declares that ever since she has, as the result of that experience, advised all her friends to take a friend on the honeymoon. Well, we "did" Nurnberg together, and much enjoyed the racy remarks of our Transatlantic friend, who, from his quaint speech and his wonderful stock of adventures, might have stepped out of a novel. We kept for the last object of interest in the city to be visited the Burg, and on the day appointed for the visit strolled round the outer wall of the city by the eastern side.

2 The Burg is seated on a rock dominating the town, and an immensely deep fosse guards it on the northern side. Nurnberg has been happy in that it was never sacked; had it been it would certainly not be so spick and span perfect as it is at present. The ditch has not been used for centuries, and now its base is spread with tea-gardens and orchards, of which some of the trees are of quite respectable growth. As we wandered round the wall, dawdling in the hot July sunshine, we often paused to admire the views spread before us, and in especial the great plain covered with towns and villages and bounded with a blue line of hills, like a landscape of Claude Lorraine. From this we always turned with new delight on the city itself, with its myriad of quaint old gables and acre-wide red roofs dotted with dormer windows, tier upon tier. A little to our right rose the towers of the Burg, and nearer still, standing grim, the Torture Tower, which was, and is, perhaps, the most interesting place in the city. For centuries the tradition of the Iron Virgin of Nurnberg has been handed down as an instance of the horrors of cruelty of which man is capable; we had long looked forward to seeing it; and here at last was its home.

3 In one of our pauses we leaned over the wall of the moat and looked down. The garden seemed quite fifty or sixty feet below us, and the sun pouring into it with an intense, moveless heat like that of an oven. Beyond rose the grey, grim wall seemingly of endless height, and losing itself right and left in the angles of bastion and counterscarp. Trees and bushes crowned the wall, and above again towered the lofty houses on whose massive beauty Time has only set the hand of approval. The sun was hot and we were lazy; time was our own, and we lingered, leaning on the wall. Just below us was a pretty sight—a great black cat lying stretched in the sun, whilst round her gambolled prettily a tiny black kitten. The mother would wave her tail for the kitten to play with, or would raise her feet and push away the little one as an encouragement to further play. They were just at the foot of the wall, and Elias P. Hutcheson, in order to help the play, stopped and took from the walk a moderate sized pebble.

4 "See!" he said, "I will drop it near the kitten, and they will both wonder where it came from."

5 "Oh, be careful," said my wife; "you might hit the dear little thing!"

6 "Not me, ma'am," said Elias P. "Why, I'm as tender as a Maine cherry-tree. Lor, bless ye, I wouldn't hurt the poor pooty little critter more'n I'd scalp a baby. An' you may bet your variegated socks on that! See, I'll drop it fur away on the outside so's not to go near her!" Thus saying, he leaned over and held his arm out at full length and dropped the stone. It may be that there is some attractive force which draws lesser matters to greater; or more probably that the wall was not plumb but sloped to its base—we not noticing the inclination from above; but the stone fell with a sickening thud that came up to us through the hot air, right on the kitten's head, and shattered out its little brains then and there. The black cat cast a swift upward glance, and we saw her eyes like green fire fixed an instant on Elias P. Hutcheson; and then her attention was given to the kitten, which lay still with just a quiver of her tiny limbs, whilst a thin red stream trickled from a gaping wound. With a muffled cry, such as a human being might give, she bent over the kitten, licking its wound and moaning. Suddenly she seemed to realise that it was dead, and again threw her eyes up at us. I shall never forget the sight, for she looked the perfect incarnation of hate. Her green eyes blazed with lurid fire, and the white, sharp teeth seemed to almost shine through the blood which dabbled her mouth and whiskers. She gnashed her teeth, and her claws stood out stark and at full length on every paw. Then she made a wild rush up the wall as if to reach us, but when the momentum ended fell back, and further added to her horrible appearance for she fell on the kitten, and rose with her back fur smeared with its brains and blood. Amelia turned quite faint, and I had to lift her back from the wall. There was a seat close by in the shade of a spreading plane-tree, and here I placed her whilst she composed herself. Then I went back to Hutcheson, who stood without moving, looking down on the angry cat below.

7 As I joined him, he said:

8 "Wall, I guess that air the savagest beast I ever see—'cept once when an Apache squaw had an edge on a half-breed what they nick-named 'Splinters' 'cos of the way he fixed up her papoose which he stole on a raid just to show that he appreciated the way they had given his mother the fire torture. She got that kinder look so set on her face that it just seemed to grow there. She followed Splinters more'n three year till at last the braves got him and handed him over

to her. They did say that no man, white or Injun, had ever been so long a-dying under the tortures of the Apaches. The only time I ever see her smile was when I wiped her out. I kem on the camp just in time to see Splinters pass in his checks, and he wasn't sorry to go either. He was a hard citizen, and though I never could shake with him after that papoose business—for it was bitter bad, and he should have been a white man, for he looked like one—I see he had got paid out in full. Durn me, but I took a piece of his hide from one of his skinnin' posts an' had it made into a pocket-book. It's here now!" and he slapped the breast pocket of his coat.

9 Whilst he was speaking the cat was continuing her frantic efforts to get up the wall. She would take a run back and then charge up, sometimes reaching an incredible height. She did not seem to mind the heavy fall which she got each time but started with renewed vigour; and at every tumble her appearance became more horrible. Hutcheson was a kind-hearted man—my wife and I had both noticed little acts of kindness to animals as well as to persons—and he seemed concerned at the state of fury to which the cat had wrought herself.

10 "Wall now!" he said, "I du declare that that poor critter seems quite desperate. There! there! poor thing, it was all an accident—though that won't bring back your little one to you. Say! I wouldn't have had such a thing happen for a thousand! Just shows what a clumsy fool of a man can do when he tries to play! Seems I'm too darned slipper-handed to even play with a cat. Say Colonel!"—it was a pleasant way he had to bestow titles freely—"I hope your wife don't hold no grudge against me on account of this unpleasantness? Why, I wouldn't have had it occur on no account."

11 He came over to Amelia and apologised profusely, and she with her usual kindness of heart hastened to assure him that she quite understood that it was an accident. Then we all went again to the wall and looked over.

12 The cat missing Hutcheson's face had drawn back across the moat, and was sitting on her haunches as though ready to spring. Indeed, the very instant she saw him she did spring, and with a blind unreasoning fury, which would have been grotesque, only that it was so frightfully real. She did not try to run up the wall, but simply launched herself at him as though hate and fury could lend her wings to pass straight through the great distance between them. Amelia, woman-like, got quite concerned, and said to Elias P. in a warning voice:

13 "Oh! you must be very careful. That animal would try to kill you if she were here; her eyes look like positive murder."

14 He laughed out jovially. "Excuse me, ma'am," he said, "but I can't

help laughin'. Fancy a man that has fought grizzlies an' Injuns bein' careful of bein' murdered by a cat!"

15 When the cat heard him laugh, her whole demeanour seemed to change. She no longer tried to jump or run up the wall, but went quietly over, and sitting again beside the dead kitten began to lick and fondle it as though it were alive.

16 "See!" said I, "the effect of a really strong man. Even that animal in the midst of her fury recognises the voice of a master, and bows to him!"

17 "Like a squaw!" was the only comment of Elias P. Hutcheson, as we moved on our way round the city fosse. Every now and then we looked over the wall and each time saw the cat following us. At first she had kept going back to the dead kitten, and then as the distance grew greater took it in her mouth and so followed. After a while, however, she abandoned this, for we saw her following all alone; she had evidently hidden the body somewhere. Amelia's alarm grew at the cat's persistence, and more than once she repeated her warning; but the American always laughed with amusement, till finally, seeing that she was beginning to be worried, he said:

18 "I say, ma'am, you needn't be skeered over that cat. I go heeled, I du!" Here he slapped his pistol pocket at the back of his lumbar region. "Why sooner'n have you worried, I'll shoot the critter, right here, an' risk the police interferin' with a citizen of the United States for carryin' arms contrairy to reg'lations!" As he spoke he looked over the wall, but the cat, on seeing him, retreated, with a growl, into a bed of tall flowers, and was hidden. He went on: "Blest if that ar critter ain't got more sense of what's good for her than most Christians. I guess we've seen the last of her! You bet, she'll go back now to that busted kitten and have a private funeral of it, all to herself!"

19 Amelia did not like to say more, lest he might, in mistaken kindness to her, fulfil his threat of shooting the cat: and so we went on and crossed the little wooden bridge leading to the gateway whence ran the steep paved roadway between the Burg and the pentagonal Torture Tower. As we crossed the bridge we saw the cat again down below us. When she saw us her fury seemed to return, and she made frantic efforts to get up the steep wall. Hutcheson laughed as he looked down at her, and said:

20 "Good-bye, old girl. Sorry I in-jured your feelin's, but you'll get over it in time! So long!" And then we passed through the long, dim archway and came to the gate of the Burg.

21 When we came out again after our survey of this most beautiful old place which not even the well-intended efforts of the Gothic

restorers of forty years ago have been able to spoil—though their restoration was then glaring white—we seemed to have quite forgotten the unpleasant episode of the morning. The old lime tree with its great trunk gnarled with the passing of nearly nine centuries, the deep well cut through the heart of the rock by those captives of old, and the lovely view from the city wall whence we heard, spread over almost a full quarter of an hour, the multitudinous chimes of the city, had all helped to wipe out from our minds the incident of the slain kitten.

22 We were the only visitors who had entered the Torture Tower that morning—so at least said the old custodian—and as we had the place all to ourselves were able to make a minute and more satisfactory survey than would have otherwise been possible. The custodian, looking to us as the sole source of his gains for the day, was willing to meet our wishes in any way. The Torture Tower is truly a grim place, even now when many thousands of visitors have sent a stream of life, and the joy that follows life, into the place; but at the time I mention it wore its grimmest and most gruesome aspect. The dust of ages seemed to have settled on it, and the darkness and the horror of its memories seemed to have become sentient in a way that would have satisfied the Pantheistic souls of Philo or Spinoza. The lower chamber where we entered was seemingly, in its normal state, filled with incarnate darkness; even the hot sunlight streaming in through the door seemed to be lost in the vast thickness of the walls, and only showed the masonry rough as when the builder's scaffolding had come down, but coated with dust and marked here and there with patches of dark stain which, if walls could speak, could have given their own dread memories of fear and pain. We were glad to pass up the dusty wooden staircase, the custodian leaving the outer door open to light us somewhat on our way; for to our eyes the one long-wick'd, evil-smelling candle stuck in a sconce on the wall gave an inadequate light. When we came up through the open trap in the corner of the chamber overhead, Amelia held on to me so tightly that I could actually feel her heart beat. I must say for my own part that I was not surprised at her fear, for this room was even more gruesome than that below. Here there was certainly more light, but only just sufficient to realise the horrible surroundings of the place. The builders of the tower had evidently intended that only they who should gain the top should have any of the joys of light and prospect. There, as we had noticed from below, were ranges of windows, albeit of mediæval smallness, but elsewhere in the tower were only a very few narrow slits such as were habitual in places of mediæval defence. A few of these only lit the chamber, and these so high up in the wall that from no part could the sky be seen through the thick-

ness of the walls. In racks, and leaning in disorder against the walls, were a number of headsmen's swords, great double-handed weapons with broad blade and keen edge. Hard by were several blocks whereon the necks of the victims had lain, with here and there deep notches where the steel had bitten through the guard of flesh and shored into the wood. Round the chamber, placed in all sorts of irregular ways, were many implements of torture which made one's heart ache to see—chairs full of spikes which gave instant and excruciating pain; chairs and couches with dull knobs whose torture was seemingly less, but which, though slower, were equally efficacious; racks, belts, boots, gloves, collars, all made for compressing at will; steel baskets in which the head could be slowly crushed into a pulp if necessary; watchmen's hooks with long handle and knife that cut at resistance—this a specialty of the old Nurnberg police system; and many, many other devices for man's injury to man. Amelia grew quite pale with the horror of the things, but fortunately did not faint, for being a little overcome she sat down on a torture chair, but jumped up again with a shriek, all tendency to faint gone. We both pretended that it was the injury done to her dress by the dust of the chair, and the rusty spikes which had upset her, and Mr. Hutcheson acquiesced in accepting the explanation with a kind-hearted laugh.

23 But the central object in the whole of this chamber of horrors was the engine known as the Iron Virgin, which stood near the centre of the room. It was a rudely-shaped figure of a woman, something of the bell order, or, to make a closer comparison, of the figure of Mrs. Noah in the children's Ark, but without that slimness of waist and perfect *rondeur* of hip which marks the æsthetic type of the Noah family. One would hardly have recognised it as intended for a human figure at all had not the founder shaped on the forehead a rude semblance of a woman's face. This machine was coated with rust without, and covered with dust; a rope was fastened to a ring in the front of the figure, about where the waist should have been, and was drawn through a pulley, fastened on the wooden pillar which sustained the flooring above. The custodian pulling this rope showed that a section of the front was hinged like a door at one side; we then saw that the engine was of considerable thickness, leaving just room enough inside for a man to be placed. The door was of equal thickness and of great weight, for it took the custodian all his strength, aided though he was by the contrivance of the pulley, to open it. This weight was partly due to the fact that the door was of manifest purpose hung so as to throw its weight downwards, so that it might shut of its own accord when the strain was released. The inside was honeycombed with

rust—nay more, the rust alone that comes through time would hardly have eaten so deep into the iron walls; the rust of the cruel stains was deep indeed! It was only, however, when we came to look at the inside of the door that the diabolical intention was manifest to the full. Here were several long spikes, square and massive, broad at the base and sharp at the points, placed in such a position that when the door should close the upper ones would pierce the eyes of the victim, and the lower ones his heart and vitals. The sight was too much for poor Amelia, and this time she fainted dead off, and I had to carry her down the stairs, and place her on a bench outside till she recovered. That she felt it to the quick was afterwards shown by the fact that my eldest son bears to this day a rude birthmark on his breast, which has, by family consent, been accepted as representing the Nurnberg Virgin.

24 When we got back to the chamber we found Hutcheson still opposite the Iron Virgin; he had been evidently philosophising, and now gave us the benefit of his thought in the shape of a sort of exordium.

25 "Well, I guess I've been learnin' somethin' here while madam has been gettin' over her faint. 'Pears to me that we're a long way behind the times on our side of the big drink. We uster think out on the plains that the Injun could give us points in tryin' to make a man oncomfortable; but I guess your old mediæval law-and-order party could raise him every time. Splinters was pretty good in his bluff on the squaw, but this here young miss held a straight flush all high on him. The points of them spikes air sharp enough still, though even the edges air eaten out by what uster be on them. It'd be a good thing for our Indian section to get some specimens of this here play-toy to send round to the Reservations jest to knock the stuffin' out of the bucks, and the squaws too, by showing them as how old civilisation lays over them at their best. Guess but I'll get in that box a minute jest to see how it feels!"

26 "Oh, no! no!" said Amelia. "It is too terrible!"

27 "Guess, ma'am, nothin's too terrible to the explorin' mind. I've been in some queer places in my time. Spent a night inside a dead horse while a prairie fire swept over me in Montana Territory—an' another time slept inside a dead buffler when the Comanches was on the war path an' I didn't keer to leave my kyard on them. I've been two days in a caved-in tunnel in the Billy Broncho gold mine in New Mexico, an' was one of the four shut up for three parts of a day in the caisson what slid over on her side when we was settin' the foundations of the Buffalo Bridge. I've not funked an odd experience yet, an' I don't propose to begin now!"

28 We saw that he was set on the experiment, so I said: "Well, hurry up, old man, and get through it quick!"

29 "All right, General," said he, "but I calculate we ain't quite ready yet. The gentlemen, my predecessors, what stood in that thar canister, didn't volunteer for the office—not much! And I guess there was some ornamental tyin' up before the big stroke was made. I want to go into this thing fair and square, so I must get fixed up proper first. I dare say this old galoot can rise some string and tie me up accordin' to sample?"

30 This was said interrogatively to the old custodian, but the latter, who understood the drift of his speech, though perhaps not appreciating to the full the niceties of dialect and imagery, shook his head. His protest was, however, only formal and made to be overcome. The American thrust a gold piece into his hand, saying, "Take it, pard! it's your pot; and don't be skeer'd. This ain't no necktie party that you're asked to assist in!" He produced some thin frayed rope and proceeded to bind our companion, with sufficient strictness for the purpose. When the upper part of his body was bound, Hutcheson said:

31 "Hold on a moment, Judge. Guess I'm too heavy for you to tote into the canister. You jest let me walk in, and then you can wash up regardin' my legs!"

32 Whilst speaking he had backed himself into the opening which was just enough to hold him. It was a close fit and no mistake. Amelia looked on with fear in her eyes, but she evidently did not like to say anything. Then the custodian completed his task by tying the American's feet together so that he was now absolutely helpless and fixed in his voluntary prison. He seemed to really enjoy it, and the incipient smile which was habitual to his face blossomed into actuality as he said:

33 "Guess this here Eve was made out of the rib of a dwarf! There ain't much room for a full-grown citizen of the United States to hustle. We uster make our coffins more roomier in Idaho Territory. Now, Judge, you just begin to let this door down, slow, on to me. I want to feel the same pleasure as the other jays had when those spikes began to move toward their eyes!"

34 "Oh no! no! no!" broke in Amelia hysterically. "It is too terrible! I can't bear to see it—I can't! I can't!"

35 But the American was obdurate. "Say, Colonel," said he, "why not take madam for a little promenade? I wouldn't hurt her feelin's for the world; but now that I am here, havin' kem eight thousand miles, wouldn't it be too hard to give up the very experience I've been pinin' and pantin' fur? A man can't get to feel like canned goods every time! Me and the Judge here'll fix up this thing in no time, an' then you'll come back, an' we'll all laugh together!"

36 Once more the resolution that is born of curiosity triumphed, and

Amelia stayed holding tight to my arm and shivering whilst the custodian began to slacken slowly inch by inch the rope that held back the iron door. Hutcheson's face was positively radiant as his eyes followed the first movement of the spikes.

[37] "Well!" he said. "I guess I've not had enjoyment like this since I left Noo York. Bar a scrap with a French sailor at Wapping—an' that warn't much of a picnic neither—I've not had a show fur real pleasure in this dod-rotted Continent, where there ain't no b'ars nor no Injuns, an' where nary man goes heeled. Slow there, Judge! Don't you rush this business! I want a show for my money this game—I du!"

[38] The custodian must have had in him some of the blood of his predecessors in that ghastly tower, for he worked the engine with a deliberate and excruciating slowness which after five minutes, in which the outer edge of the door had not moved half as many inches, began to overcome Amelia. I saw her lips whiten, and felt her hold upon my arm relax. I looked around an instant for a place whereon to lay her, and when I looked at her again found that her eye had become fixed on the side of the Virgin. Following its direction I saw the black cat crouching out of sight. Her green eyes shone like danger lamps in the gloom of the place, and their colour was heightened by the blood which still smeared her coat and reddened her mouth. I cried out:

[39] "The cat! look out for the cat!" for even then she sprang out before the engine. At this moment she looked like a triumphant demon. Her eyes blazed with ferocity, her hair bristled out till she seemed twice her normal size, and her tail lashed about as does a tiger's when the quarry is before it. Elias P. Hutcheson when he saw her was amused, and his eyes positively sparkled with fun as he said:

[40] "Darned if the squaw hain't got on all her war paint! Jest give her a shove off if she comes any of her tricks on me, for I'm so fixed everlastingly by the boss, that durn my skin if I can keep my eyes from her if she wants them! Easy there, Judge! Don't you slack that ar rope or I'm euchered!"

[41] At this moment Amelia completed her faint, and I had to clutch hold of her round the waist or she would have fallen to the floor. Whilst attending to her I saw the black cat crouching for a spring, and jumped up to turn the creature out.

[42] But at that instant, with a sort of hellish scream, she hurled herself, not as we expected at Hutcheson, but straight at the face of the custodian. Her claws seemed to be tearing wildly as one sees in the Chinese drawings of the dragon rampant, and as I looked I saw one of them light on the poor man's eye, and actually tear through it

and down his cheek, leaving a wide band of red where the blood seemed to spurt from every vein.

43 With a yell of sheer terror which came quicker than even his sense of pain, the man leaped back, dropping as he did so the rope which held back the iron door. I jumped for it, but was too late, for the cord ran like lightning through the pulley-block, and the heavy mass fell forward from its own weight.

44 As the door closed I caught a glimpse of our poor companion's face. He seemed frozen with terror. His eyes stared with a horrible anguish as if dazed, and no sound came from his lips.

45 And then the spikes did their work. Happily the end was quick, for when I wrenched open the door they had pierced so deep that they had locked in the bones of the skull through which they had crushed, and actually tore him—it—out of his iron prison till, bound as he was, he fell at full length with a sickly thud upon the floor, the face turning upward as he fell.

46 I rushed to my wife, lifted her up and carried her out, for I feared for her very reason if she should wake from her faint to such a scene. I laid her on the bench outside and ran back. Leaning against the wooden column was the custodian moaning in pain whilst he held his reddening handkerchief to his eyes. And sitting on the head of the poor American was the cat, purring loudly as she licked the blood which trickled through the gashed sockets of his eyes.

47 I think no one will call me cruel because I seized one of the old executioner's swords and shore her in two as she sat. □

The Punch

by Bruce Jay Friedman

1 It seemed to Harris that their short life together could be charted by a series of tense situations in which he came close, but finally failed to smash another man's face.

2 Not particularly well-muscled, he was a tall and hulking man given to making disagreeable faces when problems arose; the combination of his height and scowling countenance tended to keep trouble at a distance. But once, in wartime and before they were married, he had been sitting beside her at a bar when a great hawk of a man, with black, tunneled eyes and skin pulled firm over the cave of his cheeks, swooped down upon them and asked Harris if he could dance with her.

3 "I don't think so," said Harris. "I'm with her."

4 The man turned to her and said, "I'd like to dance with you."

5 "Not just now," she said. Harris caught the man by the arm and said, "Do I have to put it in writing? I told you for her." But then something poured up from his stomach to his throat and he dropped the man's arm. "Let's get out of here," Harris said to her.

6 "It's lucky we're leaving," she said as they searched the street for a cab. "You might really have knocked him unconscious."

7 "I probably would have," said Harris. "Only it isn't a good idea to hit anyone when you're in uniform. You can get into bad trouble."

8 Months later, on their honeymoon, they stayed one night at a Georgia motel. She was a slender, blonde girl with indecently young tennis-playing legs and wide, confidential eyes that made even the passing of a saltshaker seem shamefully intimate. Her skin was ovenlike in its heat and as she fitted herself against him, he reeled in voluptuous guilt and said, "We're in bed together. And it's all right."

9 "I know," she said. "We're allowed."

10 There was a click then and a shuffle outside their room and Harris rose, instinctively reaching for a shampoo bottle. "I'm turning off the lights," he whispered and then flattened himself against the wall, inching up toward the door with bottle raised and finally thrusting it open to peer around in the darkness. Convinced there was no prowler about, he returned to the room a moment later.

11 "How come you took the shampoo bottle?" she asked.

12 "What do you mean," he said. "Any defense is good in a deal like this."

13 "I thought you'd want to fight with your bare fists."

14 "Believe me, a bottle's better."

15 "In the movies they do it with fists," she said.

16 "That's the movies. Say, you're kidding around with this, aren't you?"

17 "Sort of," she said.

18 She teased him many times about the bottle through the first year of their marriage and it became a private joke between them. Once, when some children were making noise outside their garden-apartment window, he said, "I'll go down and shut them up," and she said, "Would you like to take along the shampoo bottle?" Another time, when cleaning out their bathroom, she lifted the bottle and said, "You'll probably want to keep this around in case there's trouble." He grabbed and pulled her down on the bed, doing something foolproof to her neck with his teeth, and then said, "Quit it, will you, about the bottle. Hey, you were really upset about it when I picked up that damned thing, weren't you?"

19 "No, I wasn't," she said. "The movies are what made it seem funny."

20 It was not a good first year for them. Harris worked for a public-relations man who paid him an unofficial amount of dollars each week, according to how things were. He paid Harris right out of his pocket, a clump of bills, sometimes a large clump and sometimes a small one, forcing Harris and his wife to live in a strange garden-apartment building, set up octopus-style, with the furnace headlike in the center and Harris' rooms way out on the end of the longest tentacle. Heat arrived in his radiators only in faint gusts, weakened from its long journey. One wintry afternoon, Harris called city officials about his cold radiators and was told to get up a committee among his neighbors and picket the landlord. "That and petitions are the only way to lick it," he was told. He suspected that his wife was pregnant and when there was no one left to call, he looked over at her bathrobed figure, saw her warming her hands over the kitchen gas jet, and fell upon the bed, biting the sheets in frustration and trying not to cry. "It's the superintendent," she said. "He could build a bigger furnace fire, but he's got a hot apartment so why should he care. I'd go over there and really get him."

21 Harris swept outside to the street and found his way to the superintendent's flat. Blasts of warmth washed against him as the small, wry man opened the door. "I'm not getting any heat," said Harris. "You ought to be ashamed letting the furnace get so low. I ought to grab you by the neck and drag you over there to make a bigger fire."

22 "Weekend, weekend," said the man.

23 "I don't care about that. You're nice and warm, I see. I ought to grab you by the neck."

24 "Okay, okay," said the man, closing the door. "Weekend."

25 Back in his own apartment, his wife asked, "Did you punch him right in the face?"

26 "Sort of," said Harris.

27 "What do you mean?" she asked. "What did you do?"

28 "I let him know how I felt."

29 "Is he going to do anything about it?"

30 "I think so," said Harris.

31 Months later, when winter had disappeared, Harris stepped off the bus one night to find his wife in front of their apartment, standing alongside a handyman. "Do you know what he won't do?" she said, her face choked with anger. "He won't take away the garbage."

32 "It's not my area," said the handyman.

33 "Will you make him take it away," she said. "Will you please

punch him or something so we don't have to have garbage here overnight."

34 "Look, will you take the garbage away," Harris said.

35 "That isn't what I mean," she said, crying now. "That isn't anything. I could have done that. It's like the shampoo bottle."

36 "Mister," said Harris, taking the man's arm. "I'm asking you nicely to pick up the damned garbage."

37 "Not my area," said the man, wrenching away and walking off.

38 "It isn't his area," Harris said to his wife. "You can't expect a man to work outside his area."

39 "Oh God," she said, running upstairs.

40 The situations began to come up, in his second year of marriage, with some regularity; he knew that no matter how smoothly things were running, always, at a party, in a theatre, in broad daylight, there would arise some confrontation in which he would be brought to the edge of violence and then, in some way or other, fail to throw a punch. It was not that he lacked victories. He could remember two in particular that second year, but both were unsatisfactory. One was a clear verbal triumph and the other a kind of vaguely physical but only temporarily pleasing one. The first took place at an art exhibit. He had begun to have words with a heavyset man and finally said, "I don't need your damned advice."

41 "I get paid for my advice," said the man and Harris had answered, "Then you must starve to death." The argument picked up steam until the man's wife, an aging woman with a headful of Shirley Temple ringlets, seized a bourbon bottle and ran toward Harris screaming, "Leave my husband alone."

42 "He's all yours," said Harris with great calm, heading for another part of the gallery with his own wife. "I'm going to call you 'Hammering Harris,'" she said, squeezing his arm in delight.

43 The second of his victories came after an evening of entertaining a college friend he had not seen for twelve years. The friend, nicknamed "Fritters" at school, was a sports announcer who had done quite well in the Midwest and come east to try his luck in New York City. After a dinner in Greenwich Village with Harris and his wife, Fritters walked along at their side, telling them how he would do a pro-football championship game. "The ball's handed back to Conerly, the old pro fades back with good blocking, sees Rote running the long pattern and lets a deep one go. . . ." As they were crossing the street, a car lurched around a corner and, with double brights full in their faces, bore down upon them at top speed, stopping only at the last moment with a great shriek. Peals of laughter came from inside the car and

Harris reached in through the open driver's window, felt some skin and twisted it in rage until its owner screamed in pain. The car took off then as though from a launching pad.

44 "What did you do?" his wife said, running to him, her eyes wild. "What did you do to them?"

45 "I fixed them," said Harris.

46 "How?" she said. "I saw you reach in there."

47 "I just fixed them, that's all. And I guarantee you they won't do that again to people."

48 "Bastards," said Fritters. "All right, the old trickster Y. A. Tittle is in replacing Conerly now. Giants operating out of a Split T. Tittle takes the pass from center. . . ."

49 But the exhilaration following both episodes was short-lived; by this time, it had become fairly apparent to Harris that what really mattered was smashing someone in the face. Nothing less. A verbal flourish wouldn't do it. A skin-twist or bringing your chin right up to another man's and arguing nose to nose with him wasn't the idea either. Even a numb and blinding fist deep into a soft belly and all the way back to something spinal wouldn't turn the trick. A punch high on the forehead? A heavy, wet one on the ear? Arguable. What he was after was one on the front of a man's face, a clean one on the point of the jaw, movie style. That is what had become obsessional to him, and although his wife did not phrase it formally, that is what she seemed to need herself.

50 One evening, when things had begun to pick up for him, the clumps of bills having given way to a weekly check of unvarying denomination, his wife curled against him and said, "Let me just see something." She doubled up her fist and hit him lightly on the chin, then tried it a little harder. "Is that how it is?" she asked. "Try it to me." He hit her lightly that way and she said, "Can a man really knock out a man by hitting him that way? I like it when they do that in the movies."

51 "It's not that way in real life," said Harris. "In real life when a man gets hit on the chin, he usually gets carted off to the hospital with a concussion and the hitter breaks his fist or something."

52 "Have you ever hit someone that way?"

53 "Sure. Haven't you ever seen me do it?"

54 "No, I haven't," she said.

55 "I thought you had."

56 He could not remember when he had thrown his last punch. He knew there had been a cluster of them when he was around thirteen. One

had been directed at a boy named Smollie who had great numbers of electric games in his apartment. He had more under his bed than Harris had in his whole room, and one day Harris hit him in the eye for having so many. Smollie had grown bored with a six-player field-hockey set and was kneeling to slip it under his bed when Harris let him have one in the eye. "Why did you do that?" the boy asked, holding his eye. "You were getting smart," said Harris.

57 Outside the infirmary at summer camp, he could remember hitting a handsome boy with wavy hair on some pretext involving Band-Aid allotments, but actually for being too relaxed with girls at a time when they made Harris tense. He could recall, too, a slow-acting giant of a boy named Nit who stood flailing his arms on the handball court after school each day while other boys lined up to take turns hitting him in the face. Harris had gotten in line once and when his turn came, said, "I'm doing it, too," and hit the slow boy on the cheek, getting his hand wet.

58 But then the punches had stopped and he had gone into a long Gandhi-like conciliatory period in which he somehow managed to slip out of things, to let them drop at the exquisitely correct moment, somehow to wind up reaching for his coat at the first smell of tension. What troubled him is that it had gone on now for twenty-five years. He said that often to himself. "I haven't actually punched anyone in twenty-five years." The thought tore at him and sometimes he would go home and stand throwing punches at his reflection in the mirror, putting everything behind them and wincing at the effort. It did not help to think of himself as having behaved with Stevensonian dignity. That would cover you perhaps for ten years or so, but it seemed to him that even Adlai himself must have had occasion to let someone have it in the face once or twice over a twenty-five-year span. There was something terribly wrong with not having had a single fistfight in four years of college. And in three years of the Air Force, too. The military was a place where on at least one damned occasion you stood back to back with friends and took on people, civilians and men from other services. One night he had walked into a small bar in Southern Illinois and stood outside a circle of airmen who had surrounded a mammoth girl named Rona. She sat in the center of them like a great many-spigoted pleasure fountain; the idea seemed to be that people were allowed to let their hands travel over her freely—as though she were a new kind of concession. Harris went in for a turn and a sergeant whispered in his ear, "There's a bunch here that don't like you. I'm on your side if there's trouble. We'll take 'em back to back, but I thought I'd tell you." It was a perfect, swashbuckling kind of situation, tailor-made

for ending his long abstinence, but the back of his neck got cold and he walked away from the circle to get a drink. "You get tired of lushing it up night after night," he told his sergeant informant and then walked to the door in a lazy, cowpuncher's gait. It did not come off as a cowardly move, and for all he knew the "bunch" that didn't like him had looked upon him as a man who had come in and had a few drinks and quickly grown bored. He himself did not see anything wrong with the maneuver. By this time, he had gotten used to bored exits, to dropping things quietly, pretending certain remarks had never been made and certain tense situations were only imaginary. It had not worked out too badly for a long time, except that now his wife was there to keep score. And in the years since he had gotten married, the need to hit someone had gathered up like an abscess.

59 He searched his memory at night for something that might have qualified as a punch, coming up with shoves and arm wrestles and football arguments, but there wasn't a genuine one in the carload; and in any case, it would have to be a married one, one during which his wife would be on hand to make a notebook notation.

60 It became, after awhile, as black and white a problem as having a splinter in his toe. ("I will never be completely comfortable until I have this splinter out. I will never be completely at ease until I smash someone in the face.") It was not even necessary that he be enraged, and there were times he thought he would simply go ahead and schedule it like a barbershop appointment. He would call his wife, tell her to meet him that night, that he was going to pick out someone, have a little argument, and smash him in the face to clear his record.

61 There was no way to pick his man quite that mechanically, of course; and yet, since he knew he was going to punch *someone,* he began to wonder if he would be lucky enough to get the right man; someone tall enough, let's say, to be impressive, yet not quite so formidable that he would have a full-scale fight on his hands . . . with broken teeth and facial scars to worry about. He began to size up potential nominees and wonder how he would do against them; after a short argument over incorrect change with a slender newsstand attendant, he kicked himself for letting the man get away. He lost a heavy-set but soft-looking cabdriver who'd been ill-mannered over his tip and thought how ironic it would be to have let this man slip by and wind up taking on someone deceptively slender who had received years of commando training.

62 Another thought plagued him: what if he sneaked over a real clean one, only to have his man hit the pavement and die—or have to be kept in expensive institutions for forty years.

63 As it turned out, he got a fine break in each of the particulars he had been concerned about. His man was of good size. It happened quite suddenly so that he did not have time to get nervous about it. The affair lasted one punch and Harris was the one who threw it. No heads hit the pavement. If there was any dental work, he never knew about it. No cops. No crowds. A snotty doorman, but easily handled.

64 He had met his wife in a hotel lobby one evening and gone outside to hail a cab that would take them to a restaurant for dinner. It was a cold, skin-pinching kind of evening and no taxis came by; after about ten minutes, two college-age boys appeared and took a position on the street about fifteen paces uptown which would have allowed them to beat out Harris for the first unoccupied cab. When a taxi did draw near, the boys made for it and Harris yelled, "Hey, get in line." A tall, redheaded man suddenly emerged from the shadows and said, "Who are you yelling at? They're with me."

65 "They jumped in ahead of me, though," said Harris. "I've been waiting for ten minutes."

66 The man's face suddenly changed. He put his hands on his hips, drew back his lips and opened his eyes wide enough for them to fall out. Then he moved his face close to Harris' and screamed, *"Well, fwrraurke you."* It was a perfect cue for Harris to do one of his casual shuffle-offs, and he did take a step or two away, but then he said, "Oh hell," and without thinking too much about it, threw a punch so neatly timed and placed it was as though he had spent if not twenty-five, then seven or so years preparing for it. The man fell back against the fender of the cab and said, "Oh yeah," what seemed to be at least a dozen times, trying in a vague, slow-motion way to get out of his overcoat. The two college boys ran swiftly toward Harris, but then seemed to feel they had fulfilled their obligation to make a show of force; they scooped their defender into the cab and sped off.

67 The doorman said, "You get in there," to Harris who did as he was told, going into the lobby where he began, for the first time, to breathe with some difficulty.

68 "Something happened," his wife said. "I can always tell."

69 "Something sure did," he said. "I hit a guy."

70 "What do you mean you hit him?"

71 "I hit him. Right outside. He tried to sneak in ahead of me on a cab and I let him have it."

72 "Oh God," she said. "It's lucky I didn't see it. I'd have fainted."

73 "I don't do that often," he said. "But I swear I had provocation. You should have seen the kind of face he had. Let me calm down a little here. It was some punch. Below the nose and I didn't crack his teeth either."

74 He sat on a couch and wiped his head, the pounds of joy so forceful in his chest he was certain people in the lobby could hear them.

75 "I don't know if I can eat," he said, getting to his feet. "I'm pretty excited."

76 "You must be," she said. "Did anyone see it?"

77 "The doorman," said Harris. "I hope he doesn't remember my face."

78 She freshened her makeup in the lobby mirror; outside, she asked, "Where did you say it happened?"

79 "Right up the street," he said, "about fifteen yards up in front of that cigar store."

80 "Didn't a crowd collect or anything?" she asked.

81 "It was over fast. Say, listen," he said. "I'll bet you don't believe me."

82 "Of course I do," she said. "I know *something* happened the way you came into the lobby."

83 "You want me to stand right in the place where it happened? I'll tell you what. I'll get the doorman and he'll settle it right there. I know you. You don't believe me."

84 "Don't be silly," she said. "If you say it happened, it happened. I believe you. It's just that I thought there'd be a whole bunch of people when there's a fight. Now let's eat," she said, taking his arm. "I'm starved."

85 "I was, but I'm not," he said, tearing her arm away. They glared at each other in the cold of Lexington Avenue and it seemed to Harris that for the first time he saw her tight and puckered face in a new light. What happened, he wondered, when you smacked wives in the jaw. Would they automatically walk out and never see you again after they got out of hospitals? Did they get divorces? And what about the physical end of it. Maybe they weren't so fragile. Some wives had hard, cold, mean little faces and could probably take a punch better than you thought. A well-timed one that missed the teeth and passed up the nose, yet got the job done just the same. □

Incident on the Tenth Floor

by Jeff Brown

1 The lobby ceiling was made up of tricky lighting panels—one moment blue and orange, the next gold and red—and Arthur, waiting for an elevator, said to the pretty Negro starter, "I wish that ceiling would make up its mind." The girl smiled. A good omen, he thought. Small, but good.

2 On the tenth floor, in the reception room of Hugh T. Loeffler, Inc., a hawk-faced lady with no lips said that Mr. Loeffler would be free in a moment, please come this way. She led him down a long corridor and left him in a big office with windows that looked out over Fifth Avenue.

3 He tried a cream-leather sofa, then moved to an armchair in front of the desk. The desk was a slab of white marble on wrought-iron legs, bare except for a pipe rack, an onyx pen stand, a telephone with four buttons, and an intercom box. The walls weren't very informative about Loeffler either—a few modern pictures, bold splashes of color on sheets of unframed glass; photographs of housing developments, shopping centers, and skyscrapers in various stages of completion. It was a cold room, Arthur thought, but there was no denying the sense of power and importance in the air. God's office would be like this if He had lost interest in everything except commercial real estate.

4 Fifteen minutes went by, and he wished Loeffler would come and give him a job or *not* give him a job, just get it over with, either way. Then it struck him that he had been headed toward this interview for several years, ever since he'd met Grace Dangerfield at Ann Tenney's cocktail party in the Village; it was silly to fret about a few more minutes now.

5 "Come on, help me," Ann Tenney said. "Please! She's not having any fun at all!"

6 In a corner of the room, looking very out of place among the sweater-and-blue-jean types, stood a plump, well-dressed girl wearing heavy horn-rim glasses. "Grace, this is Arthur!" Ann shouted before she darted off. "He's an actor, or at least he would be if anybody'd give him a chance. Arthur, this is Grace. I went to school with her."

7 He did his best to make conversation, but the party was noisy and Grace offered only uneasy smiles and nods. He had begun to wonder if she was not quite bright, when she said suddenly, "I guess Ann didn't tell you I was deaf. I have hearing aids, but they don't help much in crowds. You can't tune out what you *don't* want to hear, the way you can with ears." She said it not angrily, but with resignation, as if she were used to having to explain herself; he was touched by her manner, and charmed as well. When the party broke up, they had dinner together at a little Armenian restaurant down the street.

8 For several months his days had been particularly long and dull—making the rounds of agents and casting offices, from midafternoon till ten at night clerking in a bookstore on Eighth Street, after that sitting sleepily in a tiny hall bedroom trying to write—and it was comforting to be with someone who seemed interested in all his grievances and

hopes. For almost an hour he explained them; then, over the *baklava* and coffee, he made her talk about herself.

9 She had been hard-of-hearing from birth. There had been three operations, two in New York when she was very young, another in Switzerland four years ago; that one had helped a little, but she still needed hearing aids—miniature batteries and transistors built into her glasses; that was why they had such heavy frames. She had had one job since she finished college a year ago, doing research for a news magazine, but it had lasted only a few months; working in a room with four other girls, she had not been able to hear well enough.

10 They went to a movie after dinner, and halfway through it, without turning toward him, she put her hand in his.

11 Grace lived with her family in Connecticut; he saw her off from Grand Central after the movie. At the last minute, remembering that they had not arranged to meet again, he ran along the platform shouting, "What's your phone number?" above the clatter of the train. She could not have heard him—no one could have heard him—but through the window he saw her pantomime dialing, then the searching of a heavy book. The telephone directory, he realized, and it pleased him enormously —though he was not sure why—that she had been able to read his lips.

12 Two months later, after he had seen Grace a dozen times, he met her parents. They had asked about him, she said, and wanted him to come to Stamford for dinner. Arthur knew by then that her father was a corporation lawyer and the senior partner in his firm but the reality of Mr. Dangerfield's success did not fully dawn on him until he saw the chauffeured limousine waiting at the Stamford station and, fifteen minutes later, the handsome house and grounds of the Dangerfield estate.

13 Mr. Dangerfield was tall, bald, and stern. Mrs. Dangerfield was slim and chic; she spoke with a throaty drawl, her lips scarcely moving, and several times, over dinner, Grace was forced to say, "I'm sorry. What—?" Whenever she did, her parents looked annoyed, and Arthur realized how very vulnerable Grace was; it was her habit to watch people's lips, so she was bound to notice when their faces showed impatience or that they were saying things they did not mean.

14 Mr. Dangerfield took him into the library after dinner, lighted a cigar, and asked Arthur to talk about himself, about what he did, about his prospects. He listened quietly to an explanation of the difficulties of making a career as an actor, but when Arthur mentioned his interest in writing and his hopes for the play he had outlined in his mind and was almost ready to begin, Mr. Dangerfield said, "Interesting. Thank you. Good Lord, it's ten o'clock! You must be anxious to get back to town."

15 Grace and her mother were waiting in the living room. Grace looked as if she were about to cry, and Mrs. Dangerfield looked embarrassed, but only good-nights were spoken. The chauffeur drove Arthur back to the station.

16 Early the next morning Grace telephoned.

17 "They don't want me to see you any more," she said. "I'd hate that, wouldn't you?" He certainly would hate that, he said. Then she said, "Do you love me, Arthur? I love you very much and I want to know," and he knew suddenly that he loved her more than he had ever loved anyone or anything in his whole life. Marveling, he said so into the telephone. "Let's get married then," Grace said. "Right away."

18 She picked him up in her car that afternoon, and they drove to Maryland.

19 A big man with a tanned, healthy face strode into the office. "Hugh Loeffler. Sorry to keep you waiting, son."

20 "That's all right," Arthur said as they shook hands. "How do you do, sir. Grace asked to be remembered to you."

21 Loeffler sat down behind the white-marble desk, took a pipe from the rack and began to fill it, chuckling. "I'm not likely to forget Grace. Tyler Dangerfield and I got drunk together the night she was born—did you know that?"

22 "I knew you were old friends," Arthur said. "But I didn't know *that.*"

23 Loeffler wore a gray suit, a pale-blue shirt, and a maroon tie. Face, suit, shirt, tie, pipe—they all went together, he thought. People like Loeffler were probably born at Abercrombie & Fitch and went back there to die.

24 "Well, now," Loeffler said. "Let's get to know each other a little, and then I'll try to figure out where a fellow like you might fit into a business like mine. You've been an actor, Tyler tells me. How'd you get into that?"

25 "It was sort of a family thing," Arthur said. "I don't really remember my father—he died when I was five—but he was a director, in radio. And my mother was—Oh, she was an actress, I guess you'd say."

26 "You *guess?"*

27 "She could do all kinds of tricks with her voice, and in radio she played kids mostly, or babies crying—things like that. In television, the only real break she had was a weekend show for children. She wore a clown outfit—you know, white makeup and all—and told stories. *The Queen Koko Show.* It lasted four years."

28 "Never heard of it. Is she still—uh—performing?"

29 Arthur watched a puff of pipe smoke sail across the desk and spike itself on the fountain pen. Loeffler's tone annoyed him; so did the little smile, and he decided to wipe the smile off.

30 "She's dead," he said. "She killed herself. That's all I can tell you about my family. I have some cousins in Ohio, but I haven't seen them since I was a kid."

31 Loeffler blinked. "I see. Well, I'm sorry to have—Let's fill in some other parts of the picture, shall we? When did you—" The intercom box said, "Mr. Reeder, sir," and he pressed a button on his telephone and picked it up.

32 "Dave? Those Cleveland half-wits are stalling, and Farnum's on his way up here now! What are your latest figures?" Listening, he made notes.

33 Part of a picture, Arthur thought. He wondered how hard Loeffler would have blinked if that first part had *really* been filled in.

34 There had always been some drinking, but it wasn't out of control until the last years of the Queen Koko show. Success should have steadied her, people said, not made her weak. They didn't know, as he did, that television terrified her as radio never had, that she hated to be *seen,* that she was embarrassed by the ludicrous makeup, by the lisping fairy tales she told. The last year, the year he started college at Columbia, she was almost always drunk. He had done what he could—cooked their meals, cleaned the apartment, put her to bed at night, escorted her to rehearsals and shows—but there was a limit to the protection he could give. One morning, on camera, with children clustered before her little throne, Queen Koko began to snore; when a child tugged at her clown costume, she rose, swayed, and struck the child in the face.

35 Old friends tried to help. She was called for a few bit parts that next year, but she was rarely sober, and at last every casting office in town had scratched her name.

36 She stayed home then, and hung on to him. Her Arthur. Her Arthur who would go on taking care of her, wouldn't he? Her baby who wouldn't leave her, who'd stay with her always, wasn't that right, honey, please? For more than a year he'd taken it, knowing that he was cutting too many classes and that the Army would get him if Columbia flunked him out, knowing too that at least the Army would be an excuse to get away. Then it happened, but even after he had been given a reporting date he did not tell her; each day, the telling was more than he could face. The night before he was to report he made no effort to keep the bottle away from her; when she passed out, he left a note under the empty bottle and went downtown to the terminal to wait for the Fort Dix bus.

37 Three weeks later he was summoned from an Oklahoma drill field into a chaplain's office, and the chaplain told him what she had done. Arthur had seen it very clearly in his mind—the frowzy woman shuffling out into the little kitchen, sealing up the door and window cracks, turning on the stove; he had imagined even the faint, sickening smell of gas and the sound of weeping. The worst of it was that he pictured her dressed as Queen Koko, the chalk-white makeup and the floppy suit, and the weeping was the kind he remembered hearing when he was a kid, listening to her on the radio; he heard, not a grown woman, but a baby whimpering for someone to come.

38 ". . . hell with that!" Loeffler said. "Tell him to knock off five percent or we don't go along. Let me know, Dave."

39 He hung up and lighted his pipe again. "Let's see . . . You were talking about being an actor, I think."

40 "I didn't actually decide on it until I got back to New York after my Army training," Arthur said. "I didn't want to go back to college; I kept wondering what it *would* make sense to do. Then I thought: I still have some contacts in show business. Why not have a go at that?"

41 "Seems like a damn careless way to choose a career," Loeffler said.

42 "I don't think most people really *choose* their careers," Arthur said. "Things happen that they can't control; they get influenced by other people without realizing it. It gets decided *for* them, if you know what I mean."

43 "That's one way of looking at it," Loeffler said.

44 "Well, anyhow, I got a few bit parts in television and some extra work in movies that were being made in New York, but that didn't bring in enough to live on, so I had all kinds of other jobs on the side. And in my spare time I tried to write. I've always—"

45 "What kind of writing?"

46 "There was a play I worked on for a long time, but I never finished it. And I wrote some poetry."

47 Loeffler frowned briefly. Probably, Arthur thought, he was the type who thought only fairies wrote poetry.

48 "These 'on the side' jobs," Loeffler said. "What were they?"

49 He wondered what difference it made. Night clerk at a West Side hotel for elderly Jewish couples, cashier at the Village Diner, clerking at an art-supplies-and-prints shop on Lexington Avenue, all the other dreary short-term occupations . . . It wasn't the jobs themselves that mattered; it was the *feel* of those years—the sense of being wasted, the fear that his whole life was going to be lived in cheap rooming houses, that "tomorrow" would always be a word without hope in it. But that

feeling, he thought, wasn't something you could explain easily to Hugh T. Loeffler, Inc.

50 He ran down the list of jobs, simply naming them in the order they had come, and became aware that Loeffler was leaning back in his chair, studying him.

51 A moment passed, and he began to count all the things Loeffler did with his pipe: puffing, chewing the stem, tapping his teeth with it, rubbing the bowl with his thumb. Blow bubbles, he thought. Surprise me.

52 "It must be a tough way to make a living, acting," Loeffler said. "Even with all this crazy off-Broadway stuff they go in for now. My wife dragged me downtown a few weeks ago, some place up over an Italian restaurant; you could cut the cheese smell with a knife. The show was supposed to be artistic, according to the newspapers, but it was just two old colored ladies and a white man talking about race problems, and using words I didn't know you could say in public without getting arrested. You ever been in one of those off-Broadway things?"

53 "I had a small part in one, a flop, not long after Grace and I got married," Arthur said. "It was a comedy, though. No race problems."

54 "Not earning money—that must have been quite a worry after you got married?"

55 "Grace has a small income," he said. "Added to whatever I bring in, it's enough for us to squeak by. So—"

56 "I know about Grace's money," Loeffler said.

57 "You mean, did it bother me to have to depend on that?" Arthur made himself smile. "It's never been a problem. Not for us. We don't worry about what other people think."

58 "I see," Loeffler said. "So money's not your problem." He knocked out his pipe, took another from the rack and began to fill it. "Then what brings you here, son? What made you decide to go looking for a job in a business you don't know anything about? Think about that for a minute."

59 The marriage had begun well.

60 There was the sunny little apartment; there was the happiness of being with Grace; there was even, surprisingly soon, the comfort of knowing that he no longer stood between her and her parents. It seemed to dawn on the Dangerfields, after a few months, that he truly loved their daughter; a truce was arranged and they began, the four of them, to meet for dinner at least once a week. And there had been the off-Broadway play; flop or not, he had spoken lines on a New York stage. He had not been afraid, that first year, to look ahead.

61 It was all downhill after that. He made the rounds faithfully, but there were no parts, only a few auditions and one week as an extra in a television show. The months went on; at last he quit making rounds and took a series of meaningless jobs again, anything to help fill the days—selling neckties at Bloomingdale's during the Christmas season, answering telephones at a part-time-maid agency, clerking again at the bookstore on Eighth Street, the one where he had been working when he first met Grace. On the days between jobs he took long walks up and down the East River Drive, watching the barges on the river, the children playing in the little concrete parks, trying not to let himself think about anything at all.

62 The dinners with Grace's parents were more difficult to get through now. Mr. Dangerfield, though he meant well, would drone relentlessly on: The time had come for Arthur to be realistic, to accept responsibilities; there were people who might be helpful, and he had only to say the word. . . . Arthur would sit with his hands clenched, wanting to throw food, knives, forks in Mr. Dangerfield's face; later, at home with Grace, he would wait eagerly for her to say it didn't matter, that she still had faith in him, that he need not be concerned for her.

63 But there were days when she would go for hours without wearing the glasses with the hearing aids, and not bothering to look at people when they spoke; it was as if she were trying to hide somehow within herself. And he knew that he too was changing, that his strength was crumbling steadily, bit by bit. One afternoon, walking by the river, he began to tremble suddenly and then to cry. Frightened, wondering what had made it happen, he stood looking out over the greasy water, averting his face from passersby until he could control himself.

64 It happened again a few days later, and this time he was in a restaurant with Grace, and there were people at the little tables all about them. When the trembling began he bolted for the washroom, but they had noticed; he could feel their eyes on him when he came out.

65 Later that night, unable to sleep, he was sitting by the bedroom window when a shapeless figure in a long overcoat went by in the silent street below. The man seemed real only as he passed through the little circles of light the street lamps made; in the darkness between the lamps he was just a blur, and when he rounded the corner it was hard to believe that he had ever been. *I am not real either. There is nothing to show where I have been. . . .* From the bed, as if the thought had reached her, Grace said softly, "What can we do?" Turning, he said, "What? I thought you were asleep," and she said again, "What can we do?" She could not hear him, he realized, not without the hearing aids, and then he knew that she did not want to hear him, that she was lying there

in the darkness wanting only to tell him that she was afraid. "Please," she said. "I don't know what to do. . . ."

66 In the morning he telephoned Mr. Dangerfield. He was through being a fool, he said; he was ready now to look for a real job and would appreciate whatever Mr. Dangerfield could do.

67 "You all right, son?" There was impatience in Loeffler's voice, and the puffs of pipe smoke were coming fast.

68 He tried to think. *What brought me here? I was about to flip, frankly. Pretty soon they'd have had to take me away in a net.*

69 "I'm here," he said carefully, "because I've made a mess of my life, and I need a fresh start. I admit that."

70 "Let me give you some advice," Loeffler said. "Never crawl. Nobody likes a crawler."

71 Arthur made himself look at the tip of his right shoe, and keep looking at it.

72 "I'll give it to you straight. When your father-in-law and I had lunch the other day, he said he wasn't sure you'd be any use to me at all. But he asked me anyhow, as an old friend, to take you on here."

73 "It was just your lucky day, I guess."

74 Loeffler drummed his fingers on the white-marble desk. "It might interest you to know," he said slowly, "that when Tyler Dangerfield talked to me about you and Grace, he cried. I've known that man for forty years, but I've never seen him do that before. Does that mean anything to you? Or do you want to be funny again?"

75 "I'm sorry," Arthur said. "I really am."

76 "All right. Now let me give you a picture of just what this company does. The basis of our . . ."

77 He felt slightly numb; it seemed impossible, ludicrous, that Mr. Dangerfield should have cried. Loeffler went on talking about the real-estate business, and he realized suddenly that very possibly Loeffler *was* going to offer him a job. He tried to listen, but the unfamiliar phrases—site appraisal, cooperative financing, lease-backs, syndication—muddled confusingly in his mind.

78 The intercom said, "Mr. Farnum is here, Mr. Loeffler. In Mr. Hale's office."

79 "On my way," Loeffler said into the box, and stood up. At the door he turned. "Back in ten minutes. If you're sure that you really want to buckle down, we'll find something for you to do."

80 The numbness was still there, but after a moment Arthur got up and began to wander aimlessly about the room. There was a little brass model of a skyscraper on a shelf in the corner; he examined that, and

then the pipe Loeffler had left on the desk. Dunhill, not Abercrombie & Fitch. He went to the window, from which he could see down Fifth Avenue all the way to Forty-second Street, and up as far as the tangle of traffic before the Plaza Hotel. *We'll find something for you to do. . . .* I could empty ashtrays, he thought, and maybe polish the little skyscraper every day. The absurdity of it made him smile. The cars darted about in front of the Plaza, and he wondered why everybody didn't bump into everybody else. Turning from the window, he noticed a smudge on his hand and guessed that it had come from picking up Loeffler's pipe. He wiped it away, thinking about Mr. Dangerfield and Loeffler having lunch together, arranging Grace's life and his. It was no use talking to people like them, no use at all.

81 A siren wailed suddenly in the street below, and the room seemed very quiet when the wailing died.

82 He took all the pipes out of the rack and snapped the stems, one after another. They each broke the same way; the little shaft on the end of the stem would break off and remain stuck in the bowl part with a few jagged points protruding. When he was through, he laid the stems out on the white-marble desk, and the bowls in another row above them. Then he left the office and walked down the corridor and through the reception room to the elevators.

83 There were four elevators, but none stopped and the wait seemed very long. He began to feel sorry for Loeffler, who probably had wanted to help somehow, and then he felt a rush of pity for Mr. Dangerfield, weeping in a restaurant out of concern for Grace. But it was Grace, he thought suddenly, that he should be worrying about now. She would be frightened when they told her. . . .

84 An elevator arrived. Riding down, he decided that it would be better if he told her himself about what had happened this afternoon. He would begin by putting his arms around her and saying, "I love you" and "I need you," not sounding the words, but shaping them so that she could read them on his lips. It might not help much, but it was all he could think of now to do. □

Unity from Symbol

In prose, symbols serve much the same purpose as they do in poetry. Concrete details are comprehensible to a reader, while abstractions must remain forever vague. In the third chapter of Steinbeck's *The Grapes of Wrath* (pp. 86–89), you examined the description of a land turtle going toward its nameless destination. Perhaps it had no specific geographical point in mind; it was, however, intent on going in a definite direction.

As a symbol, the turtle embodied determination, single-mindedness, purposefulness. The highway, the truck, the plants which impeded the turtle's progress—all symbolized obstacles of one kind or another. And, in context, the turtle symbolized the Okies, specifically the Joads who set out for no definite location, just a promised land in the large state of California. As Steinbeck's turtle would not be stopped by obstacles, either natural or man-made, the Joads would not be stopped. The turtle transported life and planted it in passing; so did the Joads. As an object in nature, the turtle is relatively uninteresting and of little consequence to the reader. As a symbol embodying many abstract qualities, it becomes very interesting and assumes consequence. Steinbeck's attention to small detail creates a concrete picture with which the reader can be comfortable as he makes analogies and realizes "This means . . ." And thus he manages a personal application.

In the two stories which follow, examine symbolism as an element creating unity. Notice the way it allows you to establish characters as their reaction to the symbol creates a response in you. Notice also how the theme is woven around the symbol, eventually to become obvious as the symbol is explored more fully. Since you have already seen a turtle used symbolically by Steinbeck, these stories will allow you to compare and contrast the use of symbols.

Read "The Terrapin" first in its entirety. Then reread it and try to answer the questions. On your second reading, and before you answer the questions, complete the following statements on a piece of paper. Then, after you have answered the questions, see if you agree with your completion statements. In this way, you can check your analytical abilities:

a. The terrapin symbolizes ________________________________.

b. The theme of "The Terrapin" is ____________________________.

(Note: a word or phrase will not convey theme. For instance, "love" or "hate" is not a theme; "man's ability to survive" is not a theme. A complete sentence is required. "The path of true love is stony, but each stubbed toe is a painful delight" is a statement of theme. "Man needs comfort beyond physical housing and emotional understanding because his soul is a part of his being" is a statement of theme.)

The Terrapin

by Patricia Highsmith

1 Victor heard the elevator door open, his mother's quick footsteps in the hall, and he flipped his book shut. He shoved it under the sofa pillow, and winced as

he heard it slip between sofa and wall and fall to the floor with a thud. Her key was in the lock.

1. Paragraph 1 plunges the reader into the story immediately. How does the author immediately make you like Victor? How does she make you dislike Victor's mother? Examine the verbs in the sentences. What effect is achieved by using seven strong active voice verbs and a final verb-of-being?

2"Hello, Veector-r!" she cried, raising one arm in the air. Her other arm circled a big brown-paper bag, her hand held a cluster of little bags. "I have been to my publisher and to the market and also to the fish market," she told him. "Why aren't you out playing? It's a lovely, lovely day!"

2. The mother's dictatorial character is sharply drawn in sentence 1 of paragraph 2. What associations does the author force the reader to make by using the dialectical pronunciation of Victor's name ("Veector-r"), naming the child Victor in the first place, and showing the mother's arm raised in salute?

3"I was out," he said. "For a little while. I got cold."

4"Ugh!" She was unloading the grocery bag in the tiny kitchen off the foyer. "You are seeck, you know that? In the month of October, you are cold? I see all kinds of children playing on the sidewalk. Even I think that boy you like. What's his name?"

5"I don't know," Victor said.

3. How does the mother's insensitivity communicate itself to the reader in paragraphs 2–4? Explain the effect of Victor's "I don't know."

6His mother wasn't really listening, anyway. He pushed his hands into the pockets of his too-small shorts, making them tighter than ever, and walked aimlessly around the living room, looking down at his heavy, scuffed shoes. At least, his mother had to buy him shoes that fit him, and he rather liked these shoes, because they had the thickest soles of any he had ever owned, and they had heavy toes that rose up a little, like mountain climbers' shoes.

7Victor paused at the window and looked straight out at a toast-colored apartment building across Third Avenue. He and his mother lived on the eighteenth floor, just below the top floor where the penthouses were. The building across the street was even taller than this one. Victor had liked their Riverside Drive apartment better. He had liked the school he had gone to there better. Here they laughed at his clothes. In the other school they had got tired of laughing at them.

4. Is Victor's stream-of-consciousness effective in paragraphs 6 and 7? How much is indicated about him? About his mother?

8 "You don't want to go out?" asked his mother, coming into the living room, wiping her hands briskly on a wadded paper bag. She sniffed her palms. "Ugh! That stee-enk!"

5. What does "Ugh!" in paragraphs 4 and 8 foreshadow?

9 "No, Mama," Victor said patiently.

10 "Today is Saturday."

11 "I know."

12 "Can you say the days of the week?"

13 "Of course."

14 "Say them."

15 "I don't want to say them. I know them." His eyes began to sting around the edges with tears. "I've known them for years. Years and years. Kids five years old can say the days of the week."

6. Examine the dialog in paragraphs 8–15. What does it reveal about the two characters?

16 But his mother was not listening. She was bending over the drawing table in the corner of the room. She had worked late on something last night. On his sofa bed in the opposite corner of the room, Victor had not been able to sleep until two in the morning, when his mother had finally gone to bed on the studio couch.

7. In paragraphs 6 and 16, Victor's mother is "not listening." Since the story is told from Victor's point of view, what does this repetition indicate?

17 "Come here, Victor. Did you see this?"

18 Victor came on dragging feet, hands still in his pockets. No, he hadn't even glanced at her drawing board this morning, hadn't wanted to.

19 "This is Pedro, the Little Donkey. I invented him last night. What do you think? And this is Miguel, the little Mexican boy who rides him. They ride and ride over all of Mexico, and Miguel thinks they are lost, but Pedro knows the way home all the time, and . . ."

20 Victor did not listen. He deliberately shut his ears in a way he had learned to do from many years of practice; but boredom, frustration—he knew the word frustration, had read all about it—clamped his shoulders, weighed like a stone in his body, pressed hatred and tears up to his eyes as if a volcano were seething in him.

8. How does "Victor did not listen" (paragraph 20) become effective? Does Victor realize the implication?
9. Examine the poetic devices in paragraph 20. How are they effective?

21 He had hoped his mother might take a hint from his saying he was too cold in his silly shorts. He had hoped his mother might remember what he had told her—that the fellow he had wanted to get acquainted with downstairs, a fellow who looked about his own age, eleven, had laughed at his short pants on Monday afternoon. *They make you wear your kid brother's pants or something?* Victor had drifted away, mortified. What if the fellow knew he didn't even own any longer pants, not even a pair of knickers, much less *long* pants or even blue jeans!

22 His mother, for some cockeyed reason, wanted him to look "French," and made him wear shorts and stockings that came up to just below his knees, and dopey shirts with round collars. His mother wanted him to stay about six years old, forever, all his life.

23 She liked to test out her drawings on him. *Victor is my sounding board,* she sometimes said to her friends. *I show my drawings to Victor and I know if children will like them.* Often Victor said he liked stories that he did not like, or drawings that he was indifferent to, because he felt sorry for his mother and because it put her in a better mood if he said he liked them. He was quite tired now of children's book illustrations, if he had ever in his life liked them—he really couldn't remember; and now he had only two favorites—Howard Pyle's illustrations in some of Robert Louis Stevenson's books and Cruikshank's in Dickens.

24 It was too bad, Victor thought, that he was absolutely the last person his mother should have asked an opinion of, because he simply *hated* children's illustrations. And it was a wonder his mother didn't see this, because she hadn't sold any illustrations for books for years and years—not since *Wimple-Dimple,* a book whose jacket was all torn and turning yellow now from age, which sat in the center of the bookshelf in a little cleared spot, propped up against the back of the bookcase so that everyone could see it.

25 Victor had been seven years old when that book was printed. His mother liked to tell people—and remind him, too—that he had watched her make every drawing, had shown his opinion by laughing or not, and that she had been absolutely guided by him. Victor doubted this very much, because first of all the story was somebody else's and had been written before his mother did the drawings, and her drawings had had to follow the story closely.

26 Since *Wimple-Dimple,* his mother had done only a few illustrations now and then for children's magazines—how to make paper pumpkins and black paper cats for Halloween and things like that—though she took her portfolio around to publishers all the time.

27 Their income came from his father, who was a wealthy businessman in France,

an exporter of perfumes. His mother said he was very wealthy and very handsome. But he had married again, and he never wrote, and Victor had no interest in him, didn't even care if he never saw a picture of him, and he never had. His father was French with some Polish, his mother said, and she was Hungarian with some French. The word Hungarian made Victor think of gypsies, but when he had asked his mother once, she had said emphatically that she hadn't any gypsy blood, and she had been annoyed that Victor had brought the question up.

28 And now she was sounding him out again, poking him in the ribs to make him wake up, as she repeated, "Listen to me! Which do you like better, Victor? 'In all Mexico there was no bur-r-ro as wise as Miguel's Pedro,' or 'Miguel's Pedro was the wisest bur-r-ro in all Mexico'?"

10. In paragraph 22, Victor feels "His mother wanted him to stay about six years old, forever, all his life." What is the purpose of this observation? Paragraphs 21–27 combine stream-of-consciousness, panoramic flashback, and Victor's ambivalent idiom, tying them all together in a scene which becomes explosive in paragraph 28. Examine the paragraphs carefully to see the many techniques at work. Consider Victor's attitude toward his clothes. Why is "silly shorts" revealing? How is flashback dialog worked in so that the narrative flow of the scene is not disturbed? How are the words *cockeyed* and *dopey* revealing as Victor describes his Little Lord Fauntleroy costume with the Peter Pan collar? Why doesn't Victor himself allude to these literary characters? Do you feel he is unaware of them? Why is Victor's national background important? Does he suspect he has gypsy blood? Why does he think of Pyle and Cruikshank in relation to his mother?

29 "I think—I like it the first way better."

30 "Which way is that?" demanded his mother, thumping her palm down on the illustration.

31 Victor tried to remember the wording, but realized he was only staring at the pencil smudges, the thumbprints on the edges of his mother's illustration board. The colored drawing in its center did not interest him at all. He was not thinking. This was a frequent, familiar sensation to him now; there was something exciting and important about not-thinking, Victor felt, and he thought that one day he would find out something about it—perhaps under another name—in the Public Library or in the psychology books around the house that he browsed in when his mother was out.

11. What does paragraph 31 reveal? How does it give extra meaning to the following paragraphs?

32 "Veec-tor! What are you doing?"

33 "Nothing, Mama."

34 "That is exactly it! Nothing! Can you not even *think?*"

35 A warm shame spread through him. It was as if his mother read his thoughts about not-thinking. "I am thinking," he protested. "I'm thinking about *not*-thinking." His tone was defiant. What could she do about it, after all?

36 "About what?" Her black, curly head tilted, her mascaraed eyes narrowed at him.

37 "Not-thinking."

38 His mother put her jeweled hands on her hips. "Do you know, Victor, you are a leetle bit strange in the head?" She nodded. "You are seeck. Psychologically seeck. And retarded, do you know that? You have the behavior of a leetle boy five years old," she said slowly and weightily. "It is just as well you spend your Saturdays indoors. Who knows if you would not walk in front of a car, eh? But that is why I love you, little Victor."

39 She put her arm around his shoulders, pulled him against her, and for an instant Victor's nose pressed into her large, soft bosom. She was wearing her flesh-colored knitted dress, the one you could see through a little where her breast stretched it out.

12. What is the effect of Victor's description, "black curly head tilted, her mascaraed eyes narrowed"? Does the description refer to anything before it? Now associate "jeweled hands" in paragraph 38. What is Victor thinking? Why does he not tell the reader?
13. What do paragraphs 38–39 reveal about Victor's mother? Is she psychologically well? Is Victor "psychologically seeck," as she suggests? The subtleties here are deceiving.

40 Victor jerked his head away in a confusion of emotions. He did not know if he wanted to laugh or cry.

41 His mother was laughing gaily, her head back. "Seeck you are! Look at you! My lee-tle boy still, lee-tle short pants—ha! ha!"

42 Now the tears showed in his eyes, and his mother acted as if she were enjoying it! Victor turned his head away so that she would not see his eyes. Then suddenly he faced her. "Do you think I *like* these pants? *You* like them, not me, so why do you have to make fun of them?"

43 "A lee-tle boy who's crying!" she went on, laughing.

14. In light of paragraphs 27 and 39, explain paragraph 40.
15. How is Victor's ambivalence suddenly apparent in his mother's ambivalence?

44 Victor made a dash for the bathroom, then swerved away and dove onto the sofa, his face toward the pillows. He shut his eyes tight and opened his mouth, crying but not-crying in a way he had also learned through long practice. With his mouth open, his throat tight, not breathing for nearly a minute, he could somehow get the satisfaction of crying, screaming even, without anybody knowing it.

16. Paragraph 44 is a clever bit of turtle imitation. Turtles open their mouths and cry out, but the sound is not heard by human ears. Why is this description used before the reader is told a turtle is in the house? This is the third time its presence has been suggested. Why?

45 He pushed his nose, his open mouth, his teeth, against the tomato-red sofa pillow, and though his mother's voice went on in a lazily mocking tone, and her laughter went on, he imagined that it was getting fainter and more distant from him.

17. Paragraph 45 contains a suggestion of violence in the "tomato-red" pillow. Why?

46 He imagined, rigid in every muscle, that he was suffering the absolute worst that any human being could suffer. He imagined that he was dying. But he did not think of death as an escape, only as a concentrated and painful instant. This was the climax of his not-crying.

18. Paragraph 46 is a typical child's thinking. Has Victor been typical to this point? Why is this paragraph inserted?

47 Then he breathed again, and his mother's voice intruded: "Did you hear me? *Did you hear me?* Mrs. Badzerkian is coming over for tea. I want you to wash your face and put on a clean shirt. I want you to recite something for her. Now what are you going to recite?"

48 "'In winter when I go to bed,'" said Victor. She was making him memorize every poem in *A Child's Garden of Verses.* He had said the first one that came in his head, and now there was an argument, because he had recited that the last time Mrs. Badzerkian came to tea. "I said it because I couldn't think of any other one right off the bat!" Victor shouted.

19. What is the real reason for Victor's thinking of "In Winter When I Go to Bed" in paragraph 48?

[49]"Don't yell at me!" his mother cried, storming across the room at him.

[50]She slapped his face before he knew what was happening.

[51]He was up on one elbow on the sofa, on his back, his long, knobby-kneed legs splayed out in front of him. All right, he thought, if that's the way it is, that's the way it is. He looked at her with loathing.

[52]He would not show her that the slap had hurt, that it still stung. No more tears for today, he swore, not even any more not-crying. He would finish the day, go through the tea, like a stone, like a soldier, not wincing.

[53]His mother paced the room, turning one of her rings round and round, glancing at him from time to time, looking quickly away from him. But his eyes were steady on her. He was not afraid. She could even slap him again and he wouldn't move.

[54]At last she announced that she was going to wash her hair, and she went into the bathroom.

20. Explain paragraphs 49–54.

[55]Victor got up from the sofa and wandered across the room. He wished he had a room of his own to go to. In the apartment on Riverside Drive there had been two rooms, a living room and his mother's bedroom. When she was in the living room, he had been able to go into the bedroom, and vice versa, but here— They were going to tear down the old building they had lived in on Riverside Drive. It was not a pleasant thing for Victor to think about.

21. Why is the smallness of the apartment so important?

[56]Suddenly remembering the book that had fallen, he pulled out the sofa and reached for it. It was Menninger's *The Human Mind,* full of fascinating case histories of people. Victor put it back in its place on the bookshelf between a book on astrology and *How to Draw.*

22. What is the symbolic significance of the three book titles in paragraph 56? Is there a significance in the way Victor arranges them on the shelf?

[57]His mother did not like him to read psychology books, but Victor loved them, especially ones with case histories in them. The people in the case histories did what they wanted to do. They were natural. Nobody bossed them. At the local branch library he spent hours browsing through the psychology shelves. They were in the adults' section, but the librarian did not mind him sitting at the tables there, because he was always so quiet.

23. Explain "They were natural" in paragraph 57.

58 Victor went into the kitchen and got a glass of water. As he was standing there drinking it, he heard a scratching noise coming from the paper bags on the counter. A mouse, he thought, but when he moved a couple of the bags he didn't see any mouse. The scratching was coming from inside one of the bags.

59 Gingerly, he opened the bag's end with his fingers and waited for something to jump out. Looking in, he saw a white paper carton. He pulled it out slowly. Its bottom was damp. It opened like a pastry box. Victor jumped in surprise. In the box was a turtle—a live turtle!

24. Why is the turtle not introduced until paragraph 59, one-third of the way through the story?

60 It was wriggling its legs in the air, trying to turn over. Victor moistened his lips, and frowning with concentration, took the turtle by its sides with both hands, turned him over, and let him down gently into the box again. The turtle drew its feet in then and its head stretched up a little and it looked right at him.

25. Comment on the turtle's imprisonment in the box, Victor's turning it right-side-up, its looking at him in paragraph 60.

61 Victor smiled. Why hadn't his mother told him she'd brought him a present? A live turtle! Victor's eyes glazed with anticipation as he thought of taking the turtle down, maybe with a leash around its neck, to show the fellow who'd laughed at his short pants. The boy might change his mind about being friends with him, if he learned that Victor owned a live turtle.

62 "Hey, Mama! Mama!" Victor yelled at the bathroom door. "You brought me a turtle?"

63 "A what?" The water shut off.

64 "A turtle! In the kitchen!" Victor had been jumping up and down in the hall. He stopped.

65 His mother had hesitated, too. The water came on again, and she said in a shrill tone, *"C'est une terrapène! Pour un ragout!"*

66 Victor understood, and a small chill went over him because his mother had spoken in French. His mother addressed him in French only when she was giving an order that had to be obeyed, or when she anticipated resistance from him.

26. Why is the use of French, rather than English, effective in paragraph 65? What does it mean to Victor? What does this tell the reader about him? Does Victor understand more or less of the story than the reader does?
27. Comment on Victor's explanation of his mother's French.

67 So the terrapin was for a stew. Victor nodded to himself with a stunned resignation, and went back to the kitchen. For a stew. Well, the terrapin was not

long for this world, as they say. What did a terrapin like to eat? Lettuce? Raw bacon? Boiled potato? Victor peered in the refrigerator.

68 He held a piece of lettuce near the terrapin's horny mouth. The terrapin did not open its mouth, but it looked at him. Victor held it near the two little dots of its nostrils, but if the terrapin smelled the lettuce, it showed no interest. Victor looked under the sink and pulled out a round wash pan. He put two inches of water into it. Then he gently dumped the terrapin into the pan. The terrapin paddled for a few seconds, as if it had to swim; then finding that its stomach sat on the bottom of the pan, it stopped, and drew its feet in.

69 Victor got down on his knees and studied the terrapin's face. Its upper lip overhung the lower, giving it a rather stubborn and unfriendly expression; but its eyes—they were bright and shining. Victor smiled when he looked hard at them.

28. Paragraphs 67–69 and Steinbeck's description of a turtle (pp. 86–89) have much in common. Compare them.

70 "Okay, *Monsieur terrapène,*" he said, "just tell me what you'd like to eat and we'll get it for you. Maybe some tuna?"

29. What is the significance of Victor's addressing the turtle in French?

71 They had had tuna fish salad yesterday for dinner, and there was a small bowl of it left over. Victor got a little chunk of it in his fingers and offered it to the terrapin. The terrapin was not interested.

72 Victor looked around the kitchen, wondering; then seeing the sunlight on the floor of the living room, he picked up the pan and carried it to the living room and set it down so that the sunlight would fall on the terrapin's back. All turtles liked sunlight, Victor thought. He lay down on the floor on his side, propped up on an elbow.

30. Is Victor's act of placing the turtle in sunlight understood by him? What is its significance?

73 The terrapin stared at him for a moment, then very slowly and with an air of forethought and caution, put out its legs and advanced, found the circular boundary of the pan, and moved to the right, half its body out of the shallow water.

74 Obviously it wanted to get out, so Victor took it in one hand, by the sides, and said, "You can come out and have a little walk."

75 He smiled as the terrapin started to disappear under the sofa. He caught it easily, because it moved so slowly. When he put it down on the carpet, it was quite still, as if it had withdrawn a little to think what it should do next, where it should go.

31. Paragraph 75 is revealing. Are the turtle's thoughts reported by Victor? What association is Victor making?

[76]The terrapin was brownish green. Looking at it, Victor thought of river bottoms, of river water flowing. Or maybe oceans. Where did terrapins come from? He jumped up and went to the dictionary on the bookshelf. The dictionary had a picture of a terrapin, but it was a dull, black and white drawing, not so pretty as the live one. He learned nothing except that the name was of Algonquian origin, that the terrapin lived in fresh or brackish water, and that it was edible.

[77]Edible. Well, that was bad luck, Victor thought. But he was not going to eat any *terrapène* tonight. It would be all for his mother, that ragout, and even if she slapped him, scolded him, and made him learn an extra two or three poems, he would *not* eat any terrapin tonight.

[78]His mother came out of the bathroom. "What are you doing there?—Victor?"

[79]Victor put the dictionary back on the shelf. His mother had seen the pan. "I'm looking at the terrapin," he said, then realized the terrapin had disappeared. He got down on hands and knees and looked under the sofa.

[80]"Don't put it on the furniture. It makes spots," said his mother. She was standing in the foyer, rubbing her hair vigorously with a towel.

[81]Victor found the terrapin between the wastebasket and the wall. He put it back in the pan.

32. Paragraphs 76–81 indicate a great deal about Victor and his mother. Explain. Why does Victor think *terrapène* at the beginning of paragraph 77, *terrapin* at the end?

[82]"Have you changed your shirt?" asked his mother.

[83]Victor changed his shirt, and then at his mother's order sat down on the sofa with *A Child's Garden of Verses* and tackled another poem, a brand-new one for Mrs. Badzerkian. He learned two lines at a time, reading it aloud in a soft voice to himself, then repeating it, then putting two, four, and six lines together, until he had memorized the whole poem. He recited it to the terrapin. Then Victor asked his mother if he could play with the terrapin in the bathtub.

33. Why did Victor recite the poetry "to the terrapin"?

[84]"No! And get your shirt all splashed?"

[85]"I can put on my other shirt."

[86]"No! It's nearly four o'clock now. Get that pan out of the living room!"

[87]Victor carried the pan back to the kitchen. His mother took the terrapin quite fearlessly out of the pan, put it back into the white paper box, closed its lid, and stuck the box in the refrigerator.

[88]Victor jumped a little as the refrigerator door slammed. It would be awfully

cold in there for the terrapin. But then, he supposed, fresh or brackish water was cold too.

[89]"Victor, cut the lemon," said his mother. She was fixing the big round tray with cups and saucers. The water was boiling in the kettle.

[90]Mrs. Badzerkian was prompt as usual, and his mother poured the tea as soon as her guest had deposited her coat and pocketbook on the foyer chair and sat down. Mrs. Badzerkian smelled of cloves. She had a small, straight mouth and a thin mustache on her upper lip which fascinated Victor, as he had never seen one on a woman before—not at such short range, anyway. He never had mentioned Mrs. Badzerkian's mustache to his mother, knowing it was considered ugly; but in a strange way, her mustache was the thing he liked best about Mrs. Badzerkian.

34. Explain Mrs. Badzerkian's name (pronounced "badgerkun"). Why didn't the author make it Smith or Jones? Explain Victor's liking her mustache.

[91]The rest of her was dull, uninteresting, and vaguely unfriendly. She always pretended to listen carefully to his poetry recitations, but he felt that she fidgeted, thought of other things while he recited, and was glad when it was over. Today, Victor recited very well and without any hesitation, standing in the middle of the living-room floor and facing the two women, who were having their second cup of tea.

[92]"*Très bien,*" said his mother. "Now you may have a cookie."

[93]Victor chose from the plate a small round cookie with a drop of orange goo in its center. He kept his knees close together when he sat down. He always felt that Mrs. Badzerkian looked at his knees, and with distaste. He often wished she would make some remark to his mother about his being old enough for long pants, but she never had—at least, not within his hearing.

[94]Victor learned from his mother's conversation with Mrs. Badzerkian that the Lorentzes were coming for dinner tomorrow evening. It was probably for them that the terrapin stew was going to be made. Victor was glad that he would have one more day to play with the terrapin. Tomorrow morning, he thought, he would ask his mother if he could take the terrapin down on the sidewalk for a while, either on a leash or, if his mother insisted, in the paper box.

[95]"—like a chi-ild!" his mother was saying, laughing, with a glance at him, and Mrs. Badzerkian smiled shrewdly at him with her small, tight mouth.

35. Explain "Mrs. Badzerkian smiled shrewdly at him with her small, tight mouth."

[96]Victor had been excused, and was sitting across the room with a book on the studio couch. His mother was telling Mrs. Badzerkian how he had played with the

terrapin. Victor frowned down at his book, pretending not to hear. His mother did not like him to speak to her or her guests once he had been excused. But now she was calling him her "lee-tle ba-aby Veector . . ."

97 He stood up with his finger in the place in his book. "I don't see why it's childish to look at the terrapin!" he said, flushing with sudden anger. "They are very interesting animals. They—"

98 His mother interrupted him with a laugh, but at once the laugh disappeared and she said sternly, "Victor, I thought I had excused you. Isn't that correct?"

99 He hesitated, seeing in a flash the scene that was going to take place when Mrs. Badzerkian had left. "Yes, Mama. I'm sorry," he said. Then he sat down and bent over his book again.

36. Explain the scene in paragraphs 96–99.

100 Twenty minutes later Mrs. Badzerkian left. His mother scolded him for being rude, but it was not a five or ten minute scolding of the kind he had expected. It lasted barely two minutes. She had forgotten to buy heavy cream, and she wanted Victor to go downstairs and get some.

101 Victor put on his gray woolen jacket and went out. He always felt embarrassed and conspicuous in the jacket, because it came just a little bit below his short pants, and it looked as if he had nothing on underneath the coat.

102 Victor looked around for Frank on the sidewalk, but he didn't see him. He crossed Third Avenue and went to a delicatessen in the big building that he could see from the living-room window. On his way back, he saw Frank walking along the sidewalk, bouncing a ball. Victor went right up to him.

37. Explain Victor's knowing Frank's name in paragraph 102 when he had not known it earlier. He has been nowhere to learn it. Is this a flaw in the story? Careful, the answer is not simple. (There is a *logical* answer.)

103 "Hey," Victor said. "I've got a terrapin upstairs."

104 "A what?" Frank caught the ball and stopped.

105 "A terrapin. You know, like a turtle. I'll bring it down tomorrow morning and show you, if you're around. It's pretty big."

106 "Yeah? Why don't you bring it down now?"

107 "Because we're gonna eat now," said Victor. "See you."

108 He went into his building. He felt he had achieved something. Frank had looked really interested. Victor wished he could bring the terrapin down now, but his mother never liked him to go out after dark, and it was practically dark now.

109 When Victor got upstairs, his mother was still in the kitchen. Eggs were boiling and she had put a big pot of water on a back burner. "You took it out again!" Victor said, seeing the terrapin's box on the counter.

110"Yes. I prepare the stew tonight," said his mother. "That is why I need the cream."

111Victor looked at her. "You're going to—you have to kill it tonight?"

112"Yes, my little one. Tonight." She jiggled the pot of eggs.

113"Mama, can I take it downstairs to show Frank?" Victor asked quickly. "Just for five minutes, Mama. Frank's down there now."

114"Who is Frank?"

115"He's that fellow you asked me about today. The blond fellow we always see. *Please,* Mama."

116His mother's black eyebrows frowned. "Take the *terrapène* downstairs? Certainly not. Don't be absurd, my baby! The *terrapène* is not a toy!"

117Victor tried to think of some other lever of persuasion. He had not removed his coat. "You wanted me to get acquainted with Frank—"

118"Yes. What has that got to do with the *terrapène?*"

119The water on the back burner began to boil.

120"You see, I promised him I'd—" Victor watched his mother lift the terrapin from the box, and as she dropped it into the boiling water his mouth fell open. *"Mama!"*

121"What is this? What is this noise?"

122Victor, open-mouthed, stared at the terrapin whose legs were now racing against the steep sides of the pot. The terrapin's mouth opened, its eyes looked right at Victor for an instant, its head arched back in torture, then the open mouth sank beneath the seething water—and that was the end.

38. Explain "Don't be absurd, my baby! The *terrapène* is not a toy!" (paragraph 116) in relation to "his mouth fell open" (paragraph 120), "Victor, open mouthed," "the terrapin's mouth opened," and "then the open mouth sank" (all in paragraph 122).
39. Comment on "seething water" in paragraph 122; "and that was the end" refers to what different things?

123Victor blinked. The terrapin was dead. He came closer, saw the four legs and the tail stretched out in the water. He looked at his mother.

124She was drying her hands on a towel. She glanced at him, then said, "Ugh!" She smelled her hands, then hung the towel back.

40. What is the effect of "Ugh!" in paragraph 124? Associate it with its two earlier uses.

125"Did you have to kill it like that?"

126"How else? The same way you kill a lobster. Don't you know that? It doesn't hurt them."

[127]He stared at her. When she started to touch him, he stepped back. He thought of the terrapin's wide open mouth, and his eyes suddenly flooded with tears. Maybe the terrapin had been screaming and it hadn't been heard over the bubbling of the water. The terrapin had looked at him, wanting him to pull it out, and he hadn't moved to help it. His mother had tricked him, acted so fast that he couldn't save it. He stepped back again. "No, don't touch me!"

[128]His mother slapped his face, hard and quickly.

[129]Victor set his jaw. Then he about-faced and went to the closet and threw his jacket onto a hanger and hung it up. He went into the living room and fell down on the sofa. He was not crying now, but his mouth opened against the sofa pillow. Then he remembered the terrapin's mouth and he closed his lips. The terrapin had suffered, otherwise it would not have moved its legs so terribly fast to get out.

41. Comment on paragraphs 127–129.

[130]Then Victor wept, soundlessly as the terrapin, his mouth open. He put both hands over his face, so as not to wet the sofa. After a long while he got up.

42. Is there a connection between paragraphs 130 and 80? Explain.

[131]In the kitchen his mother was humming, and every few seconds he heard her quick, firm steps as she went about her work. Victor had set his teeth again. He walked slowly to the kitchen doorway.

43. Is there a connection between paragraphs 131 and 1? Explain.

[132]The terrapin was out on the wooden chopping board, and his mother, after a glance at him, still humming, took a knife and bore down on the blade, cutting off the terrapin's little nails. Victor half closed his eyes, but he watched steadily. His mother scooped the nails, with bits of skin attached to them, off the board into her palm and dumped them into the garbage bag.

[133]Then she turned the terrapin on its back and with the same sharp, pointed knife she began to cut away the pale bottom shell. The terrapin's neck was bent sideways. Victor wanted to look away, but still he stared. Now the terrapin's insides were all exposed, red and white and greenish.

[134]Victor did not listen to what his mother was saying—something about cooking terrapins in Europe before he was born. Her voice was gentle and soothing, not at all like what she was doing.

[135]"All right, don't look at me like that!" she cried out suddenly, stomping her foot. "What's the matter with you? Are you crazy? Yes, I think so! You are seeck, you know that?"

44. Explain the mother's behavior in paragraph 135.

136 Victor could not touch any of his supper, and his mother could not force him to, even though she shook him by the shoulders and threatened to slap him. They had creamed chipped beef on toast. Victor did not say a word. He felt very remote from his mother, even when she screamed right into his face. He felt very odd, the way he did sometimes when he was sick to his stomach, but he was not sick to his stomach.

45. What is the significance of "even when she screamed right into his face" (paragraph 136)? There is an answer that is more important than the obvious surface one.

137 When they went to bed that night, he felt afraid of the dark. He saw the terrapin's face very large, its mouth open, its eyes wide and full of pain. Victor wished he could walk out the window and float, go anywhere he wanted to, disappear, yet be everywhere. He imagined his mother's hands on his shoulders, jerking him back, if he tried to step out the window. He hated his mother.

46. In paragraph 37, Victor puts into words, "He hated his mother." Technically, what structural feature of the story is this sentence?

138 He got up and went quietly into the kitchen. The kitchen was absolutely dark, as there was no window, but he put his hand accurately on the knife rack and felt gently for the knife he wanted. He thought of the terrapin, in little pieces now, all mixed up in the sauce of cream and egg yolks and sherry in the pot in the refrigerator.

47. In paragraph 138, what is the significance of "the knife he wanted"?

139 His mother's cry was not silent—it seemed to tear his ears off. His second blow was in her body, and then he stabbed her throat again.

48. Discuss "His mother's cry was not silent." How does the statement complete the carefully constructed concept of silence in the story?

140 Only tiredness made him stop, and by then people were trying to bump the door in. Victor at last walked to the door, pulled the chain bolt back, and opened it for them.

141 He was taken to a large, old building full of nurses and doctors. Victor was very quiet and did everything he was asked to do, and answered the questions they put to him, but only those questions; and since they didn't ask him anything about a terrapin, he did not bring it up. □

49. Comment on "Victor was very quiet" in the final paragraph.
50. Why is litotes employed in the last sentence? Is it effective?
51. The setting of "The Terrapin" is a small apartment where privacy is impossible and imprisonment seems constant. Why is such a setting used? What does it contribute to the tone of the story? How does it help in unifying the narrative? What does it reveal as Victor and his mother each react to it? How is it comparable to the box the turtle arrives in?
52. As names are frequently important, examine Victor's for its effect in the story. Is he ever a "victor?" Is it an ironic feature? Why would the author use irony in such a fashion?
53. Four characters enter this story. Two are main characters. Frank is a stock character employed as a foil. What does his presence contribute to the story? What is the function of Mrs. Badzerkian in the story?
54. Examine the elements of conflict. Is there only one? Are complications introduced into the story? By whom? For what purpose?

The next story, Paul Brodeur's "The Turtle," is set in the vastness of nature. Space is as important in it as the lack of space was in "The Terrapin." Three characters and a huge turtle move through the incidents which make up the story's plot. Lesser symbols than the turtle are also incorporated: frogs, a dog, nature itself. Descriptions of nature serve as a unifying agent, and character is developed in direct contrast to nature. You will notice the turtle's eyes in this story are "tiny, wicked eyes." How did Steinbeck describe them? How did Victor see them? Are the eyes of a turtle wicked or wise or anything but turtle eyes? Or does the description indicate the tone of the story?

As conflict is at the heart of any short story, examine it here. Is it man against nature? Is it man against man? Is it man against Self? Is it possible that conflict exists at more than one level? If so, are the various conflicts closely allied to present an overall effect of unity?

If you have read Herman Melville's *Moby-Dick,* you may draw a parallel between the whale and the turtle and between Captain Ahab and old Hiram. The point of view is similar in this story and in Melville's novel. Here, the boys provide the focus of point of view. In *Moby-Dick,* a young sailor does. How is such a point of view effective in telling a story? You will notice, actually, that it creates two stories which are parallel. In "The Turtle," one level of the story is concerned with the development of the boys' sense of morality. A second level is the battle of old Hiram with his particular version of Evil. Why is the second level more credible as a result of the first? As you read, decide whether one level is more important than the other.

The Turtle

by Paul Brodeur

[1]The two brothers were fascinated by the pond, for it was a place where nature staged spectacles that satisfied the most savage instincts of small boys. Swallows skimmed the pond, dappling the water like skipping stones as they picked tiny insects off the surface; kingbirds chased and caught giant butterflies that undertook desperate evasive maneuvers to escape; and a belted kingfisher plunged hour after hour from the dead limb of an oak tree to spear minnows that pickerel chased inshore. Black snakes glided through the weeds, seeking frogs and baby ducks; black bass jumped for crickets and grasshoppers that tumbled off the banks; and turtles big and small sunned themselves on logs at the water's edge, and watched everything through tiny, wicked eyes.

1. The opening paragraph is poetically vibrant. How is its elaborate effect achieved? Analyze it as completely as possible. It is worth intensive study.
2. How does the first paragraph establish setting, mood, tone, atmosphere, and theme?

[2]Hiram's Pond, it was called—probably after some early settler, their father had told them—though Peter, who was eleven, and David, who was nine, preferred to think it was after the old man who tended the pumping station there that supplied water for the town. It was a small pond, half a mile long and only a couple of hundred yards across at its widest point, and it lay at the bottom of a steep hill less than a five-minute bike ride from their family's summer cottage. There were shallow parts and very deep parts in Hiram's Pond. The shallow parts were coated with lily pads that grew in sargasso-like profusion, and the deep parts lay at the foot of steep embankments that surrounded two sides of the pond. At its northern end, the pond was fed by a sluggish stream that passed through a swamp studded with water-killed trees whose foreboding trunks looked like dead sentinels. Peter and David were afraid to explore the swamp because the old man who tended the pumping station said it was full of treacherous quicksand that could swallow a man in no time. They preferred the open stretches of the pond, which lay comfortably within their capacity for awe. Hour after hour, they poled the old man's skiff through fields of lily pads and across the deep, calm coves, fishing for bass with cane poles and bobbers, and using frogs for bait.

3. Point of view is thoroughly established by the end of the second paragraph. Explain the point of view, noticing the vocabulary. Could such words as *sargasso, profusion,* and *treacherous* be employed

if the story were told from the point of view of one of the boys? On whose authority is it told? *From* whose point of view is it told?

4. How do such words as *bike* and *bobbers* lend idiomatic verisimilitude to the story?

[3]Peter and David caught the frogs in a pool near the pumping station, where bullfrogs, leopard frogs, and pickerel frogs bred in great numbers. The bass in Hiram's Pond were large and fought hard; some of them weighed nearly five pounds, and even the smallest ones came after the frogs with frightening voracity. Occasionally, the frogs attracted turtles, which ruined the bass fishing, and when this happened the boys went to the pumping station to fetch the old man, who hated turtles because his dog, Jake, had lost part of a leg to one of them, and who welcomed any excuse to shoot at them with his rifle. Peter often found himself wondering what became of the frogs that he and David impaled on their hooks by the rear leg, for the frogs almost always came off the hooks and disappeared after the bass had struck at them. Then, one day in August, he noticed that many of the frogs in the pool carried healed scars on their legs. Peter was touched by the realization that the injured creatures had swum great distances back to their cove, and for several minutes he pondered what to do about it. Finally, he decided that it would be unfair to subject any of these brave frogs to double jeopardy, and that henceforth only unscarred frogs should be used for bait. David agreed, and the two brothers went at once to the pumping station to tell the old man of their decision.

5. The first two paragraphs establish the "survival of the fittest" pattern of nature, and the third introduces old Hiram and his gun. Does the author suggest the old man is anachronistic? If such is the case, are the boys a part of the natural setting, or are they too intruders, or are they in an in-between state? In answering, consider the double-jeopardy decision of the boys. Why did they go to tell the old man?

[4]The pumping station was a small brick building surrounded by evergreen trees and shrubs. It almost looked like somebody's house until you drew close and heard the racket and rumble of the machinery inside. The old man usually sat in a wooden chair just inside the doorway, dozing in spite of the terrible clatter, and, as always, Peter had to shout to waken him. When the old man woke up, he smiled at the boys and came outside. He was a very pale old man, with watery blue eyes and a gray stubble of beard. Now, blinking his eyes in the sunlight, he listened as Peter told him of the injured frogs that had swum back to their pool all summer long.

6. Paragraph 4 contrasts the racket and rumble of the machinery with the violent tranquility of paragraph 1. Why? The old man is a

creature of the dark. How does the author establish his preference for dimness? Why? Why has narrative panorama not narrowed focus to scene yet?

5 "Sure, and what's so strange about that?" he asked with a laugh. "If you fell and cut your leg, where would *you* go?"

7. Paragraphs 5–30 constitute the first scene. Is the dialog realistic? Why? Read it aloud without narrative binding of any kind. Is it still realistic? What does your reading suggest about the illusion of reality in dialog?

6 "Home," David replied quickly. "I'd run home and tell my mother to put a bandage on it."

7 "There you are," said the old man. "Just like a little frog."

8 "Maybe we shouldn't hurt those little frogs," David said.

9 "Then what'll you use for bass bait?"

10 "We'll use worms," David replied.

11 "Or crickets," Peter said.

12 The old man shook his head. "Big bass like frogs," he declared. "They like something they can sink their teeth into. Why, there's only one thing they like *better* than a frog."

13 "What's that?" Peter asked.

14 "A mouse."

15 "A mouse!" David exclaimed.

16 "Yes, sir," the old man said, nodding his head for emphasis. "Catch yourself a nice field mouse, and tie him to your hook with some thread. Then put him on a shingle, let him float out over one of those deep spots where the bass hide, and yank him off. Before that mouse has swum five feet for shore, I guarantee you'll see the biggest bass you ever saw." The old man made a long, curving sweep with his forearm to signify the upward rush of the biggest bass in Hiram's Pond.

8. What is your reaction to old Hiram's information in paragraphs 12–16? Is the old man being merely informative or has he an ulterior motive in his recital? What makes you answer as you do?

17 Peter and David laughed with delight as they imagined a big bass opening its jaws to swallow a helplessly trussed field mouse. But a moment later David shook his head and, frowning, announced that he would prefer to continue using frogs.

18 "Well, at least you don't have to feel sorry for them," the old man replied. "Frogs can hardly feel a thing."

19 "Are you sure?" David asked.

[20] "They're cold-blooded is why," the old man said. "Fish and frogs are cold-blooded creatures. They're not like us."

9. What does paragraph 20 tell you about Hiram's character?

[21] "How about turtles?" Peter asked.

[22] It was a sly question, because he knew the old man hated turtles. But the boys loved to hear the story of how Jake had lost part of his leg, and since the merest mention of turtles always evoked the story, they sat now on the grass beside the pumping station and waited for the old man to begin.

10. Explain "It was a sly question" in paragraph 22. Before you do, notice that you can take the words out of the paragraph without changing the story at all. Why, then, does the author insert the clause, making sure the reader will evaluate the question correctly? What is the denotation of *sly?* What is its connotation?

[23] As usual, the old man commenced by calling his dog out from the pumping station. Jake was an old dog—as old for a dog as the old man was old for a man—and he came limping into the sunlight, wagging his tail, and crouched at the feet of his master. The old man bent down and lifted the dog's rear leg to show the boys where it had been severed at the lowest joint. "Look at that," he said softly. "Just like a meat cleaver had done it." The old man straightened up and pointed to the cove in front of the pumping station, where his skiff was tied to shore. "It happened five years ago—right out there," he went on. "Old Jakey was pretty old even then, but he loved to chase sunfish from those nests they build in shallow water, and he used to be wading out there all the time. Then, one day, while I was sitting inside the station, I heard this God-awful howling. I ran outside, of course, but all I could see was some terrible splashing near the boat. When I got down there, I found poor old Jake trying to make the shore. At first I couldn't make out what had got hold of him. I even thought it might be a muskrat trap someone had left in the water. Then, down below the lily pads, I saw this awful monster of a snapping turtle." The old man said this in a hushed voice, and, bringing his fingers together over his head, made an immense circle with his arms. "This big he was and he had poor old Jakey's hind paw in his jaws. He was backing out toward the deep water, and old Jake was howling for me to come help him, and trying to keep his nose above the surface. Ah, boys, it was the most awful thing I ever saw."

11. Explain the similarities in Hiram's and Jake's ages. Is there a reason for Jake to have "crouched at the feet of his master"? Is this language deliberately chosen for its connotative value?

12. Discuss "this awful monster of a snapping turtle." The word *monster* is also used by Peter near the end of the story. Assess his use in relation to Hiram's.

24 "What'd you do?" David asked.

25 "What could I do?" the old man said. "I didn't have my twenty-two in those days, so all I could do was jump into the skiff, grab old Jake by the collar, and hold on for dear life. That turtle, boys—I swear to you—was so strong he was pulling Jake and me and the skiff out through the lily pads. In the end he bit clear through the dog's leg, and that was that. I put Jake into the pickup truck and drove him over to Doc Barnes's place, and he put a tourniquet around the dog's leg and saved his life. But nobody's ever seen old Jake anywhere near the water since then. No, sir, this dog hasn't been within fifty yards of the pond in the past five years."

26 "What d'you think happened to that turtle?" Peter asked.

27 "Why, nothing happened to him!" the old man exclaimed in rage. "Nothing happened to him except he ate my poor dog's paw. He's still out there, that turtle, lurking like a reptile. They're reptiles, did you know that? Yes, sir, a turtle is nothing more than a carnivorous reptile, and that one that caught hold of poor Jake must weigh thirty pounds. Why, if a turtle that size could latch on to the ankle of a little boy like your brother here, he might even be able to drag him under."

13. Explain "the old man exclaimed in rage" (paragraph 27). Then explain "lurking like a reptile" and "nothing more than a carnivorous reptile." What does this kind of emotional invective indicate? Would the old man understand the difference between denotation and connotation? Does he distinguish between them in practice? Why does he suggest the turtle "might even be able to drag [David] under"?

28 At this point, Peter laughed at David, who had begun to shiver; then he asked, "Could that turtle upset the skiff?"

29 The old man shook his head. "If I thought so, I wouldn't let you boys use it," he said. "But turtles are cowardly, you see. They're the most cowardly creatures I know of. They just lie in ambush like crocodiles, which are reptiles, too. Did I ever tell you boys that turtles are some of the oldest living creatures known to man? It's the honest truth. I read someplace that turtles are just as they were two hundred million years ago, when the earth was crawling with dinosaurs."

14. Explain the old man's further categorizing of turtles in paragraph 29.

30 The old man breathed heavily through his nose, and turned to glare at the pond. Then he shut his dog inside the pumping station, and brought out a rusty twenty-two-caliber rifle. "C'mon, boys," he said. "We've got to keep those turtles down or they'll ruin the fishing for you."

15. What image is created by "The old man breathed heavily through his nose, and turned to glare at the pond"? Why should the author wish to create this image? Is "or they'll ruin the fishing for you" a reason or an afterthought?

31 The old man led the way to his skiff, climbed inside, and positioned himself in the bow; David got in after him and sat in the center seat; and Peter, standing in the stern, pushed off from shore with an oar. For several minutes they glided through the lily pads, while the old man, who had hunched himself up in the prow, leaned the barrel of his rifle on a gunwale and studied the shoreline. Then the rifle barked, and the boys watched breathlessly as a small spotted turtle flopped off a log and disappeared beneath the surface. For the next half hour, they proceeded slowly along the shore, toward the southern end of the pond, and every so often the stillness was punctuated by the old man's rifle. Sometimes the bullets hit their mark, but more often than not the old man muttered in disappointment because they glanced harmlessly off the turtles' shells. "You've got to hit turtles in the head," he kept saying. "And when you see a really big turtle, you have to aim for his eye—just like when you're hunting crocodiles—or else the bullets don't do any harm than they would to armor plate."

16. Explain "just like when you're hunting crocodiles" in paragraph 31.

32 "Have you ever hunted for crocodiles?" David whispered.

33 "Nope, but I've read a lot about it," the old man replied.

17. Why would Hiram have read a lot about hunting for crocodiles?

34 "Why don't we ever see any really big turtles?" Peter asked.

35 "Because they're too smart to get caught out in the open," the old man said. "The only way to attract big turtles is to put out bait for them at night."

18. In paragraph 35, Hiram says turtles are "smart." Explain. Isn't this a compliment?

36 "Have you ever done that?"

37 "I tried it after old Jakey lost his paw, but I didn't have much luck," the old man said. "I've seen it done, though. Years ago, there used to be a fellow come

down here who hunted turtles for the market. Yes, sir, believe it or not, some people *eat* turtles. They make soup from them. This fellow used to catch snappers here in Hiram's Pond and sell them to a hotel man up in Boston, and he made pretty good money doing it. He once told me that a dozen good-sized snappers brought fifty dollars."

38 "Fifty dollars!" David said. "We could buy a boat for fifty dollars."

39 They had returned to the mooring, and now, as they climbed out of the skiff and started across the grass toward the pumping station, both boys were thinking of the boat they could buy with fifty dollars, and glancing hopefully at the old man, who was squinting down the barrel of his rifle.

40 When they reached the station, the old man leaned the rifle against the wall, and filled a corncob pipe. Then he lighted it, puffed a long deep puff, and sent a plume of blue smoke into the air. Finally he smiled at Peter and David. "If you wanted to catch a big snapping turtle, how would you go about it?" he asked.

19. Is Hiram's statement about selling turtles mere information or does he have a reason for mentioning it? Before you answer, reread the final sentence of paragraph 40.

41 "I'd use a cod line," Peter answered.

42 "A cod line," the old man repeated, still smiling. "And what else?"

43 "A hook," David said helpfully.

44 "What kind of a hook?"

45 "The same kind we use for bass."

46 "And what about bait?"

47 "A big bullfrog," Peter said.

48 "No, not a bullfrog," David protested. "Not for turtles."

49 "Let me tell you something," the old man said. "You'd never catch a really big turtle that way. In the first place, a really big turtle would cut through cod line with his jaws easier than that monster cut off poor old Jakey's paw. In the second place, even if he didn't cut the cod line, he'd straighten out the hook. Why, a big turtle could straighten out one of those little bass hooks the way I could bend a coat hanger! And in the third place, if you want to attract a giant turtle, you really have to give him something to eat. Well, how about it? Shall we try our luck?"

50 The two boys sat down on the grass again and, nodding in unison, waited for the old man to continue.

51 For several moments, however, the old man contented himself with puffing on his corncob pipe; then he leaned his shoulder against the wall of the pumping station. "Here's what we're going to do," he said. "Tonight, when I shut up the station, I'll drive into town to the hardware store and buy thirty yards of thin steel wire. Then I'll drop by the tackle shop and get us a heavy-shank hook. Meanwhile, you fellows dig some worms and catch a whole batch of sunfish. We'll need at least

half a dozen, and maybe more. Put the sunfish in a basket and leave them by the door here—it doesn't matter if they get a little ripe—and tomorrow we'll set out our first trap."

52 Peter and David scarcely slept that night. In the morning, they were up at dawn, and were waiting beside the pumping station when the old man came to work in his pickup truck.

53 "Did you get the wire and the big hook?" Peter asked.

54 The old man grinned. "Did you catch enough sunfish?" he said.

55 "Yes!" David shouted. "We got a dozen of them."

56 The old man climbed out of the truck, pulled a paper bag from beneath the seat, and withdrew a long coil of steel wire and a huge hook. It was by far the largest hook that either Peter or David had ever seen, and for some moments they admired it, testing its point with the tips of their fingers.

57 The old man went into the pumping station to check the machinery, and when he came out, he and the boys climbed into the pickup and started over a rutted road that led along the edge of the pond. "We're going to have to find a place where we can set our trap," the old man told them. "It'll have to be someplace where we can drive the truck close to the water."

58 "Why do we need the truck?" Peter asked.

59 The old man smiled mysteriously. "You'll see," he said.

20. Where does the second scene end?
21. How does Hiram persuade Peter and David to help him catch the monster turtle? Why?
22. Why does a whitespace transition end the third scene?
23. Why does the old man not simply tell the boys why the truck will be needed to catch the turtle (paragraph 59)?

60 About three hundred yards from the pumping station, the old man pulled up by a clump of birch trees growing beside the water. Then he and the boys climbed out of the truck and walked to the shore. The old man threaded one end of the steel wire through the eye of the hook, and, using a pair of pliers, wrapped the excess half a dozen times around itself. Afterward, he took several sunfish and threaded them on the hook until the shank was lost from sight and the sharp point was covered. Now, unrolling the rest of the wire, he whirled the hook and its heavy load of sunfish around his head, and flung it out into the water, where it sank. Then he wrapped the loose end of the wire several times around the trunk of the thickest birch tree.

61 "How long will we have to wait?" asked David, hunkering down on his haunches, Indian-style.

62 The old man chuckled softly. "All night," he replied. "Now, don't you boys

disturb this wire until morning. Go bass fishing all you want and use the skiff, but stay away from this part of the pond. If we're going to catch a really big snapping turtle, we'll have to be very patient. Tomorrow morning, when you come down here, take a look at the wire. If it's still loose and sagging, pull it in, go catch some more sunfish, and I'll rebait the hook. If it's tight and won't budge, come and get me right away because that'll mean we've caught something."

63 "Can't we wait here if we're quiet?" Peter asked.

64 "Sure," the old man said, "but you'll be wasting your time. Big turtles only feed at night."

24. Does paragraph 60 start a new scene or is it a continuation of the fourth? Give a reason for your opinion.
25. Paragraphs 60–62 are written as process exposition. Examine the development, pointing out why this is well-done technical writing. Why is such form employed here? Is it effective? What tone does the objectivity of exposition lend to this particular scene?

65 In spite of what the old man said, neither Peter nor David could bear to stay away from the steel wire that stretched out into the murky waters of Hiram's Pond. They tried a little bass fishing to pass the time, but the turtle trap was all they really thought about, and every half hour or so they tiptoed down to the clump of birch trees to see if anything had happened. Nothing had, however, and when evening came, they reluctantly said good-bye to the old man through the doorway of the pumping station, and then pedaled home on their bicycles.

26. The scene beginning with paragraph 65 is a transition scene. What is it used for? Why did they speak to Hiram "through the doorway to the pumping station" rather than go inside? If the noise is a consideration, why did he not come out to speak to them?

66 In the morning, they arrived at the pond even earlier than on the previous day, but they were bitterly disappointed to find the wire still sagging in the same old way. When they pulled it in, however, they were somewhat heartened to see that parts of the sunfish had been eaten away. For this reason, they immediately set about catching more sunfish, and by the time the old man arrived at the station in his pickup, they were waiting for him with a fresh batch.

67 When the old man examined the half-eaten sunfish on the hook, he shook his head with disgust. "Those little spotted turtles just nibble away forever," he muttered. "This is what happened when I set out a line after Jakey lost his paw." The old man threaded half a dozen more sunfish on the hook, and, whirling it around his head again, tossed it out into the water; then he went off toward the pumping

station. "We'll try it here for the rest of the week," he told the boys. "If we don't have any luck by then, we'll have to find a new spot."

27. What is revealed by the old man's disgust and his statement that he had tried unsuccessfully to catch the turtle?
28. Is paragraph 66 a scene? Is paragraph 67? If so, why is there this series of *half-scenes* (minor scenes designed to forward narrative flow through brief focus on an incident to reveal passing time, build suspense, or show character development)?

68 For the rest of the morning, the boys continued to lurk in the vicinity of the birch clump, but by afternoon they were bored with waiting, and went off to the frog pool. As usual, they had little trouble catching frogs, but some of the old enthusiasm had gone out of the sport. David was especially solemn.

69 "Maybe we shouldn't use frogs at all." he said to Peter. "I mean maybe we should let them stay with their families."

70 Peter shook his head. "It's all right as long as we don't use the same ones twice," he replied. "That way they can't be too frightened because they won't know what to expect."

71 David agreed that this must be so, and, happily forgetting what terror they might be engendering in the frog population of Hiram's Pond, the two boys went out in the skiff and spent the remainder of the afternoon fishing for bass.

29. Explain why half-scenes are used in paragraphs 68–71.

72 On the second day, the pattern of the first repeated itself, except that after the old man rebaited the hook, the boys went off and built fluttermills to put in a tiny stream that ran out of the southern end of the pond.

30. Explain why the second day is accorded only one expository sentence. Is paragraph 72 merely a transition paragraph, or does it add information about the growing change in Peter and David? If the latter is true, why did the author not develop it into at least a half-scene?

73 But on the third day, when they arrived at the clump of birch trees, they found the steel wire stretched tight over the water. There was not the slightest bit of slack in the wire, and when Peter noticed that the anchor loop had bitten into the tough bark of the tree to which it had been fastened, he nearly fell into the water with excitement. Then, holding on to the trunk of the birch, and admonishing David to keep a tight grip on his waist, he tried pulling at the wire. But the wire might just as well have been encased in concrete. It not only refused to budge, it even gave a ping like a piano string when Peter struck it with his fishing pole.

31. Explain the use of poetic devices in paragraph 73.

74 "Can you see anything?" David asked, tightening his hold on his brother's waist, and peering out around him.

75 Peter studied the dark water beneath the lily pads, and shook his head. "It's probably just stuck on a log," he said.

76 When the boys reported their findings to the old man, however, he jumped up from his chair, hurried out of the pumping station, and drove his truck down to the clump of birches. After testing the wire, he shook his head solemnly. "There's something on the end of that wire, all right," he said, "and I'm willing to bet right here and now it's the biggest turtle you fellows ever saw."

77 "Golly," Peter said. "Will he be dangerous?"

78 "As dangerous as a reptile can be," the old man said darkly. Then he unfastened the wire from the tree, and wrapped it several times around the rear bumper of his truck. "Now I want you boys to stand over there," he said, pointing to a sandbank about thirty yards away. "When I start pulling on this wire with the truck, it could snap, and I don't want you getting hurt."

32. Explain "As dangerous as a reptile can be." What implication lies in the statement? How does "the old man said darkly" contribute to the implication?

79 Peter and David nodded obediently and ran as fast as they could for the sandbank, where, crouching down, they watched the old man get into the truck, put it in gear, and start very slowly up the road. The wire stretched taut, the truck wheels spun in the dirt ruts; but the truck began to move forward. Then, incredibly, the lily pads near the shore parted with a great threshing and thrashing, and the upper carapace of an immense turtle, whose flippers were flailing the water to a froth, came to the surface. At this point, the turtle made a last desperate effort to escape, and almost disappeared from sight in a cascade of spray and foam; but the old man kept steady pressure upon the struggling beast with the truck, until—thrashing and twisting—it was dragged entirely out of the water and onto the grass beside the shore.

33. Examine paragraph 79 as completely as possible. Is it effective? Why?

80 Now the old man shut off the engine of the truck, set the hand brake, and, climbing out of the cab, beckoned the boys to approach. Peter and David joined him by making a wide detour that never took them closer to the writhing turtle than they had been on the sandbank. The old man was laughing softly, and in his watery eyes there was a strange light that Peter had never seen. "Look at that ugly devil," he whispered. "Wouldn't he love to get ahold of one of us?"

34. Explain "The old man was laughing softly, and in his watery eyes there was a strange light that Peter had never seen." Why is mention of David omitted?

[81]The giant turtle was a horrid sight. Its great shell was bearded with algae, and dripped with slime. Its head and neck were almost as long as its tail, and each of these appendages was as long as the shell. Peter and David looked with awe at the massive, beaklike jaws that were hissing and clicking like hammers upon the shank of the big hook. The jaws were immense, with horny-plated sides and terrible cutting edges, and the mouth was pink inside, and opened and shut with the same implacable force of the giant machinery in the pumping station.

[82]Now the old man motioned the boys to follow behind him, and very slowly the three of them advanced upon the beast. When they were within ten feet, the old man told them to stop, for as they had got closer, the turtle had begun a furious thrashing that tightened the wire to what seemed to be its breaking point. The jaws continued to snap a drumbeat upon the hook, and the huge flippers dug and tore at the tough sod. When the old man picked up a branch and thrust it into the awful pink mouth, the jaws snapped shut, and the branch was instantly severed.

[83]"Well, now you see what happened to poor Jakey's paw," the old man said softly.

[84]For several moments, the old man and the two boys stood watching their captive; then the old man told the boys not to budge an inch, and started for the pumping station.

[85]"Where are you going?" Peter cried in alarm.

35. Are paragraphs 81–84 effective? Give reasons.
36. Why did Peter cry "in alarm"?

[86]"To get my rifle," the old man said. "I'm going to shoot this devil right between the eyes."

[87]"Like a crocodile," David whispered.

[88]"That's right," said the old man, with a laugh. "Right between the eyes, like a crocodile. That'll be the end of him. Just look at that devil! Why, counting the tail, he's at least three feet long. I'll bet he weighs forty pounds."

[89]"D'you think he's the one that ate old Jakey's paw?" Peter asked.

[90]"I hope so," the old man answered.

37. Explain Hiram's use of "devil" in paragraphs 80, 86, and 88.
38. Explain "I hope so" (paragraph 90).

[91]"Will we be able to sell him for a lot of money?" David wanted to know.

[92]"We'll have to see about that," the old man said. "I don't know what turtles bring these days."

93 "What'll we do with him after you shoot him in the eyes?"

94 "We'll butcher him," said the old man, gleefully. "It's a tough job and we'll need sharp knives and a meat cleaver. Then we'll scrape out the shell and clean off the weeds growing on it, and let it dry in the sun. Maybe we can sell the shell, too, but even if we can't, it'll make a nice-looking birdbath."

95 When the old man went off toward the pumping station, Peter and David backed several steps farther away from the turtle's gaping jaws. Then they watched the old man, who had begun to run. He ran awkwardly and stiffly, with his arms falling crazily at his sides, and even when he was a good distance away, they could hear the breath coming through his nose in snorts.

39. What does "it'll make a nice-looking birdbath" reveal about Hiram? Give reasons for your answer.
40. Paragraph 95 refers back to paragraph 30. Why?

96 After the old man had disappeared from view, the turtle seemed to redouble its efforts to get free of the hook and wire which held it fast. Rearing up on its hind flippers, it stretched the wire taut again, and exposed a yellow bottom that was divided into beautifully symmetrical plates. Then, suddenly, the terrible hissing noise that came from its jaws was replaced by a hoarse bellow that sounded like a cry of agony.

41. Compare paragraphs 81 and 96. What causes the change in tone?

97 When this happened, David burst into tears, and even Peter felt his eyes begin to water. Now, as David began openly to weep, Peter forced himself to look away from the turtle. But there was no escaping the sound of its desperate struggle for life, and finally he said, "Let's ask the old man not to kill it."

98 David shook his head and gave a sob. "He won't listen. He'll say it's the same turtle that bit off old Jakey's paw."

99 Peter frowned and hesitated. "Well, maybe it is," he replied.

100 "But the turtle can't help that," said David, weeping. "Can he help it if he's a turtle?"

101 "But he's a monster turtle. He'd drag you into the water if he could!"

102 "Not if I don't go wading," David said.

103 "He might catch somebody else someday."

104 "We could put up signs on all the trees," David said.

105 "How about the money for our boat?"

106 "I don't care about having a boat," David said. "Isn't there some way we can let him go?"

[107]Peter looked apprehensively at the turtle's snapping jaws, and then at the taut steel wire that stretched back to the truck. "No," he answered. "There's nothing we can do."

[108]"Can't we cut the wire?"

[109]"How?" Peter asked. Even as he spoke, he saw the old man trotting toward them along the roadway, carrying his rifle in his hand.

[110]"Is he coming?" David whispered.

[111]"Yes," Peter said quietly. "It's too late."

42. Explain Peter and David's changed attitude in paragraphs 96–111. On the surface, it may seem the boys have suddenly "come to realize" something. Such is not the case, however. The change has been progressive in that it has been built up from the beginning of the story. You have traced it; now review it.

[112]When the old man arrived, Peter put his arm around David's shoulders. Before his eyes stretched the waters of Hiram's Pond, but the pond no longer seemed familiar. The kingfisher was still plunging toward the surface after minnows, and a kingbird was pursuing a huge butterfly above the lily pads, but now it seemed to Peter that a whole chorus of scarred frogs was croaking in unison against the savage spectacle taking place on the grass before them. When the old man fired his rifle, Peter and David closed their eyes until the report had echoed and re-echoed, and died away. Then there was a moment of perfect stillness. And then they fled. □

43. Compare the final paragraph with the opening paragraph. Explain the changed mood, tone, and atmosphere.
44. Where is the climax of this story?
45. From what did the boys flee? To what did they run?
46. The theme of "The Turtle" should be apparent now. If it is not, examine "but now it seemed to Peter that a whole chorus of scarred frogs was croaking in unison against the savage spectacle taking place on the grass before them."
47. Outline the plot briefly. Examine proportion.
48. Trace the transitional devices throughout the story.
49. Identify the symbols in the story. How many are there? What is the function of each?
50. Isolate the many elements that create coherence and unity in the plot. What do they suggest about the structure of a short story?

Symbols can sometimes present truth in ways obvious didacticism would not dare to attempt. And truth has always been important to man. Sabine d'Estrée, in the translator's preface to *The Story of O,* a recent, highly controversial, sado-masochistic novel, observed:

> *Story of O* is the work of an original writer, who has dared to present us with certain truths, or intimations of truth, rarely found in literature. However much one may disagree with, or even profoundly dislike, these truths (or, if you will, these ideas), Pauline Réage has done what all good artists aim for and, when they are successful, accomplish: to arouse us from the lethargy of our set ways and routine lives, prick us into consciousness, provoke a reaction (whether positive or negative, it matters little) within us; in short, to make us think. That in itself is a rare enough occurrence so that we should be grateful indeed whenever we have the good fortune to encounter it.°

If, by analyzing the stories in this book, you have learned to allow authors to provoke a reaction in you, to make you think, you have learned much about being an educated man. You should, in the process, be learning a great deal about discrimination in your reading preferences, for that marks the educated man also. Ashley Montague, in *The Cultured Man,* argues that it is possible to read too much, for reading can become a substitute for the necessity of thinking. It should not. Discrimination will prevent the possibility and you will discover a great deal about yourself as you discover more about short stories. Montague's final judgment should be constantly in your memory, however, as you decide what to read and how to read it:

> The principal purpose of reading should be as a stimulus to thought, and only secondarily as an accretion to one's knowledge—and thinking need not be incompatible with reading for pleasure. The cultured man is necessarily a well-read man, but he knows the difference between a book that is to be tasted and one that is to be chewed and digested.°

Suggested Assignments. 1. In the following three works, hands are a symbol. Examine the works (Shapiro's poem qualifies as a short story if you examine it for the elements of the form) and analyze one author's use of symbol to create truth and make us think.

2. Compare any two of the works in any way you care to, revealing something of what you have learned.

° Pauline Réage, *The Story of O* (New York, 1965).
° New York, 1958, p. 234.

Love for a Hand

Two hands lie still, the hairy and the white,
And soon down ladders of reflected light
The sleepers climb in silence. Gradually
They separate on paths of long ago,
Each winding on his arm the unpleasant clew
That leads, live as a nerve, to memory.

But often when too steep her dream descends,
Perhaps to the grotto where her father bends
To pick her up, the husband wakes as though
He had forgotten something in the house.
Motionless he eyes the room that glows
With the little animals of light that prowl

This way and that. Soft are the beasts of light
But softer still her hand that drifts so white
Upon the whiteness. How like a water-plant
It floats upon the black canal of sleep,
Suspended upward from the distant deep
In pure achievement of its lovely want!

Quietly then he plucks it and it folds
And is again a hand, small as a child's.
He would revive it but it barely stirs
And so he carries it off a little way
And breaks it open gently. Now he can see
The sweetness of the fruit, his hand eats hers.

Karl Shapiro

Hands

(CONCERNING WING BIDDLEBAUM)

by Sherwood Anderson

1 Upon the half-decayed veranda of a small frame house that stood near the edge of a ravine near the town of Winesburg, Ohio, a fat little old man walked nervously up and down. Across a long field that had been seeded for clover but that had produced only a dense crop of yellow mustard weeds, he could see the public highway along which went a wagon filled with berry pickers returning from the fields. The berry pickers, youths and maidens, laughed and shouted boisterously.

A boy clad in a blue shirt leaped from the wagon and attempted to drag after him one of the maidens who screamed and protested shrilly. The feet of the boy in the road kicked up a cloud of dust that floated across the face of the departing sun. Over the long field came a thin girlish voice. "Oh, you Wing Biddlebaum, comb your hair, it's falling into your eyes," commanded the voice to the man, who was bald and whose nervous little hands fiddled about the bare white forehead as though arranging a mass of tangled locks.

2 Wing Biddlebaum, forever frightened and beset by a ghostly band of doubts, did not think of himself as in any way a part of the life of the town where he had lived for twenty years. Among all the people of Winesburg but one had come close to him. With George Willard, son of Tom Willard, the proprietor of the new Willard House, he had formed something like a friendship. George Willard was the reporter on the *Winesburg Eagle* and sometimes in the evenings he walked out along the highway to Wing Biddlebaum's house. Now as the old man walked up and down on the veranda, his hands moving nervously about, he was hoping that George Willard would come and spend the evening with him. After the wagon containing the berry pickers had passed, he went across the field through the tall mustard weeds and climbing a rail fence peered anxiously along the road to the town. For a moment he stood thus, rubbing his hands together and looking up and down the road, and then, fear overcoming him, ran back to walk again upon the porch of his own house.

3 In the presence of George Willard, Wing Biddlebaum, who for twenty years had been the town mystery, lost something of his timidity, and his shadowy personality, submerged in a sea of doubts, came forth to look at the world. With the young reporter at his side, he ventured in the light of day into Main Street or strode up and down on the rickety front porch of his own house, talking excitedly. The voice that had been low and trembling became shrill and loud. The bent figure straightened. With a kind of wriggle, like a fish returned to the brook by the fisherman, Biddlebaum the silent began to talk, striving to put into words the ideas that had been accumulated by his mind during long years of silence.

4 Wing Biddlebaum talked much with his hands. The slender expressive fingers, forever active, forever striving to conceal themselves in his pockets or behind his back, came forth and became the piston rods of his machinery of expression.

5 The story of Wing Biddlebaum is a story of hands. Their restless activity, like unto the beating of the wings of an imprisoned bird, had given him his name. Some obscure poet of the town had thought of it. The hands alarmed their owner. He wanted to keep them hidden

away and looked with amazement at the quiet inexpressive hands of other men who worked beside him in the fields, or passed, driving sleepy teams on country roads.

6 When he talked to George Willard, Wing Biddlebaum closed his fists and beat with them upon a table or on the walls of his house. The action made him more comfortable. If the desire to talk came to him when the two were walking in the fields, he sought out a stump or the top board of a fence and with his hands pounding busily talked with renewed ease.

7 The story of Wing Biddlebaum's hands is worth a book in itself. Sympathetically set forth it would tap many strange, beautiful qualities in obscure men. It is a job for a poet. In Winesburg the hands had attracted attention merely because of their activity. With them Wing Biddlebaum had picked as high as a hundred and forty quarts of strawberries in a day. They became his distinguishing feature, the source of his fame. Also they made more grotesque an already grotesque and elusive individuality. Winesburg was proud of the hands of Wing Biddlebaum in the same spirit in which it was proud of Banker White's new stone house and Wesley Moyer's bay stallion, Tony Tip, that had won the two-fifteen trot at the fall races in Cleveland.

8 As for George Willard, he had many times wanted to ask about the hands. At times an almost overwhelming curiosity had taken hold of him. He felt that there must be a reason for their strange activity and their inclination to keep hidden away and only a growing respect for Wing Biddlebaum kept him from blurting out the questions that were often in his mind.

9 Once he had been on the point of asking. The two were walking in the fields on a summer afternoon and had stopped to sit upon a grassy bank. All afternoon Wing Biddlebaum had talked as one inspired. By a fence he had stopped and beating like a giant woodpecker upon the top board had shouted at George Willard, condemning his tendency to be too much influenced by the people about him. "You are destroying yourself," he cried. "You have the inclination to be alone and to dream and you are afraid of dreams. You want to be like others in town here. You hear them talk and you try to imitate them."

10 On the grassy bank Wing Biddlebaum had tried again to drive his point home. His voice became soft and reminiscent, and with a sigh of contentment he launched into a long rambling talk, speaking as one lost in a dream.

11 Out of the dream Wing Biddlebaum made a picture for George Willard. In the picture men lived again in a kind of pastoral golden age. Across a green open country came clean-limbed young men, some afoot, some mounted upon horses. In crowds the young men came to

gather about the feet of an old man who sat beneath a tree in a tiny garden and who talked to them.

12 Wing Biddlebaum became wholly inspired. For once he forgot the hands. Slowly they stole forth and lay upon George Willard's shoulders. Something new and bold came into the voice that talked. "You must try to forget all you have learned," said the old man. "You must begin to dream. From this time on you must shut your ears to the roaring of the voices."

13 Pausing in his speech, Wing Biddlebaum looked long and earnestly at George Willard. His eyes glowed. Again he raised the hands to caress the boy and then a look of horror swept over his face.

14 With a convulsive movement of his body, Wing Biddlebaum sprang to his feet and thrust his hands deep into his trousers pockets. Tears came to his eyes. "I must be getting along home. I can talk no more with you," he said nervously.

15 Without looking back, the old man had hurried down the hillside and across a meadow, leaving George Willard perplexed and frightened upon the grassy slope. With a shiver of dread the boy arose and went along the road toward town. "I'll not ask him about his hands," he thought, touched by the memory of the terror he had seen in the man's eyes. "There's something wrong, but I don't want to know what it is. His hands have something to do with his fear of me and of everyone."

16 And George Willard was right. Let us look briefly into the story of the hands. Perhaps our talking of them will arouse the poet who will tell the hidden wonder story of the influence for which the hands were but fluttering pennants of promise.

17 In his youth Wing Biddlebaum had been a school teacher in a town in Pennsylvania. He was not then known as Wing Biddlebaum, but went by the less euphonic name of Adolph Myers. As Adolph Myers he was much loved by the boys of his school.

18 Adolph Myers was meant by nature to be a teacher of youth. He was one of those rare, little-understood men who rule by a power so gentle that it passes as a lovable weakness. In their feeling for the boys under their charge such men are not unlike the finer sort of women in their love of men.

19 And yet that is but crudely stated. It needs the poet there. With the boys of his school, Adolph Myers had walked in the evening or had sat talking until dusk upon the schoolhouse steps lost in a kind of dream. Here and there went his hands, caressing the shoulders of the boys, playing about the tousled heads. As he talked his voice became soft and musical. There was a caress in that also. In a way the voice and the hands, the stroking of the shoulders and the touching of the hair was a part of the schoolmaster's effort to carry a dream into

the young minds. By the caress that was in his fingers he expressed himself. He was one of those men in whom the force that creates life is diffused, not centralized. Under the caress of his hands doubt and disbelief went out of the minds of the boys and they began also to dream.

20 And then the tragedy. A half-witted boy of the school became enamored of the young master. In his bed at night he imagined unspeakable things and in the morning went forth to tell his dreams as facts. Strange hideous accusations fell from his loose-hung lips. Through the Pennsylvania town went a shiver. Hidden, shadowy doubts that had been in men's minds concerning Adolph Myers were galvanized into beliefs.

21 The tragedy did not linger. Trembling lads were jerked out of bed and questioned. "He put his arms about me," said one. "His fingers were always playing in my hair," said another.

22 One afternoon a man of the town, Henry Bradford, who kept a saloon, came to the schoolhouse door. Calling Adolph Myers into the school yard he began to beat him with his fists. As his hard knuckles beat down into the frightened face of the schoolmaster, his wrath became more and more terrible. Screaming with dismay, the children ran here and there like disturbed insects. "I'll teach you to put your hands on my boy, you beast," roared the saloon keeper, who, tired of beating the master, had begun to kick him about the yard.

23 Adolph Myers was driven from the Pennsylvania town in the night. With lanterns in their hands a dozen men came to the door of the house where he lived alone and commanded that he dress and come forth. It was raining and one of the men had a rope in his hands. They had intended to hang the schoolmaster, but something in his figure, so small, white, and pitiful, touched their hearts and they let him escape. As he ran away into the darkness they repented of their weakness and ran after him, swearing and throwing sticks and great balls of soft mud at the figure that screamed and ran faster and faster into the darkness.

24 For twenty years Adolph Myers had lived alone in Winesburg. He was but forty but looked sixty-five. The name of Biddlebaum he got from a box of goods seen at a freight station as he hurried through an eastern Ohio town. He had an aunt in Winesburg, a black-toothed old woman who raised chickens, and with her he lived until she died. He had been ill for a year after the experience in Pennsylvania, and after his recovery worked as a day laborer in the fields, going timidly about and striving to conceal his hands. Although he did not understand what had happened he felt that the hands must be to blame. Again and again the fathers of the boys had talked of the hands. "Keep your

hands to yourself," the saloon keeper had roared, dancing with fury in the schoolhouse yard.

25 Upon the veranda of his house by the ravine, Wing Biddlebaum continued to walk up and down until the sun had disappeared and the road beyond the field was lost in the gray shadows. Going into his house he cut slices of bread and spread honey upon them. When the rumble of the evening train that took away the express cars loaded with the day's harvest of berries had passed and restored the silence of the summer night, he went again to walk upon the veranda. In the darkness he could not see the hands and they became quiet. Although he still hungered for the presence of the boy, who was the medium through which he expressed his love of man, the hunger became again a part of his loneliness and his waiting. Lighting a lamp, Wing Biddlebaum washed the few dishes soiled by his simple meal and, setting up a folding cot by the screen door that led to the porch, prepared to undress for the night. A few stray white bread crumbs lay on the cleanly washed floor by the table; putting the lamp on a low stool he began to pick up the crumbs, carrying them to his mouth one by one with unbelievable rapidity. In the dense blotch of light beneath the table, the kneeling figure looked like a priest engaged in some service of his church. The nervous expressive fingers, flashing in and out of the light, might well have been mistaken for the fingers of the devotee going swiftly through decade after decade of his rosary. □

Bianca's Hands

by Theodore Sturgeon

1 Bianca's mother was leading her when Ran saw her first. Bianca was squat and small, with dank hair and rotten teeth. Her mouth was crooked and it drooled. Either she was blind or she just didn't care about bumping into things. It didn't really matter because Bianca was an imbecile. Her hands . . .

2 They were lovely hands, graceful hands, hands as soft and smooth and white as snowflakes, hands whose color was lightly tinged with pink like the glow of Mars on Snow. They lay on the counter side by side, looking at Ran. They lay there half closed and crouching, each pulsing with a movement like the panting of a field creature, and they looked. Not watched. Later, they watched him. Now they looked. They did, because Ran felt their united gaze, and his heart beat strongly.

3 Bianca's mother demanded cheese stridently. Ran brought it to her in his own time while she berated him. She was a bitter woman, as any woman has a right to be who is wife of no man and mother to

a monster. Ran gave her the cheese and took her money and never noticed that it was not enough, because of Bianca's hands. When Bianca's mother tried to take one of the hands, it scuttled away from the unwanted touch. It did not lift from the counter, but ran on its fingertips to the edge and leaped into a fold of Bianca's dress. The mother took the unresisting elbow and led Bianca out.

4 Ran stayed there at the counter unmoving, thinking of Bianca's hands. Ran was strong and bronze and not very clever. He had never been taught about beauty and strangeness, but he did not need that teaching. His shoulders were wide and his arms were heavy and thick, but he had great soft eyes and thick lashes. They curtained his eyes now. He was seeing Bianca's hands again dreamily. He found it hard to breathe . . .

5 Harding came back. Harding owned the store. He was a large man whose features barely kept his cheeks apart. He said, "Sweep up, Ran. We're closing early today." Then he went behind the counter, squeezing past Ran.

6 Ran got the broom and swept slowly.

7 "A woman bought cheese," he said suddenly. "A poor woman, with very old clothes. She was leading a girl. I can't remember what the girl looked like, except—who was she?"

8 "I saw them go out," said Harding. "The woman is Bianca's mother and the girl is Bianca. I don't know their other name. They don't talk to people much. I wish they wouldn't come in here. Hurry up, Ran."

9 Ran did what was necessary and put away his broom. Before he left he asked, "Where do they live, Bianca and her mother?"

10 "On the other side. A house on no road, away from people. Good night, Ran."

11 Ran went from the shop directly over to the other side, not waiting for his supper. He found the house easily, for it was indeed away from the road, and stood rudely by itself. The townspeople had cauterized the house by wrapping it in empty fields.

12 Harshly, "What do you want?" Bianca's mother asked as she opened the door.

13 "May I come in?"

14 "What do you want?"

15 "May I come in?" he asked again. She made as if to slam the door, and then stood aside. "Come."

16 Ran went in and stood still. Bianca's mother crossed the room and sat under an old lamp, in the shadow. Ran sat opposite her, on a three-legged stool. Bianca was not in the room.

17 The woman tried to speak, but embarrassment clutched at her

voice. She withdrew into her bitterness, saying nothing. She kept peeping at Ran, who sat quietly with his arms folded and the uncertain light in his eyes. He knew she would speak soon, and he could wait.

18 "Ah, well . . ." She was silent after that, for a time, but now she had forgiven him his intrusion. Then, "It's a great while since anyone came to see me; a great while . . . it was different before. I was a pretty girl—"

19 She bit her words off and her face popped out of the shadows, shrivelled and sagging as she leaned forward. Ran saw that she was beaten and cowed and did not want to be laughed at.

20 "Yes," he said gently. She sighed and leaned back so that her face disappeared again. She said nothing for a moment, sitting looking at Ran, liking him.

21 "We were happy, the two of us," she mused, "until Bianca came. He didn't like her, poor thing, he didn't, no more than I do now. He went away. I stayed by her because I was her mother. I'd go away myself, I would, but people know me, and I haven't a penny—not a penny. . . . They'd bring me back to her, they would, to care for her. It doesn't matter much now, though, because people don't want me any more than they want her, they don't . . ."

22 Ran shifted his feet uneasily, because the woman was crying. "Have you room for me here?" he asked.

23 Her head crept out into the light. Ran said swiftly, "I'll give you money each week, and I'll bring my own bed and things." He was afraid she would refuse.

24 She merged with the shadows again. "If you like," she said, trembling at her good fortune. "Though why you'd want to . . . still, I guess if I had a little something to cook up nice, and a good reason for it, I could make someone real cosy here. But—*why?*" She rose. Ran crossed the room and pushed her back into the chair. He stood over her, tall.

25 "I never want you to ask me that," he said, speaking very slowly. "Hear?"

26 She swallowed and nodded. "I'll come back tomorrow with the bed and things," he said.

27 He left her there under the lamp, blinking out of the dimness, folded round and about with her misery and her wonder.

28 People talked about it. People said, "Ran has moved to the house of Bianca's mother." "It must be because—" "Ah," said some, "Ran was always a strange boy. It must be because—" "Oh, *no!*" cried others appalled. "Ran is such a good boy. He wouldn't—"

29 Harding was told. He frightened the busy little woman who told him. He said, "Ran is very quiet, but he is honest and he does his

work. As long as he comes here in the morning and earns his wage, he can do what he wants, where he wants, and it is not my business to stop him." He said this so very sharply that the little woman dared not say anything more.

30 Ran was very happy, living there. Saying little, he began to learn about Bianca's hands.

31 He watched Bianca being fed. Her hands would not feed her, the lovely aristocrats. Beautiful parasites they were, taking their animal life from the heavy squat body that carried them, and giving nothing in return. They would lie one on each side of her plate, pulsing, while Bianca's mother put food into the disinterested drooling mouth. They were shy, those hands, of Ran's bewitched gaze. Caught out there naked in the light and open of the table-top, they would creep to the edge and drop out of sight—all but four rosy fingertips clutching the cloth.

32 They never lifted from a surface. When Bianca walked, her hands did not swing free, but twisted in the fabric of her dress. And when she approached a table or the mantelpiece and stood, her hands would run lightly up and leap, landing together, resting silently, watchfully, with that pulsing peculiar to them.

33 They cared for each other. They would not touch Bianca herself, but each hand groomed the other. It was the only labor to which they would bend themselves.

34 Three evenings after he came, Ran tried to take one of the hands in his. Bianca was alone in the room, and Ran went to her and sat beside her. She did not move, nor did her hands. They rested on a small table before her, preening themselves. This, then, was when they really began watching him. He felt it, right down to the depths of his enchanted heart. The hands kept stroking each other, and yet they knew he was there, they knew of his desire. They stretched themselves before him, archly, languorously, and his blood pounded hot. Before he could stay himself he reached and tried to grasp them. He was strong, and his move was sudden and clumsy. One of the hands seemed to disappear, so swiftly did it drop into Bianca's lap. But the other—

35 Ran's thick fingers closed on it and held it captive. It writhed, all but tore itself free. It took no power from the arm on which it lived, for Bianca's arms were flabby and weak. Its strength, like its beauty, was intrinsic, and it was only by shifting his grip to the puffy forearm that Ran succeeded in capturing it. So intent was he on touching it, holding it, that he did not see the other hand leap from the idiot girl's lap, land crouching at the table's edge. It reared back, fingers curling spiderlike, and sprang at him, fastening on his wrist. It clamped down agonizingly, and Ran felt bones give and crackle. With a cry he released the girl's arm. Her hands fell together and ran

over each other, feeling for any small scratch, any tiny damage he might have done them in his passion. And as he sat there clutching his wrist, he saw the hands run to the far side of the little table, hook themselves over the edge and, contracting, draw her out of her place. She had no volition of her own—ah, but her hands had! Creeping over the walls, catching obscure and precarious holds in the wainscoting, they dragged the girl from the room.

36 And Ran sat there and sobbed, not so much from the pain in his swelling arm, but in shame for what he had done. They might have been won to him in another, gentler way . . .

37 His head was bowed, yet suddenly he felt the gaze of those hands. He looked up swiftly enough to see one of them whisk round the doorpost. It had come back, then, to see . . . Ran rose heavily and took himself and his shame away. Yet he was compelled to stop in the doorway, even as had Bianca's hands. He watched covertly and saw them come into the room dragging the unprotesting idiot girl. They brought her to the long bench where Ran had sat with her. They pushed her on to it, flung themselves to the table, and began rolling and flattening themselves most curiously about. Ran suddenly realized that there was something of his there, and he was comforted, a little. They were rejoicing, drinking thirstily, revelling in his tears.

38 Afterwards for nineteen days, the hands made Ran do penance. He knew them as inviolate and unforgiving; they would not show themselves to him, remaining always hidden in Bianca's dress or under the supper table. For those nineteen days Ran's passion and desire grew. More—his love became true love, for only true love knows reverence—and the possession of the hands became his reason for living, his goal in the life which that reason had given him.

39 Ultimately they forgave him. They kissed him coyly when he was not looking, touched him on the wrist, caught and held him for one sweet moment. It was at table . . . a great power surged through him, and he gazed down at the hands, now returned to Bianca's lap. A strong muscle in his jaw twitched and twitched, swelled and fell. Happiness like a golden light flooded him; passion spurred him, love imprisoned him, reverence was the gold of the golden light. The room wheeled and whirled about him and forces unimaginable flickered through him. Battling with himself, yet lax in the glory of it, Ran sat unmoving, beyond the world, enslaved and yet possessor of all. Bianca's hands flushed pink, and if ever hands smiled to each other, then they did.

40 He rose abruptly, flinging his chair from him, feeling the strength of his back and shoulders. Bianca's mother, by now beyond surprise, looked at him and away. There was that in his eyes which she did not like, for to fathom it would disturb her, and she wanted no trouble.

Ran strode from the room and outdoors, to be by himself that he might learn more of this new thing that had possessed him.

41 It was evening. The crooked-bending skyline drank the buoyancy of the sun, dragged it down, sucking greedily. Ran stood on a knoll, his nostrils flaring, feeling the depth of his lungs. He sucked in the crisp air and it smelled new to him, as though the sunset shades were truly in it. He knotted the muscles of his thighs and stared at his smooth, solid fists. He raised his hands high over his head and, stretching, sent out such a great shout that the sun sank. He watched it, knowing how great and tall he was, how strong he was, knowing the meaning of longing and belonging. And then he lay down on the clean earth and he wept.

42 When the sky grew cold enough for the moon to follow the sun beyond the hills, and still an hour after that, Ran returned to the house. He struck a light in the room of Bianca's mother, where she slept on a pile of old clothes. Ran sat beside her and let the light wake her. She rolled over to him and moaned, opened her eyes and shrank from him. "Ran . . . what do you want?"

43 "Bianca. I want to marry Bianca."

44 Her breath hissed between her gums. "No!" It was not a refusal, but astonishment. Ran touched her arm impatiently. Then she laughed.

45 "To—marry—Bianca. It's late, boy. Go back to bed, and in the morning you'll have forgotten this thing, this dream."

46 "I've not been to bed," he said patiently, but growing angry. "Will you give me Bianca, or not?"

47 She sat up and rested her chin on her withered knees. "You're right to ask me, for I'm her mother. Still and all—Ran, you've been good to us, Bianca and me. You're—you are a good boy but—forgive me, lad, but you're something of a fool. Bianca's a monster. I say it though I am what I am to her. Do what you like, and never a word will I say. You should have known. I'm sorry you asked me, for you have given me the memory of speaking so to you. I don't understand you; but do what you like, boy."

48 It was to have been a glance, but it became a stare as she saw his face. He put his hands carefully behind his back, and she knew he would have killed her else.

49 "I'll—marry her, then?" he whispered.

50 She nodded, terrified. "As you like, boy."

51 He blew out the light and left her.

52 Ran worked hard and saved his wages, and made one room beautiful for Bianca and himself. He built a soft chair, and a table that was

like an altar for Bianca's sacred hands. There was a great bed, and heavy cloth to hide and soften the walls, and a rug.

53 They were married, though marrying took time. Ran had to go far afield before he could find one who would do what was necessary. The man came far and went again afterwards, so that none knew of it, and Ran and his wife were left alone. The mother spoke for Bianca, and Bianca's hand trembled frighteningly at the touch of the ring, writhed and struggled and then lay passive, blushing and beautiful. But it was done. Bianca's mother did not protest, for she didn't dare. Ran was happy, and Bianca—well, nobody cared about Bianca.

54 After they were married Bianca followed Ran and his two brides into the beautiful room. He washed Bianca and used rich lotions. He washed and combed her hair, and brushed it many times until it shone, to make her more fit to be with the hands he had married. He never touched the hands, though he gave them soaps and creams and tools with which they could groom themselves. They were pleased. Once one of them ran up his coat and touched his cheek and made him exultant.

55 He left them and returned to the shop with his heart full of music. He worked harder than ever, so that Harding was pleased and let him go home early. He wandered the hours away by the bank of a brook, watching the sun on the face of the chuckling water. A bird came to circle him, flew unafraid through the aura of gladness about him. The delicate tip of a wing brushed his wrist with the touch of the first secret kiss from the hands of Bianca. The singing that filled him was part of the nature of laughing, the running of water, the sound of the wind in the reeds by the edge of the stream. He yearned for the hands, and he knew he could go now and clasp them and own them; instead he stretched out on the bank and lay smiling, all lost in the sweetness and poignance of waiting, denying desire. He laughed for pure joy in a world without hatred, held in the stainless palms of Bianca's hands.

56 As it grew dark he went home. All during that nuptial meal Bianca's hands twisted about one of his while he ate with the other, and Bianca's mother fed the girl. The fingers twined about each other and about his own, so that three hands seemed to be wrought of one flesh, to become a thing of lovely weight at his arm's end. When it was quite dark they went to the beautiful room and lay where he and the hands could watch, through the window, the clean, bright stars swim up out of the forest. The house and the room were dark and silent. Ran was so happy that he hardly dared to breathe.

57 A hand fluttered up over his hair, down his cheek, and crawled into the hollow of his throat. Its pulsing matched the beat of his

heart. He opened his own hands wide and clenched his fingers, as though to catch and hold this moment.

58 Soon the other hand crept up and joined the first. For perhaps an hour they lay there passive with their coolness against Ran's warm neck. He felt them with his throat, each smooth convolution, each firm small expanse. He concentrated, with his mind and his heart on his throat, on each part of the hands that touched him, feeling with all his being first one touch and then another, though the contact was there unmoving. And he knew it would be soon now, soon.

59 As if at a command, he turned on his back and dug his head into the pillow. Staring up at the vague dark hangings on the wall, he began to realize what it was for which he had been working and dreaming so long. He put his head back yet farther and smiled, waiting. This would be possession, completion. He breathed deeply, twice, and the hands began to move.

60 The thumbs crossed over his throat and the fingertips settled one by one under his ears. For a long moment they lay there, gathering strength. Together, then, in perfect harmony, each co-operating with the other, they became rigid, rock-hard. Their touch was still light upon him, still light . . . no, now they were passing their rigidity to him, turning it to a contraction. They settled to it slowly, their pressure measured and equal. Ran lay silent. He could not breathe now, and did not want to. His great arms were crossed on his chest, his knotted fists under his armpits, his mind knowing a great peace. Soon, now . . .

61 Wave after wave of engulfing, glorious pain spread and receded. He saw color impossible, without light. He arched his back, up, up . . . the hands bore down with all their hidden strength, and Ran's body bent like a bow, resting on feet and shoulders. Up, up . . .

62 Something burst within him—his lungs, his heart—no matter. It was complete.

63 There was blood on the hands of Bianca's mother when they found her in the morning in the beautiful room, trying to soothe Ran's neck. They took Bianca away, and they buried Ran, but they hanged Bianca's mother because she tried to make them believe Bianca had done it, Bianca whose hands were quite dead, drooping like brown leaves from her wrists. □

Suggested Assignment. Read widely, discriminatingly, and with great pleasure.

Thematic Table of Contents

Index

Names of authors and titles of selections included in this book are set in **boldface.** Names of authors and works not included in this book appear in regular light-face type, as do all the terms.

1 2 3 4 5 6 7 8 9 10 11 12 13 14 15 16 17 18 19 20 21 22 23 24 25 RM 74 73 72 71 70 69 68 67